THE
PRINCIPLES
OF
SCIENCE

THE LOGICAL MACHINE.

THE PRINCIPLES OF SCIENCE
*
A TREATISE ON LOGIC AND SCIENTIFIC METHOD

by

W. Stanley Jevons

with a new introduction

by

Professor Ernest Nagel,
Columbia University

DOVER PUBLICATIONS, INC.
New York

CONSTABLE & CO LTD
10-12 ORANGE STREET, LONDON, W.C.2

This new Dover edition first published in 1958, is an unabridged and unaltered republication of the latest revision, with a new introduction by Professor Ernest Nagel, Columbia University.

Manufactured in the United States of America.

PREFACE

It may be truly asserted that the rapid progress of the physical sciences during the last three centuries has not been accompanied by a corresponding advance in the theory of reasoning. Physicists speak familiarly of Scientific Method, but they could not readily describe what they mean by that expression. Profoundly engaged in the study of particular classes of natural phenomena, they are usually too much engrossed in the immense and ever-accumulating details of their special sciences to generalise upon the methods of reasoning which they unconsciously employ. Yet few will deny that these methods of reasoning ought to be studied, especially by those who endeavour to introduce scientific order into less successful and methodical branches of knowledge.

The application of Scientific Method cannot be restricted to the sphere of lifeless objects. We must sooner or later have strict sciences of those mental and social phenomena, which, if comparison be possible, are of more interest to us than purely material phenomena. But it is the proper course of reasoning to proceed from the known to the unknown—from the evident to the obscure—from the material and palpable to the subtle and refined. The physical sciences may therefore be properly made the practice-ground of the reasoning powers, because they furnish us with a great body of precise and successful investigations. In these sciences we meet with happy instances of unquestionable deductive reasoning, of extensive generalisation, of happy prediction, of satisfactory verification, of nice calculation of probabilities. We can note how the slightest analogical clue has been followed up to a glorious discovery, how a rash generalisation has at length been exposed, or a conclusive *experimentum crucis* has decided the long-continued strife between two rival theories.

In following out my design of detecting the general methods of inductive investigation, I have found that the more elaborate and interesting processes of quantitative induction have their necessary foundation in the simpler science of Formal Logic. The earlier, and probably by far the least attractive part of this work, consists, therefore, in a statement of the so-called Fundamental Laws of Thought, and of the all-important Principle of Substitution, of which, as I think, all reasoning is a development. The whole procedure of inductive inquiry, in its most complex cases, is foreshadowed in the combinational view of Logic, which arises directly from these fundamental principles. Incidentally I have described the mechanical arrangements by which the use of the important form called the Logical Alphabet, and the whole working of the combinational system of Formal Logic, may be rendered evident to the eye, and easy to the mind and hand.

The study both of Formal Logic and of the Theory of Probabilities has led me to adopt the opinion that there is no such thing as a distinct method of induction as contrasted with deduction, but that induction is simply an inverse employment of deduction. Within the last century a reaction has been setting in against the purely empirical procedure of Francis Bacon, and physicists have learnt to advocate the use of hypotheses. I take the extreme view of holding that Francis Bacon, although he correctly insisted upon constant reference to experience, had no correct notions as to the logical method by which from particular facts we educe laws of nature. I endeavour to show that hypothetical anticipation of nature is an essential part of inductive inquiry, and that it is the Newtonian method of deductive reasoning combined with elaborate experimental verification, which has led to all the great triumphs of scientific research.

In attempting to give an explanation of this view of Scientific Method, I have first to show that the sciences of number and quantity repose upon and spring from the simpler and more general science of Logic. The Theory of Probability, which enables us to estimate and calculate quantities of knowledge, is then described, and especial attention is drawn to the Inverse Method of Probabilities, which involves, as I conceive, the true principle of inductive procedure. No inductive conclusions are more than probable, and I adopt the opinion that the theory of probability is an essential part of logical method, so that the logical value of every inductive result must be determined consciously or unconsciously, according to the principles of the inverse method of probability.

The phenomena of nature are commonly manifested in quantities of time, space, force, energy, &c., and the observation, measurement, and analysis of the various quantitative conditions or results involved, even in a simple experiment, demand much employment of systematic procedure. I devote a book, therefore, to a simple and general description of the devices by which exact measurement is effected, errors eliminated, a probable mean result attained, and the probable error of that mean ascertained. I then proceed to the principal, and probably the most interesting, subject of the book, illustrating successively the conditions and precautions requisite for accurate observation, for successful experiment, and for the sure detection of the quantitative laws of nature. As it is impossible to comprehend aright the value of quantitative laws without constantly bearing in mind the degree of quantitative approximation to the truth probably attained, I have devoted a special chapter to the Theory of Approximation, and however imperfectly I may have treated this subject, I must look upon it as a very essential part of a work on Scientific Method.

It then remains to illustrate the sound use of hypothesis, to distinguish between the portions of knowledge which we owe to empirical observation, to accidental discovery, or to scientific prediction. Interesting questions arise concerning the accordance of quantitative theories and experiments, and I point out how the successive verification of an hypothesis by distinct methods of experiment yields conclusions approximating to but never attaining certainty. Additional illustrations of the general procedure of inductive investigations are given in a chapter on the Character of the Experimentalist, in which I endeavour to show, moreover, that the inverse use of deduction was really the logical method of such great masters of experimental inquiry as Newton, Huyghens, and Faraday.

In treating Generalisation and Analogy, I consider the precautions requisite in inferring from one case to another, or from one part of the universe to another part ; the validity of all such inferences resting ultimately upon the inverse method of probabilities. The treatment of Exceptional Phenomena appeared to afford an interesting subject for a further chapter illustrating the various modes in which an outstanding fact may eventually be explained. The formal part of the book closes with the subject of Classification, which is, however, very inadequately treated. I have, in fact, almost restricted myself to showing that all classification is fundamentally carried out upon the principles of Formal Logic and the Logical Alphabet described at the outset.

In certain concluding remarks I have expressed the conviction which the study of Logic has by degrees forced upon my mind, that serious misconceptions are entertained by some scientific men as to the logical value of our knowledge of nature. We have heard much of what has been aptly called the Reign of Law, and the necessity and uniformity of natural forces has been not uncommonly interpreted as involving the non-existence of an intelligent and benevolent Power, capable of interfering with the course of natural events. Fears have been expressed that the progress of Scientific Method must therefore result in dissipating the fondest beliefs of the human heart. Even the 'Utility of Religion' is seriously proposed as a subject of discussion. It seemed to be not out of place in a work on Scientific Method to allude to the ultimate results and limits of that method. I fear that I have very imperfectly succeeded in expressing my strong conviction that before a rigorous logical scrutiny the Reign of Law will prove to be an unverified hypothesis, the Uniformity of Nature an ambiguous expression, the certainty of our scientific inferences to a great extent a delusion. The value of science is of course very high, while the conclusions are kept well within the limits of the data on which they are founded, but it is pointed out that our experience is of the most limited character compared with what there is to learn, while our mental powers seem to fall infinitely short of the task of comprehending and explaining fully the nature of any one object. I draw the conclusion that we must interpret the results of Scientific Method in an affirmative sense only. Ours must be a truly positive philosophy, not that false negative philosophy which, building on a few material facts, presumes to assert that it has compassed the bounds of existence, while it nevertheless ignores the most unquestionable phenomena of the human mind and feelings.

It is approximately certain that in freely employing illustrations drawn from many different sciences, I have frequently fallen into errors of detail. In this respect I must throw myself upon the indulgence of the reader, who will bear in mind, as I hope, that the scientific facts are generally mentioned purely for the purpose of illustration, so that inaccuracies of detail will not in the majority of cases affect the truth of the general principles illustrated.

December 15, 1872.

PREFACE

FEW alterations of importance have been made in preparing this second edition. Nevertheless, advantage has been taken . of the opportunity to revise very carefully both the language and the matter of the book. Correspondents and critics having pointed out inaccuracies of more or less importance in the first edition, suitable corrections and emendations have been made. I am under obligations to Mr. C. J. Monro, M.A., of Barnet, and to Mr. W. H. Brewer, M.A., one of Her Majesty's Inspectors of Schools, for numerous corrections.

Among several additions which have been made to the text, I may mention the abstract (p. 143) of Professor Clifford's remarkable investigation into the number of types of compound statement involving four classes of objects. This inquiry carries forward the inverse logical problem described in the preceding sections. Again, the need of some better logical method than the old Barbara Celarent, &c., is strikingly shown by Mr. Venn's logical problem, described at p. 90. A great number of candidates in logic and philosophy were tested by Mr. Venn with this problem, which, though simple in reality, was solved by very few of those who were ignorant of Boole's Logic. Other evidence could be adduced by Mr. Venn of the need for some better means of logical training. To enable the logical student to test his skill in the solution of inductive logical problems, I have given (p. 127) a series of ten problems graduated in difficulty.

To prevent misapprehension, it should be mentioned that, throughout this edition, I have substituted the name *Logical Alphabet* for *Logical Abecedarium*, the name applied in the first edition to the exhaustive series of logical combinations represented in terms of A, B, C, D (p. 94). It was objected by some readers that *Abecedarium* is a long and unfamiliar name.

To the chapter on Units and Standards of Measurement, I have added two sections, one (p. 325) containing a brief statement of the Theory of Dimensions, and the other (p. 319) discussing Professor Clerk Maxwell's very original suggestion of a Natural System of Standards for the measurement of space and time, depending upon the length and rapidity of waves of light.

In my description of the Logical Machine in the *Philosophical Transactions* (vol. 160, p. 498), I said—
" It is rarely indeed that any invention is made without some anticipation being sooner or later discovered ; but up to the present time I am totally unaware of even a single previous attempt to devise or construct a machine which should perform the operations of logical inference ; and it is only, I believe, in the satirical writings of Swift that an allusion to an actual reasoning machine is to be found."
Before the paper was printed, however, I was able to refer (p. 518) to the ingenious designs of the late Mr. Alfred Smee as attempts to represent thought mechanically. Mr. Smee's machines indeed were never constructed, and, if constructed, would not have performed actual logical inference. It has now just come to light, however, that the celebrated Lord Stanhope actually did construct a mechanical device, capable of representing syllogistic inferences in a concrete form. It appears that logic was one of the favourite studies of this truly original and ingenious nobleman. There remain fragments of a logical

work, printed by the Earl at his own press, which show that he had arrived, before the year 1800, at the principle of the quantified predicate. He puts forward this principle in the most explicit manner, and proposes to employ it throughout his syllogistic system. Moreover, he converts negative propositions into affirmative ones, and represents these by means of the copula " is identic with." Thus he anticipated, probably by the force of his own unaided insight, the main points of the logical method originated in the works of George Bentham and George Boole, and developed in this work. Stanhope, indeed, has no claim to priority of discovery, because he seems never to have published his logical writings, although they were put into print. There is no trace of them in the British Museum Library, nor in any other library or logical work, so far as I am aware. Both the papers and the logical contrivance have been placed by the present Earl Stanhope in the hands of the Rev. Robert Harley, F.R.S., who will, I hope, soon publish a description of them.[1]

By the kindness of Mr. Harley, I have been able to examine Stanhope's logical contrivance, called by him the Demonstrator. It consists of a square piece of bay-wood with a square depression in the centre, across which two slides can be pushed, one being a piece of red glass, and the other consisting of wood coloured gray. The extent to which each of these slides is pushed in is indicated by scales and figures along the edges of the aperture, and the simple rule of inference adopted by Stanhope is: " To the gray add the red and subtract the *holon*," meaning by holon (ὅλον) the whole width of the aperture. This rule of inference is a curious anticipation of De Morgan's numerically definite syllogism (see below, p. 168), and of inferences founded on what Hamilton called " Ultra-total distribution." Another curious point about Stanhope's

[1] Since the above was written Mr. Harley has read an account of Stanhope's logical remains at the Dublin Meeting (1878) of the British Association. The paper will be printed in *Mind*. (Note added November, 1878.)

device is, that one slide can be drawn out and pushed in again at right angles to the other, and the overlapping part of the slides then represents the probability of a conclusion, derived from two premises of which the• probabilities are respectively represented by the projecting parts of the slides. Thus it appears that Stanhope had studied the logic of probability as well as that of certainty, here again anticipating, however obscurely, the recent progress of logical science. It will be seen, however, that between Stanhope's Demonstrator and my Logical Machine there is no resemblance beyond the fact that they both perform logical inference.

In the first edition I inserted a section (vol. i. p. 25), on "Anticipations of the Principle of Substitution," and I have reprinted that section unchanged in this edition (p. 21). I remark therein that, "In such a subject as logic it is hardly possible to put forth any opinions which have not been in some degree previously entertained. The germ at least of every doctrine will be found in earlier writings, and novelty must arise chiefly in the mode of harmonising and developing ideas." I point out, as Professor T. M. Lindsay had previously done, that Beneke had employed the name and principle of substitution, and that doctrines closely approximating to substitution were stated by the Port Royal Logicians more than 200 years ago.

I have not been at all surprised to learn, however, that other logicians have more or less distinctly stated this principle of substitution during the last two centuries. As my friend and successor at Owens College, Professor Adamson, has discovered, this principle can be traced back to no less a philosopher than Leibnitz.

The remarkable tract of Leibnitz,[1] entitled "Non inelegans Specimen Demonstrandi in Abstractis," commences at once with a definition corresponding to the principle :—

---

[1] Leibnitii *Opera Philosophica quæ extant.* Erdmann, Pars I. Berolini, 1840, p. 94.

"Eadem sunt quorum unum potest substitui alteri salva veritate. Si sint A et B, et A ingrediatur aliquam propositionem veram, et ibi in aliquo loco ipsius A pro ipso substituendo B fiat nova propositio æque itidem vera, idque semper succedat in quacunque tali propositione, A et B dicuntur esse eadem; et contra, si eadem sint A et B, procedet substitutio quam dixi."

Leibnitz, then, explicitly adopts the principle of substitution, but he puts it in the form of a definition, saying that those things are the same which can be substituted one for the other, without affecting the truth of the proposition. It is only after having thus tested the sameness of things that we can turn round and say that A and B, being the same, may be substituted one for the other. It would seem as if we were here in a vicious circle; for we are not allowed to substitute A for B, unless we have ascertained by trial that the result is a true proposition. The difficulty does not seem to be removed by Leibnitz' proviso, "idque semper succedat in quacunque tali propositione." How can we learn that because A and B may be mutually substituted in some propositions, they may therefore be substituted in others; and what is the criterion of likeness of propositions expressed in the word "tali"? Whether the principle of substitution is to be regarded as a postulate, an axiom, or a definition, is just one of those fundamental questions which it seems impossible to settle in the present position of philosophy, but this uncertainty will not prevent our making a considerable step in logical science.

Leibnitz proceeds to establish in the form of a theorem what is usually taken as an axiom, thus (*Opera*, p. 95): "Theorema I. Quæ sunt eadem uni tertio, eadem sunt inter se. Si $A \propto B$ et $B \propto C$, erit $A \propto C$. Nam si in propositione $A \propto B$ (vera ea hypothesi) substituitur C in locum B (quod facere licet per Def. I. quia $B \propto C$ ex hypothesi) fiet $A \propto C$. Q. E. Dem." Thus Leibnitz precisely anticipates the mode of treating inference with two simple identities described at p. 51 of this work.

Even the mathematical axiom that 'equals added to equals make equals,' is deduced from the principle of substitution. At p. 95 of Erdmann's edition, we find: "Si eidem addantur coincidentia fiunt coincidentia. Si $A \propto B$, erit $A + C \propto B + C$. Nam si in propositione $A + C \propto A + C$ (quæ est vera per se) pro A semel substituas B (quod facere licet per Def. I. quia $A \propto B$) fiet $A + C \propto B + C$ Q. E. Dem." This is unquestionably the mode of deducing the several axioms of mathematical reasoning from the higher axiom of substitution, which is explained in the section on mathematical inference (p. 162) in this work, and which had been previously stated in my *Substitution of Similars*, p. 16.

There are one or two other brief tracts in which Leibnitz anticipates the modern views of logic. Thus in the eighteenth tract in Erdmann's edition (p. 92), called "Fundamenta Calculi Ratiocinatoris, he says: "Inter ea quorum unum alteri substitui potest, salvis calculi legibus, dicetur esse æquipollentiam." There is evidence, also, that he had arrived at the quantification of the predicate, and that he fully understood the reduction of the universal affirmative proposition to the form of an equation, which is the key to an improved view of logic. Thus, in the tract entitled "Difficultates Quædam Logicæ,"[1] he says : "Omne A est B; id est æquivalent AB et A, seu A non B est non-ens."

It is curious to find, too, that Leibnitz was fully acquainted with the Laws of Commutativeness and "Simplicity" (as I have called the second law) attaching to logical symbols. In the "Addenda ad Specimen Calculi Universalis" we read as follows.[2] "Transpositio literarum in eodem termino nihil mutat, ut ab coincidet cum ba, seu animal rationale et rationale animal."

"Repetitio ejusdem literæ in eodem termino est inutilis, ut b est aa; vel bb est a; homo est animal animal, vel homo homo est animal. Sufficit enim dici a est b, seu homo est animal."

---

[1] Erdmann, p. 102.   [2] Ibid p. 98.

Comparing this with what is stated in Boole's *Mathematical Analysis of Logic*, pp. 17-18, in his *Laws of Thought*, p. 29, or in this work, pp. 32-35, we find that Leibnitz had arrived two centuries ago at a clear perception of the bases of logical notation. When Boole pointed out that, in logic, $xx = x$, this seemed to mathematicians to be a paradox, or in any case a wholly new discovery; but here we have it plainly stated by Leibnitz.

The reader must not assume, however, that because Leibnitz correctly apprehended the fundamental principles of logic, he left nothing for modern logicians to do. On the contrary, Leibnitz obtained no useful results from his definition of substitution. When he proceeds to explain the syllogism, as in the paper on "Definitiones Logicæ,"[1] he gives up substitution altogether, and falls back upon the notion of inclusion of class in class, saying, "Includens includentis est includens inclusi, seu si A includit B et B includit C, etiam A includet C." He proceeds to make out certain rules of the syllogism involving the distinction of subject and predicate, and in no important respect better than the old rules of the syllogism. Leibnitz' logical tracts are, in fact, little more than brief memoranda of investigations which seem never to have been followed out. They remain as evidence of his wonderful sagacity, but it would be difficult to show that they have had any influence on the progress of logical science in recent times.

I should like to explain how it happened that these logical writings of Leibnitz were unknown to me, until within the last twelve months. I am so slow a reader of Latin books, indeed, that my overlooking a few pages of Leibnitz' works would not have been in any case surprising. But the fact is that the copy of Leibnitz' works of which I made occasional use, was one of the edition of Dutens, contained in Owens College Library. The logical tracts in question were not printed in that

[1] Erdmann, p. 100.

edition, and with one exception, they remained in manuscript in the Royal Library at Hanover, until edited by Erdmann, in 1839-40. The tract "Difficultates Quædam Logicæ," though not known to Dutens, was published by Raspe in 1765, in his collection called *Œuvres Philosophiques de feu M*ʳ *Leibnitz;* but this work had not come to my notice, nor does the tract in question seem to contain any explicit statement of the principle of substitution.

It is, I presume, the comparatively recent publication of Leibnitz' most remarkable logical tracts which explains the apparent ignorance of logicians as regards their contents and importance. The most learned logicians, such as Hamilton and Ueberweg, ignore Leibnitz' principle of substitution. In the Appendix to the fourth volume of Hamilton's *Lectures on Metaphysics and Logic,* is given an elaborate compendium of the views of logical writers concerning the ultimate basis of deductive reasoning. Leibnitz is briefly noticed on p. 319, but without any hint of substitution. He is here quoted as saying, "What are the same with the same third, are the same with each other; that is, if *A* be the same with *B*, and *C* be the same with *B*, it is necessary that *A* and *C* should also be the same with one another. For this principle flows immediately from the principle of contradiction, and is the ground and basis of all logic; if that fail, there is no longer any way of reasoning with certainty." This view of the matter seems to be inconsistent with that which he adopted in his posthumous tract.

Dr. Thomson, indeed, was acquainted with Leibnitz' tracts, and refers to them in his *Outline of the Necessary Laws of Thought.* He calls them valuable; nevertheless, he seems to have missed the really valuable point; for in making two brief quotations,[1] he omits all mention of the principle of substitution.

Ueberweg is probably considered the best authority

---

[1] Fifth Edition, 1860, p. 158.

concerning the history of logic, and in his well-known *System of Logic and History of Logical Doctrines*,[1] he gives some account of the principle of substitution, especially as it is implicitly stated in the *Port Royal Logic*. But he omits all reference to Leibnitz in this connection, nor doe : he elsewhere, so far as I can find, supply the omission. His English editor, Professor T. M. Lindsay, in referring to my *Substitution of Similars*, points out how I was anticipated by Beneke; but he also ignores Leibnitz. It is thus apparent that the most learned logicians, even when writing especially on the history of logic, displayed ignorance of Leibnitz' most valuable logical writings.

It has been recently pointed out to me, however, that the Rev. Robert Harley did draw attention, at ζhe Nottingham Meeting of the British Association, in 1866, to Leibnitz' anticipations of Boole's laws of logical notation,[2] and I am informed that Boole, about a year after the publication of his *Laws of Thought*, was made acquainted with these anticipations by R. Leslie Ellis.

There seems to have been at least one other German logician who discovered, or adopted, the principle of substitution. Reusch, in his *Systema Logicum*, published in 1734, laboured to give a broader basis to the *Dictum de Omni et Nullo*. He argues, that " the whole business of ordinary reasoning is accomplished by the substitution of ideas in place of the subject or predicate of the fundamental proposition. This some call the *equation of thoughts*." But, in the hands of Reusch, substitution does not seem to lead to simplicity, since it has to be carried on according to the rules of Equipollence, Reciprocation, Subordination, and Co-ordination.[3] Reusch is elsewhere spoken of[4] as the " celebrated Reusch "; nevertheless, I have not been able to

[1] Section 120.
[2] See his "Remarks on Boole's Mathematical Analysis of Logic." *Report of the 36th Meeting of the British Association, Transactions of the Sections*, pp. 3—6.
[3] Hamilton's Lectures, vol. iv. p. 319.
[4] Ibid. p. 326.

find a copy of his book in London, even in the British Museum Library; it is not mentioned in the printed catalogue of the Bodleian Library; Messrs. Asher have failed to obtain it for me by advertisement in Germany; and Professor Adamson has been equally unsuccessful. From the way in which the principle of substitution is mentioned by Reusch, it would seem likely that other logicians of the early part of the eighteenth century were acquainted with it; but, if so, it is still more curious that recent historians of logical science have overlooked the doctrine.

It is a strange and discouraging fact, that true views of logic should have been discovered and discussed from one to two centuries ago, and yet should have remained, like George Bentham's work in this century, without influence on the subsequent progress of the science. It may be regarded as certain that none of the discoverers of the quantification of the predicate, Bentham, Hamilton, Thomson, De Morgan, and Boole, were in any way assisted by the hints of the principle contained in previous writers. As to my own views of logic, they were originally moulded by a careful study of Boole's works, as fully stated in my first logical essay.[1] As to the process of substitution, it was not learnt from any work on logic, but is simply the process of substitution perfectly familiar to mathematicians, and with which I necessarily became familiar in the course of my long-continued study of mathematics under the late Professor De Morgan.

I find that the Theory of Number, which I explained in the eighth chapter of this work, is also partially anticipated in a single scholium of Leibnitz. He first gives as an axiom the now well-known law of Boole, as follows:—

"Axioma I. Si idem secum ipso sumatur, nihil constituitur novum, seu $A + A \propto A$." Then follows this

---

[1] *Pure Logic, or the Logic of Quality apart from Quantity; with Remarks on Boole's System, and on the Relation of Logic and Mathematics.* London, 1864, p. 3.

remarkable scholium : " Equidem in numeris 4 + 4 facit 8, seu bini nummi binis additi faciunt quatuor nummos, sed tunc bini additi sunt alii a prioribus ; si iidem essent nihil novi prodiret et perinde esset ac si joco ex tribus ovis facere vellemus sex numerando, primum 3 ova, deinde • uno sublato residua 2, ac denique uno rursus sublato residuum."

Translated this would read as follows :—

" Axiom I. If the same thing is taken together with itself, nothing new arises, or $A + A = A$.

" Scholium. In numbers, indeed, 4 + 4 makes 8, or two coins added to two coins make four coins, but then the two added are different from the former ones ; if they were the same nothing new would be produced, and it would be just as if we tried in joke to make six eggs out of three, by counting firstly the three eggs, then, one being removed, counting the remaining two, and lastly, one being again removed, counting the remaining egg."

Compare the above with pp. 156 to 162 of the present work.

M. Littré has quite recently pointed out [1] what he thinks is an analogy between the system of formal logic, stated in the following pages, and the logical devices of the celebrated Raymond Lully. Lully's method of invention was described in a great number of mediæval books, but is best stated in his *Ars Compendiosa Inveniendi Veritatem, seu Ars Magna et Major.* This method consisted in placing various names of things in the sectors of concentric circles, so that when the circles were turned, every possible combination of the things was easily produced by mechanical means. It might, perhaps, be possible to discover in this method a vague and rude anticipation of combinational logic ; but it is well known that the results of Lully's method were usually of a fanciful, if not absurd character.

A much closer analogue of the Logical Alphabet is probably to be found in the Logical Square, invented by

[1] *La Philosophie Positive* Mai-Juin, 1877, tom. xviii. p. 456.

John Christian Lange, and described in a rare and unnoticed work by him which I have recently found in the
British Museum.[1] This square involved the principle of
bifurcate classification, and was an improved form of the
Ramean and Porphyrian tree (see below, p. 702). Lange
seems, indeed, to have worked out his Logical Square
into a mechanical form, and he suggests that it might be
employed somewhat in the manner of Napier's Bones
(p. 65). There is much analogy between his Square and
my Abacus, but Lange had not arrived at a logical system
enabling him to use his invention for logical inference in
the manner of the Logical Abacus. Another work of
Lange is said to contain the first publication of the well
known Eulerian diagrams of proposition and syllogism.[2]

Since the first edition was published, an important
work by Mr. George Lewes has appeared, namely, his
Problems of Life and Mind, which to a great extent treats
of scientific method, and formulates the rules of philosophising. I should have liked to discuss the bearing
of Mr. Lewes's views upon those here propounded, but
I have felt it to be impossible in a book already filling
nearly 800 pages, to enter upon the discussion of a
yet more extensive book. For the same reason I have
not been able to compare my own treatment of the subject
of probability with the views expressed by Mr. Venn in
his *Logic of Chance*. With Mr. J. J. Murphy's profound
and remarkable works on *Habit and Intelligence*, and on
The Scientific Basis of Faith, I was unfortunately unacquainted when I wrote the following pages. They cannot safely be overlooked by any one who wishes to
comprehend the tendency of philosophy and scientific
method in the present day.

It seems desirable that I should endeavour to answer
some of the critics who have pointed out what they

[1] *Inventum Novum Quadrati Logici*, &c., Gissæ Hassorum, 1714,
8vo.
[2] See *Ueberweg's System of Logic*, &c., translated by Lindsay, p. 302.

consider defects in the doctrines of this book, especially in the first part, which treats of deduction. Some of the notices of the work were indeed rather statements of its contents than critiques. Thus, I am much indebted to M. Louis Liard, Professor of Philosophy at Bordeaux, for the very careful exposition [1] of the substitutional view of logic which he gave in the excellent *Revue Philosophique*, edited by M. Ribot. (Mars, 1877, tom. iii. p. 277.) An equally careful account of the system was given by M. Riehl, Professor of Philosophy at Graz, in his article on "Die Englische Logik der Gegenwart," published in the *Vierteljahrsschrift für wissenschaftliche Philosophie*. (1 Heft, Leipzig, 1876.) I should like to acknowledge also the careful and able manner in which my book was reviewed by the *New York Daily Tribune* and the *New York Times*.

The most serious objections which have been brought against my treatment of logic have regard to my failure to enter into an analysis of the ultimate nature and origin of the Laws of Thought. The *Spectator*,[2] for instance, in the course of a careful review, says of the principle of substitution, " Surely it is a great omission not to discuss whence we get this great principle itself; whether it is a pure law of the mind, or only an approximate lesson of experience; and if a pure product of the mind, whether there are any other products of the same kind, furnished by our knowing faculty itself." Professor Robertson, in his very acute review,[3] likewise objects to the want of

---

[1] Since the above was written M. Liard has republished this exposition as one chapter of an interesting and admirably lucid account of the progress of logical science in England. After a brief but clear introduction, treating of the views of Herschel, Mill, and others concerning Inductive Logic, M. Liard describes in succession the logical systems of George Bentham, Hamilton, De Morgan, Boole, and that contained in the present work. The title of the book is as follows :—*Les Logiciens Anglais Contemporains*. Par Louis Liard, Professeur de Philosophie à la Faculté des Lettres de Bordeaux. Paris : Librairie Germer Baillière. 1878. (Note added November, 1878.)

[2] *Spectator*, September 19, 1874, p. 1178. A second portion of the review appeared in the same journal for September 26, 1874, p. 1204.

[3] *Mind :* a Quarterly Review of Psychology and Philosophy. No. II. April 1876. Vol. I. p. 206.

psychological and philosophical analysis. "If the book really corresponded to its title, Mr. Jevons could hardly have passed so lightly over the question, which he does not omit to raise, concerning those undoubted principles of knowledge commonly called the Laws of Thought . . . . Everywhere, indeed, he appears least at ease when he touches on questions properly philosophical; nor is he satisfactory in his psychological references, as on pp. 4, 5, where he cannot commit himself to a statement without an accompaniment of 'probably,' 'almost,' or 'hardly.' Reservations are often very much in place, but there are fundamental questions on which it is proper to make up one's mind."

These remarks appear to me to be well founded, and I must state why it is that I have ventured to publish an extensive work on logic, without properly making up my mind as to the fundamental nature of the reasoning process. The fault after all is one of omission rather than of commission. It is open to me on a future occasion to supply the deficiency if I should ever feel able to undertake the task. But I do not conceive it to be an essential part of any treatise to enter into an ultimate analysis of its subject matter. Analyses must always end somewhere. There were good treatises on light which described the laws of the phenomenon correctly before it was known whether light consisted of undulations or of projected particles. Now we have treatises on the Undulatory Theory which are very valuable and satisfactory, although they leave us in almost complete doubt as to what the vibrating medium really is. So I think that, in the present day, we need a correct and scientific exhibition of the formal laws of thought, and of the forms of reasoning based on them, although we may not be able to enter into any complete analysis of the nature of those laws. What would the science of geometry be like now if the Greek geometers had decided that it was improper to publish any propositions before they had decided on

the nature of an axiom ?   Where would the science of
arithmetic be now if an analysis of the nature of number
itself were a necessary preliminary to a development of
the results of its laws ?   In recent times there have been
enormous additions to the mathematical sciences, but very
few attempts at psychological analysis.   In the Alexandrian and early mediæval schools of philosophy, much
attention was given to the nature of unity and plurality
chiefly called forth by the question of the Trinity.   In
the last two centuries whole sciences have been created
out of the notion of plurality, and yet speculation on the
nature of plurality has dwindled away.   This present
treatise contains, in the eighth chapter, one of the few
recent attempts to analyse the notion of number itself.

If further illustration is needed, I may refer to the
differential calculus.   Nobody calls in question the formal
truth of the results of that calculus.   All the more exact
and successful parts of physical science depend upon its
use, and yet the mathematicians who have created so
great a body of exact truths have never decided upon
the basis of the calculus.   What is the nature of a limit
or the nature of an infinitesimal ?   Start the question
among a knot of mathematicians, and it will be found
that hardly two agree, unless it is in regarding the question
itself as a trifling one.   Some hold that there are no such
things as infinitesimals, and that it is all a question of
limits.   Others would argue that the infinitesimal is the
necessary outcome of the limit, but various shades of
intermediate opinion spring up.

Now it is just the same with logic.   If the forms of
deductive and inductive reasoning given in the earlier
part of this treatise are correct, they constitute a definite
addition to logical science, and it would have been absurd
to decline to publish such results because I could not at
the same time decide in my own mind about the psychology and philosophy of the subject.   It comes in short
to this, that my book is a book on Formal Logic and

Scientific Method, and not a book on psychology and philosophy.

It may be objected, indeed, as the *Spectator* objects, that Mill's System of Logic is particularly strong in the discussion of the psychological foundations of reasoning, so that Mill would appear to have successfully treated that which I feel myself to be incapable of attempting at present. If Mill's analysis of knowledge is correct, then I have nothing to say in excuse for my own deficiencies. But it is well to do one thing at a time, and therefore I have not occupied any considerable part of this book with controversy and refutation. What I have to say of Mill's logic will be said in a separate work, in which his analysis of knowledge will be somewhat minutely analysed. It will then be shown, I believe, that Mill's psychological and philosophical treatment of logic has not yielded such satisfactory results as some writers seem to believe.[1]

Various minor but still important criticisms were made by Professor Robertson, a few of which have been noticed in the text (pp. 27, 101). In other cases his objections hardly admit of any other answer than such as consists in asking the reader to judge between the work and the criticism. Thus Mr. Robertson asserts[2] that the most complex logical problems solved in this book (up to p. 102 of this edition) might be more easily and shortly dealt with upon the principles and with the recognised methods of the traditional logic. The burden of proof here lies upon Mr. Robertson, and his only proof consists in a single case, where he is able, as it seems to me accidentally, to get a special conclusion by the old form of dilemma. It would be a long labour to test the old logic upon every result obtained by my notation, and I must leave such

---

[1] Portions of this work have already been published in my articles, entitled "John Stuart Mill's Philosophy Tested," printed in the *Contemporary Review* for December, 1877, vol. xxxi. p. 167, and for January and April, 1878, vol. xxxi. p. 256, and vol. xxxii. p. 88. (Note added in November, 1878.)   [2] *Mind*, vol. i. p. 222

readers as are well acquainted with the syllogistic logic to pronounce upon the comparative simplicity and power of the new and old systems.   For other acute objections brought forward by Mr. Robertson, I must refer the reader to the article in question.

One point in my last chapter, that on the Results and Limits of Scientific Method, has been criticised by Professor W. K. Clifford in his lecture[1] on "The First and the Last Catastrophe."   In vol. ii. p. 438 of the first edition (p. 744 of this edition) I referred to certain inferences drawn by eminent physicists as to a limit to the antiquity of the present order of things.   " According to Sir W. Thomson's deductions from Fourier's *theory of heat,* we can trace down the dissipation of heat by conduction and radiation to an infinitely distant time when all things will be uniformly cold.   But we cannot similarly trace the Heat-history of the Universe to an infinite distance in the past.   For a certain negative value of the time, the formulæ give impossible values, indicating that there was some initial distribution of heat which could not have resulted, according to known laws of nature, from any previous distribution."

Now according to Professor Clifford I have here misstated Thomson's results.   " It is not according to the known laws of nature, it is according to the known laws of conduction of heat, that Sir William Thomson is speaking. . . . All these physical writers, knowing what they were writing about, simply drew such conclusions from the facts which were before them as could be reasonably drawn.   They say, here is a state of things which could not have been produced by the circumstances we are at present investigating   Then your speculator comes, he reads a sentence and says, ' Here is an opportunity for me to have my fling.'   And he has his fling, and makes a purely baseless theory about the necessary origin of the

[1] *Fortnightly Review,* New Series, April 1875, p. 480.   Lecture reprinted by the Sunday Lecture Society, p. 24.

present order of nature at some definite point of time, which might be calculated."

Professor Clifford proceeds to explain that Thomson's formulæ only give a limit to the heat history of, say, the earth's crust in the solid state. We are led back to the time when it became solidified from the fluid condition. There is discontinuity in the history of the solid matter, but still discontinuity which is within our comprehension. Still further back we should come to discontinuity again, when the liquid was formed by the condensation of heated gaseous matter. Beyond that event, however, there is no need to suppose further discontinuity of law, for the gaseous matter might consist of molecules which had been falling together from different parts of space through infinite past time. As Professor Clifford says (p. 481) of the bodies of the universe, " What they have actually done is to fall together and get solid. If we should reverse the process we should see them separating and getting cool, and as a limit to that, we should find that all these bodies would be resolved into molecules, and all these would be flying away from each other. There would be no limit to that process, and we could trace it as far back as ever we liked to trace it."

Assuming that I have erred, I should like to point out that I have erred in the best company, or more strictly, being a speculator, I have been led into error by the best physical writers. Professor Tait, in his *Sketch of Thermodynamics*, speaking of the laws discovered by Fourier for the motion of heat in a solid, says, " Their mathematical expressions point also to the fact that a uniform distribution of heat, or a distribution tending to become uniform, must have arisen from some primitive distribution of heat of a kind not capable of being produced by known laws from any previous distribution." In the latter words it will be seen that there is no limitation to the laws of conduction, and, although I had carefully referred to Sir W. Thomson's original paper, it is not unnatural that I should take Professor Tait's interpretion of its meaning.[1]

In his new work *On some Recent Advances in Physical Science*, Professor Tait has recurred to the subject as follows :[2] " A profound lesson may be learned from one of the earliest little papers of Sir W. Thomson, published while he was an undergraduate at Cambridge, where he shows that Fourier's magnificent treatment of the conduction of heat [in a solid body] leads to formulæ for its distribution which are intelligible (and of course capable of being fully verified by experiment) for all time future, but which, except in particular cases, when extended to time past, remain intelligible for a finite period only, and *then* indicate a state of things which could not have resulted under known laws from any conceivable previous distribution [of heat in the body]. So far as heat is concerned, modern investigations have shown that a previous distribution of the *matter* involved may, by its potential energy, be capable of producing such a state of things at the moment of its aggregation ; but the example is now adduced not for its bearing on heat alone, but as a simple illustration of the fact that all portions of our Science, especially that beautiful one, the Dissipation of Energy, point unanimously to a beginning, to a state of things incapable of being derived by present laws [of. tangible matter and its energy] from any conceivable previous arrangement." As this was published nearly a year after Professor Clifford's lecture, it may be inferred

---

[1] Sir W. Thomson's words are as follows (*Cambridge Mathematical Journal*, Nov. 1842, vol. iii. p. 174). " When x is negative, the state represented cannot be the result of any *possible* distribution of temperature which has previously existed." There is no limitation in the sentence to the laws of conduction, but, as the whole paper treats of the results of conduction in a solid, it may no doubt be understood that there is a *tacit* limitation. See also a second paper on the subject in the same journal for February, 1844, vol. iv. p. 67, where again there is no expressed limitation.

[2] Pp. 25-26. The parentheses are in the original, and show Professor Tait's corrections in the verbatim reports of his lectures. The subject is treated again on pp. 168-9.

that Professor Tait adheres to his original opinion that the theory of heat does give evidence of " a beginning."

I may add that Professor Clerk Maxwell's words seem to countenance the same view, for he says,[1] " This is only one of the cases in which a consideration of the dissipation of energy leads to the determination of a superior limit to the antiquity of the observed order of things." The expression " observed order of things " is open to much ambiguity, but in the absence of qualification I should take it to include the aggregate of the laws of nature known to us. I should interpret Professor Maxwell as meaning that the theory of heat indicates the occurrence of some event of which our science cannot give any further explanation. The physical writers thus seem not to be so clear about the matter as Professor Clifford assumes.

So far as I may venture to form an independent opinion on the subject, it is to the effect that Professor Clifford is right, and that the known laws of nature do not enable us to assign a " beginning." Science leads us backwards into infinite past duration. But that Professor Clifford is right on this point, is no reason why we should suppose him to be right in his other opinions, some of which I am sure are wrong. Nor is it a reason why other parts of my last chapter should be wrong. The question only affects the single paragraph on pp. 744-5 of this book, which might, I believe, be struck out without necessitating any alteration in the rest of the text. It is always to be remembered that the failure of an argument in favour of a proposition does not, generally speaking, add much, if any, probability to the contradictory proposition. I cannot conclude without expressing my acknowledgments to Professor Clifford for his kind expressions regarding my work as a whole.

[1] *Theory of Heat*, 1871, p. 245.

2, THE CHESTNUTS,
  WEST HEATH,
    HAMPSTEAD, N.W.
August 15, 1877.

CONTENTS.

BOOK I.

FORMAL LOGIC, DEDUCTIVE AND INDUCTIVE.

CHAPTER I.

INTRODUCTION.

CHAPTER II.

TERMS.

CHAPTER III.

PROPOSITIONS

CHAPTER IV.

DEDUCTIVE REASONING.

CHAPTER V.

DISJUNCTIVE PROPOSITIONS.

CHAPTER VI.

THE INDIRECT METHOD OF INFERENCE.

CHAPTER VII.

INDUCTION.

BOOK II.

NUMBER, VARIETY, AND PROBABILITY.

CHAPTER VIII.

PRINCIPLES OF NUMBER.

CHAPTER IX.

THE VARIETY OF NATURE, OR THE DOCTRINE OF COMBINATIONS AND PERMUTATIONS.

CHAPTER X.

THEORY OF PROBABILITY.

CHAPTER XI.

PHILOSOPHY OF INDUCTIVE INFERENCE.

CHAPTER XII.

THE INDUCTIVE OR INVERSE APPLICATION OF THE THEORY
OF PROBABILITY.

BOOK III.

METHODS OF MEASUREMENT.

CHAPTER XIII.

THE EXACT MEASUREMENT OF PHENOMENA.

CHAPTER XIV.

UNITS AND STANDARDS OF MEASUREMENT

CHAPTER XV.

ANALYSIS OF QUANTITATIVE PHENOMENA.

CHAPTER XVI.

THE METHOD OF MEANS.

CHAPTER XVII.

THE LAW OF ERROR.

BOOK IV.

INDUCTIVE INVESTIGATION.

CHAPTER XVIII.

OBSERVATION.

CHAPTER XIX.

EXPERIMENT.

CHAPTER XX.

METHOD OF VARIATIONS.

CHAPTER XXI.

THEORY OF APPROXIMATION.

CHAPTER XXII

QUANTITATIVE INDUCTION.

CHAPTER XXIII.

THE USE OF HYPOTHESIS.

CHAPTER XXIV.

EMPIRICAL KNOWLEDGE, EXPLANATION AND PREDICTION.

CHAPTER XXV.

ACCORDANCE OF QUANTITATIVE THEORIES.

CHAPTER XXVI.

CHARACTER OF THE EXPERIMENTALIST.

BOOK V.

GENERALISATION, ANALOGY, AND CLASSIFICATION.

CHAPTER XXVII.

GENERALISATION.

CHAPTER XXVIII.

ANALOGY.

CHAPTER XXIX.

EXCEPTIONAL PHENOMENA.

CHAPTER XXX.

CLASSIFICATION.

BOOK VI.

CHAPTER XXXI.

REFLECTIONS ON THE RESULTS AND LIMITS OF SCIENTIFIC METHOD.

INTRODUCTION

TO THE DOVER EDITION

The past half century has witnessed profound advances in experimental knowledge and scientific theory, in analyses of the foundations of mathematics and of formal logic, and in conceptions concerning the nature of science and scientific method. But despite the fact that William Stanley Jevons' *The Principles of Science* was written long before these developments took place (the first edition was published in 1874, the second and final one in 1877), it is still full of valuable information about scientific practice, and continues to be of interest as an attempt to articulate the logic of scientific inquiry.

Jevons was well equipped by education and intellectual achievements to write illuminatingly on the logic of science. He was a man with versatile talents and interests, and like other British writers on logic he is a significant figure in the history of economics. He had some practical knowledge of metallurgy, did research in meteorology, and had a background of unusually wide reading in physical science. He played an important role in the development of modern symbolic logic, and pioneered in the construction of calculating machines. He broke new ground in using statistical data for the study of economic trends; his foundational contributions to the mathematical theory of economic utility, while anticipated by Walras and others elsewhere in Europe, initiated a new period in English economic theory, and assure him a secure place in the history of science.

Jevons was born in Liverpool, England, in 1835, the son of an iron merchant who was actively interested in the engineering innovations of his day as well as in the social and economic problems of the time. Jevons was thus brought up in an environment favorable to the development of a wide range of intellectual pursuits. His formal education was nevertheless chiefly in mathematics and the natural sciences, including metallurgy. The severe economic crisis of 1848 eventually bankrupted his father; and in order to lighten the financial burdens of his family Jevons interrupted his schooling at University College, London, in 1854, and accepted a desirable post as assayer in the mint in Sydney, Australia. The five years he spent away from England, though he felt lonely and cut off from his life's ambitions, were evidently profitable ones for him, for they provided a foundation for the ideas which later lifted him out of obscurity. He also found time to send weekly meteorological reports to an Australian newspaper, and to contribute papers on this and allied subjects to technical periodicals.

Jevons returned to England in 1859 in order to complete his graduate study at University College, and then sought with melancholy patience to win a place for himself in British intellectual life. His early publications on logic, the statistical study of economic fluctuations, and other scientific subjects attracted little attention at first. It was not until the appearance in 1865 of his book on *The Coal Question,* in which he argued that the industrial eminence of England was threatened by the foreseeable exhaustion of her coal mines, that he came to the notice of Gladstone and acquired national prestige as an economic thinker. Two years later he was appointed Professor of Logic, Mental and Moral Philosophy, and Political Economy at Owens College, Manchester. His marriage the same year to the daughter of the founder and owner of *The Manchester Guardian* gave him *entrée* to a politically important circle of thinkers and thereby helped spread his influence. The publication in 1871 of *The Theory of Political Economy,* a systematic exposition of his early ideas on utility as a quantity which provides the key to the understanding of the phenomena of the economic market, established him as an economic theorist of the first rank; and his later tentative speculations on the relation between sunspots and economic crises even brought him a measure of notoriety. But he did not cease to cultivate his taste for logic even after he left Manchester in 1876 to become Professor of Political Economy at University College. Indeed, the larger half of Jevons' published writings are on logical and philosophical questions; and his text-books on elementary logic, if judged by the size of their sales, are among the most successful ever written. Jevons died prematurely in 1882 by accidental drowning.

The Principles of Science is Jevons' chief logical work. Two outstanding features of the book in particular made it a work in advance of commonly held opinions in his day, and give it the accents of current modernity. It was composed when the renaissance of formal logic, effectively initiated by George Boole in 1847, had barely begun and was not widely known; and it appeared when the influence upon British thought of John Stuart Mill's views on scientific method (and through Mill, of the Baconian conceptions of experimental science) were still at their height. *The Principles of Science* has much to say, explicitly or by implication, on both these matters.

Jevons was a close student of the fresh turn in the analysis of formal inference, and *The Principles of Science* contains his most detailed account of the im-

provements he made in the Boolean algebra of logic.
Boole had adapted the notation of algebra for expressing
various logical relations between classes and between
propositions, and had thereby constructed a symbolic
instrument for handling effectively a much larger range
of deductive problems than could be solved by the traditional theory of the syllogism. But in building up his
system Boole interpreted the connective "either-or" in
the *exclusive* sense (i.e., "A or B" was taken to mean
that just one but not both of the alternatives holds); and
he also permitted his logical operations of addition and
multiplication to have inverses. He was thereby compelled to sanction formulas that could not be interpreted
in terms of the basic logical ideas he assumed. Jevons
emended the Boolean system by adopting the *inclusive*
use of "or" (i.e., "A or B" is construed as meaning that
at least one of the alternatives, and perhaps both, holds),
and by rejecting those Boolean operations which led to
logically uninterpretable formulas. These changes resulted in a great simplification of the logical algebra,
and the Jevonian modifications have been adopted by
almost all subsequent writers on the subject.

Jevons was convinced that the new logic was the true
organon of deductive reasoning, and he apparently believed that his own system was adequate for rendering
every deductive argument. In point of fact, however, he
overestimated the power of his calculus, as more recent
research makes clear. Although the Jevonian system is
certainly more comprehensive than the traditional Aris-
totelian-scholastic logic, Jevons does not develop the
analysis of logical quantification (i.e., of the structure of,
and the relations between, statements containing such
"quantifiers" as "all" and "some") beyond what this
tradition in effect achieved; and he does not even suggest
the possibility of a calculus of relations. Accordingly, it
is difficult to be sure of just what he meant by his intri-

guingly suggestive claim that the science of number "rests on logic" and that "number is but logical discrimination, and algebra a highly developed logic." This sounds as if Jevons were here anticipating the Frege-Russell thesis that number is definable in terms of the ideas of pure logic and that the propositions of arithmetic are transcriptions of logically certifiable truths. But it would be quite anachronistic to construe Jevons' dicta in this sense; and it is in any event not possible to build up even elementary arithmetic within the framework of his limited logical apparatus.

The Jevonian logic is indeed only the logic of classes (terms) and of propositions, neither of which is sufficient to analyze most of the deductions performed in modern physical science, and both of which are only elementary though important parts of the modern theory of deductive inference. Nevertheless, Jevons had a just estimate of the promise of the new logic, and he is quite admirable in his inevitably premature attempt to exhibit the deductive operations of science as illustrations of a comprehensive theory of formal logic. Moreover, although it is now known that the reduction of all deductive inference to a quasi-mechanical calculatory process is impossible, Jevons was far ahead of his time in effecting such a reduction for an important class of deductions. His discussion of the principles underlying the construction of his logical piano (a machine for automatically solving deductive problems in the logic of classes) is still a useful introduction to the principles upon which the more efficient and more powerful modern computing machines are based.

Jevons saw clearly the hopeless inadequacy of the conception that construes scientific inquiry as a routine process in which "facts" are supposedly first accumulated without benefit of any "anticipations of nature," then

classified on the basis of some manifest traits they exhibit, and finally sifted for the common properties or
"generalizations" inherent in them. In contradistinction
to such a view, he stressed the function of conjectures or
anticipatory ideas in the conduct of research, and he
recognized fully the role of hypothesis in the selection
and interpretation of factual data and in the explanation
of experimental findings. "All inductive investigation,"
he succinctly declared, "consists in the marriage of hypothesis and experiment."

Jevons describes induction as "the inference of general
from particular truths" and as "the inverse operation of
deduction." This does not mean, as a hasty reading might
lead one to suppose, that according to Jevons general
truths can be inferred deductively from particular ones.
For as he explicitly notes, "induction is the decyphering
of the hidden meaning of natural phenomena," and to
achieve the ends of this process we must invent hypotheses until we hit upon one which yields deductive results in accordance with experience. Accordingly, induction is the inverse operation of deduction in the sense
that a supposed law of nature can be established or
refuted only by deducing logical consequences of some
hypothesis and comparing some of these consequences
with the data of observation. *The Principles of Science*
is noteworthy for its vivid and richly illustrated account
of this hypothetico-deductive method which Jevons took
to be the essence of sound scientific procedure. His
analysis of the nature of explanation in science is in conformity with this emphasis, and more recent discussions
of this question add substantially little to what Jevons
contributed.

It is nevertheless surprising in this connection that
Jevons' comments on geometry are so curiously brief.
The philosophy of geometry was undergoing a funda-

mental revolution during the second half of the 19th century, as a result of the development of non-Euclidean geometries. Jevons was in a position to be familiar with these advances, especially since he corresponded with W. K. Clifford, one of the contributors to the new knowledge. Although a discussion of these developments would have fortified Jevons' analysis of scientific method (and incidentally would certainly have enabled him to score heavily against the views of John Stuart Mill, toward whom he possessed an almost pathological hostility), there is no reference to them in *The Principles of Science*.

Jevons was not the first writer to argue for the central place in the logic of science of the hypothetico-deductive method. However, unlike some of his predecessors, and especially William Whewell, he denied that this method could yield logically certain conclusions, and he maintained with great vigor that the generalizations of science could be established as only probable, at best. He based this claim on a three-fold ground. In the first place, it is a formal fallacy to hold that if the consequences of a hypothesis are in ostensible agreement with the experimental evidence, the hypothesis is necessarily true—since the evidential statements do not logically imply the hypothesis, so that the former could in fact be true and the latter false. In the second place, the empirical data used to test a hypothesis are rarely if ever known to be the complete set of relevant data, and there is no logical guarantee that the still unexamined empirical facts will be in agreement with the hypothesis under discussion. And in the third place, the agreement of experimental data with an assumed law is in most cases only approximate, and in the quantitative sciences especially it is never absolutely precise. In this connection, Jevons' account of measurement, and his discussion of how misleading is the label "exact" often used to designate some branches of science, is particularly illuminating. He was undoubtedly among the first to recognize clearly the probabilistic character of scientific inquiry; and in consequence of this important insight, *The Principles of Science* assigns a basic role in its exposition and illustration of scientific method to the mathematical theory of probability.

Jevons viewed the theory of probability, as he did formal logic, as a normative doctrine, not a descriptive one—whether of actual states of mind or of statistical frequencies. Probability for him was a measure of reasonable belief (i.e., of the belief a man *ought* to entertain) in a hypothesis relative to given evidence. He adopted without serious question the "classical" (or Laplacian) assumptions for the foundations of the probability calculus; and he made free use of the notorious and highly debatable Principle of Indifference, especially in his discussion of the probability of inductive hypotheses. Jevons' exposition of the theory is outmoded in a number of ways, and the assumptions he accepts without hesitation have been frequently subjected to fundamental criticism. His basic approach to the analysis and the use of probability nevertheless continues to be cultivated, though in a more critical spirit than he exhibited. And in any case, his vigorous insistence that probability is the very guide of science, as it is of life in general, retains for his book a current freshness.

Jevons maintained that the scope of scientific method is not restricted to the inanimate world. However, his explicit attention in *The Principles of Science* is given almost wholly to the physical sciences; and with the exception of some brief and inconclusive comments on the impossibility of a "science of history," he has practically nothing to say about the logic of social science. This

omission is surprising, in view of Jevons' eminence as an
economist and of his genuine interest in social questions;
and as far as his actual discussion goes to prove, his
claim concerning the inclusive range of scientific method
must be taken on faith. In any event, the absence of a
systematic analysis of the methods of social inquiry de-
prives *The Principles of Science* of the inclusive sweep
and direct pertinence to moral issues so notably possessed
by Mill's *System of Logic.* The lack of such an analysis
explains why Jevons' book has been largely neglected
by social scientists interested in methodological questions, although they continue to read Mill. But though
The Principles of Science undoubtedly lacks comprehensive sweep, it does possess illuminating penetration, and
it remains a richly instructive book.

Ernest Nagel

1957, Columbia University

THE
PRINCIPLES
OF
SCIENCE

THE PRINCIPLES OF SCIENCE.

CHAPTER I.

INTRODUCTION.

SCIENCE arises from the discovery of Identity amidst Diversity. The process may be described in different words, but our language must always imply the presence of one common and necessary element. In every act of inference or scientific method we are engaged about a certain identity, sameness, similarity, likeness, resemblance, analogy, equivalence or equality apparent between two objects. It is doubtful whether an entirely isolated phenomenon could present itself to our notice, since there must always be some points of similarity between object and object. But in any case an isolated phenomenon could be studied to no useful purpose. The whole value of science consists in the power which it confers upon us of applying to one object the knowledge acquired from like objects ; and it is only so far, therefore, as we can discover and register resemblances that we can turn our observations to account.

Nature is a spectacle continually exhibited to our senses, in which phenomena are mingled in combinations of endless variety and novelty. Wonder fixes the mind's attention ; memory stores up a record of each distinct impression ; the powers of association bring forth the record when the like is felt again. By the higher faculties of judgment and reasoning the mind compares the new with the old, recognises essential identity, even when disguised by diverse circumstances, and expects to find again what was before experienced. It must be the ground of all reasoning and inference that *what is true of one thing will be true of its equivalent*, and that under carefully ascertained conditions *Nature repeats herself.*

Were this indeed a Chaotic Universe, the powers of mind employed in science would be useless to us. Did Chance wholly take the place of order, and did all phenomena come out of an *Infinite Lottery*, to use Condorcet's expression, there could be no reason to expect the like result in like circumstances. It is possible to conceive a world in which no two things should be associated more often, in the long run, than any other two things. The frequent conjunction of any two events would then be purely fortuitous, and if we expected conjunctions to recur continually, we should be disappointed. In such a world we might recognise the same kind of phenomenon as it appeared from time to time, just as we might recognise a marked ball as it was occasionally drawn and re-drawn from a ballot-box; but the approach of any phenomenon would be in no way indicated by what had gone before, nor would it be a sign of what was to come after. In such a world knowledge would be no more than the memory of past coincidences, and the reasoning powers, if they existed at all, would give no clue to the nature of the present, and no presage of the future.

Happily the Universe in which we dwell is not the result of chance, and where chance seems to work it is our own deficient faculties which prevent us from recognising the operation of Law and of Design. In the material framework of this world, substances and forces present themselves in definite and stable combinations. Things are not in perpetual flux, as ancient philosophers held. Element remains element; iron changes not into gold. With suitable precautions we can calculate upon finding the same thing again endowed with the same properties. The constituents of the globe, indeed, appear in almost endless combinations; but each combination bears its fixed character, and when resolved is found to be the compound of definite substances. Misapprehensions must continually occur, owing to the limited extent of our experience. We

can never have examined and registered possible existences so thoroughly as to be sure that no new ones will
occur and frustrate our calculations. The same outward
appearances may cover any amount of hidden differences
which we have not yet suspected. To the variety of substances and powers diffused through nature at its creation,
we should not suppose that our brief experience can assign
a limit, and the necessary imperfection of our knowledge
must be ever borne in mind.

Yet there is much to give us confidence in Science. The
wider our experience, the more minute our examination of
the globe, the greater the accumulation of well-reasoned
knowledge,—the fewer in all probability will be the failures
of inference compared with the successes. Exceptions
to the prevalence of Law are gradually reduced to Law
themselves. Certain deep similarities have been detected
among the objects around us, and have never yet been
found wanting. As the means of examining distant parts
of the universe have been acquired, those similarities have
been traced there as here. Other worlds and stellar
systems may be almost incomprehensively different from
ours in magnitude, condition and disposition of parts, and
yet we detect there the same elements of which our own
limbs are composed. The same natural laws can be
detected in operation in every part of the universe within
the scope of our instruments ; and doubtless these laws are
obeyed irrespective of distance, time, and circumstance.

It is the prerogative of Intellect to discover what is uniform and unchanging in the phenomena around us. So
far as object is different from object, knowledge is useless
and inference impossible. But so far as object resembles
object, we can pass from one to the other. In proportion
as resemblance is deeper and more general, the com-
manding powers of knowledge become more wonderful.
Identity in one or other of its phases is thus always
the bridge by which we pass in inference from case to
case ; and it is my purpose in this treatise to trace out the
various forms in which the one same process of reasoning
presents itself in the ever-growing achievements of Scientific
Method.

The Powers of Mind concerned in the Creation of Science.

It is no part of the purpose of this work to investigate the nature of mind. People not uncommonly suppose that logic is a branch of psychology, because reasoning is a mental operation. On the same ground, however, we might argue that all the sciences are branches of psychology. As will be further explained, I adopt the opinion of Mr. Herbert Spencer, that logic is really an objective science, like mathematics or mechanics. Only in an incidental manner, then, need I point out that the mental powers employed in the acquisition of knowledge are probably three in number. They are substantially as Professor Bain has stated them [1] :—

1. The Power of Discrimination.
2. The Power of Detecting Identity.
3. The Power of Retention.

We exert the first power in every act of perception. Hardly can we have a sensation or feeling unless we discriminate it from something else which preceded. Consciousness would almost seem to consist in the break between one state of mind and the next, just as an induced current of electricity arises from the beginning or the ending of the primary current. We are always engaged in discrimination; and the rudiment of thought which exists in the lower animals probably consists in their power of feeling difference and being agitated by it.

Yet had we the power of discrimination only, Science could not be created. To know that one feeling differs from another gives purely negative information. It cannot teach us what will happen. In such a state of intellect each sensation would stand out distinct from every other; there would be no tie, no bridge of affinity between them. We want a unifying power by which the present and the future may be linked to the past; and this seems to be accomplished by a different power of mind. Lord Bacon has pointed out that different men possess in very different degrees the powers of discrimination and identification. It may be said indeed that discrimination necessarily implies the action of the opposite process of identification; and so

[1] *The Senses and the Intellect,* Second Ed., pp. 5, 325, &c.

it doubtless does in negative points. But there is a rare property of mind which consists in penetrating the disguise of variety and seizing the common elements of sameness; and it is this property which furnishes the true measure of intellect. The name of "intellect" expresses the interlacing of the general and the single, which is the peculiar province of mind.[1] To *cogitate* is the Latin *co-agitare*, resting on a like metaphor. Logic, also, is but another name for the same process, the peculiar work of reason; for λογος is derived from λεγειν, which like the Latin *legere* meant originally to gather. Plato said of this unifying power, that if he met the man who could detect *the one in the many*, he would follow him as a god.

Laws of Identity and Difference.

At the base of all thought and science must lie the laws which express the very nature and conditions of the discriminating and identifying powers of mind. These are the so-called Fundamental Laws of Thought, usually stated as follows :—

1. The Law of Identity. *Whatever is, is.*
2. The Law of Contradiction. *A thing cannot both be and not be.*
3. The Law of Duality. *A thing must either be or not be.*

The first of these statements may perhaps be regarded as a description of identity itself, if so fundamental a notion can admit of description. A thing at any moment is perfectly identical with itself, and, if any person were unaware of the meaning of the word "identity," we could not better describe it than by such an example.

The second law points out that contradictory attributes can never be joined together. The same object may vary in its different parts; here it may be black, and there white; at one time it may be hard and at another time

---

[1] Max Müller, *Lectures on the Science of Language*, Second Series, vol. ii. p. 63 ; or Sixth Edition, vol. ii. p. 67. The view of the etymological meaning of "intellect" is given above on the authority of Professor Max Müller. It seems to be opposed to the ordinary opinion, according to which the Latin *intelligere* means to choose between, to see a difference between, to discriminate, instead of to unite.

soft; but at the same time and place an attribute cannot be both present and absent. Aristotle truly described this law as the first of all axioms—one of which we need not seek for any demonstration. All truths cannot be proved, otherwise there would be an endless chain of demonstration; and it is in self-evident truths like this that we find the simplest foundations.

The third of these laws completes the other two. It asserts that at every step there are two possible alternatives—presence or absence, affirmation or negation. Hence I propose to name this law the Law of Duality, for it gives to all the formulæ of reasoning a dual character. It asserts also that between presence and absence, existence and non-existence, affirmation and negation, there is no third alternative. As Aristotle said, there can be no mean between opposite assertions: we must either affirm or deny. Hence the inconvenient name by which it has been known—The Law of Excluded Middle.

It may be allowed that these laws are not three independent and distinct laws; they rather express three different aspects of the same truth, and each law doubtless presupposes and implies the other two. But it has not hitherto been found possible to state these characters of identity and difference in less than the threefold formula. The reader may perhaps desire some information as to the mode in which these laws have been stated, or the way in which they have been regarded, by philosophers in different ages of the world. Abundant information on this and many other points of logical history will be found in Ueberweg's *System of Logic,* of which an excellent translation has been published by Professor T. M. Lindsay (see pp. 228-281).

The Nature of the Laws of Identity and Difference.

I must at least allude to the profoundly difficult question concerning the nature and authority of these Laws of Identity and Difference. Are they Laws of Thought or Laws of Things? Do they belong to mind or to material nature? On the one hand it may be said that science is a purely mental existence, and must therefore conform to the laws of that which formed it. Science is in the mind and not in the things, and the properties of mind are therefore all important. It is true that these laws are verified in the observation of the exterior world; and it would seem that they might have been gathered and proved by generalisation, had they not already been in our possession. But on the other hand, it may well be urged that we cannot prove these laws by any process of reasoning or observation, because the laws themselves are presupposed, as Leibnitz acutely remarked, in the very notion of a proof. They are the prior conditions of all thought and all knowledge, and even to question their truth is to allow them true. Hartley ingeniously refined upon this argument, remarking that if the fundamental laws of logic be not certain, there must exist a logic of a second order whereby we may determine the degree of uncertainty : if the second logic be not certain, there must be a third ; and so on *ad infinitum*. Thus we must suppose either that absolutely certain laws of thought exist, or that there is no such thing as certainty whatever.[1]

Logicians, indeed, appear to me to have paid insufficient attention to the fact that mistakes in reasoning are always possible, and of not unfrequent occurrence. The Laws of Thought are often called necessary laws, that is, laws which cannot but be obeyed. Yet as a matter of fact, who is there that does not often fail to obey them ? They are the laws which the mind ought to obey rather than what it always does obey. Our thoughts cannot be the criterion of truth, for we often have to acknowledge mistakes in arguments of moderate complexity, and we sometimes only discover our mistakes by collision between our expectations and the events of objective nature.

Mr. Herbert Spencer holds that the laws of logic are objective laws,[2] and he regards the mind as being in a state of constant education, each act of false reasoning or miscalculation leading to results which are likely to prevent similar mistakes from being again committed. I am quite inclined to accept such ingenious views ; but at the same time it is necessary to distinguish between the accumulation of knowledge, and the constitution of the mind which allows of the acquisition of knowledge. Before the mind can perceive or reason at all it must have

---

[1] Hartley on Man, vol. i. p. 359.
[2] *Principles of Psychology*, Second Ed., vol. ii. p. 86.

the conditions of thought impressed upon it. Before a
mistake can be committed, the mind must clearly distinguish the mistaken conclusion from all other assertions.
Are not the Laws of Identity and Difference the prior
conditions of all consciousness and all existence? Must
they not hold true, alike of things material and immaterial?
and if so, can we say that they are only subjectively true
or objectively true? I am inclined, in short, to regard
them as true both "in the nature of thought and things,"
as I expressed it in my first logical essay;[1] and I hold
that they belong to the common basis of all existence.
But this is one of the most difficult questions of psychology
and metaphysics which can be raised, and it is hardly one
for the logician to decide. As the mathematician does not
inquire into the nature of unity and plurality, but develops
the formal laws of plurality, so the logician, as I conceive,
must assume the truth of the Laws of Identity and
Difference, and occupy himself in developing the variety
of forms of reasoning in which their truth may be
manifested.

Again, I need hardly dwell upon the question whether
logic treats of language, notions, or things. As reasonably
might we debate whether a mathematician treats of
symbols, quantities, or things. A mathematician certainly
does treat of symbols, but only as the instruments
whereby to facilitate his reasoning concerning quantities;
and as the axioms and rules of mathematical science must
be verified in concrete objects in order that the calculations founded upon them may have any validity or utility,
it follows that the ultimate objects of mathematical science
are the things themselves. In like manner I conceive that
the logician treats of language so far as it is essential for the
embodiment and exhibition of thought. Even if reasoning
can take place in the inner consciousness of man without
the use of any signs, which is doubtful, at any rate it
cannot become the subject of discussion until by some
system of material signs it is manifested to other persons.
The logician then uses words and symbols as instruments
of reasoning, and leaves the nature and peculiarities of
language to the grammarian. But signs again must

[1] *Pure Logic, or the Logic of Quality apart from Quantity*, 1864,
pp. 10, 16, 22, 29, 30, &c.

correspond to the thoughts and things expressed, in order that they shall serve their intended purpose. We may therefore say that logic treats ultimately of thoughts and things, and immediately of the signs which stand for them. Signs, thoughts, and exterior objects may be regarded as parallel and analogous series of phenomena, and to treat any one of the three series is equivalent to treating either of the other series.

The Process of Inference.

The fundamental action of our reasoning faculties consists in inferring or carrying to a new instance of a phenomenon whatever we have previously known of its like, analogue, equivalent or equal. Sameness or identity presents itself in all degrees, and is known under various names; but the great rule of inference embraces all degrees, and affirms that *so far as there exists sameness, identity or likeness, what is true of one thing will be true of the other.* The great difficulty doubtless consists in ascertaining that there does exist a sufficient degree of likeness or sameness to warrant an intended inference; and it will be our main task to investigate the conditions under which reasoning is valid. In this place I wish to point out that there is something common to all acts of inference, however different their apparent forms. The one same rule lends itself to the most diverse applications.

The simplest possible case of inference, perhaps, occurs in the use of a *pattern, example,* or, as it is commonly called, a *sample.* To prove the exact similarity of two portions of commodity, we need not bring one portion beside the other. It is sufficient that we take a sample which exactly represents the texture, appearance, and general nature of one portion, and according as this sample agrees or not with the other, so will the two portions of commodity agree or differ. Whatever is true as regards the colour, texture, density, material of the sample will be true of the goods themselves. In such cases likeness of quality is the condition of inference.

Exactly the same mode of reasoning holds true of magnitude and figure. To compare the sizes of two objects, we need not lay them beside each other. A

staff, string, or other kind of measure may be employed
to represent the length of one object, and according as it
agrees or not with the other, so must the two objects
agree or differ. In this case the proxy or sample represents
length; but the fact that lengths can be added and
multiplied renders it unnecessary that the proxy should
always be as large as the object. Any standard of
convenient size, such as a common foot-rule, may be made
the medium of comparison. The height of a church in
one town may be carried to that in another, and objects
existing immovably at opposite sides of the earth may be
vicariously measured against each other. We obviously
employ the axiom that whatever is true of a thing as
regards its length, is true of its equal.

To every other simple phenomenon in nature the same
principle of substitution is applicable. We may compare
weights, densities, degrees of hardness, and degrees of all
other qualities, in like manner. To ascertain whether two
sounds are in unison we need not compare them directly,
but a third sound may be the go-between. If a tuning-
fork is in unison with the middle C of York Minster
organ, and we afterwards find it to be in unison with the
same note of the organ in Westminster Abbey, then it
follows that the two organs are tuned in unison. The
rule of inference now is, that what is true of the tuning-
fork as regards the tone or pitch of its sound, is true of
any sound in unison with it.

The skilful employment of this substitutive process
enables us to make measurements beyond the powers of
our senses. No one can count the vibrations, for instance,
of an organ-pipe. But we can construct an instrument
called the *siren*, so that, while producing a sound of any
pitch, it shall register the number of vibrations constituting the sound. Adjusting the sound of the siren in
unison with an organ-pipe, we measure indirectly the
number of vibrations belonging to a sound of that pitch.
To measure a sound of the same pitch is as good as to
measure the sound itself.

Sir David Brewster, in a somewhat similar manner,
succeeded in measuring the refractive indices of irregular
fragments of transparent minerals. It was a troublesome,
and sometimes impracticable work to grind the minerals

into prisms, so that the power of refracting light could be directly observed; but he fell upon the ingenious device of compounding a liquid possessing the same refractive power as the transparent fragment under examination. The moment when this equality was attained could be known by the fragments ceasing to reflect or refract light when immersed in the liquid, so that they became almost invisible in it. The refractive power of the liquid being then measured gave that of the solid. A more beautiful instance of representative measurement, depending immediately upon the principle of inference, could not be found.[1]

Throughout the various logical processes which we are about to consider—Deduction, Induction, Generalisation, Analogy, Classification, Quantitative Reasoning—we shall find the one same principle operating in a more or less disguised form.

Deduction and Induction.

The processes of inference always depend on the one same principle of substitution ; but they may nevertheless be distinguished according as the results are inductive or deductive. As generally stated, deduction consists in passing from more general to less general truths ; induction is the contrary process from less to more general truths. We may however describe the difference in another manner. In deduction we are engaged in developing the consequences of a law. We learn the meaning, contents, results or inferences, which attach to any given proposition. Induction is the exactly inverse process. Given certain results or consequences, we are required to discover the general law from which they flow.

In a certain sense all knowledge is inductive. We can only learn the laws and relations of things in nature by observing those things. But the knowledge gained from the senses is knowledge only of particular facts, and we require some process of reasoning by which we may collect out of the facts the laws obeyed by them.

---

[1] Brewster, *Treatise on New Philosophical Instruments*, p. 273. Concerning this method see also Whewell, *Philosophy of the Inductive Sciences*, vol. ii. p. 355 ; Tomlinson, *Philosophical Magazine*, Fourth Series, vol. xl. p. 328 ; Tyndall, in Youmans' *Modern Culture*, p. 16.

Experience gives us the materials of knowledge : induction digests those materials, and yields us general knowledge. When we possess such knowledge, in the form of general propositions and natural laws, we can usefully apply the reverse process of deduction to ascertain the exact information required at any moment. In its ultimate foundation, then, all knowledge is inductive—in the sense that it is derived by a certain inductive reasoning from the facts of experience.

It is nevertheless true,—and this is a point to which insufficient attention has been paid, that all reasoning is founded on the principles of deduction. I call in question the existence of any method of reasoning which can be carried on without a knowledge of deductive processes. I shall endeavour to show that *induction is really the inverse process of deduction.* There is no mode of ascertaining the laws which are obeyed in certain phenomena, unless we have the power of determining what results would follow from a given law. Just as the process of division necessitates a prior knowledge of multiplication, or the integral calculus rests upon the observation and remembrance of the results of the differential calculus, so induction requires a prior knowledge of deduction. An inverse process is the undoing of the direct process. A person who enters a maze must either trust to chance to lead him out again, or he must carefully notice the road by which he entered. The facts furnished to us by experience are a maze of particular results ; we might by chance observe in them the fulfilment of a law, but this is scarcely possible, unless we thoroughly learn the effects which would attach to any particular law.

Accordingly, the importance of deductive reasoning is doubly supreme. Even when we gain the results of induction they would be of no use unless we could deduc-- tively apply them. But before we can gain them at all we must understand deduction, since it is the inversion of deduction which constitutes induction. Our first task in this work, then, must be to trace out fully the nature of identity in all its forms of occurrence. Having given any series of propositions we must be prepared to develop deductively the whole meaning embodied in them, and the whole of the consequences which flow from them.

Symbolic Expression of Logical Inference.

In developing the results of the Principle of Inference we require to use an appropriate language of signs. It would indeed be quite possible to explain the processes of reasoning by the use of words found in the dictionary. Special examples of reasoning, too, may seem to be more readily apprehended than general symbolic forms. But it has been shown in the mathematical sciences that the attainment of truth depends greatly upon the invention of a clear, brief, and appropriate system of symbols. Not only is such a language convenient, but it is almost essential to the expression of those general truths which are the very soul of science. To apprehend the truth of special cases of inference does not constitute logic; we must apprehend them as cases of more general truths. The object of all science is the separation of what is common and general from what is accidental and different. In a system of logic, if anywhere, we should esteem this generality, and strive to exhibit clearly what is similar in very diverse cases. Hence the great value of *general symbols* by which we can represent the form of a reasoning process, disentangled from any consideration of the special subject to which it is applied.

The signs required in logic are of a very simple kind. As sameness or difference must exist between two things or notions, we need signs to indicate the things or notions compared, and other signs to denote the relations between them. We need, then, (1) symbols for terms, (2) a symbol for sameness, (3) a symbol for difference, and (4) one or two symbols to take the place of conjunctions.

Ordinary nouns substantive, such as *Iron, Metal, Electricity, Undulation,* might serve as terms, but, for the reasons explained above, it is better to adopt blank letters, devoid of special signification, such as A, B, C, &c. Each letter must be understood to represent a noun, and, so far as the conditions of the argument allow, *any noun*. Just as in Algebra, *x, y, z, p, q,* &c. are used for *any quantities*, undetermined or unknown, except when the special conditions of the problem are taken into account, so will our letters stand for undetermined or unknown things.

These letter-terms will be used indifferently for nouns substantive and adjective. Between these two kinds of nouns there may perhaps be differences in a metaphysical or grammatical point of view. But grammatical usage sanctions the conversion of adjectives into substantives, and *vice versâ;* we may avail ourselves of this latitude without in any way prejudging the metaphysical difficulties which may be involved. Here, as throughout this work, I shall devote my attention to truths which I can exhibit in a clear and formal manner, believing that in the present condition of logical science, this course will lead to greater advantage than discussion upon the metaphysical questions which may underlie any part of the subject.

Every noun or term denotes an object, and usually implies the possession by that object of certain qualities or circumstances common to all the objects denoted. There are certain terms, however, which imply the absence of qualities or circumstances attaching to other objects. It will be convenient to employ a special mode of indicating these *negative terms,* as they are called. If the general name A denotes an object or class of objects possessing certain defined qualities, then the term Not A will denote any object which does not possess the whole of those qualities; in short, Not A is the sign for anything which differs from A in regard to any one or more of the assigned qualities. If A denote " transparent object," Not A will denote " not transparent object." Brevity and facility of expression are of no slight importance in a system of notation, and it will therefore be desirable to substitute for the negative term Not A a briefer symbol. De Morgan represented negative terms by small Roman letters, or sometimes by small italic letters;[1] as the latter seem to be highly convenient, I shall use $a, b, c, \ldots p, q,$ &c., as the negative terms corresponding to A, B, C, . . . P, Q, &c. Thus if A means " fluid," a will mean " not fluid."

Expression of Identity and Difference.

To denote the relation of sameness or identity I unhesitatingly adopt the sign =, so long used by mathematicians to denote equality. This symbol was originally appropriated

[1] *Formal Logic,* p. 38.

by Robert Recorde in his *Whetstone of Wit*, to avoid the tedious repetition of the words "is equal to;" and he chose a pair of parallel lines, because no two things can be more equal.[1] The meaning of the sign has however been gradually extended beyond that of equality of quantities ; mathematicians have themselves used it to indicate equivalence of operations. The force of analogy has been so great that writers in most other branches of science have employed the same sign. The philologist uses it to indicate the equivalence of meaning of words : chemists adopt it to signify identity in kind and equality in weight of the elements which form two different compounds. Not a few logicians, for instance Lambert, Drobitsch, George Bentham,[2] Boole,[3] have employed it as the copula of propositions. De Morgan declined to use it for this purpose, but still further extended its meaning so as to include the equivalence of a proposition with the premises from which it can be inferred ;[4] and Herbert Spencer has applied it in a like manner.[5]

Many persons may think that the choice of a symbol is a matter of slight importance or of mere convenience ; but I hold that the common use of this sign = in so many different meanings is really founded upon a generalisation of the widest character and of the greatest importance— one indeed which it is a principal purpose of this work to explain. The employment of the same sign in different cases would be unphilosophical unless there were some real analogy between its diverse meanings. If such analogy exists, it is not only allowable, but highly desirable and even imperative, to use the symbol of equivalence with a generality of meaning corresponding to the generality of the principles involved. Accordingly De Morgan's refusal to use the symbol in logical propositions indicated his opinion that there was a want of analogy between logical propositions and mathematical equations. I use the sign because I hold the contrary opinion.

---

[1] Hallam's *Literature of Europe*, First Ed., vol. ii. p. 444.
[2] *Outline of a New System of Logic*, London, 1827, pp. 133, &c.
[3] *An Investigation of the Laws of Thought*, pp. 27, &c.
[4] *Formal Logic*, pp. 82, 106. In his later work, *The Syllabus of a New System of Logic*, he discontinued the use of the sign.
[5] *Principles of Psychology*, Second Ed., vol. ii. pp. 54, 55.

I conceive that the sign = as commonly employed, always denotes some form or degree of sameness, and the particular form is usually indicated by the nature of the terms joined by it. Thus " 6,720 pounds = 3 tons" is evidently an equation of quantities. The formula — × — = + expresses the equivalence of operations. " Exogens = Dicotyledons " is a logical identity expressing a profound truth concerning the character and origin of a most important group of plants.

We have great need in logic of a distinct sign for the copula, because the little verb *is* (or *are*), hitherto used both in logic and ordinary discourse, is thoroughly ambiguous. It sometimes denotes identity, as in " St. Paul's is the *chef-d'œuvre* of Sir Christopher Wren ; " but it more commonly indicates inclusion of class within class, or partial identity, as in " Bishops are members of the House of Lords." This latter relation involves identity, but requires careful discrimination from simple identity, as will be shown further on.

When with this sign of equality we join two nouns or logical terms, as in

$$\text{Hydrogen} = \text{The least dense element,}$$

we signify that the object or group of objects denoted by one term is identical with that denoted by the other, in everything except the names. The general formula

$$A = B$$

must be taken to mean that A and B are symbols for the same object or group of objects. This identity may sometimes arise from the mere imposition of names, but it may also arise from the deepest laws of the constitution of nature ; as when we say

$$\text{Gravitating matter} = \text{Matter possessing inertia,}$$
$$\text{Exogenous plants} = \text{Dicotyledonous plants,}$$
$$\text{Plagihedral quartz crystals} = \text{Quartz crystals causing}$$
the plane of polarisation of light to rotate.

We shall need carefully to distinguish between relations of terms which can be modified at our own will and those which are fixed as expressing the laws of nature ; but at present we are considering only the mode of expression which may be the same in either case.

Sometimes, but much less frequently, we require a symbol to indicate difference or the absence of complete sameness. For this purpose we may generalise in like manner the symbol ~, which was introduced by Wallis to signify difference between quantities. The general formula

$$B \sim C$$

denotes that B and C are the names of two objects or groups which are not identical with each other. Thus we may say

Acrogens ~ Flowering plants.

Snowdon ~ The highest mountain in Great Britain.

I shall also occasionally use the sign ∽ to signify in the most general manner the existence of any relation between the two terms connected by it. Thus ∽ might mean not only the relations of equality or inequality, sameness or difference, but any special relation of time, place, size, causation, &c. in which one thing may stand to another. By A ∽ B I mean, then, any two objects of thought related to each other in any conceivable manner.

General Formula of Logical Inference.

The one supreme rule of inference consists, as I have said, in the direction to affirm of anything whatever is known of its like, equal or equivalent. The *Substitution of Similars* is a phrase which seems aptly to express the capacity of mutual replacement existing in any two objects which are like or equivalent to a sufficient degree. It is matter for further investigation to ascertain when and for what purposes a degree of similarity less than complete identity is sufficient to warrant substitution. For the present we think only of the exact sameness expressed in the form

$$A = B.$$

Now if we take the letter C to denote any third conceivable object, and use the sign ∽ in its stated meaning of *indefinite relation*, then the general formula of all inference may be thus exhibited:—

From $A = B \mathbin{\infty} C$

we may infer $A \mathbin{\infty} C$

or, in words—*In whatever relation a thing stands to a second thing, in the same relation it stands to the like or equivalent of that second thing.* The identity between A

and B allows us indifferently to place A where B was, or
B where A was ; and there is no limit to the variety of
special meanings which we can bestow upon the signs
used in this formula consistently with its truth.   Thus if
we first specify only the meaning of the sign ∞, we may
say that if *C is the weight of B*, then *C is also the weight
of A.*   Similarly
> If C is the father of B, C is the father of A ;
> If C is a fragment of B, C is a fragment of A ;
> If C is a quality of B, C is a quality of A ;
> If C is a species of B, C is a species of A ;
> If C is the equal of B, C is the equal of A ;

and so on *ad infinitum.*

We may also endow with special meanings the letter-
terms A, B, and C, and the process of inference will never
be false.   Thus let the sign ∞ mean " is height of," and let
> A = Snowdon,
> B = Highest mountain in England or Wales,
> C = 3,590 feet;

then it obviously follows since " 3,590 feet is the neight
of Snowdon," and " Snowdon = the highest mountain in
England or Wales," that, " 3,590 feet is the height of the
highest mountain in England or Wales."

One result of this general process of inference is that we
may in any aggregate or complex whole replace any part
by its equivalent without altering the whole.   To alter is
to make a difference ; but if in replacing a part I make no
difference, there is no alteration of the whole.   Many
inferences which have been very imperfectly included in
logical formulas at once follow.   I remember the late Prof.
De Morgan remarking that all Aristotle's logic could not
prove that " Because a horse is an animal, the head of a
horse is the head of an animal."   I conceive that this
amounts merely to replacing in the complete notion *head of
a horse,* the term " horse," by its equivalent *some animal* or
an animal.   Similarly, since
> The Lord Chancellor = The Speaker of the House of
> Lords,

it follows that
> The death of the Lord Chancellor = The death of the
> Speaker of the House of Lords ;

and any event, circumstance or thing, which stands in a

certain relation to the one will stand in like relation to the other. Milton reasons in this way when he says, in his Areopagitica, " Who kills a man, kills a reasonable creature, God's image." If we may suppose him to mean

God's image = man = some reasonable creature,

it follows that " The killer of a man is the killer of some reasonable creature," and also " The killer of God's image."

This replacement of equivalents may be repeated over and over again to any extent. Thus if *person* is identical in meaning with *individual*, it follows that

Meeting of persons = meeting of individuals ;

and if *assemblage = meeting*, we may make a new replacement and show that

Meeting of persons = assemblage of individuals.

We may in fact found upon this principle of substitution a most general axiom in the following terms [1] :—

Same parts samely related make same wholes.

If, for instance, exactly similar bricks and other materials be used to build two houses, and they be similarly placed in each house, the two houses must be similar. There are millions of cells in a human body, but if each cell of one person were represented by an exactly similar cell similarly placed in another body, the two persons would be undistinguishable, and would be only *numerically* different. It is upon this principle, as we shall see, that all accurate processes of measurement depend. If for a weight in a scale of a balance we substitute another weight, and the equilibrium remains entirely unchanged, then the weights must be exactly equal. The general test of equality is substitution. Objects are equally bright when on replacing one by the other the eye perceives no difference. Objects are equal in dimensions when tested by the same gauge they fit in the same manner. Generally speaking, two objects are alike so far as when substituted one for another no alteration is produced, and *vice versâ* when alike no alteration is produced by the substitution.

1 *Pure Logic, or the Logic of Quality*, p. 14.

The Propagating Power of Similarity.

The relation of similarity in all its degrees is reciprocal. So far as things are alike, either may be substituted for the other; and this may perhaps be considered the very meaning of the relation. But it is well worth notice that there is in similarity a peculiar power of extending itself among all the things which are similar. To render a number of things similar to each other we need only render them similar to one standard object. Each coin struck from a pair of dies not only resembles the matrix or original pattern from which the dies were struck, but resembles every other coin manufactured from the same original pattern. Among a million such coins there are not less than 499,999,500,000 *pairs of coins* resembling each other. Similars to the same are similars to all. It is one great advantage of printing that all copies of a document struck from the same type are necessarily identical each with each, and whatever is true of one copy will be true of every copy. Similarly, if fifty rows of pipes in an organ be tuned in perfect unison with one row, usually the Principal, they must be in unison with each other. Similarity can also reproduce or propagate itself *ad infinitum :* for if a number of tuning-forks be adjusted in perfect unison with one standard fork, all instruments tuned to any one fork will agree with any instrument tuned to any other fork. Standard measures of length, capacity, weight, or any other measurable quality, are propagated in the same manner. So far as copies of the original standard, or copies of copies, or copies again of those copies, are accurately executed, they must all agree each with every other.

It is the capability of mutual substitution which gives such great value to the modern methods of mechanical construction, according to which all the parts of a machine are exact facsimiles of a fixed pattern. The rifles used in the British army are constructed on the American inter-changeable system, so that any part of any rifle can be substituted for the same part of another. A bullet fitting one rifle will fit all others of the same bore. Sir J.

Whitworth has extended the same system to the screws and screw-bolts used in connecting together the parts of machines, by establishing a series of standard screws.

Anticipations of the Principle of Substitution.

In such a subject as logic it is hardly possible to put forth any opinions which have not been in some degree previously entertained. The germ at least of every doctrine will be found in earlier writers, and novelty must arise chiefly in the mode of harmonising and developing ideas. When I first employed the process and name of *substitution* in logic,[1] I was led to do so from analogy with the familiar mathematical process of substituting for a symbol its value as given in an equation. In writing my first logical essay I had a most imperfect conception of the importance and generality of the process, and I described, as if they were of equal importance, a number of other laws which now seem to be but particular cases of the one general rule of substitution.

My second essay, " The Substitution of Similars," was written shortly after I had become aware of the great simplification which may be effected by a proper application of the principle of substitution. I was not then acquainted with the fact that the German logician Beneke had employed the principle of substitution, and had used the word itself in forming a theory of the syllogism. My imperfect acquaintance with the German language had prevented me from acquiring a complete knowledge of Beneke's views ; but there is no doubt that Professor Lindsay is right in saying that he, and probably other logicians, were in some degree familiar with the principle.[2] Even Aristotle's dictum may be regarded as an imperfect statement of the principle of substitution; and, as I have pointed out, we have only to modify that dictum in accordance with the quantification of the predicate in order to arrive at the complete

[1] *Pure Logic*, pp. 18, 19.
[2] Ueberweg's *System of Logic*, transl. by Lindsay, pp. 442—446, 571, 572. The anticipations of the principle of substitution to be found in the works of Leibnitz, Reusch, and perhaps other German logicians, will be noticed in the preface to this second edition.

process of substitution.[1] The Port-Royal logicians appear
to have entertained nearly equivalent views, for they
considered that all moods of the syllogism might be
reduced under one general principle.[2] Of two premises
they regard one as the *containing proposition* (propositio
continens), and the other as the *applicative proposition.*
The latter proposition must always be affirmative, and
represents that by which a substitution is made; the
former may or may not be negative, and is that in
which a substitution is effected. They also show that
this method will embrace certain cases of complex reasoning which had no place in the Aristotelian syllogism.
Their views probably constitute the greatest improvement
in logical doctrine made up to that time since the days
of Aristotle. But a true reform in logic must consist,
not in explaining the syllogism in one way or another,
but in doing away with all the narrow restrictions of
the Aristotelian system, and in showing that there exists
an infinite variety of logical arguments immediately
deducible from the principle of substitution of which the
ancient syllogism forms but a small and not even the
most important part.

The Logic of Relatives.

There is a difficult and important branch of logic
which may be called the Logic of Relatives. If I argue,
for instance, that because Daniel Bernoulli was the son
of John, and John the brother of James, therefore Daniel
was the nephew of James, it is not possible to prove
this conclusion by any simple logical process. We require at any rate to assume that the son of a brother is
a nephew. A simple logical relation is that which exists
between properties and circumstances of the same object
or class. But objects and classes of objects may also be
related according to all the properties of time and space.
I believe it may be shown, indeed, that where an inference
concerning such relations is drawn, a process of substitution is really employed and an identity must exist;

[1] *Substitution of Similars* (1869), p. 9.
[2] *Port-Royal Logic,* transl. by Spencer Baynes, pp. 212—219.
Part III. chap. x. and xi.

but I will not undertake to prove the assertion in this work. The relations of time and space are logical relations of a complicated character demanding much abstract and difficult investigation. The subject has been treated with such great ability by Peirce,[1] De Morgan,[2] Ellis,[3] and Harley, that I will not in the present work attempt any review of their writings, but merely refer the reader to the publications in which they are to be found.

[1] *Description of a Notation for the Logic of Relatives, resulting from an Amplification of the Conceptions of Boole's Calculus of Logic.* By C. S. Peirce. *Memoirs of the American Academy*, vol. ix. Cambridge, U.S., 1870.

[2] *On the Syllogism No IV., and on the Logic of Relations.* By Augustus De Morgan. *Transactions of the Cambridge Philosophical Society*, vol. x. part ii., 1860.

[3] *Observations on Boole's Laws of Thought.* By the late R. Leslie Ellis ; communicated by the Rev. Robert Harley, F.R.S. *Report of the British Association*, 1870. *Report of Sections*, p. 12. Also, *On Boole's Laws of Thought.* By the Rev. Robert Harley, F.R.S., *ibid.* p. 14.

CHAPTER II.

EVERY proposition expresses the resemblance or difference of the things denoted by its terms. As inference
treats of the relation between two or more propositions, so
a proposition expresses a relation between two or more
terms. In the portion of this work which treats of
deduction it will be convenient to follow the usual order
of exposition. We will consider in succession the various
kinds of terms, propositions, and arguments, and we commence in this chapter with terms.

The simplest and most palpable meaning which can
belong to a term consists of some single material object,
such as Westminster Abbey, Stonehenge, the Sun, Sirius,
&c. It is probable that in early stages of intellect only
concrete and palpable things are the objects of thought.
The youngest child knows the difference between a hot and
a cold body. The dog can recognise his master among a
hundred other persons, and animals of much lower intelligence know and discriminate their haunts. In all such
acts there is judgment concerning the likeness of physical
objects, but there is little or no power of analysing each
object and regarding it as a group of qualities.

The dignity of intellect begins with the power of
separating points of agreement from those of difference.
Comparison of two objects may lead us to perceive that
they are at once like and unlike. Two fragments of rock
may differ entirely in outward form, yet they may have the
same colour, hardness, and texture. Flowers which agree
in colour may differ in odour. The mind learns to regard

each object as an aggregate of qualities, and acquires the
power of dwelling at will upon one or other of those
qualities to the exclusion of the rest. Logical abstraction,
in short, comes into play, and the mind becomes capable of
reasoning, not merely about objects which are physically
complete and concrete, but about things which may be
thought of separately in the mind though they exist not
separately in nature. We can think of the hardness of
a rock, or the colour of a flower, and thus produce
abstract notions, denoted by abstract terms, which will
form a subject for further consideration.

At the same time arise general notions and classes of
objects. We cannot fail to observe that the quality *hardness* exists in many objects, for instance in many fragments
of rock ; mentally joining these together, we create the
class *hard object,* which will include, not only the actual
objects examined, but all others which may happen to
agree with them, as they agree with each other. As our
senses cannot possibly report to us all the contents of
space, we cannot usually set any limits to the number of
objects which may fall into any such class. At this point
we begin to perceive the power and generality of thought,
which enables us in a single act to treat of indefinitely
or even infinitely numerous objects. We can safely assert
that whatever is true of any one object coming under a
class is true of any of the other objects so far as they
possess the common qualities implied in their belonging to
the class. We must not place a thing in a class unless
we are prepared to believe of it all that is believed of the
class in general ; but it remains a matter of important
consideration to decide how far and in what manner we
can safely undertake thus to assign the place of objects in
that general system of classification which constitutes the
body of science.

Twofold Meaning of General Names.

Etymologically the *meaning* of a name is that which we
are caused to think of when the name is used. Now every
general name causes us to think of some one or more of
the objects belonging to a class ; it may also cause us to
think of the common qualities possessed by those objects

A name is said to *denote* the object of thought to which it may be applied; it *implies* at the same time the possession of certain qualities or circumstances. The objects denoted form the *extent* of meaning of the term; the qualities implied form the *intent* of meaning. Crystal is the name of any substance of which the molecules are arranged in a regular geometrical manner. The substances or objects in question form the extent of meaning ; the circumstance of having the molecules so arranged forms the intent of meaning.

When we compare general terms together, it may often be found that the meaning of one is included in the meaning of another. Thus all *crystals* are included among *material substances,* and all *opaque crystals* are included among *crystals;* here the inclusion is in extension. We may also have inclusion of meaning in regard to intension. For, as all crystals are material substances, the qualities implied by the term material substance must be among those implied by crystal. Again, it is obvious that while in extension of meaning opaque crystals are but a part of crystals, in intension of meaning crystal is but part of opaque crystal. We increase the intent of meaning of a term by joining to it adjectives, or phrases equivalent to adjectives, and the removal of such adjectives of course decreases the intensive meaning. Now, concerning such changes of meaning, the following all-important law holds universally true :— *When the intent of meaning of a term is increased the extent is decreased;* and vice versâ, *when the extent is increased the intent is decreased.* In short, as one is increased the other is decreased.

This law refers only to logical changes. The number of steam-engines in the world may be undergoing a rapid increase without the intensive meaning of the name being altered. The law will only be verified, again, when there is a real change in the intensive meaning, and an adjective may often be joined to a noun without making a change. *Elementary metal* is identical with *metal; mortal man* with *man;* it being a *property* of all metals to be elements, and of all men to be mortals.

There is no limit to the amount of meaning which a term may have. A term may denote one object, or many, or an infinite number ; it may imply a single quality, if such

there be, or a group of any number of qualities, and yet
the law connecting the extension and intension will infallibly apply. Taking the general name *planet,* we
increase its intension and decrease its extension by
prefixing the adjective *exterior ;* and if we further add
nearest to the earth, there remains but one planet, *Mars,* to
which the name can then be applied. Singular terms,
which denote a single individual only, come under the
same law of meaning as general names. They may be
regarded as general names of which the meaning in extension is reduced to a minimum. Logicians have erroneously
asserted, as it seems to me, that singular terms are devoid
of meaning in intension, the fact being that they exceed
all other terms in that kind of meaning, as I have elsewhere tried to show.[1]

Abstract Terms.

Comparison of objects, and analysis of the complex
resemblances and differences which they present, lead us
to the conception of *abstract qualities.* We learn to think
of one object as not only different from another, but as
differing in some particular point, such as colour, or
weight, or size. We may then convert points of agreement
or difference into separate objects of thought which we
call qualities and denote by *abstract terms.* Thus the term
redness means something in which a number of objects
agree as to colour, and in virtue of which they are called
red. Redness forms, in fact, the intensive meaning of the
term red.

Abstract terms are strongly distinguished from general
terms by possessing only one kind of meaning; for as they
denote qualities there is nothing which they cannot in
addition imply. The adjective " red " is the name of red
objects, but it implies the possession by them of the quality

---

[1] Jevons' *Elementary Lessons in Logic,* pp. 41—43; *Pure Logic,* p. 6.
See also J. S. Mill, *System of Logic,* Book 1. chap. ii. section 5, and
Shedden's *Elements of Logic,* London, 1864, pp. 14, &c. Professor
Robertson objects (*Mind,* vol. i. p. 210) that I confuse *singular* and
proper names ; if so, it is because I hold that the same remarks apply
to proper names, which do not seem to me to differ logically from
singular names.

redness ; but this latter term has one single meaning—the quality alone.   Thus it arises that abstract terms are incapadle of plurality.   Red objects are numerically distinct each from each, and there are multitudes of such objects•; but redness is a single quality which runs through all those objects, and is the same in one as it is in another. It is true that we may speak of *rednesses,* meaning different kinds or tints of redness, just as we may speak of *colours,* meaning different kinds of colours.   But in distinguishing kinds, degrees, or other differences, we render the terms so far concrete.   In that they are merely red there is but a single nature in red objects, and so far as things are merely coloured, colour is a single indivisible quality.   Redness, so far as it is redness merely, is one and the same everywhere, and possesses absolute oneness.   In virtue of this unity we acquire the power of treating all instances of such quality as we may treat any one.   We possess, in short, general knowledge.

Substantial Terms.

Logicians appear to have taken little notice of a class of terms which partake in certain respects of the character of abstract terms and yet are undoubtedly the names of concrete existing things.   These terms are the names of substances, such as gold, carbonate of lime, nitrogen, &c. We cannot speak of two golds, twenty carbonates of lime, or a hundred nitrogens.   There is no such distinction between the parts of a uniform substance as will allow of a discrimination of numerous individuals.   The qualities of colour, lustre, malleability, density, &c., by which we recognise gold, extend through its substance irrespective of particular size or shape.   So far as a substance is gold, it is one and the same everywhere ; so that terms of this kind, which I propose to call *substantial terms,* possess the peculiar unity of abstract terms.   Yet they are not abstract ; for gold is of course a tangible visible body, entirely concrete, and existing independently of other bodies.

It is only when, by actual mechanical division, we break up the uniform whole which forms the meaning of a substantial term, that we introduce number.   *Piece of gold*

is a term capable of plurality; for there may be a great
many pieces discriminated either by their various shapes
and sizes, or, in the absence of such marks, by simultaneously occupying different parts of space. In substance
they are one; as regards the properties of space they are
many.[1] We need not further pursue this question, which
involves the distinction between unity and plurality, until
we consider the principles of number in a subsequent
chapter.

Collective Terms.

We must clearly distinguish between the *collective* and
the *general meanings* of terms. The same name may be
used to denote the whole body of existing objects of a
certain kind, or any one of those objects taken separately.
"Man" may mean the aggregate of existing men, which we
sometimes describe as *mankind;* it is also the general
name applying to any man. The vegetable kingdom is
the name of the whole aggregate of *plants,* but "plant"
itself is a general name applying to any one or other plant.
Every material object may be conceived as divisible into
parts, and is therefore collective as regards those parts.
The animal body is made up of cells and fibres, a crystal
of molecules; wherever physical division, or as it has been
called *partition,* is possible, there we deal in reality with a
collective whole. Thus the greater number of general
terms are at the same time collective as regards each
individual whole which they denote.

It need hardly be pointed out that we must not infer of
a collective whole what we know only of the parts, nor of
the parts what we know only of the whole. The relation
of whole and part is not one of identity, and does not
allow of substitution. There may nevertheless be qualities
which are true alike of the whole and of its parts. A
number of organ-pipes tuned in unison produce an aggregate of sound which is of exactly the same pitch as each

---

[1] Professor Robertson has criticised my introduction of "Substantial
Terms" (*Mind*, vol. i. p. 210), and objects, perhaps correctly, that the
distinction if valid is extra-logical. I am inclined to think, however,
that the doctrine of terms is, strictly speaking, for the most part
extra-logical.

separate sound. In the case of substantial terms, certain qualities may be present equally in each minutest part as in the whole. The chemical nature of the largest mass of pure carbonate of lime is the same as the nature of the smallest particle. In the case of abstract terms, again, we cannot draw a distinction between whole and part; what is true of redness in any case is always true of redness, so far as it is merely red.

Synthesis of Terms.

We continually combine simple terms together so as to form new terms of more complex meaning. Thus, to increase the intension of meaning of a term we write it with an adjective or a phrase of adjectival nature. By joining "brittle" to "metal," we obtain a combined term, "brittle metal," which denotes a certain portion of the metals, namely, such as are selected on account of possessing the quality of *brittleness*. As we have already seen, "brittle metal" possesses less extension and greater intension than metal. Nouns, prepositional phrases, participial phrases and subordinate propositions may also be added to terms so as to increase their intension and decrease their extension.

In our symbolic language we need some mode of indicating this junction of terms, and the most convenient device will be the juxtaposition of the letter-terms. Thus if A mean brittle, and B mean metal, then AB will mean brittle metal. Nor need there be any limit to the number of letters thus joined together, or the complexity of the notions which they may represent.

Thus if we take the letters

P = metal,
Q = white,
R = monovalent,
S = of specific gravity 10·5,
T = melting above 1000° C.,
V = good conductor of heat and electricity,

then we can form a combined term PQRSTV, which will denote "a white monovalent metal, of specific gravity 10·5, melting above 1000° C., and a good conductor of heat and electricity."

There are many grammatical usages concerning the junction of words and phrases to which we need pay no attention in logic. We can never say in ordinary language "of wood table," meaning "table of wood;" but we may consider "of wood" as logically an exact equivalent of "wooden"; so that if

$$X = \text{of wood},$$
$$Y = \text{table},$$

there is no reason why, in our symbols, XY should not be just as correct an expression for "table of wood" as YX. In this case indeed we might substitute for "of wood" the corresponding adjective "wooden," but we should often fail to find any adjective answering exactly to a phrase. There is no single word by which we could express the notion "of specific gravity 10·5 :" but logically we may consider these words as forming an adjective; and denoting this by S and metal by P, we may say that SP means "metal of specific gravity 10·5." It is one of many advantages in these blank letter-symbols that they enable us completely to neglect all grammatical peculiarities and to fix our attention solely on the purely logical relations involved. Investigation will probably show that the rules of grammar are mainly founded upon traditional usage and have little logical signification. This indeed is sufficiently proved by the wide grammatical differences which exist between languages, though the logical foundation must be the same.

Symbolic Expression of the Law of Contradiction.

The synthesis of terms is subject to the all-important Law of Thought, described in a previous section (p. 5) and called the Law of Contradiction. It is self-evident that no quality can be both present and absent at the same time and place. This fundamental condition of all thought and of all existence is expressed symbolically by a rule that a term and its negative shall never be allowed to come into combination. Such combined terms as Aa, Bb, Cc, &c., are self-contradictory and devoid of all intelligible meaning. If they could represent anything, it would be what cannot exist, and cannot even be imagined in the mind. They can therefore only enter into our consideration to suffer immediate exclusion. The criterion of false reasoning, as we shall find, is that it involves self-contradiction, the affirming and denying of the same statement. We might represent tne object of all reasoning as the separation of the consistent and possible from the inconsistent and impossible; and we cannot make any statement except a truism without implying that certain combinations of terms are contradictory and excluded from thought. To assert that " all A's are B's " is equivalent to the assertion that " A's which are not B's cannot exist."

It will be convenient to have the means of indicating the exclusion of the self-contradictory, and we may use the familiar sign for *nothing*, the cipher o. Thus the second law of thought may be symbolised in the forms

$$Aa = 0 \qquad ABb = 0 \qquad ABCa = 0$$

We may variously describe the meaning of o in logic as the *non-existent*, the *impossible*, the *self-inconsistent*, the *inconceivable*. Close analogy exists between this meaning and its mathematical signification.

Certain Special Conditions of Logical Symbols.

In order that we may argue and infer truly we must treat our logical symbols according to the fundamental laws of Identity and Difference. But in thus using our symbols we shall frequently meet with combinations of which the meaning will not at first sight be apparent. If in one case we learn that an object is " yellow and round," and in another case that it is " round and yellow," there arises the question whether these two descriptions are identical in meaning or not. Again, if we proved that an object was " round round," the meaning of such an expression would be open to doubt. Accordingly we must take notice, before proceeding further, of certain special laws which govern the combination of logical terms.

In the first place the combination of a logical term with itself is without effect, just as the repetition of a statement does not alter the meaning of the statement; " a round round object " is simply " a round object." What is yellow yellow is merely yellow; metallic metals cannot differ from metals, nor circular circles from circles. In our symbolic language we may similarly hold that AA is identical with A, or

$$A = AA = AAA = \&c.$$

The late Professor Boole is the only logician in modern times who has drawn attention to this remarkable property of logical terms ; [1] but in place of the name which he gave to the law, I have proposed to call it The Law of Simplicity.[2] Its high importance will only become apparent when we attempt to determine the relations of logical and mathematical science. Two symbols of quantity, and only two, seem to obey this law ; we may say that $1 \times 1 = 1$, and $0 \times 0 = 0$ (taking 0 to mean absolute zero or $1 - 1$); there is apparently no other number which combined with itself gives an unchanged result. I shall point out, however, in the chapter upon Number, that in reality all numerical symbols obey this logical principle.

It is curious that this Law of Simplicity, though almost unnoticed in modern times, was known to Boëthius, who makes a singular remark in his treatise *De Trinitate et Unitate Dei* (p. 959). He says : "If I should say sun, sun, sun, I should not have made three suns, but I should have named one sun so many times." [3] Ancient discussions about the doctrine of the Trinity drew more attention to subtle questions concerning the nature of unity and plurality than has ever since been given to them.

It is a second law of logical symbols that order of combination is a matter of indifference. "Rich and rare gems" are the same as "rare and rich gems," or even as "gems, rich and rare." Grammatical, rhetorical, or poetic usage may give considerable significance to order of expression. The limited power of our minds prevents our grasping many ideas at once, and thus the order of statement may produce some effect, but not in a simply logical manner. All life proceeds in the succession of time, and we are obliged to write, speak, or even think of things and their qualities one after the other ; but between the things and their qualities there need be no such relation of order in

---

[1] *Mathematical Analysis of Logic*, Cambridge, 1847, p. 17. *An Investigation of the Laws of Thought*, London, 1854, p. 31.

[2] *Pure Logic*, p. 15.

[3] "Velut si dicam, Sol, Sol, Sol, non tres soles effecerim, sed uno toties prædicaverim."

time or space. The sweetness of sugar is neither before
nor after its weight and solubility. The hardness of a
metal, its colour, weight, opacity, malleability, electric and
chemical properties, are all coexistent and coextensive, pervading the metal and every part of it in perfect community,
none before nor after the others. In our words and symbols
we cannot observe this natural condition ; we must name
one quality first and another second, just as some one must
be the first to sign a petition, or to walk foremost in a pro-
cession. In nature there is no such precedence.

I find that the opinion here stated, to the effect that
relations of space and time do not apply to many of our
ideas, is clearly adopted by Hume in his celebrated *Treatise on Human Nature* (vol. i. p. 410). He says :[1]—" An
object may be said to be no where, when its parts are not so
situated with respect to each other, as to form any figure
or quantity ; nor the whole with respect to other bodies so
as to answer to our notions of contiguity or distance. Now
this is evidently the case with all our perceptions and
objects, except those of sight and feeling. A moral reflection
cannot be placed on the right hand or on the left hand
of a passion, nor can a smell or sound be either of a circular
or a square figure. These objects and perceptions, so far
from requiring any particular place, are absolutely incompatible with it, and even the imagination cannot attribute
it to them."

A little reflection will show that knowledge in the
highest perfection would consist in the *simultaneous* possession of a multitude of facts. To comprehend a
science perfectly we should have every fact present with
every other fact. We must write a book and we must read
it successively word by word, but how infinitely higher
would be our powers of thought if we could grasp the
whole in one collective act of consciousness ! Compared
with the brutes we do possess some slight approximation
to such power, and it is conceivable that in the indefinite
future mind may acquire an increase of capacity, and be
less restricted to the piecemeal examination of a subject.
But I wish here to make plain that there is no logical
foundation for the successive character of thought and
reasoning unavoidable under our present mental conditions.

[1] Book i., Part iv., Section 5.

*We are logically weak, and imperfect in respect of the fact
that we are obliged to think of one thing after another.* We
must describe metal as " hard and opaque," or " opaque and
hard," but in the metal itself there is no such difference of
order ; the properties are simultaneous and coextensive in
existence.

Setting aside all grammatical peculiarities which render
a substantive less moveable than an adjective, and dis-
regarding any meaning indicated by emphasis or marked
order of words, we may state, as a general law of logic,
that AB is identical with BA, or AB = BA. Similarly,
ABC = ACB = BCA = &c.

Boole first drew attention in recent years to this property of logical terms, and he called it the property of
Commutativeness.[1] He not only stated the law with the
utmost clearness, but pointed out that it is a Law of
Thought rather than a Law of Things. I shall have in
various parts of this work to show how the necessary imperfection of our symbols expressed in this law clings to
our modes of expression, and introduces complication into
the whole body of mathematical formulæ, which are really
founded on a logical basis.

It is of course apparent that the power of commutation
belongs only to terms related in the simple logical mode of
synthesis. No one can confuse " a house of bricks" with
" bricks of a house," " twelve square feet " with " twelve feet
square," "the water of crystallization" with " the crystallization of water." All relations which involve differences of time
and space are inconvertible ; the higher must not be made to
change places with the lower, nor the first with the last. For
the parties concerned there is all the difference in the world
between A killing B and B killing A. The law of commutativeness simply asserts that difference of order does
not attach to the connection between the properties and
circumstances of a thing—to what I call *simple logical
relation.*

[1] *Laws of Thought*, p. 29. It is pointed ᴗat in the preface to this
Second Edition that Leibnitz was acquainted with the Laws of
Simplicity and of Commutativeness.

CHAPTER III.

WE now proceed to consider the variety of forms of propositions in which the truths of science must be expressed. I shall endeavour to show that, however diverse these forms may be, they all admit the application of the one same principle of inference that what is true of a thing is true of the like or same. This principle holds true whatever be the kind or manner of the likeness, provided proper regard be had to its nature. Propositions may assert an identity of time, space, manner, quantity, degree, or any other circumstance in which things may agree or differ.

We find an instance of a proposition concerning time in the following :—" The year in which Newton was born, was the year in which Galileo died." This proposition expresses an approximate identity of time between two events; hence whatever is true of the year in which Galileo died is true of that in which Newton was born, and *vice versâ*. " Tower Hill is the place where Raleigh was executed " expresses an identity of place; and whatever is true of the one spot is true of the spot otherwise defined, but in reality the same. In ordinary language we have many propositions obscurely expressing identities of number, quantity, or degree. " So many men, so many minds," is a proposition concerning number, that is to say, an equation; whatever is true of the number of men is true of the number of minds, and *vice versâ*. " The density of Mars is (nearly) the same as that of the Earth," " The force of gravity is directly as the product of the masses, and

inversely as the square of the distance," are propositions
concerning magnitude or degree. Logicians have not paid
adequate attention to the great variety of propositions
which can·be stated by the use of the little conjunction
as, together with *so*. "As the home so the people," is a
proposition expressing identity of manner; and a great
number of similar propositions all indicating some kind of
resemblance might be quoted. Whatever be the special
kind of identity, all such expressions are subject to the
great principle of inference; but as we shall in later
parts of this work treat more particularly of inference in
cases of number and magnitude, we will here confine our
attention to logical propositions which involve only notions
of quality.

Simple Identities.

The most important class of propositions consists of
those which fall under the formula

$$A = B,$$

and may be called *simple identities*. I may instance, in
the first place, those most elementary propositions which
express the exact similarity of a quality encountered in
two or more objects. I may compare the colour of the
Pacific Ocean with that of the Atlantic, and declare them
identical. I may assert that "the smell of a rotten egg is
like that of hydrogen sulphide; " " the taste of silver hypo-
sulphite is like that of cane sugar; " "the sound of an
earthquake resembles that of distant artillery." Such are
propositions stating, accurately or otherwise, the identity
of simple physical sensations. Judgments of this kind
are necessarily pre-supposed in more complex judgments.
If I declare that "this coin is made of gold," I must base
the judgment upon the exact likeness of the substance in
several qualities to other pieces of substance which are
undoubtedly gold. I must make judgments of the colour,
the specific gravity, the hardness, and of other mechanical
and chemical properties; each of these judgments is expressed in an elementary proposition, "the colour of this
coin is the colour of gold," and so on. Even when we
establish the identity of a thing with itself under a
different name or aspect, it is by distinct judgments

concerning single circumstances. To prove that the Homeric χαλκός is copper we must show the identity of each quality recorded of χαλκός with a quality of copper. To establish Deal as the landing-place of Cæsar, all material circumstances must be shown to agree. If the modern Wroxeter is the ancient Uriconium, there must be the like agreement of all features of the country not subject to alteration by time.

Such identities must be expressed in the form $A = B$. We may say

Colour of Pacific Ocean = Colour of Atlantic Ocean.

Smell of rotten egg = Smell of hydrogen sulphide.

In these and similar propositions we assert identity of single qualities or causes of sensation. In the same form we may also express identity of any group of qualities, as in

χαλκός = Copper.

Deal = Landing-place of Cæsar.

A multitude of propositions involving singular terms fall into the same form, as in

The Pole star = The slowest-moving star.

Jupiter = The greatest of the planets.

The ringed planet = The planet having seven satellites.

The Queen of England = The Empress of India.

The number two = The even prime number.

Honesty = The best policy.

In mathematical and scientific theories we often meet with simple identities capable of expression in the same form. Thus in mechanical science " The process for finding the resultant of forces = the process for finding the resultant of simultaneous velocities." Theorems in geometry often give results in this form, as

Equilateral triangles = Equiangular triangles.

Circle = Finite plane curve of constant curvature.

Circle = Curve of least perimeter.

The more profound and important laws of nature are often expressible in the form of simple identities; in addition to some instances which have already been given, I may suggest,

Crystals of cubical system = Crystals not possessing the power of double refraction.

All definitions are necessarily of this form, whether the objects defined be many, few, or singular. Thus we may say,

Common salt = Sodium chloride.
Chlorophyl = Green colouring matter of leaves.
Square = Equal-sided rectangle.

It is an extraordinary fact that propositions of this elementary form, all-important and very numerous as they are, had no recognised place in Aristotle's system of Logic. Accordingly their importance was overlooked until very recent times, and logic was the most deformed of sciences. But it is impossible that Aristotle or any other person should avoid constantly using them; not a term could be defined without their use. In one place at least Aristotle actually notices a proposition of the kind. He observes : " We sometimes say that that white thing is Socrates, or that the object approaching is Callias."[1] Here we certainly have simple identity of terms ; but he considered such propositions purely accidental, and came to the unfortunate conclusion, that " Singulars cannot be predicated of other terms."

Propositions may also express the identity of extensive groups of objects taken collectively or in one connected whole ; as when we say,

The Queen, Lords, and Commons = The Legislature of the United Kingdom.

When Blackstone asserts that " The only true and natural foundation of society are the wants and fears of individuals," we must interpret him as meaning that the whole of the wants and fears of individuals in the aggregate form the foundation of society. But many propositions which might seem to be collective are but groups of singular propositions or identities. When we say " Potassium and sodium are the metallic bases of potash and soda," we obviously mean,

Potassium = Metallic base of potash ;
Sodium = Metallic base of soda.

It is the work of grammatical analysis to separate the various propositions often combined into a single sentence. Logic cannot be properly required to interpret the forms and devices of language, but only to treat the meaning when clearly exhibited.

Prior Analytics, i. cap. xxvii. 3.

Partial Identities.

A second highly important kind of proposition is that which I propose to call *a partial identity*. When we say that "All mammalia are vertebrata," we do not mean that mammalian animals are identical with vertebrate animals, but only that the mammalia form a *part of the class vertebrata*. Such a proposition was regarded in the old logic as asserting the inclusion of one class in another, or of an object in a class. It was called a universal affirmative proposition, because the attribute *vertebrate* was affirmed of the whole subject *mammalia ;* but the attribute was said to be *undistributed*, because not all vertebrata were of necessity involved in the proposition. Aristotle, overlooking the importance of simple identities, and indeed almost denying their existence, unfortunately founded his system upon the notion of inclusion in a class, instead of adopting the basis of identity. He regarded inference as resting upon the rule that what is true of the containing class is true of the contained, in place of the vastly more general rule that what is true of a class or thing is true of the like. Thus he not only reduced logic to a fragment of its proper self, but destroyed the deep analogies which bind together logical and mathematical reasoning. Hence a crowd of defects, difficulties and errors which will long disfigure the first and simplest of the sciences.

It is surely evident that the relation of inclusion rests upon the relation of identity. Mammalian animals cannot be included among vertebrates unless they be identical with part of the vertebrates. Cabinet Ministers are included almost always in the class Members of Parliament, because they are identical with some who sit in Parliament. We may indicate this identity with a part of the larger class in various ways ; as for instance,

Mammalia = part of the vertebrata.

Diatomaceæ = a class of plants.

Cabinet Ministers = some members of Parliament.

Iron = a metal.

In ordinary language the verbs *is* and *are* express mere inclusion more often than not. *Men are mortals*, means

that *men* form a part of the class *mortal ;* but great confusion exists between this sense of the verb and that in
which it expresses identity, as in " The sun is the centre of
the planetary system." The introduction of the indefinite
article *a* often expresses partiality ; when we say " Iron is
a metal" we clearly mean that iron is *one only* of several
metals.

Certain recent logicians have proposed to avoid the
indefiniteness in question by what is called the Quantification of the Predicate, and they have generally used the
little word *some* to show that only a part of the predicate
is identical with the subject. *Some* is an *indeterminate
adjective ;* it implies unknown qualities by which we might
select the part in question if the qualities were known, but
it gives no hint as to their nature. I might make use of
such an indeterminate sign to express partial identities in
this work. Thus, taking the special symbol V = Some, the
general form of a partial identity would be A = VB, and in
Boole's Logic expressions of the kind were much used.
But I believe that indeterminate symbols only introduce
complexity, and destroy the beauty and simple universality
of the system which may be created without their use. A
vague word like *some* is only used in ordinary language by
ellipsis, and to avoid the trouble of attaining accuracy.
We can always employ more definite expressions if we
like ; but when once the indefinite *some* is introduced we
cannot replace it by the special description. We do not
know whether *some* colour is red, yellow, blue, or what it
is ; but on the other hand *red* colour is certainly *some*
colour.

Throughout this system of logic I shall dispense with
such indefinite expressions ; and this can readily be done
by substituting one of the other terms. To express the
proposition " All A's are some B's " I shall not use the form
A = VB, but

$$A = AB.$$

This formula states that the class A is identical with the
class AB ; and as the latter must be a part at least of the
class B, it implies the inclusion of the class A in that of
B. We might represent our former example thus,

$$\text{Mammalia} = \text{Mammalian vertebrata.}$$

This proposition asserts identity between a part (or it may

be the whole) of the vertebrata and the mammalia.   If it is
asked What part ? the proposition affords no answer, except
that it is the part which is mammalian; but the assertion
" mammalia = some vertebrata " tells us no more.

It is quite likely that some readers will think this
mode of representing the universal affirmative proposition
artificial and complicated.   I will not undertake to convince them of the opposite at this point of my exposition.
Justification for it will be found, not so much in the immediate treatment of this proposition, as in the general
harmony which it will enable us to disclose between all
parts of reasoning.   I have no doubt that this is the
critical difficulty in the relation of logical to other forms of
reasoning.   Grant this mode of denoting that " all A's are
B's," and I fear no further difficulties ; refuse it, and we find
want of analogy and endless anomaly in every direction. It
is on general grounds that I hope to show overwhelming
reasons for seeking to reduce every kind of proposition to
the form of an identity.

I may add that not a few logicians have accepted this
view of the universal affirmative proposition.   Leibnitz, in
his *Difficultates Quædam Logicæ*, adopts it, saying, " Omne
A est B ; id est æquivalent AB et A, seu A non B est non-
ens."   Boole employed the logical equation $x = xy$ concurrently with $x = vy$; and Spalding [1] distinctly says that
the proposition " all metals are minerals " might be described as an assertion of *partial identity* between the two
classes.   Hence the name which I have adopted for the
proposition.

Limited Identities.

An important class of propositions have the form
$$AB = AC,$$
expressing the identity of the class AB with the class AC.
In other words, " Within the sphere of the class A, all the
B's are all the C's ;" or again, " The B's and C's, which are
A's, are identical."   But it will be observed that nothing is
asserted concerning things which are outside of the class
A ; and thus the identity is of limited extent.   It is the
proposition B = C limited to the sphere of things called A.

[1] *Encyclopædia Britannica*, Eighth Ed. art. Logic, sect. 37, note.
8vo reprint, p. 79.

Thus we may say, with some approximation to truth, that " Large plants are plants devoid of locomotive power."

A barrister may make numbers of most general statements concerning the relations of persons and things in the course of an argument, but it is of course to be understood that he speaks only of persons and things under the English Law. Even mathematicians make statements which are not true with absolute generality. They say that imaginary roots enter into equations by pairs ; but this is only true under the tacit condition that the equations in question shall not have imaginary coefficients.[1] The universe, in short, within which they habitually discourse is that of equations with real coefficients. These implied limitations form part of that great mass of tacit knowledge which accompanies all special arguments.

To De Morgan is due the remark, that we do usually think and argue in a limited universe or sphere of notions, even when it is not expressly stated.[2]

It is worthy of inquiry whether all identities are not really limited to an implied sphere of meaning. When we make such a plain statement as " Gold is malleable " we obviously speak of gold only in its solid state ; when we say that " Mercury is a liquid metal " we must be understood to exclude the frozen condition to which it may be reduced in the Arctic regions. Even when we take such a fundamental law of nature as " All substances gravitate," we must mean by substance, material substance, not including that basis of heat, light, and electrical undulations which occupies space and possesses many wonderful mechanical properties, but not gravity. The proposition then is really of the form

Material substance = Material gravitating substance.

Negative Propositions.

In every act of intellect we are engaged with a certain identity or difference between things or sensations compared together. Hitherto I have treated only of identities ; and yet it might seem that the relation of difference must be

---

[1] De Morgan *On the Root of any Function.* Cambridge Philosophical Transactions, 1867, vol xi. p. 25.

[2] *Syllabus of a proposed System of Logic*, §§ 122, 123.

infinitely more common than that of likeness. One thing may resemble a great many other things, but then it differs from all remaining things in the world. Diversity may almost be said to constitute life, being to thought what motion is to a river. The perception of an object involves its discrimination from all other objects. But we may nevertheless be said to detect resemblance as often as we detect difference. We cannot, in fact, assert the existence of a difference, without at the same time implying the existence of an agreement.

If I compare mercury, for instance, with other metals, and decide that it is *not solid*, here is a difference between mercury and solid things, expressed in a negative proposition; but there must be implied, at the same time, an agreement between mercury and the other substances which are not solid. As it is impossible to separate the vowels of the alphabet from the consonants without at the same time separating the consonants from the vowels, so I cannot select as the object of thought *solid things*, without thereby throwing together into another class all things which are *not solid*. The very fact of not possessing a quality, constitutes a new quality which may be the ground of judgment and classification. In this point of view, agreement and difference are ever the two sides of the same act of intellect, and it becomes equally possible to express the same judgment in the one or other aspect.

Between affirmation and negation there is accordingly a perfect equilibrium. Every affirmative proposition implies a negative one, and *vice versa*. It is even a matter of indifference, in a logical point of view, whether a positive or negative term be used to denote a given quality and the class of things possessing it. If the ordinary state of a man's body be called *good health*, then in other circumstances he is said *not to be in good health ;* but we might equally describe him in the latter state as *sickly*, and in his normal condition he would be *not sickly*. Animal and vegetable substances are now called *organic*, so that the other substances, forming an immensely greater part of the globe, are described negatively as *inorganic*. But we might, with at least equal logical correctness, have described the preponderating class of substances as *mineral*, and then vegetable and animal substances would have been *non-mineral*.

It is plain that any positive term and its corresponding negative divide between them the whole universe of thought : whatever does not fall into one must fall into the other, by the third fundamental Law of Thought, the Law of Duality. It follows at once that there are two modes of representing a difference. Supposing that the things represented by A and B are found to differ, we may indicate (see p. 17) the result of the judgment by the notation

$$A \sim B.$$

We may now represent the same judgment by the assertion that A agrees with those things which differ from B, or that A agrees with the not-B's. Using our notation for negative terms (see p. 14), we obtain

$$A = Ab$$

as the expression of the ordinary negative proposition. Thus if we take A to mean quicksilver, and B solid, then we have the following proposition :—

Quicksilver = Quicksilver not-solid.

There may also be several other classes of negative propositions, of which no notice was taken in the old logic. We may have cases where all A's are not-B's, and at the same time all not-B's are A's ; there may, in short, be a simple identity between A and not-B, which may be expressed in the form

$$A = b.$$

An example of this form would be

Conductors of electricity = non-electrics.

We shall also frequently have to deal as results of deduction, with simple, partial, or limited identities between negative terms, as in the forms

$$a = b, \qquad a = ab, \qquad aC = bC, \quad \text{etc.}$$

It would be possible to represent affirmative propositions in the negative form. Thus "Iron is solid," might be expressed as " Iron is not not-solid," or " Iron is not fluid ; " or, taking A and b for the terms " iron," and " not-solid," the form would be $A \sim b$.

But there are very strong reasons why we should employ all propositions in their affirmative form. All inference proceeds by the substitution of equivalents, and a proposition expressed in the form of an identity is ready to yield all its consequences in the most direct manner. As will be more fully shown, we can infer *in* a negative proposition, but not *by* it. Difference is incapable of becoming the ground of inference ; it is only the implied agreement with other differing objects which admits of deductive reasoning; and it will always be found advantageous to employ propositions in the form which exhibits clearly the implied agreements.

Conversion of Propositions.

The old books of logic contain many rules concerning the conversion of propositions, that is, the transposition of the subject and predicate in such a way as to obtain a new proposition which will be true when the original proposition is true. The reduction of every proposition to the form of an identity renders all such rules and processes needless. Identity is essentially reciprocal. If the colour of the Atlantic Ocean is the same as that of the Pacific Ocean, that of the Pacific must be the same as that of the Atlantic. Sodium chloride being identical with common salt, common salt must be identical with sodium chloride. If the number of windows in Salisbury Cathedral equals the number of days in the year, the number of days in the year must equal the number of the windows. Lord Chesterfield was not wrong when he said, " I will give anybody their choice of these two truths, which amount to the same thing ; He who loves himself best is the honestest man; or, The honestest man loves himself best." Scotus Erigena exactly expresses this reciprocal character of identity in saying, " There are not two studies, one of philosophy and the other of religion; true philosophy is true religion, and true religion is true philosophy."

A mathematician would not think it worth while to mention that if $x = y$ then also $y = x$. He would not consider these to be two equations at all, but one equation accidentally written in two different manners. In written symbols one of two names must come first, and the other second, and a like succession must perhaps be observed in our thoughts : but in the relation of identity there is no need for succession in order (see p. 33) , each is simultaneously equal and identical to the other. These remarks will hold true both of logical and mathematical identity ; so that I shall consider the two forms

$$A = B \text{ and } B = A$$

to express exactly the same identity differently written. All need for rules of conversion disappears, and there will be no single proposition in the system which may not be written with either end foremost. Thus $A = AB$ is the same as $AB = A$, $aC = bC$ is the same as $bC = aC$, and so forth.

The same remarks are partially true of differences and inequalities, which are also reciprocal to the extent that one thing cannot differ from a second without the second differing from the first. Mars differs in colour from Venus, and Venus must differ from Mars. The Earth differs from Jupiter in density; therefore Jupiter must differ from the Earth. Speaking generally, if $A \sim B$ we shall also have $B \sim A$, and these two forms may be considered expressions of the same difference. But the relation of differing things is not wholly reciprocal. The density of Jupiter does not differ from that of the Earth in the same way that that of the Earth differs from that of Jupiter. The change of sensation which we experience in passing from Venus to Mars is not the same as what we experience in passing back to Venus, but just the opposite in nature. The colour of the sky is lighter than that of the ocean; therefore that of the ocean cannot be lighter than that of the sky, but darker. In these and all similar cases we gain a notion of *direction* or character of change, and results of immense importance may be shown to rest on this notion. For the present we shall be concerned with the mere fact of identity existing or not existing.

Twofold Interpretation of Propositions.

Terms, as we have seen (p. 25), may have a meaning either in extension or intension; and according as one or the other meaning is attributed to the terms of a proposition, so may a different interpretation be assigned to the proposition itself. When the terms are abstract we must read them in intension, and a proposition connecting such terms must denote the identity or non-identity of the qualities respectively denoted by the terms. Thus if we say

$$\text{Equality} = \text{Identity of magnitude,}$$

the assertion means that the circumstance of being equal
exactly corresponds with the circumstance of being
identical in magnitude.   Similarly in

Opacity = Incapability of transmitting light,

the quality of being incapable of transmitting light is declared to be the same as the intended meaning of the word
opacity.

When general names form the terms of a proposition we
may apply a double interpretation.   Thus

Exogens = Dicotyledons

means either that the qualities which belong to all exogens
are the same as those which belong to all dicotyledons, or else
that every individual falling under one name falls equally
under the other.   Hence it may be said that there are two
distinct fields of logical thought.   We may argue either by
the qualitative meaning of names or by the quantitative,
that is, the extensive meaning.   Every argument involving concrete plural terms might be converted into
one involving only abstract singular terms, and *vice
versâ*.   But there are reasons for believing that the
intensive or qualitative form of reasoning is the primary
and fundamental one.   It is sufficient to point out that the
extensive meaning of a name is a changeable and fleeting
thing, while the intensive meaning may nevertheless remain
fixed.   Very numerous additions have been lately made
to the extensive meanings both of planet and element.
Every iron steam-ship which is made or destroyed adds to
or subtracts from the extensive meaning of the name
steam-ship, without necessarily affecting the intensive
meaning.   Stage coach means as much as ever in one way,
but in extension the class is nearly extinct.   Chinese
railway, on the other hand, is a term represented only by a
single instance; in twenty years it may be the name of a
large class.

CHAPTER IV.

DEDUCTIVE REASONING.

THE general principle of inference having been explained in the previous chapters, and a suitable system of symbols provided, we have now before us the comparatively easy task of tracing out the most common and important forms of deductive reasoning. The general problem of deduction is as follows:—*From one or more propositions called premises to draw such other propositions as will necessarily be true when the premises are true.* By deduction we investigate and unfold the information contained in the premises; and this we can do by one single rule—*For any term occurring in any proposition substitute the term which is asserted in any premise to be identical with it.* To obtain certain deductions, especially those involving negative conclusions, we shall require to bring into use the second and third Laws of Thought, and the process of reasoning will then be called *Indirect Deduction.* In the present chapter, however, I shall confine my attention to those results which can be obtained by the process of *Direct Deduction,* that is, by applying to the premises themselves the rule of substitution. It will be found that we can combine into one harmonious system, not only the various moods of the ancient syllogism, but a great number of equally important forms of reasoning, which had no recognised place in the old logic. We can at the same time dispense entirely with the elaborate apparatus of logical rules and mnemonic lines, which were requisite so long as the vital principle of reasoning was not clearly expressed.

Immediate Inference.

Probably the simplest of all forms of inference is that
which has been called *Immediate Inference,* because it can
be performed upon a single proposition. It consists in
joining an adjective, or other qualifying clause of the same
nature, to both sides of an identity, and asserting the
equivalence of the terms thus produced. For instance,
since

Conductors of electricity = Non-electrics,
it follows that

Liquid conductors of electricity = Liquid non-electrics.
If we suppose that

Plants = Bodies decomposing carbonic acid,
it follows that

Microscopic plants = Microscopic bodies decomposing
carbonic acid.
In general terms, from the identity

$$A = B$$

we can infer the identity

$$AC = BC.$$

This is but a case of plain substitution; for by the first
Law of Thought it must be admitted that

$$AC = AC,$$

and if, in the second side of this identity, we substitute
for A its equivalent B, we obtain

$$AC = BC.$$

In like manner from the partial identity

$$A = AB$$

we may obtain

$$AC = ABC$$

by an exactly similar act of substitution; and in every
other case the rule will be found capable of verification by
the principle of inference.   The process when performed as
here described will be quite free from the liability to error
which I have shown [1] to exist in " Immediate Inference by
added Determinants," as described by Dr. Thomson.[2]

---

[1] *Elementary Lessons in Logic,* p. 86.
[2] *Outline of the Laws of Thought,* § 87

Inference with Two Simple Identities.

One of the most common forms of inference, and one to which I shall especially direct attention, is practised with two simple identities. From the two statements that " London is the capital of England " and " London is the most populous city in the world," we instantaneously draw the conclusion that " The capital of England is the most populous city in the world." Similarly, from the identities

Hydrogen = Substance of least density,

Hydrogen = Substance of least atomic weight,

we infer

Substance of least density = Substance of least atomic weight.

The general form of the argument is exhibited in the symbols

$$B = A \qquad (1)$$
$$B = C \qquad (2)$$
$$\text{hence} \qquad A = C. \qquad (3)$$

We may describe the result by saying that terms identical with the same term are identical with each other; and it is impossible to overlook the analogy to the first axiom of Euclid that " things equal to the same thing are equal to each other." It has been very commonly supposed that this is a fundamental principle of thought, incapable of reduction to anything simpler. But I entertain no doubt that this form of reasoning is only one case of the general rule of inference. We have two propositions, $A = B$ and $B = C$, and we may for a moment consider the second one as affirming a truth concerning B, while the former one informs us that B is identical with A; hence by substitution we may affirm the same truth of A. It happens in this particular case that the truth affirmed is identity to C, and we might, if we preferred it, have considered the substitution as made by means of the second identity in the first. Having two identities we have a choice of the mode in which we will make the substitution, though the result is exactly the same in either case.

Now compare the three following formulæ,

(1) $A = B = C$, hence $A = C$
(2) $A = B \sim C$, hence $A \sim C$
(3) $A \sim B \sim C$, no inference.

In the second formula we have an identity and a difference, and we are able to infer a difference ; in the third we have two differences and are unable to make any inference at all. Because A and C both differ from B, we cannot tell whether they will or will not differ from each other. The flowers and leaves of a plant may both differ in colour from the earth in which the plant grows, and yet they may differ from each other; in other cases the leaves and stem may both differ from the soil and yet agree with each other. Where we have difference only we can make no inference ; where we have identity we can infer.   This fact gives great countenance to my assertion that inference proceeds always through identity, but may be equally well effected in propositions asserting difference or identity.

Deferring a more complete discussion of this point, I will only mention now that arguments from double identity occur very frequently, and are usually taken for granted, owing to their extreme simplicity.   In regard to the equivalence of words this form of inference must be constantly employed.   If the ancient Greek χαλκός is our *copper*, then it must be the French *cuivre*, the German *kupfer*, the Latin *cuprum*, because these are words, in one sense at least, equivalent to copper.   Whenever we can give two definitions or expressions for the same term, the formula applies ; thus Senior defined wealth as " All those things, and those things only, which are transferable, are limited in supply, and are directly or indirectly productive of pleasure or preventive of pain."   Wealth is also equivalent to "things which have value in exchange ; " hence obviously, "things which have value in exchange = all those things, and those things only, which are transferable, &c."   Two expressions for the same term are often given in the same sentence, and their equivalence implied.   Thus Thomson and Tait say,[1] 'The naturalist may be content to know matter as that which can be perceived by the senses, or as that which can be acted upon by or can exert force."   I take this to mean—

> Matter = what can be perceived by the senses ;
> Matter = what can be acted upon by or can exert force.

[1] *Treatise on Natural Philosophy*, vol. i. p. 161.

For the term "matter" in either of these identities we may substitute its equivalent given in the other definition. Elsewhere they often employ sentences of the form exemplified in the following:[1] "The integral curvature, or whole change of direction of an arc of a plane curve, is the angle through which the tangent has turned as we pass from one extremity to the other." This sentence is certainly of the form—

The integral curvature = the whole change of direction, &c. = the angle through which the tangent has turned, &c.

Disguised cases of the same kind of inference occur throughout all sciences, and a remarkable instance is found in algebraic geometry. Mathematicians readily show that every equation of the form $y = mx + c$ corresponds to or represents a straight line; it is also easily proved that the same equation is equivalent to one of the general form $Ax + By + C = 0$, and *vice versâ*. Hence it follows that every equation of the form in question, that is to say, every equation of the first degree, corresponds to or represents a straight line.[2]

Inference with a Simple and a Partial Identity.

A form of reasoning somewhat different from that last considered consists in inference between a simple and a partial identity. If we have two propositions of the forms

$$A = B,$$
$$B = BC,$$

we may then substitute for B in either proposition its equivalent in the other, getting in both cases $A = BC$; in this we may if we like make a second substitution for B, getting

$$A = AC.$$

Thus, since "The Mont Blanc is the highest mountain in Europe, and the Mont Blanc is deeply covered with snow," we infer by an obvious substitution that "The highest mountain in Europe is deeply covered with snow." These propositions when rigorously stated fall into the forms above exhibited.

This mode of inference is constantly employed when for

---

[1] *Treatise on Natural Philosophy*, vol. i. p. 6.
[2] Todhunter's *Plane Co-ordinate Geometry*, chap. ii. pp. 11—14.

a term we substitute its definition, or *vice versâ.* The very purpose of a definition is to allow a single noun to be employed in place of a long descriptive phrase. Thus, when we say " A circle is a curve of the second degree," we may substitute a definition of the circle, getting " A curve, all points of which are at equal distances from one point, is a curve of the second degree." The real forms of the propositions here given are exactly those shown in the symbolic statement, but in this and many other cases it will be sufficient to state them in ordinary elliptical language for sake of brevity. In scientific treatises a term and its definition are often both given in the same sentence, as in " The weight of a body in any given locality, or the force with which the earth attracts it, is proportional to its mass." The conjunction *or* in this statement gives the force of equivalence to the parenthetic phrase, so that the propositions really are

> Weight of a body = force with which the earth attracts it.

> Weight of a body = weight, &c. proportional to its mass.

A slightly different case of inference consists in substituting in a proposition of the form $A = AB$, a definition of the term B. Thus from $A = AB$ and $B = C$ we get $A = AC$. For instance, we may say that " Metals are elements " and " Elements are incapable of decomposition."

> Metal = metal element.

> Element = what is incapable of decomposition.

Hence

> Metal = metal incapable of decomposition.

It is almost needless to point out that the form of these arguments does not suffer any real modification if some of the terms happen to be negative; indeed in the last example " incapable of decomposition" may be treated as a negative term. Taking

> A = metal C = capable of decomposition

> B = element c = incapable of decomposition ;

the propositions are of the forms

$$A = AB$$
$$B = c$$

whence, by substitution.

$$A = Ac.$$

Inference of a Partial from Two Partial Identities.

Howevef common be the cases of inference already noticed, there is a form occurring almost more frequently, and which deserves much attention, because it occupied a prominent place in the ancient syllogistic system. That system strangely overlooked all the kinds of argument we have as yet considered, and selected, as the type of all reasoning, one which employs two partial identities as premises. Thus from the propositions

Sodium is a metal   (1)
Metals conduct electricity,   (2)

we may conclude that

Sodium conducts electricity.   (3)

Taking A, B, C to represent the three terms respectively, the premises are of the forms

$$A = AB \qquad (1)$$
$$B = BC. \qquad (2)$$

Now for B in (1) we can substitute its expression as given in (2), obtaining

$$A = ABC, \qquad (3)$$

or, in words, from

Sodium = sodium metal,   (1)
Metal = metal conducting electricity,   (2)

we infer

Sodium = sodium metal conducting electricity, (3)

which, in the elliptical language of common life, becomes " Sodium conducts electricity."

The above is a syllogism in the mood called Barbara [1] in the truly barbarous language of ancient logicians ; and the first figure of the syllogism contained Barbara and three other moods which were esteemed distinct forms of argument. But it is worthy of notice that, without any real change in our form of inference, we readily include these three other moods under Barbara. The negative mood Celarent will be represented by the example

Neptune is a planet,   (1)
No planet has retrograde motion ;   (2)
Hence   Neptune has not retrograde motion. (3)

---

[1] An explanation of this and other technical terms of the old logic will be found in my *Elementary Lessons in Logic.* Sixth Edition, 1876 : Macmillan.

If we put A for Neptune, B for planet, and C for "having
retrograde motion," then by the corresponding negative
term c, we denote " not having retrograde motion." The
premises now fall into the forms

$$A = AB \qquad (1)$$
$$B = Bc, \qquad (2)$$

and by substitution for B, exactly as before, we obtain

$$A = ABc. \qquad (3)$$

What is called in the old logic a particular conclusion
may be deduced without any real variation in the symbols.
Particular quantity is indicated as before mentioned
(p. 41), by joining to the term an indefinite adjective of
quantity, such as *some, a part of, certain*, &c., meaning that
an unknown part of the term enters into the proposition
as subject. Considerable doubt and ambiguity arise out of
the question whether the part may not in some cases be
the whole, and in the syllogism at least it must be understood in this sense.[1] Now, if we take a letter to represent
this indefinite part, we need make no change in our
formulæ to express the syllogisms Darii and Ferio. Consider the example—

Some metals are of less density than water,   (1)
All bodies of less density than water will float
upon the surface of water; hence   (2)
Some metals will float upon the surface of
water.   (3)

Let   A = some metals,
B = body of less density than water,
C = floating on the surface of water

then the propositions are evidently as before,

$$A = AB, \qquad (1)$$
$$B = BC; \qquad (2)$$
$$\text{hence} \qquad A = ABC, \qquad (3)$$

Thus the syllogism Darii does not really differ from Barbara. If the reader prefer it, we can readily employ a
distinct symbol for the indefinite sign of quantity.

Let   P = some,
Q = metal,

B and C having the same meanings as before. Then the
premises become

---

[1] *Elementary Lessons in Logic*, pp. 67, 79.

$$PQ = PQB, \qquad (1)$$
$$B = BC; \qquad (2)$$
hence, by substitution, as before,
$$PQ = PQBC. \qquad (3)$$
Except that the formulæ look a little more complicated there is no difference whatever.

The mood Ferio is of exactly the same character as Darii or Barbara, except that it involves the use of a negative term. Take the example,

Bodies which are equally elastic in all directions do not doubly refract light;

Some crystals are bodies equally elastic in all directions; therefore, some crystals do not doubly refract light.

Assigning the letters as follows :—

A = some crystals,

B = bodies equally elastic in all directions.

C = doubly refracting light,

c = not doubly refracting light.

Our argument is of the same form as before, and may be concisely stated in one line,

$$A = AB = ABc.$$

If it is preferred to put PQ for the indefinite *some crystals* we have

$$PQ = PQB = PQBc.$$

The only difference is that the negative term c takes the place of C in the mood Darii.

Ellipsis of Terms in Partial Identities.

The reader will probably have noticed that the conclusion which we obtain from premises is often more full than that drawn by the old Aristotelian processes. Thus from "Sodium is a metal," and "Metals conduct electricity," we inferred (p. 55) that "Sodium = sodium, metal, conducting electricity," whereas the old logic simply concludes that "Sodium conducts electricity." Symbolically, from $A = AB$, and $B = BC$, we get $A = ABC$, whereas the old logic gets at the most $A = AC$. It is therefore well to show that without employing any other principles of inference than those already described, we may infer $A = AC$ from $A = ABC$, though we cannot infer the latter

more full and accurate result from the former. We may
show this most simply as follows :—
By the first Law of Thought it is evident that
$$AA = AA;$$
and if we have given the proposition A = ABC, we may
substitute for both the A's in the second side of the above,
obtaining
$$AA = ABC . ABC.$$
But from the property of logical symbols expressed in the
Law of Simplicity (p. 33) some of the repeated letters may
be made to coalesce, and we have
$$A = ABC . C.$$
Substituting again for ABC its equivalent A, we obtain
$$A = AC,$$
the desired result.

By a similar process of reasoning it may be shown that
we can always drop out any term appearing in one member
of a proposition, provided that we substitute for it the
whole of the other member.   This process was described in
my first logical Essay,[1] as *Intrinsic Elimination*, but it
might perhaps be better entitled the *Ellipsis of Terms*.
It enables us to get rid of needless terms by strict
substitutive reasoning.

Inference of a Simple from Two Partial Identities.

Two terms may be connected together by two partial
identities in yet another manner, and a case of inference
then arises which is of the highest importance.   In the
two premises
$$A = AB \qquad (1)$$
$$B = AB \qquad (2)$$
the second member of each is the same; so that we can by
obvious substitution obtain
$$A = B.$$
Thus, in plain geometry we readily prove that "Every
equilateral triangle is also an equiangular triangle," and we
can with equal ease prove that "Every equiangular triangle
is an equilateral triangle." Thence by substitution, as
explained above, we pass to the simple identity,
Equilateral triangle = equiangular triangle.

Pure Logic. p 19.

We thus prove that one class of triangles is entirely identical with another class ; that is to say, they differ only in our way of naming and regarding them.

The great importance of this process of inference arises from the fact that the conclusion is more simple and general than either of the premises, and contains as much information as both of them put together. It is on this account constantly employed in inductive investigation, as will afterwards be more fully explained, and it is the natural mode by which we arrive at a conviction of the truth of simple identities as existing between classes of numerous objects.

Inference of a Limited from Two Partial Identities.

We have considered some arguments which are of the type treated by Aristotle in the first figure of the syllogism. But there exist two other types of argument which employ a pair of partial identities. If our premises are as shown in these symbols,

$$B = AB \qquad (1)$$
$$B = CB, \qquad (2)$$

we may substitute for B either by (1) in (2) or by (2) in (1), and by both modes we obtain the conclusion

$$AB = CB, \qquad (3)$$

a proposition of the kind which we have called a limited identity (p. 42). Thus, for example,

Potassium = potassium metal   (1)
Potassium = potassium capable of floating on
            water ;   (2)

hence

Potassium metal = potassium capable of float-
            ing on water.   (3)

This is really a syllogism of the mood Darapti in the third figure, except that we obtain a conclusion of a more exact character than the old syllogism gives. From the premises " Potassium is a metal " and " Potassium floats on water," Aristotle would have inferred that " Some metals float on water." But if inquiry were made what the " some metals " are, the answer would certainly be " Metal which is potassium." Hence Aristotle's conclusion simply leaves out some of the information afforded in the premises ; it

even leaves us open to interpret the *some metals* in a wider
sense than we are warranted in doing. From these distinct
defects of the old syllogism the process of substitution is
free, and the new process only incurs the possible objection
of being tediously minute and accurate.

Miscellaneous Forms of Deductive Inference.

The more common forms of deductive reasoning having
been exhibited and demonstrated on the principle of
substitution, there still remain many, in fact an indefinite
number, which may be explained with nearly equal ease.
Such as involve the use of disjunctive propositions will be
described in a later chapter, and several of the syllogistic
moods which include negative terms will be more conveniently treated after we have introduced the symbolic
use of the second and third laws of thought.

We sometimes meet with a chain of propositions which
allow of repeated substitution, and form an argument
called in the old logic a Sorites. Take, for instance, the
premises

Iron is a metal,   (1)
Metals are good conductors of electricity,   (2)
Good conductors of electricity are useful for
        telegraphic purposes.   (3)
It obviously follows that
Iron is useful for telegraphic purposes.   (4)
Now if we take our letters thus,

A = Iron, B = metal, C = good conductor of
        electricity, D = useful for telegraphic purposes,
the premises will assume the forms

$$A = AB,$$ (1)
$$B = BC,$$ (2)
$$C = CD.$$ (3)

For B in (1) we can substitute its equivalent in (2)
obtaining, as before,

$$A = ABC.$$

Substituting for C in this intermediate result its equivalent
as given in (3), we obtain the complete conclusion

$$A = ABCD.$$ (4)

The full interpretation is that *Iron is iron, metal, good
conductor of electricity, useful for telegraphic purposes,* which

is abridged in common language by the ellipsis of the
circumstances which are not of immediate importance.
   Instead of all the propositions being exactly of the same
kind as in the last example, we may have a series of
premises of various character ; for instance,
       Common salt is sodium chloride,   (1)
       Sodium chloride crystallizes in a cubical form, (2)
       What crystallizes in a cubical form does not
            possess the power of double refraction ;   (3
it will follow that
       Common salt does not possess the power of double
            refraction.   (4)
Taking our letter-terms thus,
       A = Common salt,
       B = Sodium chloride,
       C = Crystallizing in a cubical form,
       D = Possessing the power of double refraction,
we may state the premises in the forms
                  $A = B$,   (1)
                  $B = BC$,   (2)
                  $C = Cd$.   (3)
Substituting by (3) in (2) and then by (2) as thus altered
in (1) we obtain
                  $A = BCd$,   (4)
which is a more precise version of the common conclusion.
   We often meet with a series of propositions describing
the qualities or circumstances of the one same thing, and
we may combine them all into one proposition by the
process of substitution. This case is, in fact, that which
Dr. Thomson has called "Immediate Inference by the
sum of several predicates," and his example will serve my
purpose well.[1] He describes copper as "A metal—of a
red colour—and disagreeable smell—and taste—all the
preparations of which are poisonous—which is highly
malleable—ductile—and tenacious—with a specific gravity
of about 8.83." If we assign the letter A to copper, and the
succeeding letters of the alphabet in succession to the series
of predicates, we have nine distinct statements, of the form
$A = AB$ (1) $A = AC$ (2) $A = AD$ (3) . . . . . $A = AK$ (9).
We can readily combine these propositions into one by

---

[1] *An Outline of the Necessary Laws of Thought*, Fifth Ed. p. 161.

substituting for A in the second side of (1) its expression
in (2). We thus get

$$A = ABC,$$

and by repeating the process over and over again we
obviously get the single proposition

$$A = ABCD \, . . \, JK.$$

But Dr. Thomson is mistaken in supposing that we can
obtain in this manner a *definition* of copper. Strictly
speaking, the above proposition is only a *description* of
copper, and all the ordinary descriptions of substances in
scientific works may be summed up in this form. Thus we
may assert of the organic substances called Paraffins that
they are all saturated hydrocarbons, incapable of uniting
with other substances, produced by heating the alcoholic
iodides with zinc, and so on. It may be shown that no
amount of ordinary description can be equivalent to a definition of any substance.

Fallacies.

I have hitherto been engaged in showing that all the
forms of reasoning of the old syllogistic logic, and an
indefinite number of other forms in addition, may be
readily and clearly explained on the single principle of
substitution. It is now desirable to show that the same
principle will prevent us falling into fallacies. So long
as we exactly observe the one rule of substitution of
equivalents it will be impossible to commit a *paralogism*,
that is to break any one of the elaborate rules of the
ancient system. The one new rule is thus proved to be as
powerful as the six, eight, or more rules by which the correctness of syllogistic reasoning was guarded.

It was a fundamental rule, for instance, that two negative premises could give no conclusion. If we take the
propositions

Granite is not a sedimentary rock,   (1)

Basalt is not a sedimentary rock,   (2)

we ought not to be able to draw any inference concerning
the relation between granite and basalt. Taking our
letter-terms thus:

$$A = \text{granite}, \quad B = \text{sedimentary rock}, \quad C = \text{basalt},$$

the premises may be expressed in the forms

$$A \sim B, \qquad\qquad (1)$$
$$C \sim B. \qquad\qquad (2)$$

We have in this form two statements of difference; but the principle of inference can only work with a statement of agreement or identity (p. 63). Thus our rule gives us no power whatever of drawing any inference; this is exactly in accordance with the fifth rule of the syllogism.

It is to be remembered, indeed, that we claim the power of always turning a negative proposition into an affirmative one (p. 45); and it might seem that the old rule against negative premises would thus be circumvented. Let us try. The premises (1) and (2) when affirmatively stated take the forms

$$A = Ab \qquad\qquad (1)$$
$$C = Cb. \qquad\qquad (2)$$

The reader will find it impossible by the rule of substitution to discover a relation between A and C. Three terms occur in the above premises, namely A, b, and C; but they are so combined that no term occurring in one has its exact equivalent stated in the other. No substitution can therefore be made, and the principle of the fifth rule of the syllogism holds true. Fallacy is impossible.

It would be a mistake, however, to suppose that the mere occurrence of negative terms in both premises of a syllogism renders them incapable of yielding a conclusion. The old rule informed us that from two negative premises no conclusion could be drawn, but it is a fact that the rule in this bare form does not hold universally true; and I am not aware that any precise explanation has been given of the conditions under which it is or is not imperative. Consider the following example:

Whatever is not metallic is not capable of powerful magnetic influence, (1)
Carbon is not metallic, (2)
Therefore, carbon is not capable of powerful magnetic influence. (3)

Here we have two distinctly negative premises (1) and (2), and yet they yield a perfectly valid negative conclusion (3). The syllogistic rule is actually falsified in its bare and general statement. In this and many other cases we can convert the propositions into affirmative ones which will yield a conclusion by substitution without any difficulty.

To show this let

$$A = \text{carbon}, \qquad\qquad B = \text{metallic},$$
$$C = \text{capable of powerful magnetic influence.}$$

The premises readily take the forms

$$b = bc, \qquad\qquad (1)$$
$$A = Ab, \qquad\qquad (2)$$

and substitution for b in (2) by means of (1) gives the conclusion

$$A = Abc. \qquad\qquad (3)$$

Our principle of inference then includes the rule of negative premises whenever it is true, and discriminates correctly between the cases where it does and does not hold true.

The paralogism, anciently called *the Fallacy of Undis-tributed Middle*, is also easily exhibited and infallibly avoided by our system. Let the premises be

Hydrogen is an element, $\qquad\qquad (1)$
All metals are elements. $\qquad\qquad (2)$

According to the syllogistic rules the middle term "element " is here undistributed, and no conclusion can be obtained; we cannot tell then whether hydrogen is or is not a metal. Represent the terms as follows

$$A = \text{hydrogen},$$
$$B = \text{element},$$
$$C = \text{metal}.$$

The premises then become

$$A = AB, \qquad\qquad (1)$$
$$C = CB. \qquad\qquad (2)$$

The reader will here, as in a former page (p. 62), find it impossible to make any substitution. The only term which occurs in both premises is B, but it is differently combined in the two premises. For B we must not substitute A, which is equivalent to AB, not to B. Nor must we confuse together CB and AB, which, though they contain one common letter, are different aggregate terms. The rule of substitution gives us no right to decompose combinations; and if we adhere rigidly to the rule, that if two terms are stated to be equivalent we may substitute one for the other, we cannot commit the fallacy. It is apparent that the form of premises stated above is the same as that which we obtained by translating two negative premises into the affirmative form.

The old fallacy, technically called the *Illicit Process of the Major Term,* is more easy to commit and more difficult to detect than any other breach of the syllogistic rules. In our system it could hardly occur. From the premises

All planets are subject to gravity, (1)

Fixed stars are not planets, (2)

we might inadvertently but fallaciously infer that, " Fixed stars are not subject to gravity." To reduce the premises to symbolic form, let

A = planet

B = fixed star

C = subject to gravity ;

then we have the propositions

$A = AC$ (1)

$B = Ba.$ (2)

The reader will try in vain to produce from these premises by legitimate substitution any relation between B and C ; he could not then commit the fallacy of asserting that B is not C.

There remain two other kinds of paralogism, commonly known as the fallacy of Four Terms and the Illicit Process of the Minor Term. They are so evidently impossible while we obey the rule of the substitution of equivalents, that it is not necessary to give any illustrations. When there are four distinct terms in two propositions as in $A = B$ and $C = D$, there could evidently be no opening for substitution. As to the Illicit Process of the Minor Term it consists in a flagrant substitution for a term of another wider term which is not known to be equivalent to it, and which is therefore not allowed by our rule to be substituted for it.

CHAPTER V.

In the previous chapter I have exhibited various cases of deductive reasoning by the process of substitution, avoiding the introduction of disjunctive propositions; but we cannot long defer the consideration of this more complex class of identities. General terms arise, as we have seen (p. 24), from classifying or mentally uniting together all objects which agree in certain qualities, the value of this union consisting in the fact that the power of knowledge is multiplied thereby. In forming such classes or general notions, we overlook or abstract the points of difference which exist between the objects joined together, and fix our attention only on the points of agreement. But every process of thought may be said to have its inverse process, which consists in undoing the effects of the direct process. Just as division undoes multiplication, and evolution undoes involution, so we must have a process which undoes generalization, or the operation of forming general notions. This inverse process will consist in distinguishing the separate objects or minor classes which are the constituent parts of any wider class. If we mentally unite together certain objects visible in the sky and call them planets, we shall afterwards need to distinguish the contents of this general notion, which we do in the disjunctive proposition—

A planet is either Mercury or Venus or the Earth or . . . . . or Neptune.

Having formed the very wide class "vertebrate animal," we may specify its subordinate classes thus :—" A verte-

brate animal is either a mammal, bird, reptile, or fish."
Nor is there any limit to the number of possible alterna
tives. "An exogenous plant is either a ranunculus, a
poppy, a crucifer, a rose, or it belongs to some one of the
other seventy natural orders of exogens at present recognized by botanists." A cathedral church in England must
be either that of London, Canterbury, Winchester, Salisbury, Manchester, or of one of about twenty-four cities
possessing such churches. And if we were to attempt to
specify the meaning of the term "star," we should require
to enumerate as alternatives, not only the many thousands
of stars recorded in catalogues, but the many millions un-
named.

Whenever we thus distinguish the parts of a general
notion we employ a disjunctive proposition, in at least one
side of which are several alternatives joined by the so-
called disjunctive conjunction *or*, a contracted form of *other*.
There must be some relation between the parts thus connected in one proposition ; we may call it the *disjunctive* or
alternative relation, and we must carefully inquire into its
nature. This relation is that of ignorance and doubt,
giving rise to choice. Whenever we classify and abstract
we must open the way to such uncertainty. By fixing our
attention on certain attributes to the exclusion of others,
we necessarily leave it doubtful what those other attributes
are. The term "molar tooth" bears upon the face of it
that it is a part of the wider term "tooth." But if we
meet with the simple term "tooth" there is nothing to indicate whether it is an incisor, a canine, or a molar tooth.
This doubt, however, may be resolved by further information, and we have to consider what are the appropriate
logical processes for treating disjunctive propositions in
connection with other propositions disjunctive or otherwise.

Expression of the Alternative Relation.

In order to represent disjunctive propositions with convenience we require a sign of the alternative relation,
equivalent to one meaning at least of the little conjunction *or* so frequently used in common language. I propose to use for this purpose the symbol $\cdot\vdash\cdot$. In my first
logical essay I followed the practice of Boole and adopted

the sign +; but this sign should not be employed unless there exists exact analogy between mathematical addition and logical alternation.   We shall find that the analogy is imperfect, and that there is such profound difference between logical and mathematical terms as should prevent our uniting them by the same symbol.   Accordingly I have chosen a sign ·|·, which seems aptly to suggest whatever degree of analogy may exist without implying more. The exact meaning of the symbol we will now proceed to investigate.

Nature of the Alternative Relation.

Before treating disjunctive propositions it is indispensable to decide whether the alternatives must be considered exclusive or unexclusive.   By *exclusive alternatives* we mean those which cannot contain the same things.   If we say "Arches are circular or pointed," it is certainly to be understood that the same arch cannot be described as both circular and pointed.   Many examples, on the other hand, can readily be suggested in which two or more alternatives may hold true of the same object.   Thus

Luminous bodies are self-luminous or luminous by reflection.

It is undoubtedly possible, by the laws of optics, that the same surface may at one and the same moment give off light of its own and reflect light from other bodies.   We speak familiarly of *deaf or dumb* persons, knowing that the majority of those who are deaf from birth are also dumb.

There can be no doubt that in a great many cases, perhaps the greater number of cases, alternatives are exclusive as a matter of fact.   Any one number is incompatible with any other ; one point of time or place is exclusive of all others.   Roger Bacon died either in 1284 or 1292 ; it is certain that he could not die in both years.   Henry Fielding was born either in Dublin or Somersetshire ; he could not be born in both places. There is so much more precision and clearness in the use of exclusive alternatives that we ought doubtless to select them when possible.   Old works on logic accordingly contained a rule directing that the *Membra dividentia*, the

parts of a division or the constituent species of a genus,
should be exclusive of each other.

It is no doubt owing to the great prevalence and convenience of exclusive divisions that the majority of logicians have held it necessary to make every alternative in
a disjunctive proposition exclusive of every other one.
Aquinas considered that when this was not the case the
proposition was actually *false*, and Kant adopted the
same opinion.[1] A multitude of statements to the same
effect might readily be quoted, and if the question were
to be determined by the weight of historical evidence,
it would certainly go against my view. Among recent
logicians Hamilton, as well as Boole, took the exclusive
side. But there are authorities to the opposite effect.
Whately, Mansel, and J. S. Mill have all pointed out that
we may often treat alternatives as *Compossible*, or true at
the same time. Whately gives us an example,[2] " Virtue
tends to procure us either the esteem of mankind, or the
favour of God," and he adds—" Here both members are
true, and consequently from one being affirmed we are not
authorized to deny the other. Of course we are left to
conjecture in each case, from the context, whether it is
meant to be implied that the members are or are not
exclusive." Mansel says,[3] "*We may happen to know* that
two alternatives cannot be true together, so that the
affirmation of the second necessitates the denial of the
first; but this, as Boethius observes, is a *material*, not a
formal consequence." Mill has also pointed out the
absurdities which would arise from always interpreting
alternatives as exclusive. " If we assert," he says,[4] " that
a man who has acted in some particular way must be
either a knave or a fool, we by no means assert, or intend
to assert, that he cannot be both." Again, " to make an
entirely unselfish use of despotic power, a man must be
either a saint or a philosopher. . . . . . . Does the disjunctive premise necessarily imply, or must it be construed
as supposing, that the same person cannot be both a

---

[1] Mansel's *Aldrich*, p. 103, and *Prolegomena Logica*, p. 221.
[2] *Elements of Logic*, Book II. chap. iv. sect. 4.
[3] Aldrich, *Artis Logicæ Rudimenta*, p. 104.
[4] *Examination of Sir W. Hamilton's Philosophy*, pp. 452-454.

saint and a philosopher ? Such a construction would be
ridiculous."

I discuss this subject fully because it is really the point
which separates my logical system from that of Boole.
In his *Laws of Thought* (p. 32) he expressly says,
" In strictness, the words ' and,' ' or,' interposed between
the terms descriptive of two or more classes of objects,
imply that those classes are quite distinct, so that no
member of one is found in another." This I altogether
dispute. In the ordinary use of these conjunctions we do
not join distinct terms only ; and when terms so joined
do prove to be logically distinct, it is by virtue of a *tacit
premise*, something in the meaning of the names and
our knowledge of them, which teaches us that they are
distinct. If our knowledge of the meanings of the
words joined is defective it will often be impossible
to decide whether terms joined by conjunctions are
exclusive or not.

In the sentence " Repentance is not a single act, but
a habit or virtue," it cannot be implied that a virtue is
not a habit ; by Aristotle's definition it is. Milton has the
expression in one of his sonnets, " Unstain'd by gold or
fee," where it is obvious that if the fee is not always gold,
the gold is meant to be a fee or bribe. Tennyson has the
expression " wreath or anadem." Most readers would be
quite uncertain whether a wreath may be an anadem, or
an anadem a wreath, or whether they are quite distinct or
quite the same. From Darwin's *Origin of Species*, I
take the expression, " When we see any *part or organ*
developed in a remarkable *degree or manner*." In this, *or*
is used twice, and neither time exclusively. For if *part*
and *organ* are not synonymous, at any rate an organ is a
part. And it is obvious that a part may be developed at
the same time both in an extraordinary degree and an
extraordinary manner, although such cases may be comparatively rare.

From a careful examination of ordinary writings, it will
thus be found that the meanings of terms joined by "and,"
" or " vary from absolute identity up to absolute contrariety.
There is no logical condition of distinctness at all, and
when we do choose exclusive alternatives, it is because
our subject demands it. The matter, not the form of an

expression, points out whether terms are exclusive or not.[1] In bills, policies, and other kinds of legal documents, it is sometimes necessary to express very distinctly that alternatives are not exclusive. The form $\frac{and}{or}$ is then used, and, as Mr. J. J. Murphy has remarked, this form coincides exactly in meaning with the symbol ·|·.

In the first edition of this work (vol. i., p. 81), I took the disjunctive proposition " Matter is solid, or liquid, or gaseous," and treated it as an instance of exclusive alternatives, remarking that the same portion of matter cannot be at once solid and liquid, properly speaking, and that still less can we suppose it to be solid and gaseous, or solid, liquid, and gaseous all at the same time.   But the experiments of Professor Andrews show that, under certain conditions of temperature and pressure, there is no abrupt change from the liquid to the gaseous state.   The same substance may be in such a state as to be indifferently described as liquid and gaseous.   In many cases, too, the transition from solid to liquid is gradual, so that the properties of solidity are at least partially joined with those of liquidity.   The proposition then, instead of being an instance of exclusive alternatives, seems to afford an excellent instance to the opposite·effect. When such doubts can arise, it is evidently impossible to treat alternatives as absolutely exclusive by the logical nature of the relation.   It becomes purely a question of the matter of the proposition.

The question, as we shall afterwards see more fully, is one of the greatest theoretical importance, because it concerns the true distinction between the sciences of Logic and Mathematics.   It is the foundation of number that every unit shall be distinct from every other unit; but Boole imported the conditions of number into the science of Logic, and produced a system which, though wonderful in its results, was not a system of logic at all.

Laws of the Disjunctive Relation.

In considering the combination or synthesis of terms (p. 30), we found that certain laws, those of Simplicity

[1] *Pure Logic,* pp 76, 77.

and Commutativeness, must be observed. In uniting terms by the disjunctive symbol we shall find that the same or closely similar laws hold true. The alternatives of either member of a disjunctive proposition are certainly commutative. Just as we cannot properly distinguish between *rich and rare gems* and *rare and rich gems,* so we must consider as identical the expression *rich or rare gems,* and *rare or rich gems.* In our symbolic language we may say

$$A + B = B + A.$$

The order of statement, in short, has no effect upon the meaning of an aggregate of alternatives, so that the Law of Commutativeness holds true of the disjunctive symbol.

As we have admitted the possibility of joining as alternatives terms which are not really different, the question arises, How shall we treat two or more alternatives when they are clearly shown to be the same? If we have it asserted that P is Q or R, and it is afterwards proved that Q is but another name for R, the result is that P is either R or R. How shall we interpret such a statement? What would be the meaning, for instance, of " wreath or anadem " if, on referring to a dictionary, we found *anadem* described as a wreath? I take it to be self-evident that the meaning would then become simply "wreath." Accordingly we may affirm the general law

$$A + A = A.$$

Any number of identical alternatives may always be reduced to, and are logically equivalent to, any one of those alternatives. This is a law which distinguishes mathematical terms from logical terms, because it obviously does not apply to the former. I propose to call it the *Law of Unity,* because it must really be involved in any definition of a mathematical unit. This law is closely analogous to the Law of Simplicity, $AA = A$; and the nature of the connection is worthy of attention.

Few or no logicians except De Morgan have adequately noticed the close relation between combined and disjunctive terms, namely, that every disjunctive term is the negative of a corresponding combined term, and *vice versâ.* Consider the term

Malleable dense metal.

How shall we describe the class of things which are not malleable-dense-metals? Whatever is included under that term must have all the qualities of malleability, denseness, and metallicity. Wherever any one or more of the qualities is wanting, the combined term will not apply. Hence the negative of the whole term is

Not-malleable or not-dense or not-metallic.

In the above the conjunction *or* must clearly be interpreted as unexclusive; for there may readily be objects which are both not-malleable, and not-dense, and perhaps not-metallic at the same time. If in fact we were required to use *or* in a strictly exclusive manner, it would be requisite to specify seven distinct alternatives in order to describe the negative of a combination of three terms. The negatives of four or five terms would consist of fifteen or thirty-one alternatives. This consideration alone is sufficient to prove that the meaning of *or* cannot be always exclusive in common language.

Expressed symbolically, we may say that the negative of

$$A B C$$

is   not-A or not-B or not-C;

that is, $a \mid b \mid c.$

Reciprocally the negative of

$$P \mid Q \mid R$$

is $pqr.$

Every disjunctive term, then, is the negative of a combined term, and *vice versâ*.

Apply this result to the combined term AAA, and its negative is

$$a \mid a \mid a.$$

Since AAA is by the Law of Simplicity equivalent to A, so $a \mid a \mid a$ must be equivalent to a, and the Law of Unity holds true. Each law thus necessarily presupposes the other.

Symbolic expression of the Law of Duality.

We may now employ our symbol of alternation to express in a clear and formal manner the third Fundamental Law of Thought, which I have called the Law of Duality (p. 6). Taking A to represent any class or object or quality, and B any other class, object or quality, we may always assert that A either agrees with B, or does not agree. Thus we may say

$$A = AB \,\cdot\!\!\mid\, Ab.$$

This is a formula which will henceforth be constantly employed, and it lies at the basis of reasoning.

The reader may perhaps wish to know why A is inserted in both alternatives of the second member of the identity, and why the law is not stated in the form

$$A = B \,\cdot\!\!\mid\, b.$$

But if he will consider the contents of the last section (p. 73), he will see that the latter expression cannot be correct, otherwise no term could have a corresponding negative term. For the negative of B $\cdot\!\mid$ b is bB, or a self-contradictory term; thus if A were identical with B $\cdot\!\mid$ b its negative a would be non-existent. To say the least, this result would in most cases be an absurd one, and I see much reason to think that in a strictly logical point of view it would always be absurd. In all probability we ought to assume as a fundamental logical axiom that *every term has its negative in thought.* We cannot think at all without separating what we think about from other things, and these things necessarily form the negative notion.[1] It follows that any proposition of the form A = B $\cdot\!\mid$ b is just as self-contradictory as one of the form A = Bb.

It is convenient to recapitulate in this place the three Laws of Thought in their symbolic form, thus

Law of Identity $A = A.$
Law of Contradiction $Aa = O.$
Law of Duality $A = AB \cdot\!\mid Ab.$

Various Forms of the Disjunctive Proposition.

Disjunctive propositions may occur in a great variety of forms, of which the old logicians took insufficient notice. There may be any number of alternatives, each of which may be a combination of any number of simple terms. A proposition, again, may be disjunctive in one or both members. The proposition

---

[1] *Pure Logic,* p. 65. See also the criticism of this point by De Morgan in the *Athenæum,* No. 1892, 30th January, 1864; p. 155.

Solids or liquids or gases are electrics or conductors
of electricity

is an example of the doubly disjunctive form. The meaning of such a proposition is that whatever falls under any
one or more alternatives on one side must fall under one
or more alternatives on the other side. From what has
been said before, it is apparent that the proposition

$$A + B = C + D$$

will correspond to

$$ab = cd,$$

each member of the latter being the negative of a member
of the former proposition.

As an instance of a complex disjunctive proposition I
may give Senior's definition of wealth, which, briefly
stated, amounts to the proposition " Wealth is what is
transferable, limited in supply, and either productive of
pleasure or preventive of pain." [1]

Let A = wealth
  B = transferable
  C = limited in supply
  D = productive of pleasure
  E = preventive of pain.

The definition takes the form

$$A = BC(D + E);$$

but if we develop the alternatives by a méthod to be
afterwards more fully considered, it becomes

$$A = BCDE + BCDe + BCdE.$$

An example of a still more complex proposition is
found in De Morgan's writings,[2] as follows:—" He must
have been rich, and if not absolutely mad was weakness
itself, subjected either to bad advice or to most unfavourable circumstances."

If we assign the letters of the alphabet in succession,
thus,

A = he
B = rich
C = absolutely mad
D = weakness itself
E = subjected to bad advice

[1] Boole's *Laws of Thought*, p. 106. Jevons' *Pure Logic*, p. 69.
[2] *On the Syllogism*, No. iii. p. 12. Camb. Phil. Trans. vol. x.
part i

F = subjected to most unfavourable circumstances, the proposition will take the form

$$A = AB\{C + D (E + F)\},$$

and if we develop the alternatives, expressing some of the different cases which may happen, we obtain

$$A = ABC + AB c DEF + AB c DE f + AB c D c F.$$

The above gives the strict logical interpretation of the sentence, and the first alternative ABC is capable of development into eight cases, according as D, E and F are or are not present. Although from our knowledge of the matter, we may infer that weakness of character cannot be asserted of a person absolutely mad, there is no explicit statement to this effect.

Inference by Disjunctive Propositions.

Before we can make a free use of disjunctive propositions in the processes of inference we must consider how disjunctive terms can be combined together or with simple terms. In the first place, to combine a simple term with a disjunctive one, we must combine it with every alternative of the disjunctive term. A vegetable, for instance, is either a herb, a shrub, or a tree. Hence an exogenous vegetable is either an exogenous herb, or an exogenous shrub, or an exogenous tree. Symbolically stated, this process of combination is as follows,

$$A(B + C) = AB + AC.$$

Secondly, to combine two disjunctive terms with each other, combine each alternative of one with each alternative of the other. Since flowering plants are either exogens or endogens, and are at the same time either herbs, shrubs or trees, it follows that there are altogether six alternatives—namely, exogenous herbs, exogenous shrubs, exogenous trees, endogenous herbs, endogenous shrubs, endogenous trees. This process of combination is shown in the general form

$$(A + B) (C + D + E) = AC + AD + AE + BC + BD + BE.$$

It is hardly necessary to point out that, however numerous the terms combined, or the alternatives in those terms, we may effect the combination, provided each alternative is combined with each alternative of the other terms, as in the algebraic process of multiplication.

Some processes of deduction may be at once exhibited. We may always, for instance, unite the same qualifying term to each side of an identity even though one or both members of the identity be disjunctive. Thus let
$$A = B + C.$$
Now it is self-evident that
$$AD = AD,$$
and in one side of this identity we may for A substitute its equivalent B + C, obtaining
$$AD = BD + CD.$$

Since " a gaseous element is either hydrogen, or oxygen, or nitrogen, or chlorine, or fluorine," it follows that " a free gaseous element is either free hydrogen, or free oxygen, or free nitrogen, or free chlorine, or free fluorine."

This process of combination will lead to most useful inferences when the qualifying adjective combined with both sides of the proposition is a negative of one or more alternatives. Since chlorine is a coloured gas, we may infer that " a colourless gaseous element is either (colourless) hydrogen, oxygen, nitrogen, or fluorine." The alternative chlorine disappears because colourless chlorine does not exist. Again, since " a tooth is either an incisor, canine, bicuspid, or molar," it follows that " a not-incisor tooth is either canine, bicuspid, or molar." The general rule is that from the denial of any of the alternatives the affirmation of the remainder can be inferred. Now this result clearly follows from our process of substitution; for if we have the proposition
$$A = B + C + D,$$
and we insert this expression for A on one side of the self-evident identity
$$Ab = Ab,$$
we obtain $$Ab = ABb + AbC + AbD ;$$
and, as the first of the three alternatives is self-contradictory, we strike it out according to the law of contradiction : there remains
$$Ab = AbC + AbD.$$
Thus our system fully includes and explains that mood of the Disjunctive Syllogism technically called the *modus tollendo ponens.*

But the reader must carefully observe that the Disjunctive Syllogism of the mood *ponendo tollens,* which affirms

one alternative, and thence infers the denial of the rest, cannot be held true in this system. If I say, indeed, that
<blockquote>Water is either salt or fresh water,</blockquote>
it seems evident that " water which is salt is not fresh." But this inference really proceeds from our knowledge that water cannot be at once salt and fresh. This inconsistency of the alternatives, as I have fully shown, will not always hold. Thus, if I say
<blockquote>Gems are either rare stones or beautiful stones, (1)</blockquote>
it will obviously not follow that
<blockquote>A rare gem is not a beautiful stone,   (2)</blockquote>
nor that
<blockquote>A beautiful gem is not a rare stone.   (3)</blockquote>
Our symbolic method gives only true conclusions ; for if we take

$$A = gem$$
$$B = rare\ stone$$
$$C = beautiful\ stone,$$

the proposition (1) is of the form
$$A = B + C$$
hence $$AB = B + BC$$
and $$AC = BC + C\ ;$$
but these inferences are not equivalent to the false ones (2) and (3).

We can readily represent disjunctive reasoning by the *modus ponendo tollens,* when it is valid, by expressing the inconsistency of the alternatives explicitly. Thus if we resort to our instance of
<blockquote>Water is either salt or fresh,</blockquote>
and take
$$A = Water \qquad B = salt \qquad C = fresh,$$
then the premise is apparently of the form
$$A = AB + AC\ ;$$
but in reality there is an unexpressed condition that " what is salt is not fresh," from which follows, by a process of inference to be afterwards described, that " what is fresh is not salt." We have then, in letter-terms, the two propositions
$$B = Bc$$
$$C = bC.$$

If we substitute these descriptions in the original proposition, we obtain

$$A = ABc + AbC;$$
uniting B to each side we infer
$$AB = ABc + ABbC$$
$$\text{or} \qquad AB = ABc;$$
that is,

Water which is salt is water salt and not fresh.

I should weary the reader if I attempted to illustrate the multitude of forms which disjunctive reasoning may take; and as in the next chapter we shall be constantly treating the subject, I must here restrict myself to a single instance. A very common process of reasoning consists in the determination of the name of a thing by the successive exclusion of alternatives, a process called by the old name *abscissio infiniti.* Take the case:

Red-coloured metal is either copper or gold   (1)
Copper is dissolved by nitric acid   (2)
This specimen is red-coloured metal   (3)
This specimen is not dissolved by nitric acid   (4)
Therefore, this specimen consists of gold   (5)

Let us assign the letter-symbols thus—

A = this specimen D = gold
B = red-coloured metal E = dissolved by nitric acid.
C = copper

Assuming that the alternatives copper or gold are intended to be exclusive, as just explained in the case of fresh and salt water, the premises may be stated in the forms

$$B = BCd + BcD \qquad (1)$$
$$C = CE \qquad (2)$$
$$A = AB \qquad (3)$$
$$A = Ae \qquad (4)$$

Substituting for C in (1) by means of (2) we get
$$B = BCdE + BcD$$
From (3) and (4) we may infer likewise
$$A = ABe$$
and if in this we substitute for B its equivalent just stated, it follows that
$$A = ABCdEe + ABcDe$$
The first of the alternatives being contradictory the result is
$$A = ABcDe$$

which contains a full description of "this specimen," as furnished in the premises, but by ellipsis asserts that it is gold.   It will be observed that in the symbolic expression (1) I have explicitly stated what is certainly implied, that copper is not gold, and gold not copper, without which condition the inference would not hold good.

CHAPTER VI.

THE forms of deductive reasoning as yet considered, are mostly cases of Direct Deduction as distinguished from those which we are now about to treat. The method of Indirect Deduction may be described as that which points out what a thing is, by showing that it cannot be anything else. We can define a certain space upon a map, either by colouring that space, or by colouring all except the space ; the first mode is positive, the second negative. The difference, it will be readily seen, is exactly analogous to that between the direct and indirect modes of proof in geometry. Euclid often shows that two lines are equal, by showing that they cannot be unequal, and the proof rests upon the known number of alternatives, greater, equal or less, which are alone conceivable. In other cases, as for instance in the seventh proposition of the first book, he shows that two lines must meet in a particular point, by showing that they cannot meet elsewhere.

In logic we can always define with certainty the utmost number of alternatives which are conceivable. The Law of Duality (pp. 6, 74) enables us always to assert that any quality or circumstance whatsoever is either present or absent. Whatever may be the meaning of the terms A and B it is certainly true that

$$A = AB + Ab$$
$$B = AB + aB.$$

These are universal tacit premises which may be employed in the solution of every problem, and which are such invariable and necessary conditions of all thought,

that they need not be specially laid down. The Law of
Contradiction is a further condition of all thought and of
all logical symbols ; it enables, and in fact obliges, us to
reject from further consideration all terms which imply the
presence and absence of the same quality. Now, whenever we bring both these Laws of Thought into explicit
action by the method of substitution, we employ the
Indirect Method of Inference. It will be found that we
can treat not only those arguments already exhibited
according to the direct method, but we can include an
infinite multitude of other arguments which are incapable
of solution by any other means.

Some philosophers, especially those of France, have held
that the Indirect Method of Proof has a certain inferiority
to the direct method, which should prevent our using it
except when obliged. But there are many truths which
we can prove only indirectly. We can prove that a
number is a prime only by the purely indirect method of
showing that it is not any of the numbers which have
divisors, and the remarkable process known as Eratosthenes' Sieve is the only mode by which we can select the
prime numbers.[1] It bears a strong analogy to the indirect
method here to be described. We can prove that the side
and diameter of a square are incommensurable, but only in
the negative or indirect manner, by showing that the contrary supposition inevitably leads to contradiction.[2] Many
other demonstrations in various branches of the mathematical sciences proceed upon a like method. Now, if
there is only one important truth which must be, and can
only be, proved indirectly, we may say that the process is a
necessary and sufficient one, and the question of its comparative excellence or usefulness is not worth discussion.
As a matter of fact I believe that nearly half our logical
conclusions rest upon its employment.

    [1] See Horsley, *Philosophical Transactions*, 1772 ; vol. lxii. p. 327.
Montucla, *Histoire des Mathematiques*, vol. i p 239. *Penny*
Cyclopædia, article " Eratosthenes."
    [2] Euclid, Book x. Prop. 117.

Simple Illustrations.

In tracing out the powers and results of this method, we will begin with the simplest possible instance. Let us take a proposition of the common form, A = AB, say,

A Metal is an Element.

and let us investigate its full meaning. Any person who has had the least logical training, is aware that we can draw from the above proposition an apparently different one, namely,

A Not-element is a Not-metal.

While some logicians, as for instance De Morgan,[1] have considered the relation of these two propositions to be purely self-evident, and neither needing nor allowing analysis, a great many more persons, as I have observed while teaching logic, are at first unable to perceive the close connection between them. I believe that a true and complete system of logic will furnish a clear analysis of this process, which has been called *Contrapositive Conversion;* the full process is as follows :—

Firstly, by the Law of Duality we know that

Not-element is either Metal or Not-metal.

If it be metal, we know that it is by the premise *an element;* we should thus be supposing that the same thing is an element and a not-element, which is in opposition to the Law of Contradiction. According to the only other alternative, then, the not-element must be a not-metal.

To represent this process of inference symbolically we take the premise in the form

$$A = AB. \qquad (1)$$

We observe that by the Law of Duality the term not-B is thus described

$$b = Ab + ab. \qquad (2)$$

For A in this proposition we substitute its description as given in (1), obtaining

$$b = ABb + ab.$$

But according to the Law of Contradiction the term ABb must be excluded from thought, or

---

[1] *Philosophical Magazine,* December 1852 ; Fourth Series, vol. iv. p. 435, "On Indirect Demonstration."

$$AB b = 0.$$

Hence it results that b is either nothing at all, or it is ab; and the conclusion is

$$b = ab.$$

As it will often be necessary to refer to a conclusion of this kind I shall call it, as is usual, the *Contrapositive Proposition* of the original. The reader need hardly be cautioned to observe that from all A's are B's it does not follow that all not-A's are not-B's. For by the Law of Duality we have

$$a = a B + a b,$$

and it will not be found possible to make any substitution in this by our original premise $A = A B$. It still remains doubtful, therefore, whether not-metal is element or not-element.

The proof of the Contrapositive Proposition given above is exactly the same as that which Euclid applies in the case of geometrical notions. De Morgan describes Euclid's process as follows [1] :—" From every not-B is not-A he produces Every A is B, thus: If it be possible, let this A be not-B, but every not-B is not-A, therefore this A is not-A, which is absurd : whence every A is B." Now De Morgan thinks that this proof is entirely needless, because common logic gives the inference without the use of any geometrical reasoning. I conceive however that logic gives the inference only by an indirect process. De Morgan claims " to see identity in Every A is B and every not-B is not-A, by a process of thought prior to syllogism." Whether prior to syllogism or not, I claim that it is not prior to the laws of thought and the process of substitutive inference, by which it may be undoubtedly demonstrated.

Employment of the Contrapositive Proposition.

We can frequently employ the contrapositive form of a proposition by the method of substitution; and certain moods of the ancient syllogism, which we have hitherto passed over, may thus be satisfactorily comprehended in our system. Take for instance the following syllogism in the mood Camestres :—

[1] *Philosophical Magazine*, Dec. 1852 ; p. 437.

" Whales are not true fish; for they do not respire water,
whereas true fish do respire water."

Let us take

$$A = \text{whale}$$
$$B = \text{true fish}$$
$$C = \text{respiring water}$$

The premises are of the forms

$$A = Ac \qquad\qquad (1)$$
$$B = BC \qquad\qquad (2)$$

Now, by the process of contraposition we obtain from
the second premise

$$c = bc$$

and we can substitute this expression for c in (1), obtaining

$$A = Abc$$

or " Whales are not true fish, not respiring water."

The mood Cesare does not really differ from Camestres
except in the order of the premises, and it could be exhibited in an exactly similar manner.

The mood Baroko gave much trouble to the old logicians,
who could not *reduce* it to the first figure in the same
manner as the other moods, and were obliged to invent,
specially for it and for Bokardo, a method of Indirect
Reduction closely analogous to the indirect proof of Euclid.
Now these moods require no exceptional treatment in this
system. Let us take as an instance of Baroko, the argu
ment

All heated solids give continuous spectra   (1)
Some nebulæ do not give continuous spectra   (2)
Therefore, some nebulæ are not heated solids   (3)

Treating the little word *some* as an indeterminate adjective of selection, to which we assign a symbol like any
other adjective, let

$$A = \text{some}$$
$$B = \text{nebulæ}$$
$$C = \text{giving continuous spectra}$$
$$D = \text{heated solids}$$

The premises then become

$$D = DC \qquad\qquad (1)$$
$$AB = ABc \qquad\qquad (2)$$

Now from (1) we obtain by the indirect method the contrapositive proposition

$$c = cd$$
and if we substitute this expression for c in (2) we have
$$AB = ABcd$$
the full meaning of which is that "some nebulæ do not give continuous spectra and are not heated solids."

We might similarly apply the contrapositive in many other instances. Take the argument, "All fixed stars are self-luminous; but some of the heavenly bodies are not self-luminous, and are therefore not fixed stars." Taking our terms

$$A = \text{fixed stars}$$
$$B = \text{self-luminous}$$
$$C = \text{some}$$
$$D = \text{heavenly bodies}$$

we have the premises

$$A = AB, \tag{1}$$
$$CD = bCD \tag{2}$$

Now from (1) we can draw the contrapositive
$$b = ab$$
and substituting this expression for b in (2) we obtain
$$CD = abCD$$
which expresses the conclusion of the argument that some heavenly bodies are not fixed stars.

Contrapositive of a Simple Identity.

The reader should carefully note that when we apply the process of Indirect Inference to a simple identity of the form
$$A = B$$
we may obtain further results. If we wish to know what is the term not-B, we have as before, by the Law of Duality,
$$b = Ab + ab$$
and substituting for A we obtain
$$b = Bb + ab = ab.$$

But we may now also draw a second contrapositive; for we have
$$a = aB + ab,$$
and substituting for B its equivalent A we have
$$a = aA + ab = ab.$$

Hence from the single identity $A = B$ we can draw the two propositions

$$a = ab$$
$$b = ab,$$

and observing that these propositions have a common term *ab* we can make a new substitution, getting

$$a = b.$$

This result is in strict accordance with the fundamental principles of inference, and it may be a question whether it is not a self-evident result, independent of the steps of deduction by which we have reached it. For where two classes are coincident like A and B, whatever is true of the one is true of the other ; what is excluded from the one must be excluded from the other similarly. Now as *a* bears to A exactly the same relation that *b* bears to B, the identity of either pair follows from the identity of the other pair. In every identity, equality, or similarity, we may argue from the negative of the one side to the nega- tive of the other. Thus at ordinary temperatures

Mercury = liquid-metal,

hence obviously

Not-mercury = not liquid-metal ;

or since

Sirius = brightest fixed star,

it follows that whatever star is not the brightest is not Sirius, and *vice versâ*. Every correct definition is of the form A = B, and may often require to be applied in the equivalent negative form.

Let us take as an illustration of the mode of using this result the argument following :

Vowels are letters which can be sounded alone, (1)
The letter *w* cannot be sounded alone ; (2)
Therefore the letter *w* is not a vowel. (3)

Here we have a definition (1), and a comparison of a thing with that definition (2), leading to exclusion of the thing from the class defined.

Taking the terms

A = vowel,
B = letter which can be sounded alone,
C = letter *w*,

the premises are plainly of the forms

$$A = B, \quad\quad (1)$$
$$C = bC. \quad\quad (2)$$

Now by the Indirect method we obtain from (1) the Contrapositive

$$b = a,$$

and inserting in (2) the equivalent for b we have

$$C = aC, \tag{3}$$

or " the letter w is not a vowel."

Miscellaneous Examples of the Method.

We can apply the Indirect Method of Inference however many may be the terms involved or the premises containing those terms. As the working of the method is best learnt from examples, I will take a case of two premises forming the syllogism Barbara : thus

Iron is metal   (1)

Metal is element.   (2)

If we want to ascertain what inference is possible concerning the term *Iron*, we develop the term by the Law of Duality. Iron must be either metal or not-metal ; iron which is metal must be either element or not-element ; and similarly iron which is not-metal must be either element or not-element. There are then altogether four alternatives among which the description of iron must be contained ; thus

Iron, metal, element, (a)

Iron, metal, not-element, (β)

Iron, not-metal, element, (γ)

Iron, not-metal, not-element. (δ)

Our first premise informs us that iron is a metal, and if we substitute this description in (γ) and (δ) we shall have self-contradictory combinations. Our second premise likewise informs us that metal is element, and applying this description to (β) we again have self-contradiction, so that there remains only (a) as a description of iron—our inference is

Iron = iron, metal, element.

To represent this process of reasoning in general symbols, let

A = iron

B = metal

C = element,

The premises of the problem take the forms

$$A = AB \qquad (1)$$
$$B = BC. \qquad (2)$$

By the Law of Duality we have

$$A = AB + Ab \qquad (3)$$
$$A = AC + Ac. \qquad (4)$$

Now, if we insert for A in the second side of (3) its description in (4), we obtain what I shall call the *development of A with respect to B and C*, namely

$$A = ABC + ABc + AbC + Abc. \qquad (5)$$

Wherever the letters A or B appear in the second side of (5) substitute their equivalents given in (1) and (2), and the results stated at full length are

$$A = ABC + ABCc + ABbC + ABbCc.$$

The last three alternatives break the Law of Contradiction, so that

$$A = ABC + o + o + o = ABC.$$

This conclusion is, indeed, no more than we could obtain by the direct process of substitution, that is by substituting for B in (1), its description in (2) as in p. 55 ; it is the characteristic of the Indirect process that it gives all possible logical conclusions, both those which we have previously obtained, and an immense number of others or which the ancient logic took little or no account. From the same premises, for instance, we can obtain a description of the class *not-element* or *c*. By the Law of Duality we can develop *c* into four alternatives, thus

$$c = ABc + Abc + aBc + abc.$$

If we substitute for A and B as before, we get

$$c = ABCc + ABbc + aBCc + abc,$$

and, striking out the terms which break the Law of Contradiction, there remains

$$c = abc,$$

or what is not element is also not iron and not metal. This Indirect Method of Inference thus furnishes a complete solution of the following problem—*Given any number of logical premises or conditions, required the description of any class of objects, or of any term, as governed by those conditions.*

The steps of the process of inference may thus be concisely stated—

1. By the Law of Duality develop the utmost number of alternatives which may exist in the description of the

required class or term as regards the terms involved in the premises.

2. For each term in these alternatives substitute its description as given in the premises.

3. Strike out every alternative which is then found to break the Law of Contradiction.

4. The remaining terms may be equated to the term in question as the desired description.

Mr. Venn's Problem.

The need of some logical method more powerful and comprehensive than the old logic of Aristotle is strikingly illustrated by Mr. Venn in his most interesting and able article on Boole's logic.[1] An easy example, originally got, as he says, by the aid of my method as simply described in the *Elementary Lessons in Logic,* was proposed in examination and lecture-rooms to some hundred and fifty students as a problem in ordinary logic. It was answered by, at most, five or six of them. It was afterwards set, as an example on Boole's method, to a small class who had attended a few lectures on the nature of these symbolic methods. It was readily answered by half or more of their number.

The problem was as follows:—" The members of a board were all of them either bondholders, or shareholders, but not both ; and the bondholders as it happened, were all on the board. What conclusion can be drawn ? " The conclusion wanted is, " No shareholders are bondholders." Now, as Mr. Venn says, nothing can look simpler than the following reasoning, *when stated :—*" There can be no bondholders who are shareholders ; for if there were they must be either on the board, or off it. But they are not on it, by the first of the given statements ; nor off it, by the second." Yet from the want of any systematic mode of treating such a question only five or six of some hundred and fifty students could succeed in so simple a problem.

---

[1] *Mind ;* a Quarterly Review of Psychology and Philosophy ; October, 1876, vol. i. p. 487.

By symbolic statement the problem is instantly solved. Taking

$$A = \text{member of board}$$
$$B = \text{bondholder}$$
$$C = \text{shareholder}$$

the premises are evidently

$$A = ABc + AbC$$
$$B = AB.$$

The class C or shareholders may in respect of A and B be developed into four alternatives,

$$C = ABC + AbC + aBC + abC.$$

But substituting for A in the first and for B in the third alternative we get

$$C = ABCc + ABbC + AbC + aABC + abC.$$

The first, second, and fourth alternatives in the above are self-contradictory combinations, and only these; striking them out there remain

$$C = AbC + abC = bC,$$

the required answer. This symbolic reasoning is, I believe, the exact equivalent of Mr. Venn's reasoning, and I do not believe that the result can be attained in a simpler manner. Mr. Venn adds that he could adduce other similar instances, that is, instances showing the necessity of a better logical method.

Abbreviation of the Process.

Before proceeding to further illustrations of the use of this method, I must point out how much its practical employment can be simplified, and how much more easy it is than would appear from the description. When we want to effect at all a thorough solution of a logical problem it is best to form, in the first place, a complete series of all the combinations of terms involved in it. If there be two terms A and B, the utmost variety of combinations in which they can appear are

$$AB \qquad aB$$
$$Ab \qquad ab.$$

The term A appears in the first and second; B in the first and third; a in the third and fourth; and b in the second and fourth. Now if we have any premise, say

$$A = B,$$

we must ascertain which of these combinations will be rendered self-contradictory by substitution; the second and third will have to be struck out, and there will remain only   AB
                                ba.
Hence we draw the following inferences
                A = AB,   B = AB, $a = ab$, $b = ab$.
Exactly the same method must be followed when a question involves a greater number of terms. Thus by the Law of Duality the three terms A, B, C, give rise to eight conceivable combinations, namely

ABC	(a)	aBC	(ϵ)
ABc	(β)	aBc	(ζ)
AbC	(γ)	abC	(η)
Abc	(δ)	abc.	(θ)

The development of the term A is formed by the first four of these; for B we must select (a), (β), (ϵ), (ζ); C consists of (a), (γ), (ϵ), (η); b of (γ), (δ), (η), (θ), and so on.

Now if we want to investigate completely the meaning of the premises   A = AB   (1)
                                B = BC   (2)
we examine each of the eight combinations as regards each premise; (γ) and (δ) are contradicted by (1), and (β) and (ζ) by (2), so that there remain only

ABC	(a)
aBC	(ϵ)
abC	(η)
abc.	(θ)

To describe any term under the conditions of the premises (1) and (2), we have simply to draw out the proper combinations from this list; thus, A is represented only by ABC, that is to say
                        A = ABC,
        similarly $c = abc$.
For B we have two alternatives thus stated,
                    B = ABC + aBC ;
and for b we have

            $b = ab$C + abc.

When we have a problem involving four distinct terms we need to double the number of combinations, and as we add each new term the combinations become twice as numerous. Thus

A, B	produce	four combinations
A, B, C,	„	eight „
A, B, C, D	„	sixteen „
A, B, C, D, E	„	thirty-two „
A, B, C, D, E, F	„	sixty-four „

and so on.

I propose to call any such series of combinations the *Logical Alphabet*. It holds in logical science a position the importance of which cannot be exaggerated, and as we proceed from logical to mathematical considerations, it will become apparent that there is a close connection between these combinations and the fundamental theorems of mathematical science. For the convenience of the reader who may wish to employ the *Alphabet* in logical questions, I have had printed on the next page a complete series of the combinations up to those of six terms. At the very commencement, in the first column, is placed a single letter X, which might seem to be superfluous. This letter serves to denote that it is always some higher class which is divided up. Thus the combination AB really means ABX, or that part of some larger class, say X, which has the qualities of A and B present. The letter X is omitted in the greater part of the table merely for the sake of brevity and clearness. In a later chapter on Combinations it will become apparent that the introduction of this unit class is requisite in order to complete the analogy with the Arithmetical Triangle there described.

The reader ought to bear in mind that though the Logical Alphabet seems to give mere lists of combinations, these combinations are intended in every case to constitute the development of a term of a proposition. Thus the four combinations AB, Ab, aB, ab really mean that any class X is described by the following proposition,

$$X = XAB + XA b + XaB + Xab.$$

If we select the A's, we obtain the following proposition

$$AX = XAB + XAb.$$

Thus whatever group of combinations we treat must be conceived as part of a higher class, *summum genus* or universe symbolised in the term X ; but, bearing this in mind, it is needless to complicate our formulæ by always introducing the letter. All inference consists in passing from propositions to propositions, and combinations *per se* have no meaning. They are consequently to be regarded in all cases as forming parts of propositions.

The Logical Alphabet.

I.	II.	III.	IV.	V.	VI.	VII.
X	A X	A B	A B C	A B C D	A B C D E	A B C D E F
	a X	A b	A B c	A B C d	A B C D e	A B C D E f
		a B	A b C	A B c D	A B C d E	A B C D e F
		a b	A b c	A B c d	A B C d e	A B C D e f
			a B C	A b C D	A B c D E	A B C d E F
			a B c	A b C d	A B c D e	A B C d E f
			a b C	A b c D	A B c d E	A B C d e F
			a b c	A b c d	A B c d e	A B C d e f
				a B C D	A b C D E	A B c D E F
				a B C d	A b C D e	A B c D E f
				a B c D	A b C d E	A B c D e F
				a B c d	A b C d e	A B c D e f
				a b C D	A b c D E	A B c d E F
				a b C d	A b c D e	A B c d E f
				a b c D	A b c d E	A B c d e F
				a b c d	A b c d e	A B c d e f
					a B C D E	A b C D E F
					a B C D e	A b C D E f
					a B C d E	A b C D e F
					a B C d e	A b C D e f
					a B c D E	A b C d E F
					a B c D e	A b C d E f
					a B c d E	A b C d e F
					a B c d e	A b C d e f
					a b C D E	A b c D E F
					a b C D e	A b c D E f
					a b C d E	A b c D e F
					a b C d e	A b c D e f
					a b c D E	A b c d E F
					a b c D e	A b c d E f
					a b c d E	A b c d e F
					a b c d e	A b c d e f
						a B C D E F
						a B C D E f
						a B C D e F
						a B C D e f
						a B C d E F
						a B C d E f
						a B C d e F
						a B C d e f
						a B c D E F
						a B c D E f
						a B c D e F
						a B c D e f
						a B c d E F
						a B c d E f
						a B c d e F
						a B c d e f
						a b C D E F
						a b C D E f
						a b C D e F
						a b C D e f
						a b C d E F
						a b C d E f
						a b C d e F
						a b C d e f
						a b c D E F
						a b c D E f
						a b c D e F
						a b c D e f
						a b c d E F
						a b c d E f
						a b c d e F
						a b c d e f

In a theoretical point of view we may conceive that the Logical Alphabet is infinitely extended. Every new quality or circumstance which can belong to an object, subdivides each combination or class, so that the number of such combinations, when unrestricted by logical conditions, is represented by an infinitely high power of two. The extremely rapid increase in the number of subdivisions obliges us to confine our attention to a few qualities at a time.

When contemplating the properties of this Alphabet I am often inclined to think that Pythagoras perceived the deep logical importance of duality; for while unity was the symbol of identity and harmony, he described the number two as the origin of contrasts, or the symbol of diversity, division and separation. The number four, or the *Tetractys*, was also regarded by him as one of the chief elements of existence, for it represented the generating virtue whence come all combinations In one of the golden verses ascribed to Pythagoras, he conjures his pupil to be virtuous:[1]

> " By him who stampt *The Four* upon the Mind,
> *The Four*, the fount of Nature's endless stream."

Now four and the higher powers of duality do represent in this logical system the numbers of combinations which can be generated in the absence of logical restrictions. The followers of Pythagoras may have shrouded their master's doctrines in mysterious and superstitious notions, but in many points these doctrines seem to have some basis in logical philosophy.

The Logical Slate.

To a person who has once comprehended the extreme significance and utility of the Logical Alphabet the indirect process of inference becomes reduced to the repetition of a few uniform operations of classification, selection, and elimination of contradictories. Logical deduction, even in the most complicated questions, becomes a matter of mere routine, and the amount of

---

[1] Whewell, *History of the Inductive Sciences*, vol. i. p. 222.

labour required is the only impediment, when once the meaning of the premises is rendered clear. But the amount of labour is often found to be considerable. The mere writing down of sixty-four combinations of six letters each is no small task, and, if we had a problem of five premises, each of the sixty-four combinations would have to be examined in connection with each premise. The requisite comparison is often of a very tedious character, and considerable chance of error intervenes.

I have given much attention, therefore, to lessening both the manual and mental labour of the process, and I shall describe several devices which may be adopted for saving trouble and risk of mistake.

In the first place, as the same sets of combinations occur over and over again in different problems, we may avoid the labour of writing them out by having the sets of letters ready printed upon small sheets of writing-paper. It has also been suggested by a correspondent that, if any one series of combinations were marked upon the margin of a sheet of paper, and a slit cut between each pair of combinations, it would be easy to fold down any particular combination, and thus strike it out of view. The combinations consistent with the premises would then remain in a broken series. This method answers sufficiently well for occasional use.

A more convenient mode, however, is to have the series of letters shown on p. 94, engraved upon a common school writing slate, of such a size, that the letters may occupy only about a third of the space on the left hand side of the slate. The conditions of the problem can then be written down on the unoccupied part of the slate, and the proper series of combinations being chosen, the contradictory combinations can be struck out with the pencil. I have used a slate of this kind, which I call a *Logical Slate*, for more than twelve years, and it has saved me much trouble. It is hardly possible to apply this process to problems of more than six terms, owing to the large number of combinations which would require examination.

Abstraction of Indifferent Circumstances.

There is a simple but highly important process of inference which enables us to abstract, eliminate or disregard all circumstances indifferently present and absent. Thus if I were to state that "a triangle is a three-sided rectilinear figure, either large or not large," these two alternatives would be superfluous, because, by the Law of Duality, I know that everything must be either large or not large. To add the qualification gives no new knowledge, since the existence of the two alternatives will be understood in the absence of any information to the contrary. Accordingly, when two alternatives differ only as regards a single component term which is positive in one and negative in the other, we may reduce them to one term by striking out their indifferent part. It is really a process of substitution which enables us to do this; for having any proposition of the form

$$A = ABC \,\,+\, ABc, \qquad (1)$$

we know by the Law of Duality that

$$AB = ABC \,\,+\, ABc. \qquad (2)$$

As the second member of this is identical with the second member of (1) we may substitute, obtaining

$$A = AB.$$

This process of reducing useless alternatives may be applied again and again; for it is plain that

$$A = AB \,(CD \,\,+\, Cd \,\,+\, cD \,\,+\, cd)$$

communicates no more information than that A is B. Abstraction of indifferent terms is in fact the converse process to that of development described in p. 89; and it is one of the most important operations in the whole sphere of reasoning.

The reader should observe that in the proposition

$$AC = BC$$

we cannot abstract C and infer

$$A = B;$$

but from

$$AC \,\,+\, Ac = BC \,\,+\, Bc$$

we may abstract all reference to the term C.

It ought to be carefully remarked, however, that alternatives which seem to be without meaning often imply important knowledge. Thus if I say that " a triangle is a

three-sided rectilinear figure, with or without three equal
angles," the last alternatives really express a property of
triangles, namely, that some triangles have three equal
angles, and some do not have them.   If we put P =
"Some," meaning by the indefinite adjective "Some," one
or more of the undefined properties of triangles with three
equal angles, and take

$$A = \text{triangle}$$
$$B = \text{three-sided rectilinear figure,}$$
$$C = \text{with three equal angles,}$$

then the knowledge implied is expressed in the two
propositions

$$PA = PBC$$
$$pA = pBc.$$

These may also be thrown into the form of one proposition, namely,

$$A = PBC + pBc;$$

but these alternatives cannot be reduced, and the proposition is quite different from

$$A = BC + Bc.$$

Illustrations of the Indirect Method.

A great variety of arguments and logical problems
might be introduced here to show the comprehensive
character and powers of the Indirect Method.   We can
treat either a single premise or a series of premises.

Take in the first place a simple definition, such as "a
triangle is a three-sided rectilinear figure."   Let

$$A = \text{triangle}$$
$$B = \text{three-sided}$$
$$C = \text{rectilinear figure};$$

then the definition is of the form

$$A = BC.$$

If we take the series of eight combinations of three
letters in the Logical Alphabet (p. 94) and strike out
those which are inconsistent with the definition, we have
the following result :—   ABC
$$aBc$$
$$abC$$
$$abc.$$

For the description of the class C we have
$$C = ABC \;\cdot\!\!\!\!\cdot\; abC,$$
that is, "a rectilinear figure is either a triangle and three-sided, or not a triangle and not three-sided."
For the class b we have
$$b = abC \;\cdot\!\!\!\!\cdot\; abc.$$
To the second side of this we may apply the process of simplification by abstraction described in the last section; for by the Law of Duality
$$ab = abC \;\cdot\!\!\!\!\cdot\; abc \;;$$
and as we have two propositions identical in the second side of each we may substitute, getting
$$b = ab,$$
or what is not three-sided is not a triangle (whether it be rectilinear or not).

Second Example.

Let us treat by this method the following argument :—
   " Blende is not an elementary substance ; elementary
      substances are those which are undecomposable ;
      blende, therefore, is decomposable."
Taking our letters thus—
$$A = \text{blende},$$
$$B = \text{elementary substance},$$
$$C = \text{undecomposable},$$
the premises are of the forms

$$A = Ab, \hfill (1)$$
$$B = C. \hfill (2)$$

No immediate substitution can be made ; but if we take the contrapositive of (2) (see p. 86), namely
$$b = c, \hfill (3)$$
we can substitute in (1) obtaining the conclusion
$$A = Ac.$$
But the same result may be obtained by taking the eight combinations of A, B, C, of the Logical Alphabet ; it will be found that only three combinations, namely,
$$Abc$$
$$aBC$$
$$abc,$$
are consistent with the premises, whence it results that
$$A = Abc,$$

or by the process of Ellipsis before described (p. 57)
$$A = Ac.$$

Third Example.

As a somewhat more complex example I take the argument thus stated, one which could not be thrown into the syllogistic form :—

"All metals except gold and silver are opaque ; therefore what is not opaque is either gold or silver or is not-metal."

There is more implied in this statement than is distinctly asserted, the full meaning being as follows :

All metals not gold or silver are opaque,   (1)
Gold is not opaque but is a metal,   (2)
Silver is not opaque but is a metal,   (3)
Gold is not silver.   (4)

Taking our letters thus—

A = metal C = silver
B = gold D = opaque,

we may state the premises in the forms

$$Abc = AbcD \qquad (1)$$
$$B = ABd \qquad (2)$$
$$C = ACd \qquad (3)$$
$$B = Bc. \qquad (4)$$

To obtain a complete solution of the question we take the sixteen combinations of A, B, C, D, and striking out those which are inconsistent with the premises, there remain only

ABcd
AbCd
AbcD
abcD
abcd.

The expression for not-opaque things consists of the three combinations containing d, thus

$$d = ABcd \ +\ AbCd \ +\ abcd,$$
or $$d = Ad \ (Bc \ +\ bC) \ +\ abcd.$$

In ordinary language, what is not-opaque is either metal which is gold, and then not-silver, or silver and then not gold, or else it is not-metal and neither gold nor silver.

Fourth Example.

A good example for the illustration of the Indirect Method is to be found in De Morgan's *Formal Logic* (p. 123), the premises being substantially as follows:—

From A follows B, and from C follows D; but B and D are inconsistent with each other; therefore A and C are inconsistent.

The meaning no doubt is that where A is, B will be found, or that every A is a B, and similarly every C is a D; but B and D cannot occur together. The premises therefore appear to be of the forms

$$A = AB, \qquad\qquad (1)$$
$$C = CD, \qquad\qquad (2)$$
$$B = B d. \qquad\qquad (3)$$

On examining the series of sixteen combinations, only five are found to be consistent with the above conditions namely,

ABcd
aBcd
abCD
abcD
abcd.

In these combinations the only A which appears is joined to c, and similarly C is joined to a, or A is inconsistent with C.

Fifth Example.

A more complex argument, also given by De Morgan,[1] contains five terms, and is as stated below. except that the letters are altered.

Every A is one only of the two B or C; D is both B and C, except when B is E, and then it is neither; therefore no A is D.

The meaning of the above premises is difficult to interpret, but seems to be capable of expression in the following symbolic forms—

[1] *Formal Logic*, p. 124. As Professor Croom Robertson has pointed out to me, the second and third premises may be thrown into a single proposition, D = DeBC + DEbc.

$$A = ABc + AbC, \qquad (1)$$
$$De = DeBC, \qquad (2)$$
$$DE = DEbc. \qquad (3)$$

As five terms enter into these premises it is requisite to treat their thirty-two combinations, and it will be found that fourteen of them remain consistent with the premises, namely

ABcdE	aBCDe	abCdE
ABcde	aBCdE	abCde
AbCdE	aBCde	abcDE
AbCde	aBcdE	abcdE
	aBcde	abcde.

If we examine the first four combinations, all of which contain A, we find that they none of them contain D; or again, if we select those which contain D, we have only two, thus—

$$D = aBCDe + abcDE.$$

Hence it is clear that no A is D, and *vice versâ* no D is A. We might draw many other conclusions from the same premises; for instance—

$$DE = abcDE,$$

or D and E never meet but in the absence of A, B, and C.

Fallacies analysed by the Indirect Method.

It has been sufficiently shown, perhaps, that we can by the Indirect Method of Inference extract the whole truth from a series of propositions, and exhibit it anew in any required form of conclusion. But it may also need to be shown by examples that so long as we follow correctly the almost mechanical rules of the method, we cannot fall into any of the fallacies or paralogisms which are often committed in ordinary discussion. Let us take the example of a fallacious argument, previously treated by the Method of Direct Inference (p. 62),

Granite is not a sedimentary rock,   (1

Basalt is not a sedimentary rock,   (2)

and let us ascertain whether any precise conclusion can be drawn concerning the relation of granite and basalt. Taking as before

$$A = \text{granite,}$$
$$B = \text{sedimentary rock,}$$
$$C = \text{basalt,}$$

the premises become $\qquad$ A = Ab,   (1)

$\qquad\qquad\qquad\qquad$ C = Cb.   (2)

Of the eight conceivable combinations of A, B. C. five agree with these conditions, namely

$\qquad\qquad$ AbC $\qquad\qquad$ aBc

$\qquad\qquad$ Abc $\qquad\qquad$ abC

$\qquad\qquad\qquad\qquad$ abc.

Selecting the combinations which contain A, we find the description of granite to be

$\qquad$ A = AbC $+$ Abc = Ab(C $+$ c),

that is, granite is not a sedimentary rock, and is either basalt or not-basalt. If we want a description of basalt the answer is of like form

$\qquad$ C = AbC $+$ abC = bC (A $+$ a),

that is basalt is not a sedimentary rock, and is either granite or not-granite. As it is already perfectly evident that basalt must be either granite or not, and *vice versâ*, the premises fail to give us any information on the point, that is to say the Method of Indirect Inference saves us from falling into any fallacious conclusions. This example sufficiently illustrates both the fallacy of Negative premises and that of Undistributed Middle of the old logic.

The fallacy called the Illicit Process of the Major Term is also incapable of commission in following the rules of the method. Our example was (p. 65)

$\qquad$ All planets are subject to gravity,   (1)

$\qquad$ Fixed stars are not planets.   (2)

The false conclusion is that "fixed stars are not subject to gravity." The terms are

$\qquad\qquad$ A = planet

$\qquad\qquad$ B = fixed star

$\qquad\qquad$ C = subject to gravity.

And the premises are $\qquad$ A = AC,   (1)

$\qquad\qquad\qquad\qquad$ B = aB.   (2)

The combinations which remain uncontradicted on comparison with these premises are

$\qquad\qquad$ AbC $\qquad\qquad$ aBc

$\qquad\qquad$ aBC $\qquad\qquad$ abC

$\qquad\qquad\qquad\qquad$ abc.

For fixed star we have the description

$\qquad\qquad$ B = aBC $+$ aBc,

that is, " a fixed star is not a planet, but is either subject
or not, as the case may be, to gravity." Here we have no
conclusion concerning the connection of fixed stars and
gravity.

The Logical Abacus.

The Indirect Method of Inference has now been sufficiently described, and a careful examination of its powers
will show that it is capable of giving a full analysis and
solution of every question involving only logical relations.
The chief difficulty of the method consists in the great
number of combinations which may have to be examined ;
not only may the requisite labour become formidable, but
a considerable chance of mistake arises. I have therefore
given much attention to modes of facilitating the work,
and have succeeded in reducing the method to an almost
mechanical form. It soon appeared obvious that if the
conceivable combinations of the Logical Alphabet, for any
number of letters, instead of being printed in fixed order
on a piece of paper or slate, were marked upon light
movable pieces of wood, mechanical arrangements could
readily be devised for selecting any required class of the
combinations. The labour of comparison and rejection
might thus be immensely reduced. This idea was first
carried out in the Logical Abacus, which I have found
useful in the lecture-room for exhibiting the complete
solution of logical problems. A minute description of the
construction and use of the Abacus, together with figures
of the parts, has already been given in my essay called
The Substitution of Similars,[1] and I will here give only
a general description.

The Logical Abacus consists of a common school black-
board placed in a sloping position and furnished with four
horizontal and equi-distant ledges. The combinations
of the letters shown in the first four columns of the
Logical Alphabet are printed in somewhat large type,
so that each letter is about an inch from the neighbouring one, but the letters are placed one above the other
instead of being in horizontal lines as in p. 94. Each
combination of letters is separately fixed to the surface of

[1] Pp. 55—59, 81—86.

a thin slip of wood one inch broad and about one-eighth inch thick. Short steel pins are then driven in an inclined position into the wood. When a letter is a large capital representing a positive term, the pin is fixed in the upper part of its space; when the letter is a small italic representing a negative term, the pin is fixed in the lower part of the space. Now, if one of the series of combinations be ranged upon a ledge of the black-board, the sharp edge of a flat rule can be inserted beneath the pins belonging to any one letter—say A, so that all the combinations marked A can be lifted out and placed upon a separate ledge. Thus we have represented the act of thought which separates the class A from what is not-A. The operation can be repeated; out of the A's we can in like manner select those which are B's, obtaining the AB's; and in like manner we may select any other classes such as the aB's, the ab's, or the abc's.

If now we take the series of eight combinations of the letters A, B, C, a, b, c, and wish to analyse the argument anciently called Barbara, having the premises

$$A = AB \qquad\qquad (1)$$
$$B = BC, \qquad\qquad (2)$$

we proceed as follows—We raise the combinations marked a, leaving the A's behind; out of these A's we move to a lower ledge such as are b's, and to the remaining AB's we join the a's which have been raised. The result is that we have divided all the combinations into two classes, namely, the Ab's which are incapable of existing consistently with premise (1), and the combinations which are consistent with the premise. Turning now to the second premise, we raise out of those which agree with (1) the b's, then we lower the Bc's; lastly we join the b's to the BC's. We now find our combinations arranged as below.

A B C				a B C		a b C	a b c
	A B c	A b C	A b c		a B c		

The lower line contains all the combinations which are inconsistent with either premise; we have carried out in a

mechanical manner that exclusion of self-contradictories
which was formerly done upon the slate or upon paper.
Accordingly, from the combinations remaining in the upper
line we can draw any inference which the premises yield.
If we raise the A's we find only one, and that is C, so
that A must be C. If we select the c's we again find only
one, which is a and also b; thus we prove that not-C is
not-A and not-B.

When a disjunctive proposition occurs among the
premises the requisite movements become rather more
complicated. Take the disjunctive argument

A is either B or C or D,
A is not C and not D,
Therefore A is B.

The premises are represented accurately as follows :—

$$A = AB \cdot|\cdot AC \cdot|\cdot AD \qquad (1)$$
$$A = Ac \qquad (2)$$
$$A = Ad. \qquad (3)$$

As there are four terms, we choose the series of sixteen
combinations and place them on the highest ledge of the
board but one. We raise the a's and out of the A's, which
remain, we lower the b's. But we are not to reject all the
Ab's as contradictory, because by the first premise A's
may be either B's or C's or D's. Accordingly out of the
Ab's we must select the c's, and out of these again the d's,
so that only Abcd will remain to be rejected finally.
Joining all the other fifteen combinations together again,
and proceeding to premise (2), we raise the a's and lower
the AC's, and thus reject the combinations inconsistent
with (2) ; similarly we reject the AD's which are inconsistent with (3). It will be found that there remain, in
addition to all the eight combinations containing a, only
one containing A, namely

ABcd,

whence it is apparent that A must be B, the ordinary
conclusion of the argument.

In my " Substitution of Similars " (pp. 56—59) I have
described the working upon the Abacus of two other
logical problems, which it would be tedious to repeat in
this place.

The Logical Machine.

Although the Logical Abacus considerably reduced the labour of using the Indirect Method, it was not free from the possibility of error. I thought moreover that it would afford a conspicuous proof of the generality and power of the method if I could reduce it to a purely mechanical form. Logicians had long been accustomed to speak of Logic as an Organon or Instrument, and even Lord Bacon, while he rejected the old syllogistic logic, had insisted, in the second aphorism of his " New Instrument," that the mind required some kind of systematic aid. In the kindred science of mathematics mechanical assistance of one kind or another had long been employed. Orreries, globes, mechanical clocks, and such like instruments, are really aids to calculation and are of considerable antiquity. The Arithmetical Abacus is still in common use in Russia and China. The calculating machine of Pascal is more than two centuries old, having been constructed in 1642–45. M. Thomas of Colmar manufactures an arithmetical machine on Pascal's principles which is employed by engineers and others who need frequently to multiply or divide. To Babbage and Scheutz is due the merit of embodying the Calculus of Differences in a machine, which thus became capable of calculating the most complicated tables of figures. It seemed strange that in the more intricate science of quantity mechanism should be applicable, whereas in the simple science of qualitative reasoning, the syllogism was only called an instrument by a figure of speech. It is true that Swift satirically described the Professors of Laputa as in possession of a thinking machine, and in 1851 Mr. Alfred Smee actually proposed the construction of a Relational machine and a Differential machine, the first of which would be a mechanical dictionary and the second a mode of comparing ideas; but with these exceptions I have not yet met with so much as a suggestion of a reasoning machine. It may be added that Mr. Smee's designs, though highly ingenious, appear to be impracticable, and in any case they do not attempt the performance of logical inference.[1]

[1] See his work called *The Process of Thought adapted to Words and Language, together with a Description of the Relational and Differ-*

The Logical Abacus soon suggested the notion of a Logical Machine, which, after two unsuccessful attempts, I succeeded in constructing in a comparatively simple and effective form. The details of the Logical Machine have been fully described by the aid of plates in the Philosophical Transactions,[1] and it would be needless to repeat the account of the somewhat intricate movements of the machine in this place.

The general appearance of the machine is shown in a plate facing the title-page of this volume. It somewhat resembles a very small upright piano or organ, and has a keyboard containing twenty-one keys. These keys are of two kinds, sixteen of them representing the terms or letters A, a, B, b, C, c, D, d, which have so often been employed in our logical notation. When letters occur on the left-hand side of a proposition, formerly called the subject, each is represented by a key on the left-hand half of the keyboard; but when they occur on the right-hand side, or as it used to be called the predicate of the proposition, the letter-keys on the right-hand side of the keyboard are the proper representatives. The five other keys may be called operation keys, to distinguish them from the letter or term keys. They stand for the stops, copula, and disjunctive conjunctions of a proposition. The middle key of all is the copula, to be pressed when the verb *is* or the sign = is met. The key to the extreme right-hand is called the Full Stop, because it should be pressed when a proposition is completed, in fact in the proper place of the full stop. The key to the extreme left-hand is used to terminate an argument or to restore the machine to its initial condition; it is called the Finis key. The last keys but one on the right and left complete the whole series, and represent the conjunction *or* in its unexclusive meaning, or the sign + which I have employed, according as it occurs in the right or left hand side of the proposition. The whole keyboard is arranged as shown on the next page—

ential Machines. Also *Philosophical Transactions,* [1870] vol. 160, p. 518.
  [1] *Philosophical Transactions* [1870], vol. 160, p. 497. *Proceedings of the Royal Society,* vol. xviii. p. 166, Jan. 20 1870. *Nature,* vol. i. p. 343.

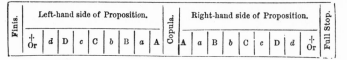

Finis.	Left-hand side of Proposition.							Copula.	Right-hand side of Proposition.								Full Stop.
	·|· Or	d	D	c	C	b	B	a	A		A	a	B	b	C	c	D	d	·|· Or	

To work the machine it is only requisite to press the keys in succession as indicated by the letters and signs of a symbolical proposition. All the premises of an argument are supposed to be reduced to the simple notation which has been employed in the previous pages. Taking then such a simple proposition as

$$A = AB,$$

we press the keys A (left), copula, A (right), B (right), and full stop.

If there be a second premise, for instance

$$B = BC,$$

we press in like manner the keys—

B (left), copula, B (right), C (right), full stop.

The process is exactly the same however numerous the premises may be. When they are completed the operator will see indicated on the face of the machine the exact combinations of letters which are consistent with the premises according to the principles of thought.

As shown in the figure opposite the title-page, the machine exhibits in front a Logical Alphabet of sixteen combinations, exactly like that of the Abacus, except that the letters of each combination are separated by a certain interval. After the above problem has been worked upon the machine the Logical Alphabet will have been modified so as to present the following appearance—

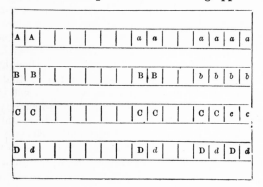

The operator will readily collect the various conclusions in the manner described in previous pages, as, for instance that A is always C, that not-C is not-B and not-A ; and not-B is not-A but either C or not-C. The results are thus to be read off exactly as in the case of the Logical Slate, or the Logical Abacus.

Disjunctive propositions are to be treated in an exactly similar manner. Thus, to work the premises

$$A = AB + AC$$
$$B + C = BD + CD,$$

it is only necessary to press in succession the keys

A (left), copula, A (right), B, + , A,C, full stop.

B (left), + , C, copula, B (right), D, + , C,D, full stop.

The combinations then remaining will be as follows

ABCD	aBCD	abcD
ABcD	aBcD	abcd.
AbCD	abCD	

On pressing the left-hand key A, all the possible combinations which do not contain A will disappear, and the description of A may be gathered from what remain, namely that it is always D.   The full-stop key restores all combinations consistent with the premises and any other selection may be made, as say not-D, which will be found to be always not-A, not-B, and not-C.

At the end of every problem, when no further questions need be addressed to the machine, we press the Finis key, which has the effect of bringing into view the whole of the conceivable combinations of the alphabet. This key in fact obliterates the conditions impressed upon the machine by moving back into their ordinary places those combinations which had been rejected as inconsistent with the premises. Before beginning any new problem it is requisite to observe that the whole sixteen combinations are visible. After the Finis key has been used the machine represents a mind endowed with powers of thought, but wholly devoid of knowledge. It would not in that condition give any answer but such as would consist in the primary laws of thought themselves. But when any proposition is worked upon the keys, the machine analyses and digests the meaning of it and becomes charged with the knowledge embodied in that proposition. Accordingly it is able to return as an answer any description of a term or class so far as furnished by that proposition in accordance with the Laws of Thought. The machine is thus the embodiment of a true logical system. The combinations are classified, selected or rejected, just as they should be by a reasoning mind, so that at each step in a problem, the Logical Alphabet represents the proper condition of a mind exempt from mistake. It cannot be asserted indeed that the machine entirely supersedes the agency of conscious thought; mental labour is required in interpreting the meaning of grammatical expressions, and in correctly impressing that meaning on the machine; it is further required in gathering the conclusion from the remaining combinations. Nevertheless the true process of logical inference is really accomplished in a purely mechanical manner.

It is worthy of remark that the machine can detect any self-contradiction existing between the premises presented to it; should the premises be self-contradictory it will be found that one or more of the letter-terms disappears entirely from the Logical Alphabet. Thus if we work the two propositions, A is B, and A is not-B, and then inquire for a description of A, the machine will refuse to give it by exhibiting no combination at all containing A. This result is in agreement with the law, which I have explained, that every term must have its negative (p. 74). Accordingly, whenever any one of the letters A, B, C, D, a, b, c, d, wholly disappears from the alphabet, it may be safely inferred that some act of self-contradiction has been committed.

It ought to be carefully observed that the logical machine cannot receive a simple identity of the form A = B except in the double form of A = B and B = A. To work the proposition A = B, it is therefore necessary to press the keys—

    A (left), copula, B (right), full stop ;
    B (left), copula, A (right), full stop.

The same double operation will be necessary whenever the proposition is not of the kind called a partial identity (p. 40). Thus AB = CD, AB = AC, A = B $+$ C, A $+$ B = C $+$ D, all require to be read from both ends separately.

The proper rule for using the machine may in fact be given in the following way :—(1) *Read each proposition as it stands, and play the corresponding keys :* (2) *Convert the proposition and read and play the keys again in the trans-posed order of the terms.* So long as this rule is observed the true result must always be obtained. There can be no mistake. But it will be found that in the case of partial identities, and some other similar forms of propositions, the transposed reading has no effect upon the combinations of the Logical Alphabet. One reading is in such cases all that is practically needful. After some experience has been gained in the use of the machine, the worker naturally saves himself the trouble of the second reading when possible.

It is no doubt a remarkable fact that a simple identity cannot be impressed upon the machine except in the form of two partial identities, and this may be thought by some logicians to militate against the equational mode of repre-senting propositions.

Before leaving the subject I may remark that these mechanical devices are not likely to possess much practical utility. We do not require in common life to be constantly solving complex logical questions. Even in mathematical calculation the ordinary rules of arithmetic are generally sufficient, and a calculating machine can only be used with advantage in peculiar cases. But the machine and abacus have nevertheless two important uses.

In the first place I hope that the time is not very far distant when the predominance of the ancient Aristotelian Logic will be a matter of history only, and when the teaching of logic will be placed on a footing more worthy of its supreme importance. It will then be found that the solution of logical questions is an exercise of mind at least as valuable and necessary as mathematical calculation. I believe that these mechanical devices, or something of the same kind, will then become useful for exhibiting to a class of students a clear and visible analysis of logical problems of any degree of complexity, the nature of each step being rendered plain to the eyes of the students. I often used the machine or abacus for this purpose in my class lectures while I was Professor of Logic at Owens College.

Secondly, the more immediate importance of the machine seems to consist in the unquestionable proof which it affords that correct views of the fundamental principles of reasoning have now been attained, although they were unknown to Aristotle and his followers. The time must come when the inevitable results of the admirable investigations of the late Dr. Boole must be recognised at their true value, and the plain and palpable form in which the machine presents those results will, I hope, hasten the time. Undoubtedly Boole's life marks an era in the science of human reason. It may seem strange that it had remained for him first to set forth in its full extent the problem of logic, but I am not aware that anyone before him had treated logic as a symbolic method for evolving from any premises the description of any class whatsoever as defined by those premises. In spite of several serious errors into which he fell, it will probably be allowed that Boole discovered the true and general form of logic, and put the science substantially into the form which it must hold for evermore. He thus effected a reform with which there is hardly anything comparable in the history of logic between his time and the remote age of Aristotle.

Nevertheless, Boole's quasi-mathematical system could hardly be regarded as a final and unexceptionable solution of the problem. Not only did it require the manipulation of mathematical symbols in a very intricate and perplexing manner, but the results when obtained were devoid of demonstrative force, because they turned upon the employment of unintelligible symbols, acquiring meaning only by analogy. I have also pointed out that he imported into his system a condition concerning the exclusive nature of alternatives (p. 70), which is not necessarily true of logical terms. I shall have to show in the next chapter that logic is really the basis of the whole science of mathematical reasoning, so that Boole inverted the true order of proof when he proposed to infer logical truths by algebraic processes. It is wonderful evidence of his mental power that by methods fundamentally false he should have succeeded in reaching true conclusions and widening the sphere of reason.

The mechanical performance of logical inference affords a demonstration both of the truth of Boole's results and of the mistaken nature of his mode of deducing them. Conclusions which he could obtain only by pages of intricate calculation, are exhibited by the machine after one or two minutes of manipulation. And not only are those conclusions easily reached, but they are demonstratively true, because every step of the process involves nothing more obscure than the three fundamental Laws of Thought.

The Order of Premises.

Before quitting the subject of deductive reasoning, I may remark that the order in which the premises of an argument are placed is a matter of logical indifference. Much discussion has taken place at various times concerning the arrangement of the premises of a syllogism; and it has been generally held, in accordance with the opinion of Aristotle, that the so-called major premise, containing the major term, or the predicate of the conclusion, should stand first. This distinction however falls to the ground in our system, since the proposition is reduced to an identical form, in which there is no distinction of subject and predicate. In a strictly logical point of view the order of statement is wholly devoid of significance. The premises are simultaneously coexistent, and are not related to each other according to the properties of space and time. Just as the qualities of the same object are neither before nor after each other in nature (p. 33), and are only thought of in some one order owing to the limited capacity of mind, so the premises of an argument are neither before nor after each other, and are only thought of in succession because the mind cannot grasp many ideas at once. The combinations of the logical alphabet are exactly the same in whatever order the premises be treated on the logical slate or machine. Some difference may doubtless exist as regards convenience to human memory. The mind may take in the results of an argument more easily in one mode of statement than another, although there is no real difference in the logical results. But in this point of view I think that Aristotle and the old logicians were clearly wrong. It is more easy to gather the conclusion that " all A's are C's " from " all A's are B's and all B's are C's," than from the same propositions in inverted order, " all B's are C's and all A's are B's.

The Equivalence of Propositions

One great advantage which arises from the study of this Indirect Method of Inference consists in the clear notion which we gain of the Equivalence of Propositions. The older logicians showed how from certain simple premises we might draw an inference, but they failed to point out whether that inference contained the whole, or only a part, of the information embodied in the premises. Any one proposition or group of propositions may be classed with respect to another proposition or group of propositions, as

1. Equivalent,
2. Inferrible,
3. Consistent,
4. Contradictory.

Taking the proposition " All men are mortals " as the original, then " All immortals are not men " is its equivalent; " Some mortals are men " is inferrible, or capable of inference, but is not equivalent; " All not-men are not mortals " cannot be inferred, but is consistent, that is, may be true at the same time ; " All men are immortals " is of course contradictory.

One sufficient test of equivalence is capability of mutual inference.   Thus from

All electrics = all non-conductors,

I can infer

All non-electrics = all conductors,

and *vice versâ* from the latter I can pass back to the former.   In short, A = B is equivalent to $a = b$.   Again, from the union of the two propositions, A = AB and B = AB, I get A = B, and from this I might as easily deduce the two with which I started.   In this case one proposition is equivalent to two other propositions.   There are in fact no less than four modes in which we may express the identity of two classes A and B, namely,

FIRST MODE.	SECOND MODE.	THIRD MODE.	FOURTH MODE.
A = B	$a = b$	$\left. \begin{array}{l} A = AB \\ B = AB \end{array} \right\}$	$\left. \begin{array}{l} a = ab \\ b = ab \end{array} \right\}$

The Indirect Method of Inference furnishes a universal and clear criterion as to the relationship of propositions. The import of a statement is always to be measured by the combinations of terms which it destroys. Hence two propositions are equivalent when they remove the same combinations from the Logical Alphabet, and neither more nor less. A proposition is inferrible but not equivalent to another when it removes some but not all the combinations which the other removes, and none except what this other removes. Again, propositions are consistent provided that they jointly allow each term and the negative of each term to remain somewhere in the Logical Alphabet. If after all the combinations inconsistent with two propositions are struck out, there still appears each of the letters A, a, B, b, C, c, D, d, which were there before, then no inconsistency between the propositions exists, although they may not be equivalent or even inferrible. Finally, contradictory propositions are those which taken together remove any one or more letter-terms from the Logical Alphabet.

What is true of single propositions applies also to groups of propositions, however large or complicated; that is to say, one group may be equivalent, inferrible, consistent, or contradictory as regards another, and we may similarly compare one proposition with a group of propositions.

To give in this place illustrations of all the four kinds of relation would require much space : as the examples given in previous sections or chapters may serve more or less to explain the relations of inference, consistency, and contradiction, I will only add a few instances of equivalent propositions or groups.

In the following list each proposition or group of propositions is exactly equivalent in meaning to the corresponding one in the other column, and the truth of this statement may be tested by working out the combinations of the alphabet, which ought to be found exactly the same in the case of each pair of equivalents.

$$A = Ab \ . \ . \ . \ . \ . \ B = aB$$
$$A = b \ . \ . \ . \ . \ . \ a = B$$
$$A = BC \ . \ . \ . \ . \ a = b + c$$
$$A = AB + AC \ . \ . \ . \ b = ab + AbC$$
$$A + B = C + D \ . \ . \ . \ . \ ab = cd$$
$$A + c = B + d \ . \ . \ . \ . \ aC = bD$$
$$A = ABc + AbC \quad \left\{ \begin{array}{l} A = AB + AC \\ AB = ABc \end{array} \right.$$

$$\left.\begin{array}{l} A = B \\ B = C \end{array}\right\} \quad \cdot \quad \cdot \quad \left\{\begin{array}{l} A = B \\ A = C \end{array}\right.$$

$$\left.\begin{array}{l} A = AB \\ B = BC \end{array}\right\} \quad \cdot \quad \cdot \quad \left\{\begin{array}{l} A = AC \\ B = A + aBC \end{array}\right.$$

Although in these and many other cases the equivalents of certain propositions can readily be given, yet I believe that no uniform and infallible process can be pointed out by which the exact equivalents of premises can be ascertained. Ordinary deductive inference usually gives us only a portion of the contained information. It is true that the combinations consistent with a set of premises may always be thrown into the form of a proposition which must be logically equivalent to those premises, but the difficulty consists in detecting the other forms of propositions which will be equivalent to the premises. The task is here of a different character from any which we have yet attempted. It is in reality an inverse process, and is just as much more troublesome and uncertain than the direct process, as seeking is compared with hiding. Not only may several different answers equally apply, but there is no method of discovering any of those answers except by repeated trial. The problem which we have here met is really that of induction, the inverse of deduction ; and, as I shall soon show, induction is always tentative, and, unless conducted with peculiar skill and insight, must be exceedingly laborious in cases of complexity.

De Morgan was unfortunately led by this equivalence of propositions. into the most serious error of his ingenious system of Logic. He held that because the proposition " All A's are all B's," is but another expression for the two propositions " All A's are B's " and " All B's are A's, it must be a composite and not really an elementary form of proposition.[1] But on taking a general view of the equivalence of propositions such an objection seems to have no weight. Logicians have, with few exceptions, persistently upheld the original error of Aristotle in rejecting from their science the one simple relation of identity on which all more complex logical relations must really rest.

[1] *Syllabus of a proposed system of Logic*, §§ 57, 121, &c.   *Formal Logic*, p. 66.

The Nature of Inference.

The question, What is Inference? is involved, even to the present day, in as much uncertainty as that ancient question, What is Truth? I shall in more than one part of this work endeavour to show that inference never does more than explicate, unfold, or develop the information contained in certain premises or facts. Neither in deductive nor inductive reasoning can we add a tittle to our implicit knowledge, which is like that contained in an unread book or a sealed letter. Sir W. Hamilton has well said, "Reasoning is the showing out explicitly that a proposition not granted or supposed, is implicitly contained in something different, which is granted or supposed." [1]

Professor Bowen has explained [2] with much clearness that the conclusion of an argument states explicitly what is virtually or implicitly thought. "The process of reasoning is not so much a mode of evolving a new truth, as it is of establishing or proving an old one, by showing how much was admitted in the concession of the two premises taken together." It is true that the whole meaning of these statements rests upon that of such words as "explicit," "implicit," "virtual." That is implicit which is wrapped up, and we render it explicit when we unfold it. Just as the conception of a circle involves a hundred important geometrical properties, all following from what we know, if we have acuteness to unfold the results, so every fact and statement involves more meaning than seems at first sight. Reasoning explicates or brings to conscious possession what was before unconscious. It does not create, nor does it destroy, but it transmutes and throws the same matter into a new form.

The difficult question still remains, Where does novelty of form begin? Is it a case of inference when we pass from "Sincerity is the parent of truth" to "The parent of truth is sincerity?" The old logicians would have called this change *conversion*, one case of immediate inference. But as all identity is necessarily reciprocal, and the very meaning of such a proposition is that the two terms are

---

[1] Lectures on Metaphysics, vol. iv. p. 369.
[2] Bowen, *Treatise on Logic*, Cambridge, U.S., 1866 ; p. 362.

identical in their signification, I fail to see any difference between the statements whatever. As well might we say that $x = y$ and $y = x$ are different equations.

Another point of difficulty is to decide when a change is merely grammatical and when it involves a real logical transformation. Between a *table of wood* and a *wooden table* there is no logical difference (p. 31), the adjective being merely a convenient substitute for the prepositional phrase. But it is uncertain to my mind whether the change from "All men are mortal" to "No men are not mortal" is purely grammatical. Logical change may perhaps be best described as consisting in the determination of a relation between certain classes of objects from a relation between certain other classes. Thus I consider it a truly logical inference when we pass from "All men are mortal" to "All immortals are not-men," because the classes *immortals* and *not-men* are different from *mortals* and *men*, and yet the propositions contain at the bottom the very same truth, as shown in the combinations of the Logical Alphabet.

The passage from the qualitative to the quantitative mode of expressing a proposition is another kind of change which we must discriminate from true logical inference. We state the same truth when we say that "mortality belongs to all men," as when we assert that "all men are mortals." Here we do not pass from class to class, but from one kind of term, the abstract, to another kind, the concrete. But inference probably enters when we pass from either of the above propositions to the assertion that the class of immortal men is zero, or contains no objects.

It is of course a question of words to what processes we shall or shall not apply the name "inference," and I have no wish to continue the trifling discussions which have already taken place upon the subject. What we need to do is to define accurately the sense in which we use the word "inference," and to distinguish the relation of in-ferrible propositions from other possible relations. It seems to be sufficient to recognise four modes in which two apparently different propositions may be related. Thus two propositions may be—

1. *Tautologous* or *identical*, involving the same relation between the same terms and classes, and only differing in

the order of statement; thus " Victoria is the Queen of England " is tautologous with " The Queen of England is Victoria."

2. *Grammatically related,* when the classes or objects are the same and similarly related, and the only difference is in the words; thus " Victoria is the Queen of England " is grammatically equivalent to " Victoria is England's Queen."

3. *Equivalents* in qualitative and quantitative form, the classes being the same, but viewed in a different manner.

4. *Logically inferrible,* one from the other, or it may be *equivalent,* when the classes and relations are different, but involve the same knowledge of the possible combinations

CHAPTER VII.

INDUCTION.

WE enter in this chapter upon the second great department of logical method, that of Induction or the Inference of general from particular truths. It cannot be said that the Inductive process is of greater importance than the Deductive process already considered, because the latter process is absolutely essential to the existence of the former. Each is the complement and counterpart of the other. The principles of thought and existence which underlie them are at the bottom the same, just as subtraction of numbers necessarily rests upon the same principles as addition. Induction is, in fact, the inverse operation of deduction, and cannot be conceived to exist without the corresponding operation, so that the question of relative importance cannot arise. Who thinks of asking whether addition or subtraction is the more important process in arithmetic? But at the same time much difference in difficulty may exist between a direct and inverse operation; the integral calculus, for instance, is infinitely more difficult than the differential calculus of which it is the inverse. Similarly, it must be allowed that inductive investigations are of a far higher degree of difficulty and complexity than any questions of deduction; and it is this fact no doubt which led some logicians, such as Francis Bacon, Locke, and J. S. Mill, to erroneous opinions concerning the exclusive importance of induction.

Hitherto we have been engaged in considering how from certain conditions, laws, or identities governing the combinations of qualities, we may deduce the nature of the combinations agreeing with those conditions. Our work has been to unfold the results of what is contained in any statements, and the process has been one of *Synthesis*. The terms or combinations of which the character has been determined have usually, though by no means always, involved more qualities, and therefore, by the relation of extension and intension, fewer objects than the terms in which they were described. The truths inferred were thus usually less general than the truths from which they were inferred.

In induction all is inverted. The truths to be ascertained are more general than the data from which they are drawn. The process by which they are reached is *analytical,* and consists in separating the complex combinations in which natural phenomena are presented to us, and determining the relations of separate qualities. Given events obeying certain unknown laws, we have to discover the laws obeyed. Instead of the comparatively easy task of finding what effects will follow from a given law, the effects are now given and the law is required. We have to interpret the will by which the conditions of creation were laid down.

Induction an Inverse Operation

I have already asserted that induction is the inverse operation of deduction, but the difference is one of such great importance that I must dwell upon it. There are many cases in which we can easily and infallibly do a certain thing but may have much trouble in undoing it. A person may walk into the most complicated labyrinth or the most extensive catacombs, and turn hither and thither at his will; it is when he wishes to return that doubt and difficulty commence. In entering, any path served him; in leaving, he must select certain definite paths, and in this selection he must either trust to memory of the way he entered or else make an exhaustive trial of all possible ways. The explorer entering a new country makes sure his line of return by barking the trees.

The same difficulty arises in many scientific processes. Given any two numbers, we may by a simple and infallible process obtain their product; but when a large number

is given it is quite another matter to determine its factors.
Can the reader say what two numbers multiplied together
will produce the number 8,616,460,799? I think it
unlikely that anyone but myself will ever know; for
they are two large prime numbers, and can only be re-
discovered by trying in succession a long series of prime
divisors until the right one be fallen upon. The work
would probably occupy a good computer for many weeks,
but it did not occupy me many minutes to multiply the
two factors together. Similarly there is no direct process
for discovering whether any number is a prime or not; it
is only by exhaustively trying all inferior numbers which
could be divisors, that we can show there is none, and the
labour of the process would be intolerable were it not performed systematically once for all in the process known as
the Sieve of Eratosthenes, the results being registered in
tables of prime numbers.

The immense difficulties which are encountered in the
solution of algebraic equations afford another illustration.
Given any algebraic factors, we can easily and infallibly
arrive at the product; but given a product it is a matter
of infinite difficulty to resolve it into factors. Given any
series of quantities however numerous, there is very little
trouble in making an equation which shall have those
quantities as roots. Let a, b, c, d, &c., be the quantities;
then $(x - a)\ (x - b)\ (x - c)\ (x - d)\ldots\ldots = 0$
is the equation required, and we only need to multiply out
the expression on the left hand by ordinary rules. But
having given a complex algebraic expression equated to
zero, it is a matter of exceeding difficulty to discover all
the roots. Mathematicians have exhausted their highest
powers in carrying the complete solution up to the fourth
degree. In every other mathematical operation the inverse
process is far more difficult than the direct process, subtraction than addition, division than multiplication, evolution than involution; but the difficulty increases vastly
as the process becomes more complex. Differentiation,
the direct process, is always capable of performance by
fixed rules, but as these rules produce considerable variety
of results, the inverse process of integration presents immense difficulties, and in an infinite majority of cases
surpasses the present resources of mathematicians. There

are no infallible and general rules for its accomplishment ; it must be done by trial, by guesswork, or by remembering the results of differentiation, and using them as a guide.

Coming more nearly to our own immediate subject, exactly the same difficulty exists in determining the law which certain things obey. Given a general mathematical expression, we can infallibly ascertain its value for any required value of the variable. But I am not aware that mathematicians have ever attempted to lay down the rules of a process by which, having given certain numbers, one might discover a rational or precise formula from which they proceed. The reader may test his power of detecting a law, by contemplation of its results, if he, not being a mathematician, will attempt to point out the law obeyed by the following numbers:

$$\frac{1}{6}, \quad \frac{1}{30}, \quad \frac{1}{42}, \quad \frac{1}{30}, \quad \frac{5}{66}, \quad \frac{691}{2730}, \quad \frac{7}{6}, \quad \frac{3617}{510}, \quad \frac{43867}{798}, \quad \text{etc.}$$

These numbers are sometimes in low terms, but unexpectedly spring up to high terms ; in absolute magnitude they are very variable. They seem to set all regularity and method at defiance, and it is hardly to be supposed that anyone could, from contemplation of the numbers, have detected the relations between them. Yet they are derived from the most regular and symmetrical laws of relation, and are of the highest importance in mathematical analysis, being known as the numbers of Bernoulli.

Compare again the difficulty of deciphering with that of cyphering. Anyone can invent a secret language, and with a little steady labour can translate the longest letter into the character. But to decypher the letter, having no key to the signs adopted, is a wholly different matter. As the possible modes of secret writing are infinite in number and exceedingly various in kind, there is no direct mode of discovery whatever. Repeated trial, guided more or less by knowledge of the customary form of cypher, and resting entirely on the principles of probability and logical induction, is the only resource. A peculiar tact or skill is requisite for the process, and a few men, such as Wallis or Wheatstone, have attained great success.

Induction is the decyphering of the hidden meaning of natural phenomena. Given events which happen in certain

definite combinations, we are required to point out the
laws which govern those combinations. Any laws being
supposed, we can, with ease and certainty, decide whether
the phenomena obey those laws. But the laws which may
exist are infinite in variety, so that the chances are immensely against mere random guessing. The difficulty is
much increased by the fact that several laws will usually
be in operation at the same time, the effects of which
are complicated together. The only modes of discovery
consist either in exhaustively trying a great number of
supposed laws, a process which is exhaustive in more
senses than one, or else in carefully contemplating the
effects, endeavouring to remember cases in which like
effects followed from known laws. In whatever manner
we accomplish the discovery, it must be done by the more
or less conscious application of the direct process of
deduction.

The Logical Alphabet illustrates induction as well as
deduction. In considering the Indirect Process of Inference
we found that from certain propositions we could infallibly
determine the combinations of terms agreeing with those
premises. The inductive problem is just the inverse.
Having given certain combinations of terms, we need to
ascertain the propositions with which the combinations are
consistent, and from which they may have proceeded.
Now, if the reader contemplates the following combinations,

$$\begin{array}{ll} \text{ABC} & ab\text{C} \\ a\text{BC} & abc, \end{array}$$

he will probably remember at once that they belong to the
premises A = AB, B = BC (p. 92). If not, he will require
a few trials before he meets with the right answer, and
every trial will consist in assuming certain laws and
observing whether the deduced results agree with the data.
To test the facility with which he can solve this inductive
problem, let him casually strike out any of the combinations of the fourth column of the Logical Alphabet, (p. 94),
and say what laws the remaining combinations obey,
observing that every one of the letter-terms and their
negatives ought to appear in order to avoid self-contradiction in the premises (pp. 74, 111). Let him say, for
instance, what laws are embodied in the combinations

$$\begin{array}{ll} \text{ABC} & a\text{BC} \\ \text{A}bc & ab\text{C.} \end{array}$$

The difficulty becomes much greater when more terms enter into the combinations. It would require some little examination to ascertain the complete conditions fulfilled in the combinations

$$\begin{array}{ll} \text{AC}e & ab\text{C}e \\ a\text{BC}e & abc\text{E.} \\ a\text{B}cd\text{E} & \end{array}$$

The reader may discover easily enough that the principal laws are C = e, and A = Ae; but he would hardly discover without some trouble the remaining law, namely, that BD = BDe.

The difficulties encountered in the inductive investigations of nature, are of an exactly similar kind. We seldom observe any law in uninterrupted and undisguised operation. The acuteness of Aristotle and the ancient Greeks did not enable them to detect that all terrestrial bodies tend to fall towards the centre of the earth. A few nights of observation might have convinced an astronomer viewing the solar system from its centre, that the planets travelled round the sun; but the fact that our place of observation is one of the travelling planets, so complicates the apparent motions of the other bodies, that it required all the sagacity of Copernicus to prove the real simplicity of the planetary system. It is the same throughout nature; the laws may be simple, but their combined effects are not simple, and we have no clue to guide us through their intricacies. "It is the glory of God," said Solomon, "to conceal a thing, but the glory of a king to search it out." The laws of nature are the invaluable secrets which God has hidden, and it is the kingly prerogative of the philosopher to search them out by industry and sagacity.

Inductive Problems for Solution by the Reader.

In the first edition (vol. ii. p. 370) I gave a logical problem involving six terms, and requested readers to discover the laws governing the combinations given. I received satisfactory replies from readers both in the United States and in England. I formed the combinations deductively from four laws of correction, but my correspondents found that three simpler laws, equivalent to the four more complex ones, were the best answer; these laws are as follows : $a = ac,\ b = cd,\ d = \mathrm{E}f$.

In case other readers should like to test their skill in the inductive or inverse problem, I give below several series of combinations forming problems of graduated difficulty.

PROBLEM 1.

A b C D
A b c D
a B C D
a B c D
a B c d
a b C d

PROBLEM 1.

A B c
A b C
a B C

PROBLEM II.

A B C
A b C
a B C
a B c

PROBLEM III

A B C
A b C
a B C
a B c
a b c

PROBLEM IV

A B C D
A b c D
a B c d
a b C d

PROBLEM V.

A B C D
A B C d
A B c d

PROBLEM VI.

A B C D E
A B C d e
A B c D E
A B c d e
A b C D E
a B C D E
a B C d e
a b C D E
a b c d e

PROBLEM VII.

A b c D e
a B C d E
a b C d E

PROBLEM VIII.

A B C D E
A B C D e
A B C d e
A B c d e
A b C D E
A b c d E
A b c d e
a B C D e
a B C d e
a B c D e

a b C D e
a b C d E
a b c D e
a b c d E

PROBLEM IX.

A B c D E F
A B c D e F
A b C D e f
A b c D E f
A b c D e f
A b c d E F
A b c d e F
a B c D E F
a B c D e F
a B c d E F
a b C D E F
a b C D e F
a b C D e f
a b c D e f
a b c D E f
a b c d e F

PROBLEM X.

A B C D e F
A B c D E f
A b C D E F
A b C D e F
A b c D e F
a B C D E J
a B c D E f
a b C D e F
a b C d e F
a b c D e f
a b c d e f

Induction of Simple Identities.

Many important laws of nature are expressible in the form of simple identities, and I can at once adduce them as examples to illustrate what I have said of the difficulty of the inverse process of induction. Two phenomena are conjoined. Thus all gravitating matter is exactly co-incident with all matter possessing inertia; where one property appears, the other likewise appears. All crystals of the cubical system, are all the crystals which do not doubly refract light. All exogenous plants are, with some exceptions, those which have two cotyledons or seed-leaves.

A little reflection will show that there is no direct and infallible process by which such complete coincidences may be discovered. Natural objects are aggregates of many qualities, and any one of those qualities may prove to be in close connection with some others. If each of a numerous group of objects is endowed with a hundred distinct physical or chemical qualities, there will be no less than $\frac{1}{2}$ (100 × 99) or 4950 pairs of qualities, which may be connected, and it will evidently be a matter of great intricacy and labour to ascertain exactly which qualities are connected by any simple law.

One principal source of difficulty is that the finite powers of the human mind are not sufficient to compare by a single act any large group of objects with another large group. We cannot hold in the conscious possession of the mind at any one moment more than five or six different ideas. Hence we must treat any more complex group by successive acts of attention. The reader will perceive by an almost individual act of comparison that the words *Roma* and *Mora* contain the same letters. He may perhaps see at a glance whether the same is true of *Causal* and *Casual*, and of *Logica* and *Caligo*. To assure himself that the letters in *Astronomers* make *No more stars*, that *Serpens in akuleo* is an anagram of *Joannes Keplerus*, or *Great gun do us a sum* an anagram of *Augustus de Morgan*, it will certainly be necessary to break up the act of comparison into several successive acts. The process will acquire a double character, and will consist in ascertaining that each letter of the first group is among the letters of the second group, and *vice versâ*, that each letter of the second is among those of the first group. In the same way we can only prove that two long lists of names are identical, by showing that each name in one list occurs in the other, and *vice versâ*.

This process of comparison really consists in establishing two partial identities, which are, as already shown (p. 58), equivalent in conjunction to one simple identity. We first ascertain the truth of the two propositions $A = AB$,

$B = AB$, and we then rise by substitution to the single law $A = B$.

There is another process, it is true, by which we may get to exactly the same result; for the two propositions $A = AB$, $a = ab$ are also equivalent to the simple identity $A = B$. If then we can show that all objects included under A are included under B, and also that all objects not included under A are not included under B, our purpose is effected. By this process we should usually compare two lists if we are allowed to mark them. For each name in the first list we should strike off one in the second, and if, when the first list is exhausted, the second list is also exhausted, it follows that all names absent from the first must be absent from the second, and the coincidence must be complete.

These two modes of proving an identity are so closely allied that it is doubtful how far we can detect any difference in their powers and instances of application. The first method is perhaps more convenient when the phenomena to be compared are rare. Thus we prove that all the musical concords coincide with all the more simple numerical ratios, by showing that each concord arises from a simple ratio of undulations, and then showing that each simple ratio gives rise to one of the concords. To examine all the possible cases of discord or complex ratio of undulation would be impossible. By a happy stroke of induction Sir John Herschel discovered that all crystals of quartz which cause the plane of polarization of light to rotate are precisely those crystals which have plagihedral faces, that is, oblique faces on the corners of the prism unsymmetrical with the ordinary faces. This singular relation would be proved by observing that all plagihedral crystals possessed the power of rotation, and *vice versâ* all crystals possessing this power were plagihedral. But it might at the same time be noticed that all ordinary crystals were devoid of the power. There is no reason why we should not detect any of the four propositions $A = AB$, $B = AB$, $a = ab$, $b = ab$, all of which follow from $A = B$ (p. 115).

Sometimes the terms of the identity may be singular objects; thus we observe that diamond is a combustible gem, and being unable to discover any other that is, we affirm—

Diamond = combustible gem.

In a similar manner we ascertain that

Mercury = metal liquid at ordinary temperatures,

Substance of least density = substance of least atomic weight.

Two or three objects may occasionally enter into the induction, as when we learn that

Sodium + potassium = metal of less density than water,

Venus + Mercury + Mars = major planet devoid of satellites.

Induction of Partial Identities.

We found in the last section that the complete identity of two classes is almost always discovered not by direct observation of the fact, but by first establishing two partial identities. There are also a multitude of cases in which the partial identity of one class with another is the only relation to be discovered. Thus the most common of all inductive inferences consists in establishing the fact that all objects having the properties of A have also those of B, or that A = AB. To ascertain the truth of a proposition of this kind it is merely necessary to assemble together, mentally or physically, all the objects included under A, and then observe whether B is present in each of them, or, which is the same, whether it would be impossible to select from among them any not-B. Thus, if we mentally assemble together all the heavenly bodies which move with apparent rapidity, that is to say, the planets, we find that they all possess the property of not scintillating. We cannot analyse any vegetable substance without discovering that it contains carbon and hydrogen, but it is not true that all substances containing carbon and hydrogen are vegetable substances.

The great mass of scientific truths consists of propositions of this form A = AB. Thus in astronomy we learn that all the planets are spheroidal bodies; that they all revolve in one direction round the sun; that they all shine by reflected light; that they all obey the law of gravitation. But of course it is not to be asserted that all bodies obeying the law of gravitation, or shining by reflected light, or revolving in a particular direction, or being spheroidal in form, are planets. In other sciences we have immense numbers of propositions of the same form, as, for instance, all substances in becoming gaseous absorb heat; all metals are elements; they are all good conductors of heat and electricity; all the alkaline metals are monad elements; all foraminifera are marine organisms; all parasitic animals are non-mammalian; lightning never issues from stratous clouds; pumice never occurs where only Labrador felspar is present; milkmaids do not suffer from small-pox; and, in the works of Darwin, scientific importance may attach even to such an apparently trifling observation as that " white tom-cats having blue eyes are deaf."

The process of inference by which all such truths are obtained may readily be exhibited in a precise symbolic form. We must have one premise specifying in a disjunctive form all the possible individuals which belong to a class; we resolve the class, in short, into its constituents. We then need a number of propositions, each of which affirms that one of the individuals possesses a certain property. Thus the premises must be of the forms

$$A = B + C + D + \ldots\ldots + P + Q$$
$$B = BX$$
$$C = CX$$
$$\ldots \quad \ldots$$
$$\ldots \quad \ldots$$
$$Q = QX.$$

Now, if we substitute for each alternative of the first premise its description as found among the succeeding premises, we obtain

$$A = BX + CX + \ldots\ldots\ldots + PX + QX$$

or

$$A = (B + C + \ldots\ldots + Q)X$$

But for the aggregate of alternatives we may now substitute their equivalent as given in the first premise, namely A, so that we get the required result:

$$A = AX.$$

We should have reached the same result if the first premise had been of the form

$$A = AB + AC + \ldots\ldots + AQ.$$

We can always prove a proposition, if we find it more convenient, by proving its equivalent. To assert that all not-B's are not-A's, is exactly the same as to assert that all A's are B's. Accordingly we may ascertain that A = AB by first ascertaining that $b = ab$. If we observe, for instance, that all substances which are not solids are also not capable of double refraction, it follows necessarily that all double refracting substances are solids. We may convince ourselves that all electric substances are nonconductors of electricity, by reflecting that all good conductors do not, and in fact cannot, retain electric excitation. When we come to questions of probability it will be found desirable to prove, as far as possible, both the original proposition and its equivalent, as there is then an increased area of observation.

The number of alternatives which may arise in the division of a class varies greatly, and may be any number from two upwards. Thus it is probable that every substance is either magnetic or diamagnetic, and no substance can be both at the same time. The division then must be made in the form

$$A = ABc + AbC.$$

If now we can prove that all magnetic substances are capable of polarity, say B = BD, and also that all diamagnetic substances are capable of polarity, C = CD, it follows by substitution that all substances are capable of polarity, or A = AD. We commonly divide the class substance into the three subclasses, solid, liquid, and gas; and if we can show that in each of these forms it obeys Carnot's thermodynamic law, it follows that all substances obey that law. Similarly we may show that all vertebrate animals possess red blood, if we can show separately that fish, reptiles, birds, marsupials, and mammals possess red blood, there being, as far as is known, only five principal subclasses of vertebrata.

Our inductions will often be embarrassed by exceptions, real or apparent. We might affirm that all gems are incombustible were not diamonds undoubtedly combustible. Nothing seems more evident than that all the metals are opaque until we examine them in fine films, when gold and silver are found to be transparent. All plants absorb carbonic acid except certain fungi; all the bodies of the

planetary system have a progressive motion from west to
east, except the satellites of Uranus and Neptune. Even
some of the profoundest laws of matter are not quite
universal; all solids expand by heat except india-rubber,
and possibly a few other substances; all liquids which have
been tested expand by heat except water below 4° C. and
fused bismuth; all gases have a coefficient of expansion
increasing with the temperature, except hydrogen. In
a later chapter I shall consider how such anomalous
cases may be regarded and classified; here we have only to
express them in a consistent manner by our notation.

Let us take the case of the transparency of metals, and
assign the terms **thus :**—

$$A = \text{metal} \qquad D = \text{iron}$$
$$B = \text{gold} \qquad E, F, \&c. = \text{copper, lead, \&c.}$$
$$C = \text{silver} \qquad X = \text{opaque.}$$

Our premises will be

$$A = B + C + D + E, \&c.$$
$$B = Bx$$
$$C = Cx$$
$$D = DX$$
$$E = EX,$$

and so on for the rest of the metals. Now evidently

$$Abc = (D + E + F + \ldots\ldots)bc,$$

and by substitution as before we shall obtain

$$Abc = AbcX,$$

or in words, " All metals not gold nor silver are opaque ;'
at the same time we have

$$A(B + C) = AB + AC = ABx + ACx = A(B + C)x,$$

or " Metals which are either gold or silver are not opaque."

In some cases the problem of induction assumes a much
higher degree of complexity. If we examine the properties
of crystallized substances we may find some properties
which are common to all, as cleavage or fracture in definite
planes; but it would soon become requisite to break up
the class into several minor ones. We should divide
crystals according to the seven accepted systems—and we
should then find that crystals of each system possess
many common properties. Thus crystals of the Regular
or Cubical system expand equally by heat, conduct heat
and electricity with uniform rapidity, and are of like
elasticity in all directions; they have but one index of

refraction for light ; and every facet is repeated in like
relation to each of the three axes. Crystals of the system
having one principal axis will be found to possess the
various physical powers of conduction, refraction, elasticity, &c., uniformly in directions perpendicular to the
principal axis ; in other directions their properties vary
according to complicated laws. The remaining systems
in which the crystals possess three unequal axes, or have
inclined axes, exhibit still more complicated results, the
effects of the crystal upon light, heat, electricity, &c.,
varying in all directions. But when we pursue induction
into the intricacies of its application to nature we really
enter upon the subject of classification, which we must
take up again in a later part of this work.

Solution of the Inverse or Inductive Problem, involving Two Classes.

It is now plain that Induction consists in passing back
from a series of combinations to the laws by which such
combinations are governed. The natural law that all
metals are conductors of electricity really means that in
nature we find three classes of objects, namely—

    1. Metals, conductors ;

    2. Not-metals, conductors ;

    3. Not-metals, not-conductors.

It comes to the same thing if we say that it excludes the
existence of the class, "metals not-conductors." In the
same way every other law or group of laws will really
mean the exclusion from existence of certain combinations
of the things, circumstances or phenomena governed by
those laws. Now in logic, strictly speaking, we treat not
the phenomena, nor the laws, but the general forms of the
laws ; and a little consideration will show that for a finite
number of things the possible number of forms or kinds
of law governing them must also be finite. Using general
terms, we know that A and B can be present or absent in
four ways and no more—thus :

$$AB, \quad Ab, \quad aB, \quad ab \;;$$

therefore every possible law which can exist concerning
the relation of A and B must be marked by the exclusion
of one or more of the above combinations. The number

of possible laws then cannot exceed the number of selections which we can make from these four combinations. Since each combination may be present or absent, the number of cases to be considered is 2 × 2 × 2 × 2, or sixteen ; and these cases are all shown in the following table, in which the sign o indicates absence or non-existence of the combination shown at the left-hand column in the same line, and the mark 1 its presence :—

	1	2	3	4	5	6	7*	8*	9	10*	11	12*	13	14*	15*	16*
AB	o	o	o	o	o	o	o	o	1	1	1	1	1	1	1	1
Ab	o	o	o	o	1	1	1	1	o	o	o	o	1	1	1	1
aB	o	o	1	1	o	o	1	1	o	o	1	1	o	o	1	1
ab	o	1	o	1	o	1	o	1	o	1	o	1	o	1	o	1

Thus in column sixteen we find that all the conceivable combinations are present, which means that there are no special laws in existence in such a case, and that the combinations are governed only by the universal Laws of Identity and Difference. The example of metals and conductors of electricity would be represented by the twelfth column ; and every other mode in which two things or qualities might present themselves is shown in one or other of the columns. More than half the cases may indeed be at once rejected, because they involve the entire absence of a term or its negative. It has been shown to be a logical principle that every term must have its negative (p. 111), and when this is not the case, inconsistency between the conditions of combination must exist. Thus if we laid down the two following propositions, " Graphite conducts electricity," and " Graphite does not conduct electricity," it would amount to asserting the impossibility of graphite existing at all ; or in general terms, A is B and A is not B result in destroying altogether the combinations containing A, a case shown in the fourth column of the above table. We therefore restrict our attention to those cases which may be represented in natural phenomena when at least two combinations are present, and which correspond to those columns of the table in which each of A, a, B, b appears. These cases are shown in the columns marked with an asterisk.

We find that seven cases remain for examination, thus characterised—

Four cases exhibiting three combinations,
Two cases exhibiting two combinations,
One case exhibiting four combinations.

It has already been pointed out that a proposition of the form A = AB destroys one combination, Ab, so that this is the form of law applying to the twelfth column. But by changing one or more of the terms in A = AB into its negative, or by interchanging A and B, a and b, we obtain no less than eight different varieties of the one form; thus—

12th case.	8th case.	15th case.	14th case.
A = AB	A = Ab	$a = a$B	$a = ab$
$b = ab$	B = aB	$b = A b$	B = AB

The reader of the preceding sections will see that each proposition in the lower line is logically equivalent to, and is in fact the contrapositive of, that above it (p. 83). Thus the propositions A = Ab and B = aB both give the same combinations, shown in the eighth column of the table, and trial shows that the twelfth, eighth, fifteenth and fourteenth columns are thus accounted for. We come to this conclusion then—*The general form of proposition A = AB admits of four logically distinct varieties, each capable of expression in two modes.*

In two columns of the table, namely the seventh and tenth, we observe that two combinations are missing. Now a simple identity A = B renders impossible both Ab and aB, accounting for the tenth case; and if we change B into b the identity A = b accounts for the seventh case. There may indeed be two other varieties of the simple identity, namely $a = b$ and $a = $ B; but it has already been shown repeatedly that these are equivalent respectively to A = B and A = b (p. 115). As the sixteenth column has already been accounted for as governed by no special conditions, we come to the following general conclusion :—The laws governing the combinations of two terms must be capable of expression either in a partial identity or a simple identity; the partial identity is capable of only four logically distinct varieties, and the simple identity of two. Every logical relation between two terms must be expressed in one of these six forms of law, or must be logically equivalent to one of them.

In short, we may conclude that in treating of partial and complete identity, we have exhaustively treated the modes in which two terms or classes of objects can be related. Of any two classes it can be said that one must either be included in the other, or must be identical with it, or a like relation must exist between one class and the negative of the other. We have thus completely solved the inverse logical problem concerning two terms.[1]

The Inverse Logical Problem involving Three Classes.

No sooner do we introduce into the problem a third term C, than the investigation assumes a far more complex character, so that some readers may prefer to pass over this section. Three terms and their negatives may be combined, as we have frequently seen, in eight different combinations, and the effect of laws or logical conditions is to destroy any one or more of these combinations. Now we may make selections from eight things in 2^8 or 256 ways; so that we have no less than 256 different cases to treat, and the complete solution is at least fifty times as troublesome as with two terms. Many series of combinations, indeed, are contradictory, as in the simpler problem, and may be passed over, the test of consistency being that each of the letters A, B, C, a, b, c, shall appear somewhere in the series of combinations.

My mode of solving the problem was as follows:— Having written out the whole of the 256 series of combinations, I examined them separately and struck out such as did not fulfil the test of consistency. I then chose some form of proposition involving two or three terms, and varied it in every possible manner, both by the circular interchange of letters (A, B, C into B, C, A and then into C, A, B), and by the substitution for any one or more of the terms of the corresponding negative terms.

[1] The contents of this and the following section nearly correspond with those of a paper read before the Manchester Literary and Philosophical Society on December 26th, 1871. See Proceedings of the Society, vol. xi. pp. 65—68, and Memoirs, Third Series, vol. v. pp. 119 —130.

For instance, the proposition AB = ABC can be first varied by circular interchange so as to give BC = BCA and then CA = CAB. Each of these three can then be thrown into eight varieties by negative change. Thus AB = ABC gives aB = aBC, Ab = AbC, AB = ABc, ab = abC, and so on. Thus there may possibly exist no less than twenty-four varieties of the law having the general form AB = ABC, meaning that whatever has the properties of A and B has those also of C. It by no means follows that some of the varieties may not be equivalent to others ; and trial shows, in fact, that AB = ABC is exactly the same in meaning as Ac = Abc or Bc = Bca. Thus the law in question has but eight varieties of distinct logical meaning. I now ascertain by actual deductive reasoning which of the 256 series of combinations result from each of these distinct laws, and mark them off as soon as found. I then proceed to some other form of law, for instance A = ABC, meaning that whatever has the qualities of A has those also of B and C. I find that it admits of twenty-four variations, all of which are found to be logically distinct ; the combinations being worked out, I am able to mark off twenty-four more of the list of 256 series. I proceed in this way to work out the results of every form of law which I can find or invent. If in the course of this work I obtain any series of combinations which had been previously marked off, I learn at once that the law giving these combinations is logically equivalent to some law previously treated. It may be safely inferred that every variety of the apparently new law will coincide in meaning with some variety of the former expression of the same law. I have sufficiently verified this assumption in some cases, and have never found it lead to error. Thus as AB = ABC is equivalent to Ac = Abc, so we find that ab = abC is equivalent to ac = acB.

Among the laws treated were the two A = AB and A = B which involve only two terms, because it may of course happen that among three things two only are in special logical relation, and the third independent ; and the series of combinations representing such cases of relation are sure to occur in the complete enumeration. All single propositions which I could invent having been treated, pairs of propositions were next investigated. Thus

we have the relations, " All A's are B's and all B's are
C's," of which the old logical syllogism is the development.
We may also have "all A's are all B's, and all B's are C's,"
or even "all A's are all B's, and all B's are all C's." All
such premises admit of variations, greater or less in
number, the logical distinctness of which can only be
determined by trial in detail. Disjunctive propositions
either singly or in pairs were also treated, but were often
found to be equivalent to other propositions of a simpler
form ; thus A = ABC $\cdot$ Abc is exactly the same in meaning
as AB = AC.

This mode of exhaustive trial bears some analogy to
that ancient mathematical process called the Sieve of
Eratosthenes. Having taken a long series of the natural
numbers, Eratosthenes is said to have calculated out in
succession all the multiples of every number, and to
have marked them off, so that at last the prime numbers
alone remained, and the factors of every number were
exhaustively discovered. My problem of 256 series of
combinations is the logical analogue, the chief points of
difference being that there is a limit to the number of cases,
and that prime numbers have no analogue in logic, since
every series of combinations corresponds to a law or group
of conditions. But the analogy is perfect in the point that
they are both inverse processes. There is no mode of
ascertaining that a number is prime but by showing that
it is not the product of any assignable factors. So there
is no mode of ascertaining what laws are embodied in any
series of combinations but trying exhaustively the laws
which would give them. Just as the results of Eratosthenes' method have been worked out to a great extent
and registered in tables for the convenience of other
mathematicians, I have endeavoured to work out the
inverse logical problem to the utmost extent which is at
present practicable or useful.

I have thus found that there are altogether fifteen conditions or series of .conditions which may govern the combinations of three terms, forming the premises of fifteen
essentially different kinds of arguments. The following
table contains a statement of these conditions, together
with the numbers of combinations which are contradicted
or destroyed by each, and the numbers of logically distinct

variations of which the law is capable. There might be also added, as a sixteenth case, that case where no special logical condition exists, so that all the eight combinations remain.

Reference Number.	Propositions expressing the general type of the logical conditions.	Number of distinct logical variations.	Number of combinations contradicted by each.
I.	$A = B$	6	4
II.	$A = AB$	12	2
III.	$A = B, \quad B = C$	4	6
IV.	$A = B, \quad B = BC$	24	5
V.	$A = AB, \quad B = BC$	24	4
VI.	$A = BC$	24	4
VII.	$A = ABC$	24	3
VIII.	$AB = ABC$	8	1
IX.	$A = AB, \quad aB = aBc$	24	3
X.	$A = ABC, \quad ab = abC$	8	4
XI.	$AB = ABC, \quad ab = abc$	4	2
XII.	$AB = AC$	12	2
XIII.	$A = BC + Abc$	8	3
XIV.	$A = BC + bc$	2	4
XV.	$A = ABC, \quad a = Bc + bC$	8	5

There are sixty-three series of combinations derived from self-contradictory premises, which with 192, the sum of the numbers of distinct logical variations stated in the third column of the table, and with the one case where there are no conditions or laws at all, make up the whole conceivable number of 256 series.

We learn from this table, for instance, that two propositions of the form $A = AB, B = BC$, which are such as constitute the premises of the old syllogism Barbara, exclude as impossible four of the eight combinations in which three terms may be united, and that these propositions are capable of taking twenty-four variations by transpositions of the terms or the introduction of negatives. This table then presents the results of a complete analysis of all the possible logical relations arising in the case of three terms, and the old syllogism forms but one out of fifteen typical forms. Generally speaking, every form can be converted into apparently different propositions; thus the fourth type $A = B, B = BC$ may appear in the form $A = ABC, a = ab$, or again in the form of three propositions $A = AB, B = BC, aB = aBc$; but all these sets of premises yield identically the same series of combinations,

and are therefore of equivalent logical meaning. The fifth
type, or Barbara, can also be thrown into the equivalent
forms $A = ABC$, $aB = aBC$ and $A = AC$, $B = A \cdot\!\!\mid aBC$.
In other cases I have obtained the very same logical
conditions in four modes of statements. As regards mere
appearance and form of statement, the number of possible
premises would be very great, and difficult to exhibit
exhaustively.

The most remarkable of all the types of logical condition
is the fourteenth, namely, $A = BC \cdot\!\!\mid bc$. It is that which
expresses the division of a genus into two doubly marked
species, and might be illustrated by the example—" Component of the physical universe = matter, gravitating, or
not-matter (ether), not-gravitating." It is capable of only
two distinct logical variations, namely, $A = BC \cdot\!\!\mid bc$ and
$A = Bc \cdot\!\!\mid bC$. By transposition or negative change of the
letters we can indeed obtain six different expressions of
each of these propositions; but when their meanings are
analysed, by working out the combinations, they are found
to be logically equivalent to one or other of the above two.
Thus the proposition $A = BC \cdot\!\!\mid bc$ can be written in any
of the following five other modes,

$$a = bC \;\cdot\!\!\mid\; Bc, \quad B = CA \;\cdot\!\!\mid\; ca, \quad b = cA \;\cdot\!\!\mid\; Ca,$$
$$C = AB \;\cdot\!\!\mid\; ab, \quad c = aB \;\cdot\!\!\mid\; Ab.$$

I do not think it needful to publish at present the complete table of 193 series of combinations and the premises
corresponding to each. Such a table enables us by mere
inspection to learn the laws obeyed by any set of combinations of three things, and is to logic what a table of
factors and prime numbers is to the theory of numbers, or
a table of integrals to the higher mathematics. The table
already given (p. 140) would enable a person with but little
labour to discover the law of any combinations. If there
be seven combinations (one contradicted) the law must be
of the eighth type, and the proper variety will be apparent.
If there be six combinations (two contradicted), either the
second, eleventh, or twelfth type applies, and a certain
number of trials will disclose the proper type and variety.
If there be but two combinations the law must be of the
third type, and so on.

The above investigations are complete as regards the
possible logical relations of two or three terms. But

when we attempt to apply the same kind of method to the relations of four or more terms, the labour becomes impracticably great. Four terms give sixteen combinations compatible with the laws of thought, and the number of possible selections of combinations is no less than 2^{16} or 65,536. The following table shows the extraordinary manner in which the number of possible logical relations increases with the number of terms involved.

Number of terms.	Number of possible combinations.	Number of possible selections of combinations corresponding to consistent or inconsistent logical relations.
2	4	16
3	8	256
4	16	65,536
5	32	4,294,967,296
6	64	18,446,744,073,709,551,616

Some years of continuous labour would be required to ascertain the types of laws which may govern the combinations of only four things, and but a small part of such laws would be exemplified or capable of practical application in science. The purely logical inverse problem, whereby we pass from combinations to their laws, is solved in the preceding pages, as far as it is likely to be for a long time to come; and it is almost impossible that it should ever be carried more than a single step further.

In the first edition, vol i. p. 158, I stated that I had not been able to discover any mode of calculating the number of cases in which inconsistency would be implied in the selection of combinations from the Logical Alphabet. The logical complexity of the problem appeared to be so great that the ordinary modes of calculating numbers of combinations failed, in my opinion, to give any aid, and exhaustive examination of the combinations in detail seemed to be the only method applicable. This opinion, however, was mistaken, for both Mr. R. B. Hayward, of Harrow, and Mr. W. H. Brewer have calculated the numbers of inconsistent cases both for three and for four terms, without much difficulty. In the case of four terms they find that there are 1761 inconsistent selections and 63,774 consistent, which with one case where no condition exists, make up the total of 65,536 possible selections.

The inconsistent cases are distributed in the manner shown in the following table :—

Number of Combinations remaining.	0	1	2	3	4	5	6	7	8	9	10, &c.
Number of Inconsistent Cases.	1	16	112	352	536	448	224	64	8	0	0, &c.

When more than eight combinations of the Logical Alphabet (p. 94, column V.) remain unexcluded, there cannot be inconsistency. The whole numbers of ways of selecting 0, 1, 2, &c., combinations out of 16 are given in the 17th line of the Arithmetical Triangle given further on in the Chapter on Combinations and Permutations, the sum of the numbers in that line being 65,536.

Professor Clifford on the Types of Compound Statement involving Four Classes.

In the first edition (vol. i. p. 163), I asserted that some years of labour would be required to ascertain even the precise number of types of law governing the combinations of four classes of things. Though I still believe that some years' labour would be required to work out the types themselves, it is clearly a mistake to suppose that the *numbers* of such types cannot be calculated with a reasonable amount of labour, Professor W. K Clifford having actually accomplished the task. His solution of the numerical problem involves the use of a complete new system of nomenclature and is far too intricate to be fully described here. I can only give a brief abstract of the results, and refer readers, who wish to follow out the reasoning, to the Proceedings of the Literary and Philosophical Society of Manchester, for the 9th January, 1877, vol. xvi., p. 88, where Professor Clifford's paper is printed in full.

By a *simple statement* Professor Clifford means the denial of the existence of any single combination or *cross-*

division, of the classes, as in ABCD = o, or A*b*C*d* = o. The denial of two or more such combinations is called a *compound statement,* and is further said to be *twofold, threefold,* &c., according to the number denied. Thus ABC = o is a twofold compound statement in regard to four classes, because it involves both ABCD = o and ABC*d* = o. When two compound statements can be converted into one another by interchange of the classes, A, B, C, D, with each other or with their complementary classes, *a, b, c, d,* they are called *similar,* and all similar statements are said to belong to the same *type.*

Two statements are called *complementary* when they deny between them all the sixteen combinations without both denying any one; or, which is the same thing, when each denies just those combinations which the other permits to exist. It is obvious that when two statements are similar, the complementary statements will also be similar, and consequently for every type of n-fold statement, there is a complementary type of $(16-n)$-fold statement. It follows that we need only enumerate the types as far as the eighth order; for the types of more-than-eight-fold statement will already have been given as complementary to types of lower orders.

One combination, ABCD, may be converted into another A*b*C*d* by interchanging one or more of the classes with the complementary classes. The number of such changes is called the *distance,* which in the above case is 2. In two similar compound statements the distances of the combinations denied must be the same; but it does not follow that when all the distances are the same, the statements are similar. There is, however, only one example of two dissimilar statements having the same distances. When the distance is 4, the two combinations are said to be *obverse* to one another, and the statements denying them are called *obverse statements,* as in ABCD = o and *abcd* = o or again A*b*C*d* = o and *a*B*c*D = o. When any one combination is given, called the *origin,* all the others may be grouped in respect of their relations to it as follows :—Four are at distance *one* from it, and may be called *proximates;* six are at distance *two,* and may be called *mediates;* four are at distance *three,* and may be called *ultimates;* finally the obverse is at distance *four.*

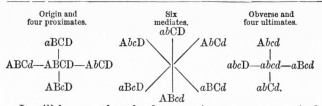

| Origin and four proximates. | Six mediates. | Obverse and four ultimates. |

It will be seen that the four proximates are respectively obverse to the four ultimates, and that the mediates form three pairs of obverses. Every proximate or ultimate is distant 1 and 3 respectively from such a pair of mediates.

Aided by this system of nomenclature Professor Clifford proceeds to an exhaustive enumeration of types, in which it is impossible to follow him. The results are as follows :—

1-fold statements		1 type	\	
2 „ „		4 types		
3 „ „		6 „		
4 „ „		19 „	}	159
5 „ „		27 „		
6 „ „		47 „		
7 „ „		55 „	/	
8-fold statements		78 „		

Now as each seven-fold or less-than-seven-fold statement is complementary to a nine-fold or more-than-nine-fold statement, it follows that the complete number of types will be $159 \times 2 + 78 = 396$.

It appears then that the types of statement concerning four classes are only about 26 times as numerous as those concerning three classes, fifteen in number, although the number of possible combinations is 256 times as great.

Professor Clifford informs me that the knowledge of the possible groupings of subdivisions of classes which he obtained by this inquiry has been of service to him in some applications of hyper-elliptic functions to which he has subsequently been led. Professor Cayley has since expressed his opinion that this line of investigation should be followed out, owing to the bearing of the theory of compound combinations upon the higher geometry.[1] It seems likely that many unexpected points of connection

---

[1] *Proceedings of the Manchester Literary and Philosophical Society,* 6th February, 1877, vol. xvi., p. 113.

will in time be disclosed between the sciences of logic and mathematics.

Distinction between Perfect and Imperfect Induction.

We cannot proceed with advantage before noticing the extreme difference which exists between cases of perfect and those of imperfect induction. We call an induction *perfect* when all the objects or events which can possibly come under the class treated have been examined. But in the majority of cases it is impossible to collect together, or in any way to investigate, the properties of all portions of a substance or of all the individuals of a race. The number of objects would often be practically infinite, and the greater part of them might be beyond our reach, in the interior of the earth, or in the most distant parts of the Universe. In all such cases induction is *imperfect*, and is affected by more or less uncertainty. As some writers have fallen into much error concerning the functions and relative importance of these two branches of reasoning, I shall have to point out that—

1. Perfect Induction is a process absolutely requisite, both in the performance of imperfect induction and in the treatment of large bodies of facts of which our knowledge is complete.

2. Imperfect Induction is founded on Perfect Induction, but involves another process of inference of a widely different character.

It is certain that if I can draw any inference at all concerning objects not examined, it must be done on the data afforded by the objects which have been examined. If I judge that a distant star obeys the law of gravity, it must be because all other material objects sufficiently known to me obey that law. If I venture to assert that all ruminant animals have cloven hoofs, it is because all ruminant animals which have come under my notice have cloven hoofs. On the other hand, I cannot safely say that all cryptogamous plants possess a purely cellular structure, because some cryptogamous plants, which have been examined by botanists, have a partially vascular structure. The probability that a new cryptogam will be cellular only can be estimated, if at all, on the ground of the comparative numbers of known cryptogams which are and are not cellular. Thus the first step in every induction will consist in accurately summing up the number of instances of a particular phenomenon which have fallen under our observation. Adams and Leverrier, for instance, must have inferred that the undiscovered planet Neptune would obey Bode's law, because *all the planets known at that time obeyed it.* On what principles the passage from the known to the apparently unknown is warranted, must be carefully discussed in the next section, and in various parts of this work.

It would be a great mistake, however, to suppose that Perfect Induction is in itself useless. Even when the enumeration of objects belonging to any class is complete, and admits of no inference to unexamined objects, the statement of our knowledge in a general proposition is a process of so much importance that we may consider it necessary. In many cases we may render our investigations exhaustive ; all the teeth or bones of an animal ; all the cells in a minute vegetable organ ; all the caves in a mountain side ; all the strata in a geological section ; all the coins in a newly found hoard, may be so completely scrutinized that we may make some general assertion concerning them without fear of mistake. Every bone might be proved to contain phosphate of lime ; every cell to enclose a nucleus ; every cave to hide remains of extinct animals ; every stratum to exhibit signs of marine origin ; every coin to be of Roman manufacture. These are cases where our investigation is limited to a definite portion of matter, or a definite area on the earth's surface.

There is another class of cases where induction is naturally and necessarily limited to a definite number of alternatives. Of the regular solids we can say without the least doubt that no one has more than twenty faces, thirty edges, and twenty corners ; for by the principles of geometry we learn that there cannot exist more than five regular solids, of each of which we easily observe that the above statements are true. In the theory of numbers, an endless variety of perfect inductions might be made ; we can show that no number less than sixty possesses so many divisors, and the like is true of 360 ; for it does not require a great amount of labour to ascertain and count all the divisors of numbers up to sixty or 360. I can assert that between 60,041 and 60,077 no prime number occurs, because the exhaustive examination of those who have constructed tables of prime numbers proves it to be so.

In matters of human appointment or history, we can frequently have a complete limitation of the number of instances to be included in an induction. We might show that the propositions of the third book of Euclid treat only of circles; that no part of the works of Galen mentions the fourth figure of the syllogism; that none of the other kings of England reigned so long as George III.; that Magna Charta has not been repealed by any subsequent statute; that the price of corn in England has never been so high since 1847 as it was in that year; that the price of the English funds has never been lower than it was on the 23rd of January, 1798, when it fell to 47¼.

It has been urged against this process of Perfect Induction that it gives no new information, and is merely a summing up in a brief form of a multitude of particulars. But mere abbreviation of mental labour is one of the most important aids we can enjoy in the acquisition of knowledge. The powers of the human mind are so limited that multiplicity of detail is alone sufficient to prevent its progress in many directions. Thought would be practically impossible if every separate fact had to be separately thought and treated. Economy of mental power may be considered one of the main conditions on which our elevated intellectual position depends. Mathematical processes are for the most part but abbreviations of the simpler acts of addition and subtraction. The invention of logarithms was one of the most striking additions ever made to human power: yet it was a mere abbreviation of operations which could have been done before had a sufficient amount of labour been available. Similar additions to our power will, it is hoped, be made from time to time; for the number of mathematical problems hitherto solved is but an indefinitely small fraction of those which await solution, because the labour they have hitherto demanded renders them impracticable. So it is throughout all regions of thought. The amount of our knowledge depends upon our power of bringing it within practicable compass. Unless we arrange and classify facts and condense them into general truths, they soon surpass our powers of memory, and serve but to confuse. Hence Perfect Induction, even as a process of abbreviation, is absolutely essential to any high degree of mental achievement.

Transition from Perfect to Imperfect Induction.

It is a question of profound difficulty on what grounds we are warranted in inferring the future from the present, or the nature of undiscovered objects from those which we have examined with our senses. We pass from Perfect to Imperfect Induction when once we allow our conclusion to apply, at all events apparently, beyond the data on which it was founded. In making such a step we seem to gain a net addition to our knowledge ; for we learn the nature of what was unknown. We reap where we have never sown. We appear to possess the divine power of creating knowledge, and reaching with our mental arms far beyond the sphere of our own observation. I shall have, indeed, to point out certain methods of reasoning in which we do pass altogether beyond the sphere of the senses, and acquire accurate knowledge which observation could never have given ; but it is not imperfect induction that accomplishes such a task. Of imperfect induction itself, I venture to assert that it never makes any real addition to our knowledge, in the meaning of the expression sometimes accepted. As in other cases of inference, it merely unfolds the information contained in past observations ; it merely renders explicit what was implicit in previous experience. It transmutes, but certainly does not create knowledge.

There is no fact which I shall more constantly keep before the reader's mind in the following pages than that the results of imperfect induction, however well authenticated and verified, are never more than probable. We never can be sure that the future will be as the present. We hang ever upon the will of the Creator : and it is only so far as He has created two things alike, or maintains the framework of the world unchanged from moment to moment, that our most careful inferences can be fulfilled. All predictions, all inferences which reach beyond their data, are purely hypothetical, and proceed on the assump tion that new events will conform to the conditions detected in our observation of past events.   No experience of finite duration can give an exhaustive knowledge of the forces which are in operation.   There is thus a double uncertainty ; even supposing the Universe as a whole to proceed unchanged, we do not really know the Universe as a whole. We know only a point in its infinite extent, and a moment in its infinite duration.   We cannot be sure, then, that our observations have not escaped some fact, which will cause the future to be apparently different from the past ; nor can we be sure that the future really will be the outcome of the past.   We proceed then in all our inferences to unexamined objects and times on the assumptions—

1. That our past observation gives us a complete knowledge of what exists.

2. That the conditions of things which did exist will continue to be the conditions which will exist.

We shall often need to illustrate the character of our knowledge of nature by the simile of a ballot-box, so often employed by mathematical writers in the theory of probability.   Nature is to us like an infinite ballot-box, the contents of which are being continually drawn, ball after ball, and exhibited to us.   Science is but the careful observation of the succession in which balls of various character present themselves ; we register the combinations, notice those which seem to be excluded from occurrence, and from the proportional frequency of those which appear we infer the probable character of future drawings. But under such circumstances certainty of prediction depends on two conditions :—

1. That we acquire a perfect knowledge of the comparative numbers of balls of each kind within the box.

2. That the contents of the ballot-box remain unchanged.

Of the latter assumption, or rather that concerning the constitution of the world which it illustrates, the logician or physicist can have nothing to say.   As the Creation of the Universe is necessarily an act passing all experience and all conception, so any change in that Universe, or, it may be, a termination of it, must likewise be infinitely beyond the bounds of our mental faculties.   No science no reasoning upon the subject, can have any validity; for without experience we are without the basis and materials of knowledge. It is the fundamental postulate accordingly of all inference concerning the future, that there shall be no arbitrary change in the subject of inference; of the probability or improbability of such a change I conceive that our faculties can give no estimate.

The other condition of inductive inference—that we acquire an approximately complete knowledge of the combinations in which events do occur, is in some degree within our power. There are branches of science in which phenomena seem to be governed by conditions of a most fixed and general character. We have ground in such cases for believing that the future occurrence of such phenomena can be calculated and predicted. But the whole question now becomes one of probability and improbability. We seem to leave the region of logic to enter one in which the number of events is the ground of inference. We do not really leave the region of logic; we only leave that where certainty, affirmative or negative, is the result, and the agreement or disagreement of qualities the means of inference. For the future, number and quantity will commonly enter into our processes of reasoning; but then I hold that number and quantity are but portions of the great logical domain. I venture to assert that number is wholly logical, both in its fundamental nature and in its developments. Quantity in all its forms is but a development of number. That which is mathematical is not the less logical; if anything it is more logical, in the sense that it presents logical results in a higher degree of complexity and variety.

Before proceeding then from Perfect to Imperfect Induction I must devote a portion of this work to treating the logical conditions of number. I shall then employ number to estimate the variety of combinations in which natural phenomena may present themselves, and the probability or improbability of their occurrence under definite circumstances. It is in later parts of the work that I must endeavour to establish the notions which I have set forth upon the subject of Imperfect Induction, as applied in the investigation of Nature, which notions may be thus briefly stated :—

1. Imperfect Induction entirely rests upon Perfect Induction for its materials.

2. The logical process by which we seem to pass directly from examined to unexamined cases consists in an inverse application of deductive inference, so that all reasoning may be said to be either directly or inversely deductive.

3. The result is always of a hypothetical character, and is never more than probable.

4. No net addition is ever made to our knowledge by reasoning; what we know of future events or unexamined objects is only the unfolded contents of our previous knowledge, and it becomes less probable as it is more boldly extended to remote cases.

BOOK II.

NUMBER, VARIETY, AND PROBABILITY.

CHAPTER VIII.

PRINCIPLES OF NUMBER.

NOT without reason did Pythagoras represent the world as ruled by number. Into almost all our acts of thought number enters, and in proportion as we can define numerically we enjoy exact and useful knowledge of the Universe. The science of numbers, too, has hitherto presented the widest and most practicable training in logic. So free and energetic has been the study of mathematical forms, compared with the forms of logic, that mathematicians have passed far in advance of pure logicians. Occasionally, in recent times, they have condescended to apply their algebraic instrument to a reflex treatment of the primary logical science. It is thus that we owe to profound mathematicians, such as John Herschel, Whewell, De Morgan, or Boole, the regeneration of logic in the present century. I entertain no doubt that it is in maintaining a close alliance with quantitative reasoning that we must look for further progress in our comprehension of qualitative inference

I cannot assent, indeed, to the common notion that certainty begins and ends with numerical determination. Nothing is more certain than logical truth. The laws of identity and difference are the tests of all that is certain throughout the range of thought, and mathematical reasoning is cogent only when it conforms to these conditions, of which logic is the first development. And if it be erroneous to suppose that all certainty is mathematical, it is equally an error to imagine that all which is mathematical is certain. Many processes of mathematical reasoning are of most doubtful validity. There are points of mathematical doctrine which must long remain matter of opinion; for instance, the best form of the definition and axiom concerning parallel lines, or the true nature of a limit. In the use of symbolic reasoning questions occur on which the best mathematicians may differ, as Bernoulli and Leibnitz differed irreconcileably concerning the existence of the logarithms of negative quantities.[1] In fact we no sooner leave the simple logical conditions of number, than we find ourselves involved in a mazy and mysterious science of symbols.

Mathematical science enjoys no monopoly, and not even a supremacy, in certainty of results. It is the boundless extent and variety of quantitative questions that delights the mathematical student. When simple logic can give but a bare answer Yes or No, the algebraist raises a score of subtle questions, and brings out a crowd of curious results. The flower and the fruit, all that is attractive and delightful, fall to the share of the mathematician, who too often despises the plain but necessary stem from which all has arisen. In no region of thought can a reasoner cast himself free from the prior conditions of logical correctness. The mathematician is only strong and true as long as he is logical, and if number rules the world, it is logic which rules number.

Nearly all writers have hitherto been strangely content to look upon numerical reasoning as something apart from logical inference. A long divorce has existed between quality and quantity, and it has not been uncommon to treat them as contrasted in nature and restricted to independent branches of thought. For my own part, I believe that all the sciences meet somewhere. No part of knowledge can stand wholly disconnected from other parts of the universe of thought; it is incredible, above all, that

---

[1] Montucla, *Histoire des Mathématiques*, vol. iii. p. 373.

the two great branches of abstract science, interlacing and co-operating in every discourse, should rest upon totally distinct foundations. I assume that a connection exists, and care only to inquire, What is its nature? Does the science of quantity rest upon that of quality; or, *vice versâ*, does the science of quality rest upon that of quantity? There might conceivably be a third view, that they both rest upon some still deeper set of principles.

It is generally supposed that Boole adopted the second view, and treated logic as an application of algebra, a special case of analytical reasoning which admits only two quantities, unity and zero. It is not easy to ascertain clearly which of these views really was accepted by Boole. In his interesting biographical sketch of Boole,[1] the Rev. R. Harley protests against the statement that Boole's logical calculus imported the conditions of number and quantity into logic. He says: " Logic is never. identified or confounded with mathematics; the two systems of thought are kept perfectly distinct, each being subject to its own laws and conditions. The symbols are the same for both systems, but they have not the same interpretation." The Rev. J. Venn, again, in his review of Boole's logical system,[2] holds that Boole's processes are at bottom logical, not mathematical, though stated in a highly generalized form and with a mathematical dress. But it is quite likely that readers of Boole should be misled. Not only have his logical works an entirely mathematical appearance, but I find on p. 12 of his *Laws of Thought* the following unequivocal statement: " That logic, as a science, is susceptible of very wide applications is admitted; but it is equally certain that its ultimate forms and processes are mathematical." A few lines below he adds, " It is not of the essence of mathematics to be conversant with the ideas of number and quantity."

The solution of the difficulty is that Boole used the term mathematics in a wider sense than that usually attributed to it. He probably adopted the third view, so that his mathematical *Laws of Thought* are the common

---

[1] *British Quarterly Review*, No. lxxxvii, July 1866.
[2] *Mind*; October 1876, vol. i. p. 484.

basis both of logic and of quantitative mathematics. But
I do not care to pursue the subject because I think that
in either case Boole was wrong. In my opinion logic is
the superior science, the general basis of mathematics as
well as of all other sciences. Number is but logical discrimination, and algebra a highly developed logic. Thus
it is easy to understand the deep analogy which Boole
pointed out between the forms of algebraic and logical
deduction. Logic resembles algebra as the mould
resembles that which is cast in it. Boole mistook the
cast for the mould. Considering that logic imposes its
own laws upon every branch of mathematical science, it
is no wonder that we constantly meet with the traces of
logical laws in mathematical processes.

The Nature of Number.

Number is but another name for *diversity*. Exact identity is unity, and with difference arises plurality. An
abstract notion, as was pointed out (p. 28), possesses a
certain *oneness*. The quality of *justice*, for instance, is one
and the same in whatever just acts it is manifested. In
justice itself there are no marks of difference by which to
discriminate justice from justice. But one just act can be
discriminated from another just act by circumstances of
time and place, and we can count many acts thus discriminated each from each. In like manner pure gold is
simply pure gold, and is so far one and the same throughout. But besides its intrinsic qualities, gold occupies
space and must have shape and size. Portions of gold
are always mutually exclusive and capable of discrimination, in respect that they mnst be each without the other.
Hence they may be numbered.

Plurality arises when and only when we detect differ-
ence. For instance, in counting a number of gold coins
I must count each coin once, and not more than once.
Let C denote a coin, and the mark above it the order of
counting. Then I must count the coins
$$C' + C'' + C''' + C'''' + \ldots \ldots$$
If I were to count them as follows
$$C' + C'' + C''' + C''' + C'''' + \ldots ,$$
I should make the third coin into two, and should imply

the existence of difference where there is no difference.[1]
C''' and C''' are but the names of one coin named twice
over.   But according to one of the conditions of logical
symbols, which I have called the Law of Unity (p. 72),
the same name repeated has no effect, and

$$A \cdot\mid\cdot A = A.$$

We must apply the Law of Unity, and must reduce all
identical alternatives before we can count with certainty
and use the processes of numerical calculation.   Identical
alternatives are harmless in logic, but are wholly inadmissible in number.   Thus logical science ascertains the
nature of the mathematical unit, and the definition may
be given in these terms—*A unit is any object of thought
which can be discriminated from every other object treated as
a unit in the same problem.*

   It has often been said that units are units in respect of
being perfectly similar to each other ; but though they
may be perfectly similar in some respects, they must be
different in at least one point, otherwise they would be
incapable of plurality.   If three coins were so similar that
they occupied the same space at the same time, they
would not be three coins, but one coin.   It is a property
of space that every point is discriminable from every other
point, and in time every moment is necessarily distinct
from any other moment before or after.   Hence we
frequently count in space or time, and Locke, with some
other philosophers, has held that number arises from
repetition in time.   Beats of a pendulum may be so
perfectly similar that we can discover no difference except
that one beat is before and another after.   Time alone is
here the ground of difference and is a sufficient foundation
for the discrimination of plurality ; but it is by no means
the only foundation.   Three coins are three coins, whether
we count them successively or regard them all simultaneously.   In many cases neither time nor space is the
ground of difference, but pure quality alone enters.   We
can discriminate the weight, inertia, and hardness of gold
as three qualities, though none of these is before nor after
the other, neither in space nor time.   Every means of
discrimination may be a source of plurality.

---

[1] *Pure Logic*, Appendix, p. 82, § 192

Our logical notation may be used to express the rise of number. The symbol A stands for one thing or one class, and in itself must be regarded as a unit, because no difference is specified. But the combinations AB and A*b* are necesssarily *two*, because they cannot logically coalesce, and there is a mark B which distinguishes one from the other. A logical definition of the number *four* is given in the combinations ABC, AB*c*, A*b*C, A*bc*, where there is a double difference. As Puck says—

> " Yet but three ?   Come one more ;
> Two of both kinds makes up four."

I conceive that all numbers might be represented as arising out of the combinations of the Logical Alphabet, more or less of each series being struck out by various logical conditions. The number three, for instance, arises from the condition that A must be either B or C, so that the combinations are ABC, AB*c*, A*b*C.

Of Numerical Abstraction.

There will now be little difficulty in forming a clear notion of the nature of numerical abstraction. It consists in abstracting the character of the difference from which plurality arises, retaining merely the fact. When I speak of *three men* I need not at once specify the marks by which each may be known from each. Those marks must exist if they are really three men and not one and the same, and in speaking of them as many I imply the existence of the requisite differences. Abstract number, then, is *the empty form of difference ;* the abstract number *three* asserts the existence of marks without specifying their kind.

Numerical abstraction is thus seen to be a different process from logical abstraction (p. 27), for in the latter process we drop out of notice the very existence of difference and plurality. In forming the abstract notion *hardness,* we ignore entirely the diverse circumstances in which the quality may appear. It is the concrete notion *three hard objects,* which asserts the existence of hardness along with sufficient other undefined qualities, to mark out *three* such objects. Numerical thought is indeed closely interwoven with logical thought. We cannot use a con-

crete term in the plural, as *men*, without implying that
there are marks of difference.   But when we use an
abstract term, we deal with unity.

The origin of the great generality of number is now
apparent.   Three sounds differ from three colours, or three
riders from three horses ; but they agree in respect of the
variety of marks by which they can be discriminated.   The
symbols $1+1+1$ are thus the empty marks asserting the
existence of discrimination.   But in dropping out of sight
the character of the differences we give rise to new
agreements on which mathematical reasoning is founded.
Numerical abstraction is so far from being incompatible
with logical abstraction that it is the origin of our widest
acts of generalization.

Concrete and Abstract Number.

The common distinction between concrete and abstract
number can now be easily stated.   In proportion as we
specify the logical characters of the things numbered, we
render them concrete.   In the abstract number *three*
there is no statement of the points in which the three
objects agree; but in *three coins, three men,* or *three horses,*
not only are the objects numbered but their nature is restricted.   Concrete number thus implies the same consciousness of difference as abstract number, but it is
mingled with a groundwork of similarity expressed in the
logical terms.   There is identity so far as logical terms
enter; difference so far as the terms are merely numerical.

The reason of the important Law of Homogeneity will
now be apparent.   This law asserts that in every arithmetical calculation the logical nature of the things numbered must remain unaltered.   The specified logical
agreement of the things must not be affected by the un-
specified numerical differences.   A calculation would be
palpably absurd which, after commencing with length,
gave a result in hours.   It is equally absurd, in a purely
arithmetical point of view, to deduce areas from the
calculation of lengths, masses from the combination of
volume and density, or momenta from mass and velocity.
It must remain for subsequent consideration to decide in
what sense we may truly say that two linear feet multi-

plied by two linear feet give four superficial feet; arith-
metically it is absurd, because there is a change of unit.

As a general rule we treat in each calculation only
objects of one nature. We do not, and cannot properly
add, in the same sum yards of cloth and pounds of sugar.
We cannot even conceive the result of adding area to
velocity, or length to density, or weight to value. The
units added must have a basis of homogeneity, or must be
reducible to some common denominator. Nevertheless it
is possible, and in fact common, to treat in one complex
calculation the most heterogeneous quantities, on the
condition that each kind of object is kept distinct, and
treated numerically only in conjunction with its own kind.
Different units, so far as their logical differences are specified, must never be substituted one for the other. Chemists
continually use equations which assert the equivalence of
groups of atoms. Ordinary fermentation is represented
by the formula

$$C^6 \ H^{12} \ O^6 = 2C^2 \ H^6 \ O + 2CO^2.$$

Three kinds of units, the atoms respectively of carbon,
hydrogen, and oxygen, are here intermingled, but there is
really a separate equation in regard to each kind. Mathematicians also employ compound equations of the same
kind; for in, $a + b \sqrt{-1} = c + d \sqrt{-1}$, it is impossible
by ordinary addition to add a to $b \sqrt{-1}$. Hence we
really have the separate equations $a = b$, and $c \sqrt{-1} = d
\sqrt{-1}$. Similarly an equation between two quaternions is
equivalent to four equations between ordinary quantities,
whence indeed the name *quaternion*.

Analogy of Logical and Numerical Terms.

If my assertion is correct that number arises out of
logical conditions, we ought to find number obeying all the
laws of logic. It is almost superfluous to point out that
this is the case with the fundamental laws of identity and
difference, and it only remains to show that mathematical
symbols do really obey the special conditions of logical
symbols which were formerly pointed out (p. 32). Thus
the Law of Commutativeness, is equally true of quality and
quantity. As in logic we have

$$AB = BA,$$

so in mathematics it is familiarly known that

$$2 \times 3 = 3 \times 2, \quad \text{or} \quad x \times y = y \times x.$$
The properties of space are as indifferent in multiplication as we found them in pure logical thought.

Similarly, as in logic

triangle or square = square or triangle,

or generally $\quad$ A $\cdot | \cdot$ B = B $\cdot | \cdot$ A,

so in quantity $\quad$ $2 + 3 = 3 + 2,$

or generally $\quad$ $x + y = y + x.$

The symbol $\cdot | \cdot$ is not identical with +, but it is thus far analogous.

How far, now, is it true that mathematical symbols obey the Law of Simplicity expressed in the form

$$AA = A,$$

or the example

Round round = round?

Apparently there are but two numbers which obey this law ; for it is certain that

$$x \times x = x$$

is true only in the two cases when $x = 1$, or $x = 0$.

In reality all numbers obey the law, for $2 \times 2 = 2$ is not really analogous to $AA = A$. According to the definition of a unit already given, each unit is discriminated from each other in the same problem, so that in $2' \times 2''$, the first *two* involves a different discrimination from the second *two*. I get four kinds of things, for instance, if I first discriminate "heavy and light" and then "cubical and spherical," for we now have the following classes—

heavy, cubical. $\quad$ light, cubical.

heavy, spherical. $\quad$ light, spherical.

But suppose that my two classes are in both cases discriminated by the same difference of light and heavy, then we have

heavy heavy = heavy,

heavy light = 0,

light heavy = 0,

light light = light.

Thus, (heavy or light) × (heavy or light) = (heavy or light).

In short, *twice two is two* unless we take care that the second two has a different meaning from the first. But under similar circumstances logical terms give the like result, and it is not true that $A'A'' = A'$, when A'' is different in meaning from A'.

In a similar manner it may be shown that the Law of
Unity   A $\cdot|\cdot$ A $=$ A.
holds true alike of logical and mathematical terms.   It is
absurd indeed to say that

$$x + x = x$$

except in the one case when $x =$ absolute zero.   But this
contradiction $x + x = x$ arises from the fact that we have
already defined the units in one x as differing from those in
the other.   Under such circumstances the Law of Unity
does not apply.   For if in

A$'$ $\cdot|\cdot$ A$'' =$ A$'$

we mean that A$''$ is in any way different from A$'$ the
assertion of identity is evidently false.

The contrast then which seems to exist between logical
and mathematical symbols is only apparent.   It is because
the Laws of Simplicity and Unity must always be observed
in the operation of counting that those laws seem no further
to apply.   This is the understood condition under which
we use all numerical symbols.   Whenever I write the
symbol 5 I really mean

$$1 + 1 + 1 + 1 + 1,$$

and it is perfectly understood that each of these units is
distinct from each other.   If requisite I might mark them
thus

$$1' + 1'' + 1''' + 1'''' + 1'''''.$$

Were this not the case and were the units really

$$1' + 1'' + 1'' + 1''' + 1'''',$$

the Law of Unity would, as before remarked, apply, and

$$1'' + 1'' = 1''.$$

Mathematical symbols then obey all the laws of logical
symbols, but two of these laws seem to be inapplicable
simply because they are presupposed in the definition of
the mathematical unit.   Logic thus lays down the conditions of number, and the science of arithmetic developed
as it is into all the wondrous branches of mathematical
calculus is but an outgrowth of logical discrimination.

Principle of Mathematical Inference.

The universal principle of all reasoning, as I have
asserted, is that which allows us to substitute like for like.
I have now to point out how in the mathematical sciences

this principle is involved in each step of reasoning. It is in these sciences indeed that we meet with the clearest cases of substitution, and it is the simplicity with which the principle can be applied which probably led to the comparatively early perfection of the sciences of geometry and arithmetic. Euclid, and the Greek mathematicians from the first, recognised *equality* as the fundamental relation of quantitative thought, but Aristotle rejected the exactly analogous, but far more general relation of identity, and thus crippled the formal science of logic as it has descended to the present day.

Geometrical reasoning starts from the axiom that " things equal to the same thing are equal to each other." Two equalities enable us to infer a third equality ; and this is true not only of lines and angles, but of areas, volumes, numbers, intervals of time, forces, velocities, degrees of intensity, or, in short, anything which is capable of being equal or unequal. Two stars equally bright with the same star must be equally bright with each other, and two forces equally intense with a third force are equally intense with each other. It is remarkable that Euclid has not explicitly stated two other axioms, the truth of which is necessarily implied. The second axiom should be that " Two things of which one is equal and the other unequal to a third common thing, are unequal to each other." An equality and inequality, in short, give an inequality, and this is equally true with the first axiom of all kinds of quantity. If Venus, for instance, agrees with Mars in density, but Mars differs from Jupiter, then Venus differs from Jupiter. A third axiom must exist to the effect that " Things unequal to the same thing may or may not be equal to each other." *Two inequalities give no ground of inference whatever.* If we only know, for instance, that Mercury and Jupiter differ in density from Mars, we cannot say whether or not they agree between themselves. As a fact they do not agree ; but Venus and Mars on the other hand both differ from Jupiter and yet closely agree with each other. The force of the axioms can be most clearly illustrated by drawing equal and unequal lines.[1]

---

[1] *Elementary Lessons in Logic* (Macmillan), p. 123. It is pointed out in the preface to this Second Edition, that the views here given were partially stated by Leibnitz.

The general conclusion then must be that where there
is equality there may be inference, but where there is not
equality there cannot be inference. A plain induction
will lead us to believe that *equality is the condition of
inference concerning quantity.* All the three axioms may
in fact be summed up in one, to the effect, that "*in
whatever relation one quantity stands to another, it stands
in the same relation to the equal of that other.*"

The active power is always the substitution of equals,
and it is an accident that in a pair of equalities we can
make the substitution in two ways. From $a = b = c$ we
can infer $a = c$, either by substituting in $a = b$ the value
of b as given in $b = c$, or else by substituting in $b = c$ the
value of b as given in $a = b$. In $a = b \sim d$ we can make
but the one substitution of a for b. In $e \sim f \sim g$ we can
make no substitution and get no inference.

In mathematics the relations in which terms may stand
to each other are far more varied than in pure logic, yet
our principle of substitution always holds true. We may
say in the most general manner that *In whatever relation
one quantity stands to another, it stands in the same relation
to the equal of that other.* In this axiom we sum up a
number of axioms which have been stated in more or less
detail by algebraists. Thus, " If equal quantities be added
to equal quantities, the sums will be equal." To explain
this, let

$$a = b, \qquad c = d.$$

Now $a + c$, whatever it means, must be identical with
itself, so that

$$a + c = a + c.$$

In one side of this equation substitute for the quantities
their equivalents, and we have the axiom proved

$$a + c = b + d.$$

The similar axiom concerning subtraction is equally evident, for whatever $a - c$ may mean it is equal to $a - c$,
and therefore by substitution to $b - d$. Again, "if equal
quantities be multiplied by the same or equal quantities,
the products will be equal." For evidently

$$ac = ac,$$

and if for c in one side we substitute its equal d, we have

$$ac = ad,$$

and a second similar substitution gives us

$$ac = bd.$$

We might prove a like axiom concerning division in an exactly similar manner. I might even extend the list of axioms and say that " Equal powers of equal numbers are equal." For certainly, whatever $a \times a \times a$ may mean, it is equal to $a \times a \times a$; hence by our usual substitution it is equal to $b \times b \times b$. The same will be true of roots of numbers and $\sqrt[c]{a} = \sqrt[d]{b}$ provided that the roots are so taken that the root of a shall really be related to a as the root of b is to b. The ambiguity of meaning of an an operation thus fails in any way to shake the universality of the principle. We may go further and assert that, not only the above common relations, but all other known or conceivable mathematical relations obey the same principle. Let Qa denote in the most general manner that we do something with the quantity a; then if $a = b$ it follows that

$$Qa = Qb.$$

The reader will also remember that one of the most frequent operations in mathematical reasoning is to substitute for a quantity its equal, as known either by assumed, natural, or self-evident conditions. Whenever a quantity appears twice over in a problem, we may apply what we learn of its relations in one place to its relations in the other. All reasoning in mathematics, as in other branches of science, thus involves the principle of treating equals equally, or similars similarly. In whatever way we employ quantitative reasoning in the remaining parts of this work, we never can desert the simple principle on which we first set out.

Reasoning by Inequalities.

I have stated that all the processes of mathematical reasoning may be deduced from the principle of substitution. Exceptions to this assertion may seem to exist in the use of inequalities. The greater of a greater is undoubtedly a greater, and what is less than a less is certainly less. Snowdon is higher than the Wrekin, and Ben Nevis than Snowdon; therefore Ben Nevis is higher than the Wrekin. But a little consideration discloses sufficient reason for believing that even in such cases, where equality does not apparently enter, the force of the reasoning entirely depends upon underlying and implied equalities.

In the first place, two statements of mere difference do not give any ground of inference. We learn nothing concerning the comparative heights of St. Paul's and Westminster Abbey from the assertions that they both differ in height from St. Peter's at Rome. We need something more than inequality; we require one identity in addition, namely the identity in direction of the two differences. Thus we cannot employ inequalities in the simple way in which we do equalities, and, when we try to express what other conditions are requisite, we find ourselves lapsing into the use of equalities or identities.

In the second place, every argument by inequalities may be represented in the form of equalities. We express that a is greater than b by the equation

$$a = b + p, \qquad (1)$$

where p is an intrinsically positive quantity, denoting the difference of a and b. Similarly we express that b is greater than c by the equation

$$b = c + q, \qquad (2)$$

and substituting for b in (1) its value in (2) we have

$$a = c + q + p. \qquad (3)$$

Now as p and q are both positive, it follows that a is greater than c, and we have the exact amount of excess specified. It will be easily seen that the reasoning concerning that which is less than a less will result in an equation of the form

$$c = a - r - s.$$

Every argument by inequalities may then be thrown into the form of an equality; but the converse is not true. We cannot possibly prove that two quantities are equal by merely asserting that they are both greater or both less than another quantity. From $e > f$ and $g > f$, or $e < f$ and $g < f$, we can infer no relation between e and g. And if the reader take the equations $x = y = 3$ and attempt to prove that therefore $x = 3$, by throwing them into inequalities, he will find it impossible to do so.

From these considerations I gather that reasoning in arithmetic or algebra by so-called inequalities, is only an imperfectly expressed reasoning by equalities, and when we want to exhibit exactly and clearly the conditions of reasoning, we are obliged to use equalities explicitly. Just as in pure logic a negative proposition, as expressing mere difference, cannot be the means of inference, so inequality can never really be the true ground of inference. I do not deny that affirmation and negation, agreement and difference, equality and inequality, are pairs of equally fundamental relations, but I assert that inference is possible only where affirmation, agreement, or equality, some species of identity in fact, is present, explicitly or implicitly.

Arithmetical Reasoning.

It may seem somewhat inconsistent that I assert number to arise out of difference or discrimination, and yet hold that no reasoning can be grounded on difference. Number, of course, opens a most wide sphere for inference, and a little consideration shows that this is due to the unlimited series of identities which spring up out of numerical abstraction. If six people are sitting on six chairs, there is no resemblance between the chairs and the people in logical character. But if we overlook all the qualities both of a chair and a person and merely remember that there are marks by which each of six chairs may be discriminated from the others, and similarly with the people, then there arises a resemblance between the chairs and the people, and this resemblance in number may be the ground of inference. If on another occasion the chairs are filled by people again, we may infer that these people resemble the others in number though they need not resemble them in any other points.

Groups of units are what we really treat in arithmetic. The number *five* is really $1 + 1 + 1 + 1 + 1$, but for the sake of conciseness we substitute the more compact sign 5, or the name *five*. These names being arbitrarily imposed in any one manner, an infinite variety of relations spring up between them which are not in the least arbitrary. If we define *four* as $1 + 1 + 1 + 1$, and *five* as $1 + 1 + 1 + 1 + 1$, then of course it follows that *five* = *four* + 1 ; but it would be equally possible to take this latter equality as a definition, in which case one of the former equalities would become an inference. It is

hardly requisite to decide how we define the names of
numbers, provided we remember that out of the infinitely
numerous relations of one number to others, some one
relation expressed in an equality must be a definition of
the number in question and the other relations immediately become necessary inferences.

In the science of number the variety of classes which
can be formed is altogether infinite, and statements of
perfect generality may be made subject only to difficulty
or exception at the lower end of the scale.   Every existing
number for instance belongs to the class $m + 7$; that is,
every number must be the sum of another number and
seven, except of course the first six or seven numbers,
negative quantities not being here taken into account.
Every number is the half of some other, and so on.   The
subject of generalization, as exhibited in mathematical
truths, is an infinitely wide one.   In number we are only
at the first step of an extensive series of generalizations.
As number is general compared with the particular things
numbered, so we have general symbols for numbers, and
general symbols for relations between undetermined
numbers.   There is an unlimited hierarchy of successive
generalizations.

Numerically Definite Reasoning.

It was first discovered by De Morgan that many arguments are valid which combine logical and numerical
reasoning, although they cannot be included in the
ancient logical formulas.   He developed the doctrine of
the " Numerically Definite Syllogism," fully explained in
his *Formal Logic* (pp. 141—170).   Boole also devoted
considerable attention to the determination of what he
called " Statistical Conditions," meaning the numerical
conditions of logical classes.   In a paper published among
the Memoirs of the Manchester Literary and Philosophical
Society, Third Series, vol. IV. p. 330 (Session 1869—70),
I have pointed out that we can apply arithmetical calculation to the Logical Alphabet.   Having given certain logical
conditions and the numbers of objects in certain classes,
we can either determine the numbers of objects in other
classes governed by those conditions, or can show what

further data are required to determine them. As an example of the kind of questions treated in numerical logic, and the mode of treatment, I give the following problem suggested by De Morgan, with my mode of representing its solution.

" For every man in the house there is a person who is aged; some of the men are not aged. It follows that some persons in the house are not men."[1]

Now let　　　　A = person in house,

　　　　　　　　B = male,

　　　　　　　　C = aged.

By enclosing a logical symbol in brackets, let us denote the number of objects belonging to the class indicated by the symbol. Thus let

　　　(A) = number of persons in house,

　　(AB) = number of male persons in house,

　(ABC) = number of aged male persons in house,

and so on. Now if we use w and w' to denote unknown numbers, the conditions of the problem may be thus stated according to my interpretation of the words—

$$(AB) = (AC) - w, \qquad (1)$$

that is to say, the number of persons in the house who are aged is at least equal to, and may exceed, the number of male persons in the house;

$$(ABc) = w', \qquad (2)$$

that is to say, the number of male persons in the house who are not aged is some unknown positive quantity.

If we develop the terms in (1) by the Law of Duality (pp. 74, 81, 89), we obtain

$$(ABC) + (ABc) = (ABC) + (AbC) - w.$$

Subtracting the common term (ABC) from each side and substituting for (ABc) its value as given in (2), we get at once

$$(AbC) = w + w',$$

and adding (Abc) to each side, we have

$$(Ab) = (Abc) + w + w'.$$

The meaning of this result is that the number of persons in the house who are not men is at least equal to $w + w'$, and exceeds it by the number of persons in the house who are neither men nor aged (Abc).

---

[1] *Syllabus of a Proposed System of Logic*, p. 29.

It should be understood that this solution applies only to the terms of the example quoted above, and not to the general problem for which De Morgan intended it to serve as an illustration.

As a second instance, let us take the following question :—The whole number of voters in a borough is a ; the number against whom objections have been lodged by liberals is b ; and the number against whom objections have been lodged by conservatives is c ; required the number, if any, who have been objected to on both sides. Taking

A = voter,
B = objected to by liberals,
C = objected to by conservatives,

then we require the value of (ABC). Now the following equation is identically true—

$$(ABC) = (AB) + (AC) + (Abc) - (A). \qquad (1)$$

For if we develop all the terms on the second side we obtain

$$(ABC) = (ABC) + (ABc) + (ABC) + (AbC) + (Abc)$$
$$- (ABC) - (ABc) - (AbC) - (Abc) ;$$

and striking out the corresponding positive and negative terms, we have left only   (ABC) = (ABC).   Since then (1) is necessarily true, we have only to insert the known values, and we have

$$(ABC) = b + c - a + (Abc).$$

Hence the number who have received objections from both sides is equal to the excess, if any, of the whole number of objections over the number of voters together with the number of voters who have received no objection (Abc).

The following problem illustrates the expression for the common part of any three classes :—The number of paupers who are blind males, is equal to the excess, if any, of the sum of the whole number of blind persons, added to the whole number of male persons, added to the number of those who being paupers are neither blind nor males, above the sum of the whole number of paupers added to the number of those who, not being paupers, are blind, and to the number of those who, not being paupers, are male.

The reader is requested to prove the truth of the above statement. (1) by his own unaided common sense ; (2) by

the Aristotelian Logic; (3) by the method of numerical
logic just expounded; and then to decide which method
is most satisfactory.

Numerical meaning of Logical Conditions.

In many cases classes of objects may exist under special logical conditions, and we must consider how these
conditions can be interpreted numerically. Every logical
proposition gives rise to a corresponding numerical
equation. Sameness of qualities occasions sameness of
numbers. Hence if

$$A = B$$

denotes the identity of the qualities of A and B, we may
conclude that

$$(A) = (B).$$

It is evident that exactly those objects, and those objects
only, which are comprehended under A must be comprehended under B. It follows that wherever we can draw
an equation of qualities, we can draw a similar equation
of numbers. Thus, from

$$A = B = C$$

we infer

$$A = C;$$

and similarly from

$$(A) = (B) = (C),$$

meaning that the numbers of A's and C's are equal to the
number of B's, we can infer

$$(A) = (C).$$

But, curiously enough, this does not apply to negative
propositions and inequalities. For if

$$A = B \sim D$$

means that A is identical with B, which differs from D, it
does not follow that

$$(A) = (B) \sim (D).$$

Two classes of objects may differ in qualities, and yet they
may agree in number. This point strongly confirms me
in the opinion which I have already expressed, that all
inference really depends upon equations, not differences.

The Logical Alphabet thus enables us to make a complete analysis of any numerical problem, and though the
symbolical statement may sometimes seem prolix, I con-

ceive that it really represents the course which the mind must follow in solving the question. Although thought may outstrip the rapidity with which the symbols can be written down, yet the mind does not really follow a different course from that indicated by the symbols. For a fuller explanation of this natural system of Numerically Definite Reasoning, with more abundant illustrations and an analysis of De Morgan's Numerically Definite Syllogism, I must refer the reader to the paper[1] in the Memoirs of the Manchester Literary and Philosophical Society, already mentioned, portions of which, however, have been embodied in the present section.

The reader may be referred, also, to Boole's writings upon the subject in the *Laws of Thought*, chap. xix. p. 295, and in a paper on "Propositions Numerically Definite," communicated by De Morgan, in 1868, to the Cambridge Philosophical Society, and printed in their *Transactions*," vol. xi. part ii.

---

[1] It has been pointed out to me by Mr. C. J. Monroe, that section 14 (p. 339) of this paper is erroneous, and ought to be cancelled. The problem concerning the number of paupers illustrates the answer which should have been obtained. Mr. A. J. Ellis, F.R.S., had previously observed that my solution in the paper of De Morgan's problem about "men in the house" did not answer the conditions intended by De Morgan, and I therefore give in the text a more satisfactory solution.

CHAPTER IX.

NATURE may be said to be evolved from the monotony
of non-existence by the creation of diversity. It is plausibly asserted that we are conscious only so far as we
experience difference. Life is change, and perfectly uniform existence would be no better than non-existence.
Certain it is that life demands incessant novelty, and that
nature, though it probably never fails to obey the same
fixed laws, yet presents to us an apparently unlimited
series of varied combinations of events. It is the work of
science to observe and record the kinds and comparative
numbers of such combinations of phenomena, occurring
spontaneously or produced by our interference. Patient
and skilful examination of the records may then disclose
the laws imposed on matter at its creation, and enable us
more or less successfully to predict, or even to regulate,
the future occurrence of any particular combination.

The Laws of Thought are the first and most important
of all the laws which govern the combinations of phenomena, and, though they be binding on the mind, they
may also be regarded as verified in the external world.
The Logical Alphabet develops the utmost variety of
things and events which may occur, and it is evident that
as each new quality is introduced, the number of combinations is doubled. Thus four qualities may occur in 16
combinations; five qualities in 32; six qualities in 64;
and so on. In general language, if n be the number of
qualities, 2^n is the number of varieties of things which

may be formed from them, if there be no conditions but those of logic. This number, it need hardly be said, increases after the first few terms, in an extraordinary manner, so that it would require 302 figures to express the number of combinations in which 1,000 qualities might conceivably present themselves.

If all the combinations allowed by the Laws of Thought occurred indifferently in nature, then science would begin and end with those laws. To observe nature would give us no additional knowledge, because no two qualities would in the long run be oftener associated than any other two. We could never predict events with more certainty than we now predict the throws of dice, and experience would be without use. But the universe, as actually created, presents a far different and much more interesting problem. The most superficial observation shows that some things are constantly associated with other things. The more mature our examination, the more we become convinced that each event depends upon the prior occurrence of some other series of events. Action and reaction are gradually discovered to underlie the whole scene, and an independent or casual occurrence does not exist except in appearance. Even dice as they fall are surely determined in their course by prior conditions and fixed laws. Thus the combinations of events which can really occur are found to be comparatively restricted, and it is the work of science to detect these restricting conditions.

In the English alphabet, for instance, we have twenty-six letters. Were the combinations of such letters perfectly free, so that any letter could be indifferently sounded with any other, the number of words which could be formed without any repetition would be $2^{26} - 1$, or 67,108,863, equal in number to the combinations of the twenty-seventh column of the Logical Alphabet, excluding one for the case in which all the letters would be absent. But the formation of our vocal organs prevents us from using the far greater part of these conjunctions of letters. At least one vowel must be present in each word; more than two consonants cannot usually be brought together; and to produce words capable of smooth utterance a number of other rules must be observed. To determine exactly how many words might exist in the English language under these circumstances, would be an exceedingly complex problem, the solution of which has never been attempted. The number of existing English words may perhaps be said not to exceed one hundred thousand, and it is only by investigating the combinations presented in the dictionary, that we can learn the Laws of Euphony or calculate the possible number of words. In this example we have an epitome of the work and method of science. The combinations of natural phenomena are limited by a great number of conditions which are in no way brought to our knowledge except so far as they are disclosed in the examination of nature.

It is often a very difficult matter to determine the numbers of permutations or combinations which may exist under various restrictions. Many learned men puzzled themselves in former centuries over what were called Protean verses, or verses admitting many variations in accordance with the Laws of Metre. The most celebrated of these verses was that invented by Bernard Bauhusius, as follows : [1]—

"Tot tibi sunt dotes, Virgo, quot sidera cœlo."

One author, Ericius Puteanus, filled forty-eight pages of a work in reckoning up its possible transpositions, making them only 1022. Other calculators gave 2196, 3276, 2580 as their results. Wallis assigned 3096, but without much confidence in the accuracy of his result.[2] It required the skill of James Bernoulli to decide that the number of transpositions was 3312, under the condition that the sense and metre of the verse shall be perfectly preserved.

In approaching the consideration of the great Inductive problem, it is very necessary that we should acquire correct notions as to the comparative numbers of combinations which may exist under different circumstances. The doctrine of combinations is that part of mathematical science which applies numerical calculation to determine the numbers of combinations under various conditions. It is a part of the science which really lies at the base not nly of other sciences, but of other branches of mathe-

---

[1] Montucla, *Histoire*, &c., vol. iii. p. 388.
[2] Wallis, *Of Combinations*, &c., p. 119.

matics. The forms of algebraical expressions are determined by the principles of combination, and Hindenburg
recognised this fact in his Combinatorial Analysis. The
greatest mathematicians have, during the last three centuries, given their best powers to the treatment of this
subject ; it was the favourite study of Pascal ; it early
attracted the attention of Leibnitz, who wrote his curious
essay, *De Arte Combinatoria*, at twenty years of age ; James
Bernoulli, one of the very profoundest mathematicians,
devoted no small part of his life to the investigation of the
subject, as connected with that of Probability ; and in his
celebrated work, *De Arte Conjectandi*, he has so finely
described the importance of the doctrine of combinations,
that I need offer no excuse for quoting his remarks at full
length.

" It is easy to perceive that the prodigious variety which
appears both in the works of nature and in the actions of
men, and which constitutes the greatest part of the beauty
of the universe, is owing to the multitude of different ways
in which its several parts are mixed with, or placed near,
each other.   But, because the number of causes that concur
in producing a given event, or effect, is oftentimes so immensely great, and the causes themselves are so different
one from another, that it is extremely difficult to reckon up
all the different ways in which they may be arranged or
combined together, it often happens that men, even of the
best understandings and greatest circumspection, are guilty
of that fault in reasoning which the writers on logic call
the insufficient or imperfect enumeration of parts or cases :
insomuch that I will venture to assert, that this is the
chief, and almost the only, source of the vast number of
erroneous opinions, and those too very often in matters
of great importance, which we are apt to form on all the
subjects we reflect upon, whether they relate to the knowledge of nature, or the merits and motives of human
actions.

It must therefore be acknowledged, that that art which
affords a cure to this weakness, or defect, of our understandings, and teaches us so to enumerate all the possible
ways in which a given number of things may be mixed
and combined together, that we may be certain that we
have not omitted any one arrangement of them that can

lead to the object of our inquiry, deserves to be considered as most eminently useful and worthy of our highest esteem and attention. And this is the business of *the art or doctrine of combinations.* Nor is this art or doctrine to be considered merely as a branch of the mathematical sciences. For it has a relation to almost every species of useful knowledge that the mind of man can be employed upon. It proceeds indeed upon mathematical principles, in calculating the number of the combinations of the things proposed : but by the conclusions that are obtained by it, the sagacity of the natural philosopher, the exactness of the historian, the skill and judgment of the physician, and the prudence and foresight of the politician may be assisted ; because the business of all these important professions is but *to form reasonable conjectures* concerning the several objects which engage their attention, and all wise conjectures are the results of a just and careful examination of the several different effects that may possibly arise from the causes that are capable of producing them." [1]

Distinction of Combinations and Permutations.

We must first consider the deep difference which exists between Combinations and Permutations, a difference involving important logical principles, and influencing the form of mathematical expressions. In *permutation* we recognise varieties of order, treating AB as a different group from BA. In *combination* we take notice only of the presence or absence of a certain thing, and pay no regard to its place in order of time or space. Thus the four letters *a, e, m, n* can form but one combination, but they occur in language in several permutations, as *name, amen, mean, mane.*

We have hitherto been dealing with purely logical questions, involving only combination of qualities. I have fully pointed out in more than one place that, though our symbols could not but be written in order of place and read in order of time, the relations expressed had no regard to place or time (pp. 33, 114). The Law of Commutativeness, in fact, expresses the condition that in logic we deal with

---

[1] James Bernoulli, *De Arte Conjectandi,* translated by Baron Maseres. London, 1795, pp. 35, 36.

combinations, and the same law is true of all the processes of algebra. In some cases, order may be a matter of indifference; it makes no difference, for instance, whether gunpowder is a mixture of sulphur, carbon, and nitre, or carbon, nitre, and sulphur, or nitre, sulphur, and carbon, provided that the substances are present in proper proportions and well mixed. But this indifference of order does not usually extend to the events of physical science or the operations of art. The change of mechanical energy into heat is not exactly the same as the change from heat into mechanical energy; thunder does not indifferently precede and follow lightning; it is a matter of some importance that we load, cap, present, and fire a rifle in this precise order. Time is the condition of all our thoughts, space of all our actions, and therefore both in art and science we are to a great extent concerned with permutations. Language, for instance, treats different permutations of letters as having different meanings.

Permutations of things are far more numerous than combinations of those things, for the obvious reason that each distinct thing is regarded differently according to its place. Thus the letters A, B, C, will make different permutations according as A stands first, second, or third; having decided the place of A, there are two places between which we may choose for B; and then there remains but one place for C. Accordingly the permutations of these letters will be altogether $3 \times 2 \times 1$ or 6 in number. With four things or letters, A, B, C, D, we shall have four choices of place for the first letter, three for the second, two for the third, and one for the fourth, so that there will be altogether, $4 \times 3 \times 2 \times 1$, or 24 permutations. The same simple rule applies in all cases; beginning with the whole number of things we multiply at each step by a number decreased by a unit. In general language, if n be the number of things in a combination, the number of permutations is

$$n \,(n - 1) \,(n - 2) \ldots \ldots 4 \cdot 3 \cdot 2 \cdot 1.$$

If we were to re-arrange the names of the days of the week, the possible arrangements out of which we should have to choose the new order, would be no less than $7 \cdot 6 \cdot 5 \cdot 4 \cdot 3 \cdot 2 \cdot 1$, or 5040, or, excluding the existing order, 5039.

The reader will see that the numbers which we reach in questions of permutation, increase in a more extraordinary manner even than in combination. Each new object or term doubles the number of combinations, but increases the permutations by a factor continually growing. Instead of $2 \times 2 \times 2 \times 2 \times \ldots$ we have $2 \times 3 \times 4 \times 5 \times \ldots$ and the products of the latter expression immensely exceed those of the former. These products of increasing factors are frequently employed, as we shall see, in questions both of permutation and combination. They are technically called *factorials*, that is to say, the product of all integer numbers, from unity up to any number n is the *factorial* of n, and is often indicated symbolically by $\lfloor n$. I give below the factorials up to that of twelve :—

$$
\begin{aligned}
24 &= 1 . 2 . 3 . 4 \\
120 &= 1 . 2 . \ldots 5 \\
720 &= 1 . 2 . \ldots 6 \\
5,040 &= \lfloor 7 \\
40,320 &= \lfloor 8 \\
362,880 &= \lfloor 9 \\
3,628,800 &= \lfloor 10 \\
39,916,800 &= \lfloor 11 \\
479,001,600 &= \lfloor 12
\end{aligned}
$$

The factorials up to $\lfloor 36$ are given in Rees's ' Cyclopædia, art. *Cipher*, and the logarithms of factorials up to $\lfloor 265$ are to be found at the end of the table of logarithms published under the superintendence of the Society for the Diffusion of Useful Knowledge (p. 215). To express the factorial $\lfloor 265$ would require 529 places of figures.

Many writers have from time to time remarked upon the extraordinary magnitude of the numbers with which we deal in this subject. Tacquet calculated [1] that the twenty-four letters of the alphabet may be arranged in more than 620 thousand trillions of orders ; and Schott estimated [2] that if a thousand millions of men were employed for the same number of years in writing out these arrangements, and each man filled each day forty pages with forty arrangements in each, they would not have accomplished the task, as they would have written only 584 thousand trillions instead of 620 thousand trillions.

[1] *Arithmeticæ Theoria.* Ed. Amsterd. 1704. p 517.
[2] Rees's *Cyclopædia*, art. *Cipher*.

In some questions the number of permutations may be
restricted and reduced by various conditions. Some
things in a group may be undistinguishable from others,
so that change of order will produce no difference. Thus
if we were to permutate the letters of the name *Ann*,
according to our previous rule, we should obtain 3 × 2 × 1,
or 6 orders ; but half of these arrangements would be
identical with the other half, because the interchange of
the two *n*'s has no effect. The really different orders will
therefore be $\frac{3 \cdot 2 \cdot 1}{1 \cdot 2}$ or 3, namely *Ann, Nan, Nna.* In
the word *utility* there are two *i*'s and two *t*'s, in respect
of both of which pairs the numbers of permutations must
be halved. Thus we obtain $\frac{7 \cdot 6 \cdot 5 \cdot 4 \cdot 3 \cdot 2 \cdot 1}{1 \cdot 2 \cdot 1 \cdot 2}$ or 1260, as
the number of permutations. The simple rule evidently
is — when some things or letters are undistinguished,
proceed in the first place to calculate all the possible
permutations as if all were different, and then divide by
the numbers of possible permutations of those series of
things which are not distinguished, and of which the
permutations have therefore been counted in excess.
Thus since the word *Utilitarianism* contains fourteen
letters, of which four are *i*'s, two *a*'s, and two *t*'s, the
number of distinct arrangements will be found by
dividing the factorial of 14, by the factorials of 4, 2,
and 2, the result being 908,107,200. From the letters
of the word *Mississippi* we can get in like manner
$\frac{\lfloor 11}{\lfloor 4 \times \lfloor 4 \times \lfloor 2}$ or 34,650 permutations, which is not the one-
thousandth part of what we should obtain were all the
letters different.

Calculation of Number of Combinations.

Although in many questions both of art and science
we need to calculate the number of permutations on
account of their own interest, it far more frequently
happens in scientific subjects that they possess but an
indirect interest. As I have already pointed out, we
almost always deal in the logical and mathematical
sciences with *combinations,* and variety of order enters

only through the inherent imperfections of our symbols and modes of calculation. Signs must be used in some order, and we must withdraw our attention from this order before the signs correctly represent the relations of things which exist neither before nor after each other. Now, it often happens that we cannot choose all the combinations of things, without first choosing them subject to the accidental variety of order, and we must then divide by the number of possible variations of order, that we may get to the true number of pure combinations.

Suppose that we wish to determine the number of ways in which we can select a group of three letters out of the alphabet, without allowing the same letter to be repeated. At the first choice we can take any one of 26 letters; at the next step there remain 25 letters, any one of which may be joined with that already taken; at the third step there will be 24 choices, so that apparently the whole number of ways of choosing is 26 × 25 × 24. But the fact that one choice succeeded another has caused us to obtain the same combinations of letters in different orders; we should get, for instance, a, p, r at one time, and p, r, a at another, and every three distinct letters will appear six times over, because three things can be arranged in six permutations. To get the number of combinations, then, we must divide the whole number of ways of choosing, by six, the number of permutations of three things, obtaining $\dfrac{26 \times 25 \times 24}{1 \times 2 \times 3}$ or 2,600.

It is apparent that we need the doctrine of combinations in order that we may in many questions counteract the exaggerating effect of successive selection. If out of a senate of 30 persons we have to choose a committee of 5, we may choose any of 30 first, any of 29 next, and so on, in fact there will be 30 × 29 × 28 × 27 × 26 selections; but as the actual character of the members of the committee will not be affected by the accidental order of their selection, we divide by 1 × 2 × 3 × 4 × 5, and the possible number of different committees will be 142,506. Similarly if we want to calculate the number of ways in which the eight major planets may come into conjunction, it is evident that they may meet either two at a time or three at a time, or four or more at a time, and as nothing is said as to

the relative order or place in the conjunction, we require
the number of combinations. Now a selection of 2 out of 8
is possible in $\frac{8.7}{1.2}$ or 28 ways; of 3 out of 8 in $\frac{8.7.6}{1.2.3}$
or 56 ways; of 4 out of 8 in $\frac{8.7.6.5}{1.2.3.4}$ or 70 ways; and it
may be similarly shown that for 5, 6, 7, and 8 planets,
meeting at one time, the numbers of ways are 56, 28, 8,
and 1. Thus we have solved the whole question of the
variety of conjunctions of eight planets; and adding all the
numbers together, we find that 247 is the utmost possible
number of modes of meeting.

In general algebraic language, we may say that a group
of m things may be chosen out of a total number of n
things, in a number of combinations denoted by the
formula

$$\frac{n \cdot (n-1)\,(n-2)\,(n-3)\ldots\ldots(n-m+1)}{1 \cdot 2 \cdot 3 \cdot 4 \ldots\ldots m}$$

The extreme importance and significance of this formula
seems to have been first adequately recognised by Pascal,
although its discovery is attributed by him to a friend, M.
de Ganières.[1] We shall find it perpetually recurring in
questions both of combinations and probability, and
throughout the formulæ of mathematical analysis traces
of its influence may be noticed.

The Arithmetical Triangle.

The Arithmetical Triangle is a name long since given to
a series of remarkable numbers connected with the subject
we are treating. According to Montucla [2] " this triangle is
in the theory of combinations and changes of order, almost
what the table of Pythagoras is in ordinary arithmetic, that
is to say, it places at once under the eyes the numbers required in a multitude of cases of this theory." As early
as 1544 Stifels had noticed the remarkable properties of
these numbers and the mode of their evolution. Briggs,
the inventor of the common system of logarithms, was so
struck with their importance that he called them the

---

[1] *Œuvres Complètes de Pascal* (1865), vol. iii. p. 302. Montucla
states the name as De Gruières, *Histoire des Mathématiques*, vol. iii.
p. 389.

[2] *Histoire des Mathématiques*, vol. iii. p. 378.

Abacus Panchrestus. Pascal, however, was the first who wrote a distinct treatise on these numbers, and gave them the name by which they are still known. But Pascal did not by any means exhaust the subject, and it remained for James Bernoulli to demonstrate fully the importance of the *figurate numbers*, as they are also called. In his treatise *De Arte Conjectandi*, he points out their application in the theory of combinations and probabilities, and remarks of the Arithmetical Triangle, " It not only contains the clue to the mysterious doctrine of combinations, but it is also the ground or foundation of most of the important and abstruse discoveries that have been made in the other branches of the mathematics." [1]

The numbers of the triangle can be calculated in a very easy manner by successive additions. We commence with unity at the apex; in the next line we place a second unit to the right of this; to obtain the third line of figures we move the previous line one place to the right, and add them to the same figures as they were before removal; we can then repeat the same process *ad infinitum*. The fourth line of figures, for instance, contains ı, 3, 3, ı; moving them one place and adding as directed we obtain :—

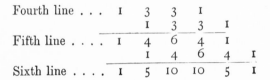

```
Fourth line . . .   ı    3    3    ı
                         ı    3    3    ı
Fifth line . . . .  ı    4    6    4    ı
                         ı    4    6    4    ı
Sixth line . . . .  ı    5   10   10    5    ı
```

Carrying out this simple process through ten more steps we obtain the first seventeen lines of the Arithmetical Triangle as printed on the next page. Theoretically speaking the Triangle must be regarded as infinite in extent, but the numbers increase so rapidly that it soon becomes impracticable to continue the table. The longest table of the numbers which I have found is in Fortia's " Traité des Progressions " (p. 80), where they are given up to the fortieth line and the ninth column.

[1] Bernoulli, *De Arte Conjectandi*, translated by Francis Maseres. London, 1795, p. 75.

THE ARITHMETICAL TRIANGLE.

Line.	First Column.	Second Column.	Third Column.	Fourth Column.	Fifth Column.	Sixth Column.	Seventh Column.	Eighth Column.	Ninth Column.	Tenth Column.	Eleventh Column.	Twelfth Column.	Thirteenth Column.	Fourteenth Column.	Fifteenth Column.	Sixteenth Column.	Seventeenth Col.
1	1																
2	1	1															
3	1	2	1														
4	1	3	3	1													
5	1	4	6	4	1												
6	1	5	10	10	5	1											
7	1	6	15	20	15	6	1										
8	1	7	21	35	35	21	7	1									
9	1	8	28	56	70	56	28	8	1								
10	1	9	36	84	126	126	84	36	9	1							
11	1	10	45	120	210	252	210	120	45	10	1						
12	1	11	55	165	330	462	462	330	165	55	11	1					
13	1	12	66	220	495	792	924	792	495	220	66	12	1				
14	1	13	78	286	715	1287	1716	1716	1287	715	286	78	13	1			
15	1	14	91	364	1001	2002	3003	3432	3003	2002	1001	364	91	14	1		
16	1	15	105	455	1365	3003	5005	6435	6435	5005	3003	1365	455	105	15	1	
17	1	16	120	560	1820	4368	8008	11440	12870	11440	8008	4368	1820	560	120	16	1

Examining these numbers, we find that they are connected by an unlimited series of relations, a few of the
more simple of which may be noticed. Each vertical
column of numbers exactly corresponds with an oblique
series descending from left to right, so that the triangle is
perfectly symmetrical in its contents. The first column
contains only *units;* the second column contains the
natural numbers, 1, 2, 3, &c.; the third column contains
a remarkable series of numbers, 1, 3, 6, 10, 15, &c.,
which have long been called *the triangular numbers,*
because they
correspond with the numbers of balls which may be
arranged in a triangular form, thus—

```
                                         o
                           o           o o
             o           o o         o o o
 o         o o         o o o       o o o o
o   o o   o o o   o o o o   o o o o o
```

The fourth column contains the *pyramidal numbers,* so
called because they correspond to the numbers of equal
balls which can be piled in regular triangular pyramids.
Their differences are the triangular numbers. The numbers
of the fifth column have the pyramidal numbers for their
differences, but as there is no regular figure of which they
express the contents, they have been arbitrarily called the
trianguli-triangular numbers. The succeeding columns
have, in a similar manner, been said to contain the
trianguli-pyramidal, the *pyramidi-pyramidal* numbers,
and so on.[1]

From the mode of formation of the table, it follows that
the differences of the numbers in each column will be
found in the preceding column to the left. Hence the
second differences, or the *differences of differences,* will be
in the second column to the left of any given column, the
third differences in the third column, and so on. Thus
we may say that unity which appears in the first column
is the *first difference* of the numbers in the second column ;
the *second difference* of those in the third column ; the *third*
difference of those in the fourth, and so on. The triangle
is seen to be a complete classification of all numbers
according as they have unity for any of their differences.

Since each line is formed by adding the previous line

[1] Wallis's *Algebra,* Discourse of Combinations, &c., p. 109.

to itself, it is evident that the sum of the numbers in each horizontal line must be double the sum of the numbers in the line next above. Hence we know, without making the additions, that the successive sums must be 1, 2, 4, 8, 16, 32, 64, &c., the same as the numbers of combinations in the Logical Alphabet. Speaking generally, the sum of the numbers in the nth line will be 2^{n-1}.

Again, if the whole of the numbers down to any line be added together, we shall obtain a number less by unity than some power of 2; thus, the first line gives 1 or $2^1 - 1$; the first two lines give 3 or $2^2 - 1$; the first three lines 7 or $2^3 - 1$; the first six lines give 63 or $2^6 - 1$; or, speaking in general language, the sum of the first n lines is $2^n - 1$. It follows that the sum of the numbers in any one line is equal to the sum of those in all the preceding lines increased by a unit. For the sum of the nth line is, as already shown, 2^{n-1}, and the sum of the first $n-1$ lines is $2^{n-1} - 1$, or less by a unit.

This account of the properties of the figurate numbers does not approach completeness; a considerable, probably an unlimited, number of less simple and obvious relations might be traced out. Pascal, after giving many of the properties, exclaims[1]: "Mais j'en laisse bien plus que je n'en donne; c'est une chose étrange combien il est fertile en propriétés! Chacun peut s'y exercer." The arithmetical triangle may be considered a natural classification of numbers, exhibiting, in the most complete manner, their evolution and relations in a certain point of view. It is obvious that in an unlimited extension of the triangle, each number, with the single exception of the number *two*, has at least two places.

Though the properties above explained are highly curious, the greatest value of the triangle arises from the fact that it contains a complete statement of the values of the formula (p. 182), for the numbers of combinations of m things out of n, for all possible values of m and n. Out of seven things one may be chosen in seven ways, and seven occurs in the eighth line of the second column. The combinations of two things chosen out of seven are $\dfrac{7 \times 6}{1 \times 2}$ or 21, which is the third number in the eighth

[1] *Œuvres Complètes*, vol. iii. p. 251.

line. The combinations of three things out of seven are $\frac{7 \times 6 \times 5}{1 \times 2 \times 3}$ or 35, which appears fourth in the eighth line. In a similar manner, in the fifth, sixth, seventh, and eighth columns of the eighth line I find it stated in how many ways I can select combinations of 4, 5, 6, and 7 things out of 7. Proceeding to the ninth line, I find in succession the number of ways in which I can select 1, 2, 3, 4, 5, 6, 7, and 8 things, out of 8 things. In general language, if I wish to know in how many ways m things can be selected in combinations out of n things, I must look in the $n + 1^{\text{th}}$ line, and take the $m + 1^{\text{th}}$ number, as the answer. In how many ways, for instance, can a sub-committee of five be chosen out of a committee of nine. The answer is 126, and is the sixth number in the tenth line; it will be found equal to $\frac{9 \cdot 8 \cdot 7 \cdot 6 \cdot 5}{1 \cdot 2 \cdot 3 \cdot 4 \cdot 5}$, which our formula (p. 182) gives.

The full utility of the figurate numbers will be more apparent when we reach the subject of probabilities, but I may give an illustration or two in this place. In how many ways can we arrange four pennies as regards head and tail ? The question amounts to asking in how many ways we can select 0, 1, 2, 3, or 4 heads, out of 4 heads, and the *fifth* line of the triangle gives us the complete answer, thus—

We can select No head and 4 tails in 1 way.
  „   1 head and 3 tails in 4 ways.
  „   2 heads and 2 tails in 6 ways.
  „   3 heads and 1 tail in 4 ways.
  „   4 heads and 0 tail in 1 way.

The total number of different cases is 16, or 2^4, and when we come to the next chapter, it will be found that these numbers give us the respective probabilities of all throws with four pennies.

I gave in p. 181 a calculation of the number of ways in which eight planets can meet in conjunction ; the reader will find all the numbers detailed in the ninth line of the arithmetical triangle. The sum of the whole line is 2^8 or 256; but we must subtract a unit for the case where no planet appears, and 8 for the 8 cases in which only one planet appears ; so that the total number of conjunctions is $2^8 - 1 - 8$ or 247. If an organ has eleven stops we find in the twelfth line the numbers of ways in which we can draw them, 1, 2, 3, or more at a time. Thus there are 462 ways of drawing five stops at once, and as many of drawing six stops. The total number of ways of varying the sound is 2048, including the single case in which no stop at all is drawn.

One of the most important scientific uses of the arithmetical triangle consists in the information which it gives concerning the comparative frequency of divergencies from an average. Suppose, for the sake of argument, that all persons were naturally of the equal stature of five feet, but enjoyed during youth seven independent chances of growing one inch in addition. Of these seven chances, one, two, three, or more, may happen favourably to any individual; but, as it does not matter what the chances are, so that the inch is gained, the question really turns upon the number of combinations of 0, 1, 2, 3, &c., things out of seven. Hence the eighth line of the triangle gives us a complete answer to the question, as follows:—

Out of every 128 people—

			Feet	Inches.
One person would have the stature of			5	0
7 persons	„	„	5	1
21 persons	„	„	5	2
35 persons	„	„	5	3
35 persons	„	„	5	4
21 persons	„	„	5	5
7 persons	„	„	5	6
1 person	„	„	5	7

By taking a proper line of the triangle, an answer may be had under any more natural supposition. This theory of comparative frequency of divergence from an average, was first adequately noticed by Quetelet, and has lately been employed in a very interesting and bold manner by Mr. Francis Galton,[1] in his remarkable work on "Hereditary Genius." We shall afterwards find that the theory of error, to which is made the ultimate appeal in cases of quantitative investigation, is founded upon the

[1] See also Galton's Lecture at the Royal Institution, 27th February, 1874; Catalogue of the Special Loan Collection of Scientific Instruments, South Kensington, Nos. 48, 49; and Galton, *Philosophical Magazine*, January 1875.

comparative numbers of combinations as displayed in the triangle.

Connection between the Arithmetical Triangle and the Logical Alphabet.

There exists a close connection between the arithmetical triangle described in the last section, and the series of combinations of letters called the Logical Alphabet. The one is to mathematical science what the other is to logical science. In fact the figurate numbers, or those exhibited in the triangle, are obtained by summing up the logical combinations. Accordingly, just as the total of the numbers in each line of the triangle is twice as great as that for the preceding line (p. 186), so each column of the Alphabet (p. 94) contains twice as many combinations as the preceding one. The like correspondence also exists between the sums of all the lines of figures down to any particular line, and of the combinations down to any particular column.

By examining any column of the Logical Alphabet we find that the combinations naturally group themselves according to the figurate numbers. Take the combinations of the letters A, B, C, D; they consist of all the ways in which I can choose four, three, two, one, or none of the four letters, filling up the vacant spaces with negative terms.

There is one combination, ABCD, in which all the positive letters are present; there are four combinations in each of which three positive letters are present; six in which two are present; four in which only one is present; and, finally, there is the single case, abcd, in which all positive letters are absent. These numbers, 1, 4, 6, 4, 1, are those of the fifth line of the arithmetical triangle, and a like correspondence will be found to exist in each column of the Logical Alphabet.

Numerical abstraction, it has been asserted, consists in overlooking the kind of difference, and retaining only a consciousness of its existence (p. 158). While in logic, then, we have to deal with each combination as a separate kind of thing, in arithmetic we distinguish only the classes which depend upon more or less positive terms being present, and the numbers of these classes immediately produce the numbers of the arithmetical triangle.

It may here be pointed out that there are two modes in which we can calculate the whole number of combinations of certain things. Either we may take the whole number at once as shown in the Logical Alphabet, in which case the number will be some power of two, or else we may calculate successively, by aid of permutations, the number of combinations of none, one, two, three things, and so on. Hence we arrive at a necessary identity between two series of numbers. In the case of four things we shall have

$$2 = 1 + \frac{4}{1} + \frac{4 \cdot 3}{1 \cdot 2} + \frac{4 \cdot 3 \cdot 2}{1 \cdot 2 \cdot 3} + \frac{4 \cdot 3 \cdot 2 \cdot 1}{1 \cdot 2 \cdot 3 \cdot 4}.$$

In a general form of expression we shall have

$$2 = 1 + \frac{n}{1} + \frac{n \cdot (n-1)}{1 \cdot 2} + \frac{n (n-1)(n-2)}{1 \cdot 2 \cdot 3} + \&c.,$$

the terms being continued until they cease to have any value. Thus we arrive at a proof of simple cases of the Binomial Theorem, of which each column of the Logical Alphabet is an exemplification. It may be shown that all other mathematical expansions likewise arise out of simple processes of combination, but the more complete consideration of this subject must be deferred to another work.

Possible Variety of Nature and Art.

We cannot adequately understand the difficulties which beset us in certain branches of science, unless we have some clear idea of the vast numbers of combinations or permutations which may be possible under certain conditions. Thus only can we learn how hopeless it would be to attempt to treat nature in detail, and exhaust the whole number of events which might arise. It is instructive to consider, in the first place, how immensely great are the numbers of combinations with which we deal in many arts and amusements.

In dealing a pack of cards, the number of hands, of thirteen cards each, which can be produced is evidently $52 \times 51 \times 50 \times \ldots \times 40$ divided by $1 \times 2 \times 3 \ldots \times 13$. or 635,013,559,600. But in whist four hands are simul-

taneously held, and the number of distinct deals becomes
so vast that it would require twenty-eight figures to express
it. If the whole population of the world, say one thousand
millions of persons, were to deal cards day and night, for
a hundred million of years, they would not in that time
have exhausted one hundred-thousandth part of the possible deals. Even with the same hands of cards the play
may be almost infinitely varied, so that the complete
variety of games at whist which may exist is almost
incalculably great. It is in the highest degree improbable
that any one game of whist was ever exactly like another,
except it were intentionally so.

The end of novelty in art might well be dreaded, did
we not find that nature at least has placed no attainable
limit, and that the deficiency will lie in our inventive
faculties. It would be a cheerless time indeed when all
possible varieties of melody were exhausted, but it is
readily shown that if a peal of twenty-four bells had been
rung continuously from the so-called beginning of the
world to the present day, no approach could have been
made to the completion of the possible changes. Nay,
had every single minute been prolonged to 10,000 years,
still the task would have been unaccomplished.[1] As
regards ordinary melodies, the eight notes of a single
octave give more than 40,000 permutations, and two
octaves more than a million millions. If we were to take
into account the semitones, it would become apparent that
it is impossible to exhaust the variety of music. When
the late Mr. J. S Mill, in a depressed state of mind, feared
the approaching exhaustion of musical melodies, he had
certainly not bestowed sufficient study on the subject of
permutations.

Similar considerations apply to the possible number of
natural substances, though we cannot always give precise
numerical results. It was recommended by Hatchett [2]
that a systematic examination of all alloys of metals
should be carried out, proceeding from the binary ones to
more complicated ternary or quaternary ones. He can
hardly have been aware of the extent of his proposed

---

[1] Wallis, *Of Combinations*, p. 116, quoting Vossius.
[2] *Philosophical Transactions* (1803), vol. xciii. p. 193.

inquiry. If we operate only upon thirty of the known
metals, the number of binary alloys would be 435, of
ternary alloys 4060, of quaternary 27,405, without paying
regard to the varying proportions of the metals, and only
regarding the kind of metal. If we varied all the ternary
alloys by quantities not less than one per cent., the
number of these alloys would be 11,445,060. An exhaustive investigation of the subject is therefore out of
the question, and unless some laws connecting the properties of the alloy and its components can be discovered, it
is not apparent how our knowledge of them can ever be
more than fragmentary.

The possible variety of definite chemical compounds,
again, is enormously great. Chemists have already examined many thousands of inorganic substances, and a
still greater number of organic compounds;[1] they have
nevertheless made no appreciable impression on the
number which may exist. Taking the number of elements at sixty-one, the number of compounds containing different selections of four elements each would
be more than half a million (521,855). As the same
elements often combine in many different proportions
and some of them, especially carbon, have the power of
forming an almost endless number of compounds, it
would hardly be possible to assign any limit to the
number of chemical compounds which may be formed.
There are branches of physical science, therefore, of which
it is unlikely that scientific men, with all their industry,
can ever obtain a knowledge in any appreciable degree
approaching to completeness.

Higher Orders of Variety.

The consideration of the facts already given in this
chapter will not produce an adequate notion of the possible variety of existence, unless we consider the comparative numbers of combinations of different orders. By
a combination of a higher order, I mean a combination
of groups, which are themselves groups. The immense
numbers of compounds of carbon, hydrogen, and oxygen,

[1] Hofmann's *Introduction to Chemistry*, p. 36.

described in organic chemistry, are combinations of a second order, for the atoms are groups of groups. The wave of sound produced by a musical instrument may be regarded as a combination of motions; the body of sound proceeding from a large orchestra is therefore a complex aggregate of sounds, each in itself a complex combination of movements. All literature may be said to be developed out of the difference of white paper and black ink. From the unlimited number of marks which might be chosen we select twenty-six conventional letters. The pronounceable combinations of letters are probably some trillions in number. Now, as a sentence is a selection of words, the possible sentences must be inconceivably more numerous than the words of which it may be composed. A book is a combination of sentences, and a library is a combination of books. A library, therefore, may be regarded as a combination of the fifth order, and the powers of numerical expression would be severely tasked in attempting to express the number of distinct libraries which might be constructed. The calculation, of course, would not be possible, because the union of letters in words, of words in sentences, and of sentences in books, is governed by conditions so complex as to defy analysis. I wish only to point out that the infinite variety of literature, existing or possible, is all developed out of one fundamental difference. Galileo remarked that all truth is contained in the compass of the alphabet. He ought to have said that it is all contained in the difference of ink and paper.

One consequence of successive combination is that the simplest marks will suffice to express any information. Francis Bacon proposed for secret writing a biliteral cipher, which resolves all letters of the alphabet into permutations of the two letters a and b. Thus A was *aaaaa*, B *aaaab*, X *babab*, and so on.[1] In a similar way, as Bacon clearly saw, any one difference can be made the ground of a code of signals; we can express, as he says, *omnia per omnia*. The Morse alphabet uses only a succession of long and short marks, and other systems of telegraphic language employ right and left strokes A single lamp obscured at various intervals, long or

---

[1] *Works*, edited by Shaw, vol. i. pp. 141—145, quoted in Rees' *Encyclopædia*. art. *Cipher*.

short, may be made to spell out any words, and with two lamps, distinguished by colour, position, or any other circumstance, we could at once represent Bacon's biliteral alphabet. Babbage ingeniously suggested that every lighthouse in the world should be made to spell out its own name or number perpetually, by flashes or obscurations of various duration and succession. A system like that of Babbage is now being applied to lighthouses in the United Kingdom by Sir W. Thomson and Dr. John Hopkinson.

Let us calculate the numbers of combinations of different orders which may arise out of the presence or absence of a single mark, say A. In these figures

$$\boxed{A \mid A} \qquad \boxed{A \mid } \qquad \boxed{ \mid A} \qquad \boxed{ \mid }$$

we have four distinct varieties. Form them into a group of a higher order, and consider in how many ways we may vary that group by omitting one or more of the component parts. Now, as there are four parts, and any one may be present or absent, the possible varieties will be $2 \times 2 \times 2 \times 2$, or 16 in number. Form these into a new whole, and proceed again to create variety by omitting any one or more of the sixteen. The number of possible changes will now be $2.2.2.2.2.2.2.2.2.2.2.2.2.2.2.2$, or 2^{16}, and we can repeat the process again and again. We are imagining the creation of objects, whose numbers are represented by the successive orders of the powers of *two*.

At the first step we have 2 ; at the next 2^2, or 4 ; at the third 2^{2^2}, or 16, numbers of very moderate amount.

Let the reader calculate the next term, $2^{2^{2^2}}$, and he will be surprised to find it leap up to 65,536. But at the next step he has to calculate the value of 65,536 *two*'s multiplied together, and it is so great that we could not possibly compute it, the mere expression of the result requiring 19,729 places of figures. But go one step more and we pass the bounds of all reason. The sixth order of the powers of *two* becomes so great, that we could not even express the number of figures required in writing it down, without using about 19,729 figures for the purpose. The successive orders of the powers of two have then the following values so far as we can succeed in describing them :—

First order	2
Second order	4
Third order	16
Fourth order	65,536

Fifth order, number expressed by 19,729 figures.

Sixth order, number expressed by figures, to express the number of which figures would require about . . . . 19,729 figures.

It may give us some notion of infinity to remember that at this sixth step, having long surpassed all bounds of intuitive conception, we make no approach to a limit. Nay, were we to make a hundred such steps, we should be as far away as ever from actual infinity.

It is well worth observing that our powers of expression rapidly overcome the possible multitude of finite objects which may exist in any assignable space. Archimedes showed long ago, in one of the most remarkable writings of antiquity, the *Liber de Arenæ Numero*, that the grains of sand in the world could be numbered, or rather, that if numbered, the result could readily be expressed in arithmetical notation. Let us extend his problem, and ascertain whether we could express the number of atoms which could exist in the visible universe. The most distant stars which can now be seen by telescopes—those of the sixteenth magnitude—are supposed to have a distance of about 33,900,000,000,000,000 miles. Sir W. Thomson has shown reasons for supposing that there do not exist more than from 3×10^{24} to 10^{26} molecules in a cubic centimetre of a solid or liquid substance.[1] Assuming these data to be true, for the sake of argument, a simple calculation enables us to show that the almost inconceivably vast sphere of our stellar system if entirely filled with solid matter, would not contain more than about 68×10^{90} atoms, that is to say, a number requiring for its expression 92 places of figures. Now, this number would be immensely less than the fifth order of the powers of two.

In the variety of logical relations, which may exist

[1] *Nature*, vol. i. p. 553

between a certain number of logical terms, we also meet a case of higher combinations. We have seen (p. 142) that with only six terms the number of possible selections of combinations is 18,446,744,073.709,551,616. Considering that it is the most common thing in the world to use an argument involving six objects or terms, it may excite some surprise that the complete investigation of the relations in which six such terms may stand to each other, should involve an almost inconceivable number of cases. Yet these numbers of possible logical relations belong only to the second order of combinations.

CHAPTER X.

THE subject upon which we now enter must not be regarded as an isolated and curious branch of speculation. It is the necessary basis of the judgments we make in the prosecution of science, or the decisions we come to in the conduct of ordinary affairs. As Butler truly said, " Probability is the very guide of life." Had the science of numbers been studied for no other purpose, it must have been developed for the calculation of probabilities. All our inferences concerning the future are merely probable, and a due appreciation of the degree of probability depends upon a comprehension of the principles of the subject. I am convinced that it is impossible to expound the methods of induction in a sound manner, without resting them upon the theory of probability. Perfect knowledge alone can give certainty, and in nature perfect knowledge would be infinite knowledge, which is clearly beyond our capacities. We have, therefore, to content ourselves with partial knowledge—knowledge mingled with ignorance, producing doubt.

A great difficulty in this subject consists in acquiring a precise notion of the matter treated. What is it that we number, and measure, and calculate in the theory of probabilities ? Is it belief, or opinion, or doubt, or knowledge, or chance, or necessity, or want of art ? Does probability exist in the things which are probable, or in the mind which regards them as such ? The etymology of the name lends us no assistance : for, curiously enough, *probable* is ultimately the same word as *provable*, a good instance of one word becoming differentiated to two opposite meanings.

Chance cannot be the subject of the theory, because there is really no such thing as chance, regarded as producing and governing events. The word chance signifies *falling*, and the notion of falling is continually used as a simile to express uncertainty, because we can seldom predict how a die, a coin, or a leaf will fall, or when a bullet will hit the mark. But everyone sees, after a little reflection, that it is in our knowledge the deficiency lies, not in the certainty of nature's laws. There is no doubt in lightning as to the point it shall strike; in the greatest storm there is nothing capricious; not a grain of sand lies upon the beach, but infinite knowledge would account for its lying there; and the course of every falling leaf is guided by the principles of mechanics which rule the motions of the heavenly bodies.

Chance then exists not in nature, and cannot coexist with knowledge; it is merely an expression, as Laplace remarked, for our ignorance of the causes in action, and our consequent inability to predict the result, or to bring it about infallibly. In nature the happening of an event has been pre-determined from the first fashioning of the universe. *Probability belongs wholly to the mind.* This is proved by the fact that different minds may regard the very same event at the same time with widely different degrees of probability. A steam-vessel, for instance, is missing and some persons believe that she has sunk in mid-ocean; others think differently. In the event itself there can be no such uncertainty ; the steam-vessel either has sunk or has not sunk, and no subsequent discussion of the probable nature of the event can alter the fact. Yet the probability of the event will really vary from day to day, and from mind to mind, according as the slightest information is gained regarding the vessels met at sea, the weather prevailing there, the signs of wreck picked up, or the previous condition of the vessel. Probability thus belongs to our mental condition, to the light in which we regard events, the occurrence or non-occurrence of which is certain in themselves. Many writers accordingly have asserted that probability is concerned with degree or quantity of belief. De Morgan says,[1] " By degree of proba-

---

[1] *Formal Logic*, p. 172.

bility we really mean or ought to mean degree of belief.'
The late Professor Donkin expressed the meaning of
probability as "quantity of belief;" but I have never felt
satisfied with such definitions of probability. The nature
of *belief* is not more clear to my mind than the notion
which it is used to define. But an all-sufficient objection
is, that *the theory does not measure what the belief is, but
what it ought to be.* Few minds think in close accordance
with the theory, and there are many cases of evidence in
which the belief existing is habitually different from what
it ought to be. Even if the state of belief in any mind
could be measured and expressed in figures, the results
would be worthless. The value of the theory consists in
correcting and guiding our belief, and rendering our states
of mind and consequent actions harmonious with our
knowledge of exterior conditions.

This objection has been clearly perceived by some of
those who still used quantity of belief as a definition of
probability. Thus De Morgan adds—"Belief is but
another name for imperfect knowledge." Donkin has
well said that the quantity of belief is "always relative
to a particular state of knowledge or ignorance; but it
must be observed that it is absolute in the sense of not
being relative to any individual mind; since, the same
information being presupposed, all minds *ought* to dis-
tribute their belief in the same way."[1] Boole seemed to
entertain a like view, when he described the theory as
engaged with "the equal distribution of ignorance;"[2]
but we may just as well say that it is engaged with the
equal distribution of knowledge.

I prefer to dispense altogether with this obscure word
belief, and to say that the theory of probability deals with
quantity of knowledge, an expression of which a precise
explanation and measure can presently be given. An
event is only probable when our knowledge of it is
diluted with ignorance, and exact calculation is needed
to discriminate how much we do and do not know. The
theory has been described by some writers as professing *to
evolve knowledge out of ignorance;* but as Donkin admirably
remarked, it is really "a method of avoiding the erection

[1] *Philosophical Magazine,* 4th Series, vol. i. p. 355.
[2] *Transactions of the Royal Society of Edinburgh,* vol. xxi. part 4.

of belief upon ignorance." It defines rational expectation by measuring the comparative amounts of knowledge and ignorance, and teaches us to regulate our actions with regard to future events in a way which will, in the long run, lead to the least disappointment. It is, as Laplace happily said, *good sense reduced to calculation.* This theory appears to me the noblest creation of intellect, and it passes my conception how two such men as Auguste Comte and J. S. Mill could be found depreciating it and vainly questioning its validity. To eulogise the theory ought to be as needless as to eulogise reason itself.

Fundamental Principles of the Theory.

The calculation of probabilities is really founded, as I conceive, upon the principle of reasoning set forth in preceding chapters. We must treat equals equally, and what we know of one case may be affirmed of every case resembling it in the necessary circumstances. The theory consists in putting similar cases on a par, and distributing equally among them whatever knowledge we possess. Throw a penny into the air, and consider what we know with regard to its way of falling. We know that it will certainly fall upon a side, so that either head or tail will be uppermost; but as to whether it will be head or tail, our knowledge is equally divided. Whatever we know concerning head, we know also concerning tail, so that we have no reason for expecting one more than the other. The least predominance of belief to either side would be irrational; it would consist in treating unequally things of which our knowledge is equal.

The theory does not require, as some writers have erroneously supposed, that we should first ascertain by experiment the equal facility of the events we are considering. So far as we can examine and measure the causes in operation, events are removed out of the sphere of probability. The theory comes into play where ignorance begins, and the knowledge we possess requires to be distributed over many cases. Nor does the theory show that the coin will fall as often on the one side as the other. It is almost impossible that this should happen, because some inequality in the form of the coin, or some uniform

manner in throwing it up, is almost sure to occasion a
slight preponderance in one direction. But as we do not
previously know in which way a preponderance will exist,
we have no reason for expecting head more than tail. Our
state of knowledge will be changed should we throw up
the coin many times and register the results. Every throw
gives us some slight information as to the probable
tendency of the coin, and in subsequent calculations we
must take this into account. In other cases experience
might show that we had been entirely mistaken ; we might
expect that a die would fall as often on each of the six
sides as on each other side in the long run ; trial might show
that the die was a loaded one, and falls most often on a
particular face. The theory would not have misled us : it
treated correctly the information we had, which is all that
any theory can do.

It may be asked, as Mill asks, Why spend so much
trouble in calculating from imperfect data, when a little
trouble would enable us to render a conclusion certain by
actual trial ? Why calculate the probability of a measurement being correct, when we can try whether it is correct ?
But I shall fully point out in later parts of this work that
in measurement we never can attain perfect coincidence.
Two measurements of the same base line in a survey may
show a difference of some inches, and there may be no
means of knowing which is the better result. A third
measurement would probably agree with neither. To
select any one of the measurements, would imply that
we knew it to be the most nearly correct one, which we
do not. In this state of ignorance, the only guide is the
theory of probability, which proves that in the long run
the mean of divergent results will come most nearly to
the truth. In all other scientific operations whatsoever,
perfect knowledge is impossible, and when we have exhausted all our instrumental means in the attainment of
truth, there is a margin of error which can only be safely
treated by the principles of probability.

The method which we employ in the theory consists in
calculating the number of all the cases or events concerning
which our knowledge is equal. If we have the slightest
reason for suspecting that one event is more likely to
occur than another, we should take this knowledge into

account. This being done, we must determine the whole number of events which are, so far as we know, equally likely. Thus, if we have no reason for supposing that a penny will fall more often one way than another, there are two cases, head and tail, equally likely. But if from trial or otherwise we know, or think we know, that of 100 throws 55 will give tail, then the probability is measured by the ratio of 55 to 100.

The mathematical formulæ of the theory are exactly the same as those of the theory of combinations. In this latter theory we determine in how many ways events may be joined together, and we now proceed to use this knowledge in calculating the number of ways in which a certain event may come about. It is the comparative numbers of ways in which events can happen which measure their comparative probabilities. If we throw three pennies into the air, what is the probability that two of them will fall tail uppermost? This amounts to asking in how many possible ways can we select two tails out of three, compared with the whole number of ways in which the coins can be placed. Now, the fourth line of the Arithmetical Triangle (p. 184) gives us the answer. The whole number of ways in which we can select or leave three things is eight, and the possible combinations of two things at a time is three; hence the probability of two tails is the ratio of three to eight. From the numbers in the triangle we may similarly draw all the following probabilities :—

One combination gives 0 tail.   Probability $\frac{1}{8}$.
Three combinations gives 1 tail.   Probability $\frac{3}{8}$.
Three combinations give 2 tails.   Probability $\frac{3}{8}$.
One combination gives 3 tails.   Probability $\frac{1}{8}$.

We can apply the same considerations to the imaginary causes of the difference of stature, the combinations of which were shown in p. 188. There are altogether 128 ways in which seven causes can be present or absent. Now, twenty-one of these combinations give an addition of two inches, so that the probability of a person under the circumstances being five feet two inches is $\frac{21}{128}$. The probability of five feet three inches is $\frac{35}{128}$; of five feet one inch $\frac{7}{128}$; of five feet $\frac{1}{128}$, and so on. Thus the eighth line of the Arithmetical Triangle gives all the probabilities arising out of the combinations of seven causes.

Rules for the Calculation of Probabilities.

I will now explain as simply as possible the rules
for calculating probabilities. The principal rule is as
follows :—

Calculate the number of events which may happen
independently of each other, and which, as far as is
known, are equally probable. Make this number the
denominator of a fraction, and take for the numerator
the number of such events as imply or constitute the
happening of the event, whose probability is required.

Thus, if the letters of the word *Roma* be thrown down
casually in a row, what is the probability that they will
form a significant Latin word ? The possible arrangements of four letters are 4 × 3 × 2 × 1, or 24 in number
(p. 178), and if all the arrangements be examined, seven
of these will be found to have meaning, namely *Roma,
ramo, oram, mora, maro, armo,* and *amor.* Hence the
probability of a significant result is $\frac{7}{24}$.

We must distinguish comparative from absolute probabilities. In drawing a card casually from a pack, there
is no reason to expect any one card more than any other.
Now, there are four kings and four queens in a pack, so
that there are just as many ways of drawing one as the
other, and the probabilities are equal. But there are
thirteen diamonds, so that the probability of a king is to
that of a diamond as four to thirteen. Thus the probabilities of each are proportional to their respective numbers
of ways of happening. Again, I can draw a king in four
ways, and not draw one in forty-eight, so that the probabilities are in this proportion, or, as is commonly said,
the *odds* against drawing a king are forty-eight to four.
The odds are seven to seventeen in favour, or seventeen to
seven against the letters R,o,m,a, accidentally forming a
significant word. The odds are five to three against two
tails appearing in three throws of a penny. Conversely,
when the odds of an event are given, and the probability is
required, *take the odds in favour of the event for numerator,
and the sum of the odds for denominator.*

It is obvious that an event is certain when all the combinations of causes which can take place produce that
event. If we represent the probability of such event

according to our rule, it gives the ratio of some number to itself, or unity. An event is certain not to happen when no possible combination of causes gives the event, and the ratio by the same rule becomes that of o to some number. Hence it follows that in the theory of probability certainty is expressed by 1, and impossibility by o; but no mystical meaning should be attached to these symbols, as they merely express the fact that *all* or *no* possible combinations give the event.

By a *compound event*, we mean an event which may be decomposed into two or more simpler events. Thus the firing of a gun may be decomposed into pulling the trigger, the fall of the hammer, the explosion of the cap, &c. In this example the simple events are not *independent*, because if the trigger is pulled, the other events will under proper conditions necessarily follow, and their probabilities are therefore the same as that of the first event. Events are *independent* when the happening of one does not render the other either more or less probable than before. Thus the death of a person is neither more nor less probable because the planet Mars happens to be visible. When the component events are independent, a simple rule can be given for calculating the probability of the compound event, thus—*Multiply together the fractions expressing the probabilities of the independent component events.*

The probability of throwing tail twice with a penny is $\frac{1}{2} \times \frac{1}{2}$, or $\frac{1}{4}$; the probability of throwing it three times running is $\frac{1}{2} \times \frac{1}{2} \times \frac{1}{2}$, or $\frac{1}{8}$; a result agreeing with that obtained in an apparently different manner (p. 202). In fact, when we multiply together the denominators, we get the whole number of ways of happening of the compound event, and when we multiply the numerators, we get the number of ways favourable to the required event.

Probabilities may be added to or subtracted from each other under the important condition that the events in question are exclusive of each other, so that not more than one of them can happen. It might be argued that, since the probability of throwing head at the first trial is $\frac{1}{2}$, and at the second trial also $\frac{1}{2}$, the probability of throwing it in the first two throws is $\frac{1}{2} + \frac{1}{2}$, or certainty. Not only is this result evidently absurd, but a repetition of the process would lead us to a probability of $1\frac{1}{2}$ or of any greater number, results which could have no meaning whatever. The probability we wish to calculate is that of one head in two throws, but in our addition we have included the case in which two heads appear. The true result is $\frac{1}{2} + \frac{1}{2} \times \frac{1}{2}$ or $\frac{3}{4}$, or the probability of head at the first throw, added to the exclusive probability that if it does not come at the first, it will come at the second. The greatest difficulties of the theory arise from the confusion of exclusive and unexclusive alternatives. I may remind the reader that the possibility of unexclusive alternatives was a point previously discussed (p. 68), and to the reasons then given for considering alternation as logically unexclusive, may be added the existence of these difficulties in the theory of probability. The erroneous result explained above really arose from overlooking the fact that the expression " head first throw or head second throw " might include the case of head at both throws.

The Logical Alphabet in questions of Probability.

When the probabilities of certain simple events are given, and it is required to deduce the probabilities of compound events, the Logical Alphabet may give assistance, provided that there are no special logical conditions so that all the combinations are possible. Thus, if there be three events, A, B, C, of which the probabilities are, a, β, γ, then the negatives of those events, expressing the absence of the events, will have the probabilities $1 - a$, $1 - \beta$, $1 - \gamma$. We have only to insert these values for the letters of the combinations and multiply, and we obtain the probability of each combination. Thus the probability of ABC is $a\beta\gamma$; of Abc, $a(1 - \beta)(1 - \gamma)$.

We can now clearly distinguish between the probabilities of exclusive and unexclusive events. Thus, if A and B are events which may happen together like rain and high tide, or an earthquake and a storm, the probability of A or B happening is not the sum of their separate probabilities. For by the Laws of Thought we develop A $\cdot|\cdot$ B into AB $\cdot|\cdot$ Ab $\cdot|\cdot$ aB, and substituting a and β, the probabilities of A and B respectively, we obtain $a.\beta + a.(1 - \beta) + (1 - a).\beta$ or $a + \beta - a.\beta$. But if events are *incompossible* or incapable of happening together, like a clear sky and rain, or a new moon and a full moon, then the events are not really A or B, but A not-B, or B not-A, or in symbols Ab + aB.   Now if we take μ = probability of Ab and ν = probability of aB, then we may add simply, and the probability of Ab + aB is $\mu + \nu$.

Let the reader carefully observe that if the combination AB cannot exist, the probability of Ab is not the product of the probabilities of A and b.   When certain combinations are logically impossible, it is no longer allowable to substitute the probability of each term for the term, because the multiplication of probabilities presupposes the independence of the events.   A large part of Boole's Laws of Thought is devoted to an attempt to overcome this difficulty and to produce a General Method in Probabilities by which from certain logical conditions and certain given probabilities it would be possible to deduce the probability of any other combinations of events under those conditions.   Boole pursued his task with wonderful ingenuity and power, but after spending much study on his work, I am compelled to adopt the conclusion that his method is fundamentally erroneous. As pointed out by Mr. Wilbraham,[1] Boole obtained his results by an arbitrary assumption, which is only the most probable, and not the only possible assumption.   The answer obtained is therefore not the real probability, which is usually indeterminate, but only, as it were, the most probable probability.   Certain problems solved by Boole are free from logical conditions and therefore may admit of valid answers.   These, as I have shown,[2] may be solved by the combinations of the Logical Alphabet, but the rest of the problems do not admit of a determinate answer, at least by Boole's method.

Comparison of the Theory with Experience.

The Laws of Probability rest upon the fundamental principles of reasoning, and cannot be really negatived by any

---

[1] *Philosophical Magazine,* 4th Series, vol. vii. p. 465 ; vol. viii. p. 91.
[2] *Memoirs of the Manchester Literary and Philosophical Society,* 3rd Series, vol. iv. p. 347

possible experience. It might happen that a person should always throw a coin head uppermost, and appear incapable of getting tail by chance. The theory would not be falsified, because it contemplates the possibility of the most extreme runs of luck. Our actual experience might be counter to all that is probable; the whole course of events might seem to be in complete contradiction to what we should expect, and yet a casual conjunction of events might be the real explanation. It is just possible that some regular coincidences, which we attribute to fixed laws of nature, are due to the accidental conjunction of phenomena in the cases to which our attention is directed. All that we can learn from finite experience is capable, according to the theory of probabilities, of misleading us, and it is only infinite experience that could assure us of any inductive truths.

At the same time, the probability that any extreme runs of luck will occur is so excessively slight, that it would be absurd seriously to expect their occurrence. It is almost impossible, for instance, that any whist player should have played in any two games where the distribution of the cards was exactly the same, by pure accident (p. 191). Such a thing as a person always losing at a game of pure chance, is wholly unknown. Coincidences of this kind are not impossible, as I have said, but they are so unlikely that the lifetime of any person, or indeed the whole duration of history, does not give any appreciable probability of their being encountered. Whenever we make any extensive series of trials of chance results, as in throwing a die or coin, the probability is great that the results will agree nearly with the predictions yielded by theory. Precise agreement must not be expected, for that, as the theory shows, is highly improbable. Several attempts have been made to test, in this way, the accordance of theory and experience. Buffon caused the first trial to be made by a young child who threw a coin many times in succession, and he obtained 1992 tails to 2048 heads. A pupil of De Morgan repeated the trial for his own satisfaction, and obtained 2044 tails to 2048 heads. In both cases the coincidence with theory is as close as could be expected, and the details may be found in De Morgan's "Formal Logic," p. 185.

Quetelet also tested the theory in a rather more complete manner, by placing 20 black and 20 white balls in an
urn and drawing a ball out time after time in an indifferent
manner, each ball being replaced before a new drawing was
made. He found, as might be expected, that the greater
the number of drawings made, the more nearly were the
white and black balls equal in number. At the termination of the experiment he had registered 2066 white
and 2030 black balls, the ratio being 1·02.[1]

I have made a series of experiments in a third manner,
which seemed to me even more interesting, and capable
of more extensive trial. Taking a handful of ten coins,
usually shillings, I threw them up time after time, and
registered the numbers of heads which appeared each
time. Now the probability of obtaining 10, 9, 8, 7, &c.,
heads is proportional to the number of combinations of
10, 9, 8, 7, &c., things out of 10 things. Consequently
the results ought to approximate to the numbers in the
eleventh line of the Arithmetical Triangle. I made
altogether 2048 throws, in two sets of 1024 throws each,
and the numbers obtained are given in the following
table :—

Character of Throw.	Theoretical Numbers.	First Series.	Second Series.	Average.	Divergence.
10 Heads 0 Tail	1	3	1	2	+ 1
9 „ 1 „	10	12	23	17½	+ 7½
8 „ 2 „	45	57	73	65	+ 20
7 „ 3 „	120	129	123	126	+ 6
6 „ 4 „	210	181	190	185½	− 25
5 „ 5 „	252	257	232	244½	− 7½
4 „ 6 „	210	201	197	199	− 11
3 „ 7 „	120	111	119	115	− 5
2 „ 8 „	45	52	50	51	+ 6
1 „ 9 „	10	21	15	18	+ 8
0 „ 10 „	1	0	1	½	− ½
Totals	1024	1024	1024	1024	− 1

The whole number of single throws of coins amounted
to 10 × 2048, or 20,480 in all, one half of which or
10,240 should theoretically give head. The total number

[1] *Letters on the Theory of Probabilities*, translated by Downes, 1849,
pp. 36, 37.

of heads obtained was actually 10,353, or 5222 in the first series, and 5131 in the second. The coincidence with theory is pretty close, but considering the large number of throws there is some reason to suspect a tendency in favour of heads.

The special interest of this trial consists in the exhibition, in a practical form, of the results of Bernoulli's theorem, and the law of error or divergence from the mean to be afterwards more fully considered. It illustrates the connection between combinations and permutations, which is exhibited in the Arithmetical Triangle, and which underlies many important theorems of science.

Probable Deductive Arguments.

With the aid of the theory of probabilities, we may extend the sphere of deductive argument. Hitherto we have treated propositions as certain, and on the hypothesis of certainty have deduced conclusions equally certain. But the information on which we reason in ordinary life is seldom or never certain, and almost all reasoning is really a question of probability. We ought therefore to be fully aware of the mode and degree in which deductive reasoning is affected by the theory of probability, and many persons may be surprised at the results which must be admitted. Some controversial writers appear to consider, as De Morgan remarked,[1] that an inference from several equally probable premises is itself as probable as any of them, but the true result is very different. If an argument involves many propositions, and each of them is uncertain, the conclusion will be of very little force.

The validity of a conclusion may be regarded as a compound event, depending upon the premises happening to be true ; thus, to obtain the probability of the conclusion, we must multiply together the fractions expressing the probabilities of the premises. If the probability is $\frac{1}{2}$ that A is B, and also $\frac{1}{2}$ that B is C, the conclusion that A is C, on the ground of these premises, is $\frac{1}{2} \times \frac{1}{2}$ or $\frac{1}{4}$. Similarly if there be any number of premises requisite to the establish-

---

[1] *Encyclopædia Metropolitana*, art. *Probabilities*, p. 396.

ment of a conclusion and their probabilities be p, q, r, &c., the probability of the conclusion on the ground of these premises is $p \times q \times r \times$...... This product has but a small value, unless each of the quantities p, q, &c., be nearly unity.

But it is particularly to be noticed that the probability thus calculated is not the whole probability of the conclusion, but that only which it derives from the premises in question. Whately's [1] remarks on this subject might mislead the reader into supposing that the calculation is completed by multiplying together the probabilities of the premises. But it has been fully explained by De Morgan [2] that we must take into account the antecedent probability of the conclusion ; A may be C for other reasons besides its being B, and as he remarks, " It is difficult, if not impossible, to produce a chain of argument of which the reasoner can rest the result on those arguments only." The failure of one argument does not, except under special circumstances, disprove the truth of the conclusion it is intended to uphold, otherwise there are few truths which could survive the ill-considered arguments adduced in their favour. As a rope does not necessarily break because one or two strands in it fail, so a conclusion may depend upon an endless number of considerations besides those immediately in view. Even when we have no other information we must not consider a statement as devoid of all probability. The true expression of complete doubt is a ratio of equality between the chances in favour of and against it, and this ratio is expressed in the probability $\frac{1}{2}$.

Now if A and C are wholly unknown things, we have no reason to believe that A is C rather than A is not C. The antecedent probability is then $\frac{1}{2}$. If we also have the probabilities that A is B, $\frac{1}{2}$ and that B is C, $\frac{1}{2}$ we have no right to suppose that the probability of A being C is reduced by the argument in its favour. If the conclusion is true on its own grounds, the failure of the argument does not affect it ; thus its total probability is its antecedent probability, added to the probability that this failing, the new argument in question establishes it. There is a pro-

[1] *Elements of Logic*, Book III. sections 11 and 18.
[2] *Encyclopædia Metropolitana*, art. *Probabilities*, p. 400.

bability $\frac{1}{2}$ that we shall not require the special argument;
a probability $\frac{1}{2}$ that we shall, and a probability $\frac{1}{4}$ that the
argument does in that case establish it. Thus the com-
plete result is $\frac{1}{2} + \frac{1}{2} \times \frac{1}{4}$, or $\frac{5}{8}$. In general language, if a
be the probability founded on a particular argument, and
c the antecedent probability of the event, the general result
is $1 - (1 - a)(1 - c)$, or $a + c - ac$.

We may put it still more generally in this way:—Let
a, b, c, &c. be the probabilities of a conclusion grounded
on various arguments. It is only when all the arguments
fail that our conclusion proves finally untrue; the probabilities of each failing are respectively, $1 - a, 1 - b, 1 - c$,
&c.; the probability that they will all fail is $(1 - a)(1 - b)$
$(1 - c)...$; therefore the probability that the conclusion
will not fail is $1 - (1 - a)(1 - b)(1 - c)...$ &c. It follows
that every argument in favour of a conclusion, however
flimsy and slight, adds probability to it. When it is
unknown whether an overdue vessel has foundered or not,
every slight indication of a lost vessel will add some probability to the belief of its loss, and the disproof of any
particular evidence will not disprove the event.

We must apply these principles of evidence with great
care, and observe that in a great proportion of cases the
adducing of a weak argument does tend to the disproof
of its conclusion. The assertion may have in itself great
inherent improbability as being opposed to other evidence
or to the supposed law of nature, and every reasoner may
be assumed to be dealing plainly, and putting forward the
whole force of evidence which he possesses in its favour.
If he brings but one argument, and its probability a is
small, then in the formula $1 - (1 - a)(1 - c)$ both a and c
are small, and the whole expression has but little value.
The whole effect of an argument thus turns upon the
question whether other arguments remain, so that we can
introduce other factors $(1 - b), (1 - d)$, &c., into the above
expression. In a court of justice, in a publication having
an express purpose, and in many other cases, it is doubtless
right to assume that the whole evidence considered to
have any value as regards the conclusion asserted, is put
forward.

To assign the antecedent probability of any proposition,
may be a matter of difficulty or impossibility, and one

with which logic and the theory of probability have little
concern. From the general body of science in our possession, we must in each case make the best judgment we
can. But in the absence of all knowledge the probability
should be considered $= \frac{1}{2}$, for if we make it less than this
we incline to believe it false rather than true. Thus, before
we possessed any means of estimating the magnitudes of
the fixed stars, the statement that Sirius was greater than
the sun had a probability of exactly $\frac{1}{2}$; it was as likely that
it would be greater as that it would be smaller; and so
of any other star. This was the assumption which Michell
made in his admirable speculations.[1] It might seem,
indeed, that as every proposition expresses an agreement,
and the agreements or resemblances between phenomena
are infinitely fewer than the differences (p. 44), every proposition should in the absence of other information be
infinitely improbable. But in our logical system every
term may be indifferently positive or negative, so that we
express under the same form as many differences as agreements. It is impossible therefore that we should have
any reason to disbelieve rather than to believe a statement
about things of which we know nothing. We can hardly
indeed invent a proposition concerning the truth of which
we are absolutely ignorant, except when we are entirely
ignorant of the terms used. If I ask the reader to assign
the odds that a " Platythliptic Coefficient is positive " he
will hardly see his way to doing so, unless he regard them
as even.

The assumption that complete doubt is properly ex-
pressed by $\frac{1}{2}$ has been called in question by Bishop Terrot,[2]
who proposes instead the indefinite symbol $\frac{0}{0}$; and he
considers that "the *à priori* probability derived from
absolute ignorance has no effect upon the force of a
subsequently admitted probability." But if we grant that
the probability may have any value between 0 and 1, and
that every separate value is equally likely, then n and
$1 - n$ are equally likely, and the average is always $\frac{1}{2}$. Or
we may take $p \cdot dp$ to express the probability that our

[1] *Philosophical Transactions* (1767). Abridg. vol. xii. p. 435.
[2] *Transactions of the Edinburgh Philosophical Society*, vol. xxi.
p. 375.

estimate concerning any proposition should lie beween p and $p + dp$. The complete probability of the proposition is then the integral taken between the limits 1 and 0, or again $\frac{1}{2}$.

Difficulties of the Theory.

The theory of probability, though undoubtedly true, requires very careful application. Not only is it a branch of mathematics in which oversights are frequently committed, but it is a matter of great difficulty in many cases, to be sure that the formula correctly represents the data of the problem. These difficulties often arise from the logical complexity of the conditions, which might be, perhaps, to some extent cleared up by constantly bearing in mind the system of combinations as developed in the Indirect Logical Method. In the study of probabilities, mathematicians had unconsciously employed logical processes far in advance of those in possession of logicians, and the Indirect Method is but the full statement of these processes.

It is very curious how often the most acute and powerful intellects have gone astray in the calculation of probabilities. Seldom was Pascal mistaken, yet he inaugurated the science with a mistaken solution.[1] Leibnitz fell into the extraordinary blunder of thinking that the number twelve was as probable a result in the throwing of two dice as the number eleven.[2] In not a few cases the false solution first obtained seems more plausible to the present day than the correct one since demonstrated. James Bernoulli candidly records two false solutions of a problem which he at first thought self-evident; and he adds a warning against the risk of error, especially when we attempt to reason on this subject without a rigid adherence to methodical rules and symbols. Montmort was not free from similar mistakes. D'Alembert constantly fell into blunders, and could not perceive, for instance, that the probabilities would be the same when

[1] Montucla, *Histoire des Mathématiques*, vol. iii. p. 386.
[2] Leibnitz *Opera*, Dutens' Edition, vol. vi. part i. p. 217. Todhunter's *History of the Theory of Probability*, p. 48. To the latter work I am indebted for many of the statements in the text.

coins are thrown successively as when thrown simultaneously.   Some men of great reputation, such as
Ancillon, Moses Mendelssohn, Garve, Auguste Comte,[1]
Poinsot, and J. S. Mill,[2] have so far misapprehended the
theory, as to question its value or even to dispute its
validity.   The erroneous statements about the theory given
in the earlier editions of Mill's *System of Logic* were partially withdrawn in the later editions.

Many persons have a fallacious tendency to believe that
when a chance event has happened several times together
in an unusual conjunction, it is less likely to happen
again.   D'Alembert seriously held that if head was thrown
three times running with a coin, tail would more probably
appear at the next trial.[3]   Bequelin adopted the same
opinion, and yet there is no reason for it whatever.   If
the event be really casual, what has gone before cannot in
the slightest degree influence it.   As a matter of fact, the
more often a casual event takes place the more likely it is
to happen again; because there is some slight empirical
evidence of a tendency.   The source of the fallacy is to be
found entirely in the feelings of surprise with which we
witness an event happening by chance, in a manner which
seems to proceed from design.

Misapprehension may also arise from overlooking the
difference between permutations and combinations.   To
throw ten heads in succession with a coin is no more
unlikely than to throw any other particular succession
of heads and tails, but it is much less likely than five
heads and five tails without regard to their order, because there are no less than 252 different particular
throws which will give this result, when we abstract
the difference of order.

Difficulties arise in the application of the theory from
our habitual disregard of slight probabilities.   We are
obliged practically to accept truths as certain which are
nearly so, because it ceases to be worth while to calculate
the difference.   No punishment could be inflicted if
absolutely certain evidence of guilt were required, and as

---

[1] *Positive Philosophy*, translated by Martineau, vol. ii. p. 120.
[2] *System of Logic*, bk. iii. chap. 18, 5th Ed. vol. ii. p. 61.
[3] Montucla, *Histoire*, vol. iii. p. 405 ; Todhunter, p. 263.

Locke remarks, "He that will not stir till he infallibly knows the . business he goes about will succeed, will have but little else to do but to sit still and perish." [1] There is not a moment of our lives when we do not lie under a slight danger of death, or some most terrible fate. There is not a single action of eating, drinking, sitting down, or standing up, which has not proved fatal to some person. Several philosophers have tried to assign the limit of the probabilities which we regard as zero ; Buffon named $\frac{1}{10.000}$, because it is the probability, practically disregarded, that a man of 56 years of age will die the next day. Pascal remarked that a man would be esteemed a fool for hesitating to accept death when three dice gave sixes twenty times running, if his reward in case of a different result was to be a crown; but as the chance of death in question is only $1 \div 6^{60}$, or unity divided by a number of 47 places of figures, we may be said to incur greater risks every day for less motives. There is far greater risk of death, for instance, in a game of cricket or a visit to the rink.

Nothing is more requisite than to distinguish carefully between the truth of a theory and the truthful application of the theory to actual circumstances. As a general rule, events in nature and art will present a complexity of relations exceeding our powers of treatment. The intricate action of the mind often intervenes and renders complete analysis hopeless. If, for instance, the probability that a marksman shall hit the target in a single shot be 1 in 10, we might seem to have no difficulty in calculating the probability of any sucession of hits; thus the probability of three successive hits would be one in a thousand. But, in reality, the confidence and experience derived from the first successful shot would render a second success more probable. The events are not really independent, and there would generally be a far greater preponderance of runs of apparent luck, than a simple calculation of probabilities could account for. In some persons, however, a remarkable series of successes will produce a degree of excitement rendering continued success almost impossible.

Attempts to apply the theory of probability to the

---

[1] *Essay concerning Human Understanding*, bk. iv. ch. 14. § 1.

results of judicial proceedings have proved of little value,
simply because the conditions are far too intricate. As
Laplace said, " Tant de passions, d'intérêts divers et de
circonstances compliquent les questions relatives à ces
objets, qu'elles sont presque toujours insolubles." Men
acting on a jury, or giving evidence before a court, are
subject to so many complex influences that no mathematical formulas can be framed to express the real conditions.
Jurymen or even judges on the bench cannot be regarded
as acting independently, with a definite probability in
favour of each delivering a correct judgment. Each man
of the jury is more or less influenced by the opinion of the
others, and there are subtle effects of character and manner
and strength of mind which defy analysis. Even in
physical science we can in comparatively few cases apply
the theory in a definite manner, because the data required
are too complicated and difficult to obtain. But such failures
in no way diminish the truth and beauty of the theory
itself ; in reality there is no branch of science in which our
symbols can cope with the complexity of Nature. As
Donkin said,—

" I do not see on what ground it can be doubted that
every definite state of belief concerning a proposed hypothesis, is in itself capable of being represented by a numerical expression, however difficult or impracticable it may
be to ascertain its actual value. It would be very difficult
to estimate in numbers the *vis viva* of all the particles of
a human body at any instant ; but no one doubts that it is
capable of numerical expression." [1]

The difficulty, in short, is merely relative to our knowledge and skill, and is not absolute or inherent in the
subject. We must distinguish between what is theoretically conceivable and what is practicable with our
present mental resources. Provided that our aspirations
are pointed in a right direction, we must not allow them
to be damped by the consideration that they pass beyond
what can now be turned to immediate use. In spite of
its immense difficulties of application, and the aspersions
which have been mistakenly cast upon it, the theory of
probabilities, I repeat, is the noblest, as it will in course

of time prove, perhaps the most fruitful branch of mathematical science.   It is the very guide of life, and hardly can we take a step or make a decision of any kind without correctly or incorrectly making an estimation of probabilities.   In the next chapter we proceed to consider how the whole cogency of inductive reasoning rests upon probabilities.   The truth or untruth of a natural law, when carefully investigated, resolves itself into a high or low degree of probability, and this is the case whether or not we are capable of producing precise numerical data.

CHAPTER XI.

PHILOSOPHY OF INDUCTIVE INFERENCE.

WE have inquired into the nature of perfect induction, whereby we pass backwards from certain observed combinations of events, to the logical conditions governing such combinations. We have also investigated the grounds of that theory of probability, which must be our guide when we leave certainty behind, and dilute knowledge with ignorance. There is now before us the difficult task of endeavouring to decide how, by the aid of that theory, we can ascend from the facts to the laws of nature; and may then with more or less success anticipate the future course of events. All our knowledge of natural objects must be ultimately derived from observation, and the difficult question arises—How can we ever know anything which we have not directly observed through one of our senses, the apertures of the mind? The utility of reasoning is to assure ourselves that, at a determinate time and place, or under specified conditions, a certain phenomenon will be observed. When we can use our senses and perceive that the phenomenon does occur, reasoning is superfluous. If the senses cannot be used, because the event is in the future, or out of reach, how can reasoning take their place? Apparently, at least, we must infer the unknown from the known, and the mind must itself create an addition to the sum of knowledge. But I hold that it is quite impossible to make any real additions to the contents of our knowledge, except through new impressions upon the senses, or upon some seat of feeling. I shall attempt to show that inference, whether inductive or deductive, is never more than an unfolding of the contents of our experience, and that it always proceeds upon the assumption that the future and the unperceived will be governed by the same conditions as the past and the perceived, an assumption which will often prove to be mistaken.

In inductive as in deductive reasoning the conclusion never passes beyond the premises. Reasoning adds no more to the implicit contents of our knowledge, than the arrangement of the specimens in a museum adds to the number of those specimens. Arrangement adds to our knowledge in a certain sense : it allows us to perceive the similarities and peculiarities of the specimens, and on the assumption that the museum is an adequate representation of nature, it enables us to judge of the prevailing forms of natural objects. Bacon's first aphorism holds perfectly true, that man knows nothing but what he has observed, provided that we include his whole sources of experience, and the whole implicit contents of his knowledge. Inference but unfolds the hidden meaning of our observations, and *the theory of probability shows how far we go beyond our data in assuming that new specimens will resemble the old ones,* or that the future may be regarded as proceeding uniformly with the past.

Various Classes of Inductive Truths.

It will be desirable, in the first place, to distinguish between the several kinds of truths which we endeavour to establish by induction. Although there is a certain common and universal element in all our processes of reasoning, yet diversity arises in their application. Similarity of condition between the events from which we argue, and those to which we argue, must always be the ground of inference ; but this similarity may have regard either to time or place, or the simple logical combination of events, or to any conceivable junction of circumstances involving quality, time, and place. Having met with many pieces of substance possessing ductility and a bright yellow colour, and having discovered, by perfect induction, that they all possess a high specific gravity, and a freedom from the corrosive action of acids, we are led to expect that every piece of substance, possessing like ductility and a similar yellow colour, will have an equally high specific gravity, and a like freedom from corrosion by acids. This is a case of the coexistence of qualities ; for the character of the specimens examined alters not with time nor place.

In a second class of cases, time will enter as a principal ground of similarity. When we hear a clock pendulum beat time after time, at equal intervals, and with a uniform sound, we confidently expect that the stroke will continue to be repeated uniformly. A comet having appeared several times at nearly equal intervals, we infer that it will probably appear again at the end of another like interval. A man who has returned home evening after evening for many years, and found his house standing, may, on like grounds, expect that it will be standing the next evening, and on many succeeding evenings. Even the continuous existence of an object in an unaltered state, or the finding again of that which we have hidden, is but a matter of inference depending on experience.

A still larger and more complex class of cases involves the relations of space, in addition to those of time and quality. Having observed that every triangle drawn upon the diameter of a circle, with its apex upon the circumference, apparently contains a right angle, we may ascertain that all triangles in similar circumstances will contain right angles. This is a case of pure space reasoning, apart from circumstances of time or quality, and it seems to be governed by different principles of reasoning. I shall endeavour to show, however, that geometrical reasoning differs but in degree from that which applies to other natural relations.

The Relation of Cause and Effect.

In a very large part of the scientific investigations which must be considered, we deal with events which follow from previous events, or with existences which succeed existences. Science, indeed, might arise even were material nature a fixed and changeless whole. Endow mind with the power to travel about, and compare part with part, and it could certainly draw inferences concerning the similarity of forms, the coexistence of qualities, or the preponderance of a particular kind of matter in a changeless world. A solid universe, in at least approximate equilibrium, is not inconceivable, and then the relation of cause and effect would evidently be no more than the relation of before and after. As nature exists, however, it is a progressive existence, ever moving and changing as time, the great independent variable, proceeds. Hence it arises that we must continually compare what is happening now with what happened a moment before, and a moment before that moment, and so on, until we reach indefinite periods of past time. A comet is seen moving in the sky, or its constituent particles illumine the heavens with their tails of fire. We cannot explain the present movements of such a body without supposing its prior existence, with a definite amount of energy and a definite direction of motion ; nor can we validly suppose that our task is concluded when we find that it came wandering to our solar system through the unmeasured vastness of surrounding space. Every event must have a cause, and that cause again a cause, until we are lost in the obscurity of the past, and are driven to the belief in one First Cause, by whom the course of nature was determined.

Fallacious Use of the Term Cause.

The words Cause and Causation have given rise to infinite trouble and obscurity, and have in no slight degree retarded the progress of science. From the time of Aristotle, the work of philosophy has been described as the discovery of the causes of things, and Francis Bacon adopted the notion when he said " *vere scire esse per causas scire.*" Even now it is not uncommonly supposed that the knowledge of causes is something different from other knowledge, and consists, as it were, in getting possession of the keys of nature. A single word may thus act as a spell, and throw the clearest intellect into confusion, as I have often thought that Locke was thrown into confusion when endeavouring to find a meaning for the word *power*.[1] In Mill's *System of*

---

[1] *Essay concerning Human Understanding,* bk. ii. chap. xxi.

Logic the term *cause* seems to have re-asserted its old noxious power. Not only does Mill treat the Laws of Causation as almost coextensive with science, but he so uses the expression as to imply that when once we pass within the circle of causation we deal with certainties.

The philosophical danger which attaches to the use of this word may be thus described. A cause is defined as the necessary or invariable antecedent of an event, so that when the cause exists the effect will also exist or soon follow. If then we know the cause of an event, we know what will certainly happen ; and as it is implied that science, by a proper experimental method, may attain to a knowledge of causes, it follows that experience may give us a certain knowledge of future events. But nothing is more unquestionable than that finite experience can never give us certain knowledge of the future, so that either a cause is not an invariable antecedent, or else we can never gain certain knowledge of causes. The first horn of this dilemma is hardly to be accepted. Doubtless there is in nature some invariably acting mechanism, such that from certain fixed conditions an invariable result always emerges. But we, with our finite minds and short experience, can never penetrate the mystery of those existences which embody the Will of the Creator, and evolve it throughout time. We are in the position of spectators who witness the productions of a complicated machine, but are not allowed to examine its intimate structure. We learn what does happen and what does appear, but if we ask for the reason, the answer would involve an infinite depth of mystery. The simplest bit of matter, or the most trivial incident, such as the stroke of two billiard balls, offers infinitely more to learn than ever the human intellect can fathom. The word cause covers just as much untold meaning as any of the words *substance, matter, thought, existence.*

Confusion of Two Questions.

The subject is much complicated, too, by the confusion of two distinct questions. An event having happened, **we** may ask—

(1) Is there any cause for the event ?

(2) Of what kind is that cause ?

No one would assert that the mind possesses any faculty capable of inferring, prior to experience, that the occurrence of a sudden noise with flame and smoke indicates the combustion of a black powder, formed by the mixture of black, white, and yellow powders. The greatest upholder of *à priori* doctrines will allow that the particular aspect, shape, size, colour, texture, and other qualities of a cause must be gathered through the senses.

The question whether there is any cause at all for an event, is of a totally different kind. If an explosion could happen without any prior existing conditions, it must be a new creation—a distinct addition to the universe. It may be plausibly held that we can imagine neither the creation nor annihilation of anything. As regards matter, this has long been held true; as regards force, it is now almost universally assumed as an axiom that energy can neither come into nor go out of existence without distinct acts of Creative Will. That there exists any instinctive belief to this effect, indeed, seems doubtful. We find Lucretius, a philosopher of the utmost intellectual power and cultivation, gravely assuming that his raining atoms could turn aside from their straight paths in a self-determining manner, and by this spontaneous origination of energy determine the form of the universe.[1] Sir George Airy, too, seriously discussed the mathematical conditions under which a perpetual motion, that is, a perpetual source of self-created energy, might exist.[2] The larger part of the philosophic world has long held that in mental acts there is free will—in short, self-causation. It is in vain to attempt to reconcile this doctrine with that of an intuitive belief in causation, as Sir W. Hamilton candidly allowed.

It is obvious, moreover, that to assert the existence of a cause for every event cannot do more than remove into the indefinite past the inconceivable fact and mystery of creation At any given moment matter and energy

---

[1] *De Rerum Natura*, bk. ii. ll. 216-293.

[2] *Cambridge Philosophical Transactions* (1830), vol. iii. pp. 369—372.

were equal to what they are at present, or they were not; if equal, we may make the same inquiry concerning any other moment, however long prior, and we are thus obliged to accept one horn of the dilemma—existence from infinity, or creation at some moment. This is but one of the many cases in which we are compelled to believe in one or other of two alternatives, both inconceivable. My present purpose, however, is to point out that we must not confuse this supremely difficult question with that into which inductive science inquires on the foundation of facts. By induction we gain no certain knowledge; but by observation, and the inverse use of deductive reasoning, we estimate the probability that an event which has occurred was preceded by conditions of specified character, or that such conditions will be followed by the event.

Definition of the Term Cause.

Clear definitions of the word cause have been given by several philosophers. Hobbes has said, " A cause is the sum or aggregate of all such accidents, both in the agents and the patients, as concur in the producing of the effect propounded; all which existing together, it cannot be understood but that the effect existeth with them; or that it can possibly exist if any of them be absent." Brown, in his *Essay on Causation,* gave a nearly corresponding statement. "A cause," he says,[1] "may be defined to be the object or event which immediately precedes any change, and which existing again in similar circumstances will be always immediately followed by a similar change." Of the kindred word *power,* he likewise says :[2] " Power is nothing more than that invariableness of antecedence which is implied in the belief of causation."

These definitions may be accepted with the qualification that our knowledge of causes in such a sense can be probable only. The work of science consists in ascertaining the combinations in which phenomena present themselves.

---

[1] *Observations on the Nature and Tendency of the Doctrine of Mr. Hume, concerning the Relation of Cause and Effect.* Second ed. p. 44.   [2] Ibid. p. 97.

Concerning every event we shall have to determine its probable conditions, or the group of antecedents from which it probably follows.   An antecedent is anything which exists prior to an event; a consequent is anything which exists subsequently to an antecedent.   It will not usually happen that there is any probable connection between an antecedent and consequent.   Thus nitrogen is an antecedent to the lighting of a common fire; but it is so far from being a cause of the lighting, that it renders the combustion less active.   Daylight is an antecedent to all fires lighted during the day, but it probably has no appreciable effect upon their burning.   But in the case of any given event it is usually possible to discover a certain number of antecedents which seem to be always present, and with more or less probability we conclude that when they exist the event will follow.

Let it be observed that the utmost latitude is at present enjoyed in the use of the term *cause*.   Not only may a cause be an existent thing endowed with powers, as oxygen is the cause of combustion, gunpowder the cause of explosion, but the very absence or removal of a thing may also be a cause.   It is quite correct to speak of the dryness of the Egyptian atmosphere, or the absence of moisture, as being the cause of the preservation of mummies, and other remains of antiquity.   The cause of a mountain elevation, Ingleborough for instance, is the excavation of the surrounding valleys by denudation.   It is not so usual to speak of the existence of a thing at one moment as the cause of its existence at the next, but to me it seems the commonest case of causation which can occur.   The cause of motion of a billiard ball may be the stroke of another ball; and recent philosophy leads us to look upon all motions and changes, as but so many manifestations of prior existing energy.   In all probability there is no creation of energy and no destruction, so that as regards both mechanical and molecular changes, the cause is really the manifestation of existing energy.   In the same way I see not why the prior existence of matter is not also a cause as regards its subsequent existence.   All science tends to show us that the existence of the universe in a particular state at one moment, is the condition of its existence at the next moment, in an apparently different state. When we analyse the meaning which we can attribute to the word *cause*, it amounts to the existence of suitable portions of matter endowed with suitable quantities of energy. If we may accept Horne Tooke's assertion, *cause* has etymologically the meaning of *thing before*. Though, indeed, the origin of the word is very obscure, its derivatives, the Italian *cosa*, and the French *chose*, mean simply *thing*. In the German equivalent *ursache*, we have plainly the original meaning of *thing before*, the *sache* denoting "interesting or important object," the English *sake*, and *ur* being the equivalent of the English *ere*, *before*. We abandon, then, both etymology and philosophy, when we attribute to the *laws of causation* any meaning beyond that of the *conditions* under which an event may be expected to happen, according to our observation of the previous course of nature.

I have no objection to use the words cause and causation, provided they are never allowed to lead us to imagine that our knowledge of nature can attain to certainty. I repeat that if a cause is an invariable and necessary condition of an event, we can never know certainly whether the cause exists or not. To us, then, a cause is not to be distinguished from the group of positive or negative conditions which, with more or less probability, precede an event. In this sense, there is no particular difference between knowledge of causes and our general knowledge of the succession of combinations, in which the phenomena of nature are presented to us, or found to occur in experimental inquiry.

Distinction of Inductive and Deductive Results.

We must carefully avoid confusing together inductive investigations which terminate in the establishment of general laws, and those which seem to lead directly to the knowledge of future particular events. That process only can be called induction which gives general laws, and it is by the subsequent employment of deduction that we anticipate particular events. If the observation of a number of cases shows that alloys of metals fuse at lower temperatures than their constituent metals, I may with more or less probability draw a general inference to that

effect, and may thence deductively ascertain the probability that the next alloy examined will fuse at a lower
temperature than its constituents.   It has been asserted,
indeed, by Mill,[1] and partially admitted by Mr. Fowler,[2]
that we can argue directly from case to case, so that what
is true of some alloys will be true of the next.   Professor
Bain has adopted the same view of reasoning.   He thinks
that Mill has extricated us from the dead lock of the
syllogism and effected a total revolution in logic.   He
holds that reasoning from particulars to particulars is not
only the usual, the most obvious and the most ready
method, but that it is the type of reasoning which best
discloses the real process.[3]   Doubtless, this is the usual
result of our reasoning, regard being had to degrees of
probability ; but these logicians fail entirely to give any
explanation of the process by which we get from case
to case.

It may be allowed that the knowledge of future particular events is the main purpose of our investigations,
and if there were any process of thought by which we
could pass directly from event to event without ascending
into general truths, this method would be sufficient, and
certainly the briefest.   It is true, also, that the laws of
mental association lead the mind always to expect the like
again in apparently like circumstances, and even animals
of very low intelligence must have some trace of such
powers of association, serving to guide them more or less
correctly, in the absence of true reasoning faculties.   But
it is the purpose of logic, according to Mill, to ascertain
whether inferences have been correctly drawn, rather than
to discover them.[4]   Even if we can, then, by habit,
association, or any rude process of inference, infer the
future directly from the past, it is the work of logic to
analyse the conditions on which the correctness of this
inference depends.   Even Mill would admit that such
analysis involves the consideration of general truths,[5] and

---

[1] *System of Logic*, bk. II. chap. iii.
[2] *Inductive Logic*, pp. 13, 14.
[3] Bain, *Deductive Logic*, pp. 208, 209.
[4] *System of Logic*. Introduction, § 4.   Fifth ed. pp. 8, 9.
[5] Ibid. bk. II. chap. iii. § 5, pp. 225, &c.

in this, as in several other important points, we might controvert Mill's own views by his own statements. It seems to me undesirable in a systematic work like this to enter into controversy at any length, or to attempt to refute the views of other logicians. But I shall feel bound to state, in a separate publication, my very deliberate opinion that many of Mill's innovations in logical science, and especially his doctrine of reasoning from particulars to particulars, are entirely groundless and false.

The Grounds of Inductive Inference.

I hold that in all cases of inductive inference we must invent hypotheses, until we fall upon some hypothesis which yields deductive results in accordance with experience. Such accordance renders the chosen hypothesis more or less probable, and we may then deduce, with some degree of likelihood, the nature of our future experience, on the assumption that no arbitrary change takes place in the conditions of nature. We can only argue from the past to the future, on the general principle set forth in this work, that what is true of a thing will be true of the like. So far then as one object or event differs from another, all inference is impossible, particulars as particulars can no more make an inference than grains of sand can make a rope. We must always rise to something which is general or same in the cases, and assuming that sameness to be extended to new cases we learn their nature. Hearing a clock tick five thousand times without exception or variation, we adopt the very probable hypothesis that there is some invariably acting machine which produces those uniform sounds, and which will, in the absence of change, go on producing them. Meeting twenty times with a bright yellow ductile substance, and finding it always to be very heavy and incorrodible, I infer that there was some natural condition which tended in the creation of things to associate these properties together, and I expect to find them associated in the next instance. But there always is the possibility that some unknown change may take place between past and future cases. The clock may run down, or be subject to a hundred accidents altering its condition. There is no reason in the nature of things, so far as known

to us, why yellow colour, ductility, high specific gravity,
and incorrodibility, should always be associated together,
and in other cases, if not in this, men's expectations
have been deceived. Our inferences, therefore, always
retain more or less of a hypothetical character, and are so
far open to doubt. Only in proportion as our induction
approximates to the character of perfect induction, does
it approximate to certainty. The amount of uncertainty
corresponds to the probability that other objects than
those examined may exist and falsify our inferences; the
amount of probability corresponds to the amount of information yielded by our examination; and the theory of
probability will be needed to prevent us from over-estimating or under-estimating the knowledge we possess.

Illustrations of the Inductive Process.

To illustrate the passage from the known to the apparently unknown, let us suppose that the phenomena
under investigation consist of numbers, and that the
following six numbers being exhibited to us, we are
required to infer the character of the next in the
series :—

$$5, \ 15, \ 35, \ 45, \ 65, \ 95.$$

The question first of all arises, How may we describe this
series of numbers? What is uniformly true of them?
The reader cannot fail to perceive at the first glance that
they all end in five, and the problem is, from the properties of these six numbers, to infer the properties of the
next number ending in five. If we test their properties
by the process of perfect induction, we soon perceive that
they have another common property, namely that of being
divisible by five without remainder. May we then assert that
the next number ending in five is also divisible by five,
and, if so, upon what grounds? Or extending the question,
Is every number ending in five divisible by five? Does it
follow that because six numbers obey a supposed law,
therefore 376,685,975 or any other number, however large,
obeys the law? I answer *certainly not*. The law in question is undoubtedly true; but its truth is not proved by
any finite number of examples. All that these six numbers
can do is to suggest to my mind the possible existence of

such a law; and I then ascertain its truth, by proving
deductively from the rules of decimal numeration, that any
number ending in five must be made up of multiples of
five, and must therefore be itself a multiple.

To make this more plain, let the reader now examine
the numbers—

$$7, 17, 37, 47, 67, 97.$$

They all end in 7 instead of 5, and though not at equal
intervals, the intervals are the same as in the previous
case. After consideration, the reader will perceive that
these numbers all agree in being *prime numbers,* or multiples of unity only. May we then infer that the next, or
any other number ending in 7, is a prime number?
Clearly not, for on trial we find that 27, 57, 117 are not
primes. Six instances, then, treated empirically, lead us
to a true and universal law in one case, and mislead us in
another case. We ought, in fact, to have no confidence in
any law until we have treated it deductively, and have
shown that from the conditions supposed the results expected must ensue. No one can show from the principles
of number, that numbers ending in 7 should be primes.

From the history of the theory of numbers some good
examples of false induction can be adduced. Taking the
following series of prime numbers,

$$41, 43, 47, 53, 61, 71, 83, 97, 113, 131, 151, \&c.,$$

it will be found that they all agree in being values of
the general expression $x^2 + x + 41$, putting for x in succession the values, 0, 1, 2, 3, 4, &c. We seem always to
obtain a prime number, and the induction is apparently
strong, to the effect that this expression always will
give primes. Yet a few more trials disprove this false conclusion. Put $x = 40$, and we obtain $40 \times 40 + 40 + 41$,
or 41×41. Such a failure could never have happened,
had we shown any deductive reason why $x^2 + x + 41$
should give primes.

There can be no doubt that what here happens with
forty instances, might happen with forty thousand or
forty million instances. An apparent law never once
failing up to a certain point may then suddenly break
down, so that inductive reasoning, as it has been described
by some writers, can give no sure knowledge of what is to
come. Babbage pointed out in his Ninth Bridgewater

Treatise, that a machine could be constructed to give a perfectly.regular series of numbers through a vast series of steps, and yet to break the law of progression suddenly at any required point. No number of particular cases as particulars enables us to pass by inference to any new case. It is hardly needful to inquire here what can be inferred from an infinite series of facts, because they are never practically within our power; but we may unhesitatingly accept the conclusion, that no finite number of instances can ever prove a general law, or can give us certain knowledge of even one other instance.

General mathematical theorems have indeed been discovered by the observation of particular cases, and may again be so discovered. We have Newton's own statement, to the effect that he was thus led to the all-important Binomial Theorem, the basis of the whole structure of mathematical analysis. Speaking of a certain series of terms, expressing the area of a circle or hyperbola, he says : " I reflected that the denominators were in arithmetical progression; so that only the numerical co-efficients of the numerators remained to be investigated. But these, in the alternate areas, were the figures of the powers of the number eleven, namely 11^0, 11^1, 11^2, 11^3, 11^4; that is, in the first 1 ; in the second 1, 1 ; in the third 1, 2, 1 ; in the fourth 1, 3, 3, 1 ; in the fifth 1, 4, 6, 4, 1.[1] I inquired, therefore, in what manner all the remaining figures could be found from the first two ; and I found that if the first figure be called m, all the rest could be found by the continual multiplication of the terms of the formula

$$\frac{m-0}{1} \times \frac{m-1}{2} \times \frac{m-2}{3} \times \frac{m-3}{4} \times \&c."[2]$$

It is pretty evident, from this most interesting statement, that Newton, having simply observed the succession of the numbers, tried various formulæ until he found one which agreed with them all. He was so little satisfied with this process, however, that he verified particular results of his new theorem by comparison with the results of common

---

[1] These are the figurate numbers considered in pages 183, 187, &c.
[2] *Commercium Epistolicum. Epistola ad Oldenburgum*, Oct. 24, 1676. Horsley's *Works of Newton*, vol. iv. p. 541. See De Morgan in *Penny Cyclovædia* art. " Binomial Theorem," p. 412.

multiplication, and the rule for the extraction of the square root. Newton, in fact, gave no demonstration of his theorem; and the greatest mathematicians of the last century, James Bernoulli, Maclaurin, Landen, Euler, Lagrange, &c., occupied themselves with discovering a conclusive method of deductive proof.

There can be no doubt that in geometry also discoveries have been suggested by direct observation. Many of the now trivial propositions of Euclid's Elements were probably thus discovered, by the ancient Greek geometers; and we have pretty clear evidence of this in the Commentaries of Proclus.[1] Galileo was the first to examine the remarkable properties of the cycloid, the curve described by a point in the circumference of a wheel rolling on a plane. By direct observation he ascertained that the area of the curve is apparently three times that of the generating circle or wheel, but he was unable to prove this exactly, or to verify it by strict geometrical reasoning. Sir George Airy has recorded a curious case, in which he fell accidentally by trial on a new geometrical property of the sphere.[2] But discovery in such cases means nothing more than suggestion, and it is always by pure deduction that the general law is really established. As Proclus puts it, *we must pass from sense to consideration.*

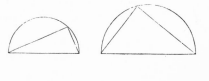

Given, for instance, the series of figures in the accompanying diagram, measurement will show that the curved lines approximate to semicircles, and the rectilinear figures to right-angled triangles. These figures may seem to suggest to the mind the general law that angles inscribed

[1] Bk. ii. chap. iv.
[2] *Philosophical Transactions* (1866), vol. 146, p. 334.

in semicircles are right angles ; but no number of instances,
and no possible accuracy of measurement would really
establish the truth of that general law. Availing ourselves
of the suggestion furnished by the figures, we can only
investigate deductively the consequences which flow from
the definition of a circle, until we discover among them the
property of containing right angles. Persons have thought
that they had discovered a method of trisecting angles by
plane geometrical construction, because a certain complex
arrangement of lines and circles had appeared to trisect an
angle in every case tried by them, and they inferred, by a
supposed act of induction, that it would succeed in all
other cases. De Morgan has recorded a proposed mode of
trisecting the angle which could not be discriminated by
the senses from a true general solution, except when it was
applied to very obtuse angles.[1] In all such cases, it has
always turned out either that the angle was not trisected
at all, or that only certain particular angles could be thus
trisected. The trisectors were misled by some apparent or
special coincidence, and only deductive proof could establish the truth and generality of the result. In this particular case, deductive proof shows that the problem
attempted is impossible, and that angles generally cannot
be trisected by common geometrical methods.

Geometrical Reasoning.

This view of the matter is strongly supported by the
further consideration of geometrical reasoning. No skill
and care could ever enable us to verify absolutely any one
geometrical proposition. Rousseau, in his *Emile*, tells us
that we should teach a child geometry by causing him to
measure and compare figures by superposition. While a
child was yet incapable of general reasoning, this would
doubtless be an instructive exercise; but it never could
teach geometry, nor prove the truth of any one proposition.
All our figures are rude approximations, and they may
happen to seem unequal when they should be equal,
and equal when they should be unequal. Moreover
figures may from chance be equal in case after case, and

[1] *Budget of Paradoxes*, p. 257.

yet there may be no general reason why they should be
so. The results of deductive geometrical reasoning are
absolutely certain, and are either exactly true or capable
of being carried to any required degree of approximation.
In a perfect triangle, the angles must be equal to one half-
revolution precisely; even an infinitesimal divergence
would be impossible; and I believe with equal confidence,
that however many are the angles of a figure, provided
there are no re-entrant angles, the sum of the angles will
be precisely and absolutely equal to twice as many right-
angles as the figure has sides, less by four right-angles.
In such cases, the deductive proof is absolute and complete ; empirical verification can at the most guard against
accidental oversights.

There is a second class of geometrical truths which can
only be proved by approximation ; but, as the mind sees
no reason why that approximation should not always go
on, we arrive at complete conviction. We thus learn that
the surface of a sphere is equal exactly to two-thirds of
the whole surface of the circumscribing cylinder, or to four
times the area of the generating circle. The area of a
parabola is exactly two-thirds of that of the circumscribing
parallelogram. The area of the cycloid is exactly three
times that of the generating circle. These are truths that
we could never ascertain, nor even verify by observation ,
for any finite amount of difference, less than what the
senses can discern, would falsify them.

There are geometrical relations again which we cannot
assign exactly, but can carry to any desirable degree of approximation. The ratio of the circumference to the diameter of a circle is that of $3\cdot14159265358979323846\ldots$
to 1, and the approximation may be carried to any extent by the expenditure of sufficient labour. Mr. W.
Shanks has given the value of this natural constant, known
as π, to the extent of 707 places of decimals.[1] Some years
since, I amused myself by trying how near I could get to
this ratio, by the careful use of compasses, and I did not
come nearer than 1 part in 540. We might imagine measurements so accurately executed as to give us eight or
ten places correctly. But the power of the hands and

[1] *Proceedings of the Royal Society* (1872-3), vol. **xxi.** p. 319.

senses must soon stop, whereas the mental powers of deductive reasoning can proceed to an unlimited degree of approximation.   Geometrical truths, then, are incapable of
verification ; and, if so, they cannot even be learnt by
observation.   How can I have learnt by observation a proposition of which I cannot even prove the truth by observation, when I am in possession of it ?   All that observation or empirical trial can do is to suggest propositions, of
which the truth may afterwards be proved deductively.

If Viviani's story is to be believed, Galileo endeavoured
to satisfy himself about the area of the cycloid by cutting
out several large cycloids in pasteboard, and then comparing the areas of the curve and the generating circle by
weighing them.   In every trial the curve seemed to be
rather less than three times the circle, so that Galileo, we
are told, began to suspect that the ratio was not precisely
3 to 1.   It is quite clear, however, that no process of
weighing or measuring could ever prove truths like these,
and it remained for Torricelli to show what his master
Galileo had only guessed at.[1]

Much has been said about the peculiar certainty of
mathematical reasoning, but it is only certainty of deductive reasoning, and equal certainty attaches to all correct
logical deduction.   If a triangle be right-angled, the
square on the hypothenuse will undoubtedly equal the
sum of the two squares on the other sides ; but I can
never be sure that a triangle is right-angled : so I can be
certain that nitric acid will not dissolve gold, provided I
know that the substances employed really correspond to
those on which I tried the experiment previously.   Here
is like certainty of inference, and like doubt as to the
facts.

Discrimination of Certainty and Probability.

We can never recur too often to the truth that our
knowledge of the laws and future events of the external
world is only probable.   The mind itself is quite capable
of possessing certain knowledge, and it is well to discriminate carefully between what we can and cannot know

[1] *Life of Galileo*, Society for the Diffusion of Useful Knowledge,
p. 102.

with certainty. In the first place, whatever feeling is actually present to the mind is certainly known to that mind. If I see blue sky, I may be quite sure that I do experience the sensation of blueness. Whatever I do feel, I do feel beyond all doubt. We are indeed very likely to confuse what we really feel with what we are inclined to associate with it, or infer inductively from it; but the whole of our consciousness, as far as it is the result of pure intuition and free from inference, is certain knowledge beyond all doubt.

In the second place, we may have certainty of inference ; the fundamental laws of thought, and the rule of substitution (p. 9), are certainly true ; and if my senses could inform me that A was indistinguishable in colour from B, and B from C, then I should be equally certain that A was indistinguishable from C. In short, whatever truth there is in the premises, I can certainly embody in their correct logical result. But the certainty generally assumes a hypothetical character. I never can be quite sure that two colours are exactly alike, that two magnitudes are exactly equal, or that two bodies whatsoever are identical even in their apparent qualities. Almost all our judgments involve quantitative relations, and, as will be shown in succeeding chapters, we can never attain exactness and certainty where continuous quantity enters. Judgments concerning discontinuous quantity or numbers, however, allow of certainty ; I may establish beyond doubt, for instance, that the difference of the squares of 17 and 13 is the product of $17 + 13$ and $17 - 13$, and is therefore 30×4, or 120.

Inferences which we draw concerning natural objects are never certain except in a hypothetical point of view. It might seem to be certain that iron is magnetic, or that gold is incapable of solution in nitric acid; but, if we carefully investigate the meanings of these statements, they will be found to involve no certainty but that of consciousness and that of hypothetical inference. For what do I mean by iron or gold? If I choose a remarkable piece of yellow substance, call it gold, and then immerse it in a liquid which I call nitric acid, and find that there is no change called solution, then consciousness has certainly informed me that, with my meaning of the terms, "Gold is insoluble in nitric acid." I may further

be certain of something else; for if this gold and nitric
acid remain what they were, I may be sure there will be
no solution on again trying the experiment. If I take other
portions of gold and nitric acid, and am sure that they really
are identical in properties with the former portions, I can
be certain that there will be no solution. But at this point
my knowledge becomes purely hypothetical; for how can I
be sure without trial that the gold and acid are really
identical in nature with what I formerly called gold and
nitric acid. How do I know gold when I see it? If I
judge by the apparent qualities—colour, ductility, specific
gravity, &c., I may be misled, because there may always
exist a substance which to the colour, ductility, specific
gravity, and other specified qualities, joins others which we
do not expect. Similarly, if iron is magnetic, as shown by
an experiment with objects answering to those names, then
all iron is magnetic, meaning all pieces of matter identical
with my assumed piece. But in trying to identify iron, I
am always open to mistake. Nor is this liability to mistake a matter of speculation only.[1]

The history of chemistry shows that the most confident
inferences may have been falsified by the confusion of one
substance with another. Thus strontia was never discriminated from baryta until Klaproth and Haüy detected
differences between some of their properties. Accordingly
chemists must often have inferred concerning strontia
what was only true of baryta, and *vice versâ*. There is
now no doubt that the recently discovered substances,
cæsium and rubidium, were long mistaken for potassium.[2]
Other elements have often been confused together—for
instance, tantalum and niobium; sulphur and selenium;
cerium, lanthanum, and didymium; yttrium and erbium.

Even the best known laws of physical science do
not exclude false inference. No law of nature has been
better established than that of universal gravitation, and
we believe with the utmost confidence that any body
capable of affecting the senses will attract other bodies,
and fall to the earth if not prevented. Euler remarks

---

[1] Professor Bowen has excellently stated this view. *Treatise on
Logic*. Cambridge, U.S.A., 1866, p. 354.
[2] Roscoe's *Spectrum Analysis*, 1st edit., p. 98.

that, although he had never made trial of the stones which compose the church of Magdeburg, yet he had not the least doubt that all of them were heavy, and would fall if unsupported. But he adds, that it would be extremely difficult to give any satisfactory explanation of this confident belief.[1] The fact is, that the belief ought not to amount to certainty until the experiment has been tried, and in the meantime a slight amount of uncertainty enters, because we cannot be sure that the stones of the Magdeburg Church resemble other stones in all their properties.

In like manner, not one of the inductive truths which men have established, or think they have established, is really safe from exception or reversal. Lavoisier, when laying the foundations of chemistry, met with so many instances tending to show the existence of oxygen in all acids, that he adopted a general conclusion to that effect, and devised the name oxygen accordingly. He entertained no appreciable doubt that the acid existing in sea salt also contained oxygen;[2] yet subsequent experience falsified his expectations. This instance refers to a science in its infancy, speaking relatively to the possible achievements of men. But all sciences are and ever will remain in their infancy, relatively to the extent and complexity of the universe which they undertake to investigate. Euler expresses no more than the truth when he says that it would be impossible to fix on any one thing really existing, of which we could have so perfect a knowledge as to put us beyond the reach of mistake.[3] We may be quite certain that a comet will go on moving in a similar path *if* all circumstances remain the same as before ; but if we leave out this extensive qualification, our predictions will always be subject to the chance of falsification by some unexpected event, such as the division of Biela's comet or the interference of an unknown gravitating body.

---

[1] Euler's *Letters to a German Princess*, translated by Hunter. 2nd ed., vol. ii. pp. 17, 18.
[2] Lavoisier's *Chemistry*, translated by Kerr. 3rd ed., pp. 114, 121, 123.
[3] Euler's *Letters*, vol. ii. p. 21.

Inductive inference might attain to certainty if our knowledge of the agents existing throughout the universe were complete, and if we were at the same time certain that the same Power which created the universe would allow it to proceed without arbitrary change. There is always a possibility of causes being in existence without our knowledge, and these may at any moment produce an unexpected effect. Even when by the theory of probabilities we succeed in forming some notion of the comparative confidence with which we should receive inductive results, it yet appears to me that we must make an assumption. Events come out like balls from the vast ballot-box of nature, and close observation will enable us to form some notion, as we shall see in the next chapter, of the contents of that ballot-box. But we must still assume that, between the time of an observation and that to which our inferences relate, no change in the ballot-box has been made.

CHAPTER XII.

THE INDUCTIVE OR INVERSE APPLICATION OF THE THEORY OF PROBABILITY.

WE have hitherto considered the theory of probability only in its simple deductive employment, in which it enables us to determine from given conditions the probable character of events happening under those conditions. But as deductive reasoning when inversely applied constitutes the process of induction, so the calculation of probabilities may be inversely applied; from the known character of certain events we may argue backwards to the probability of a certain law or condition governing those events. Having satisfactorily accomplished this work, we may indeed calculate forwards to the probable character of future events happening under the same conditions ; but this part of the process is a direct use of deductive reasoning (p. 226).

Now it is highly instructive to find that whether the theory of probability be deductively or inductively applied, the calculation is always performed according to the principles and rules of deduction. The probability that an event has a particular condition entirely depends upon the probability that if the condition existed the event would follow. If we take up a pack of common playing cards, and observe that they are arranged in perfect numerical order, we conclude beyond all reasonable doubt that they have been thus intentionally arranged by some person acquainted with the usual order of sequence. This conclusion is quite irresistible, and rightly so; for there are but two suppositions which we can make as to the reason of the cards being in that particular order :—

1. They may have been intentionally arranged by some one who would probably prefer the numerical order.

2. They may have fallen into that order by chance, that is, by some series of conditions which, being unknown to us, cannot be known to lead by preference to the particular order in question.

The latter supposition is by no means absurd, for any one order is as likely as any other when there is no preponderating tendency. But we can readily calculate by the doctrine of permutations the probability that fifty-two objects would fall by chance into any one particular order. Fifty-two objects can be arranged in $52 \times 51 \times . . \times 3 \times 2 \times 1$ or about $8066 \times (10)^{64}$ possible orders, the number obtained requiring 68 places of figures for its full expression. Hence it is excessively unlikely that anyone should ever meet with a pack of cards arranged in perfect order by accident. If we do meet with a pack so arranged, we inevitably adopt the other supposition, that some person, having reasons for preferring that special order, has thus put them together.

We know that of the immense number of possible orders the numerical order is the most remarkable ; it is useful as proving the perfect constitution of the pack, and it is the intentional result of certain games. At any rate, the probability that intention should produce that order is incomparably greater than the probability that chance should produce it ; and as a certain pack exists in that order, we rightly prefer the supposition which most probably leads to the observed result.

By a similar mode of reasoning we every day arrive, and validly arrive, at conclusions approximating to certainty. Whenever we observe a perfect resemblance between two objects, as, for instance, two printed pages, two engravings, two coins, two foot-prints, we are warranted in asserting that they proceed from the same type, the same plate, the same pair of dies, or the same boot. And why ? Because it is almost impossible that with different types, plates, dies, or boots some apparent distinction of form should not be produced. It is impossible for the hand of the most skilful artist to make two objects alike, so that mechanical repetition is the only probable explanation of exact similarity.

We can often establish with extreme probability that one document is copied from another. Suppose that each document contains 10,000 words, and that the same word is incorrectly spelt in each. There is then a probability of less than 1 in 10,000 that the same mistake should be made in each. If we meet with a second error occurring in each document, the probability is less than 1 in 10,000 × 9999, that two such coincidences should occur by chance, and the numbers grow with extreme rapidity for more numerous coincidences. We cannot make any precise calculations without taking into account the character of the errors committed, concerning the conditions of which we have no accurate means of estimating probabilities. Nevertheless, abundant evidence may thus be obtained as to the derivation of documents from each other. In the examination of many sets of logarithmic tables, six remarkable errors were found to be present in all but two, and it was proved that tables printed at Paris, Berlin, Florence, Avignon, and even in China, besides thirteen sets printed in England between the years 1633 and 1822, were derived directly or indirectly from some common source.[1] With a certain amount of labour, it is possible to establish beyond reasonable doubt the relationship or genealogy of any number of copies of one document, proceeding possibly from parent copies now lost. The relations between the manuscripts of the New Testament have been elaborately investigated in this manner, and the same work has been performed for many classical writings, especially by German scholars.

Principle of the Inverse Method.

The inverse application of the rules of probability entirely depends upon a proposition which may be thus stated, nearly in the words of Laplace.[2] *If an event can*

---

[1] Lardner, *Edinburgh Review*, July 1834, p. 277.
[2] *Mémoires par divers Savans*, tom. vi. ; quoted by Todhunter in his *History of the Theory of Probability*, p. 458.

be produced by any one of a certain number of different causes, all equally probable à priori, the probabilities of the existence of these causes as inferred from the event, are proportional to the probabilities of the event as derived from these causes. In other words, the most probable cause of an event which has happened is that which would most probably lead to the event supposing the cause to exist; but all other possible causes are also to be taken into account with probabilities proportional to the probability that the event would happen if the cause existed. Suppose, to fix our ideas clearly, that E is the event, and C_1 C_2 C_3 are the three only conceivable causes. If C exist, the probability is p_1 that E would follow ; if C_2 or C_3 exist, the like probabilities are respectively p_2 and p_3. Then as p_1 is to p_2, so is the probability of C_1 being the actual cause to the probability of C_2 being it; and, similarly, as p_2 is to p_3, so is the probability of C_2 being the actual cause to the probability of C_3 being it. By a simple mathematical process .we arrive at the conclusion that the actual probability of C_1 being the cause is

$$\frac{p_1}{p_1 + p_2 + p_3} ;$$

and the similar probabilities of the existence of C_2 and C_3 are,

$$\frac{p_2}{p_1 + p_2 + p_3} \text{ and } \frac{p_3}{p_1 + p_2 + p_3}.$$

The sum of these three fractions amounts to unity, which correctly expresses the certainty that one cause or other must be in operation.

We may thus state the result in general language *If it is certain that one or other of the supposed causes exists, the probability that any one does exist is the probability that if it exists the event happens, divided by the sum of all the similar probabilities.* There may seem to be an intricacy in this subject which may prove distasteful to some readers ; but this intricacy is essential to the subject in hand. No one can possibly understand the principles of inductive reasoning, unless he will take the trouble to master the meaning of this rule, by which we recede from an event to the probability of each of its possible causes.

This rule or principle of the indirect method is that which common sense leads us to adopt almost instinctively, before we have any comprehension of the principle in its general form. It is easy to see, too, that it is the rule which will, out of a great multitude of cases, lead us most often to the truth, since the most probable cause of an event really means that cause which in the greatest number of cases produces the event. Donkin and Boole have given demonstrations of this principle, but the one most easy to comprehend is that of Poisson. He imagines each possible cause of an event to be represented by a distinct ballot-box, containing black and white balls, in such a ratio that the probability of a white ball being drawn is equal to that of the event happening. He further supposes that each box, as is possible, contains the same total number of balls, black and white ; then, mixing all the contents of the boxes together, he shows that if a white ball be drawn from the aggregate ballot-box thus formed, the probability that it proceeded from any particular ballot-box is represented by the number of white balls in that particular box, divided by the total number of white balls in all the boxes. This result corresponds to that given by the principle in question.[1]

Thus, if there be three boxes, each containing ten balls in all, and respectively containing seven, four, and three white balls, then on mixing all the balls together we have fourteen white ones ; and if we draw a white ball, that is if the event happens, the probability that it came out of the first box is $\frac{7}{14}$; which is exactly equal to $\dfrac{\frac{7}{10}}{\frac{7}{10}+\frac{4}{10}+\frac{3}{10}}$, the fraction given by the rule of the Inverse Method.

Simple Applications of the Inverse Method.

In many cases of scientific induction we may apply the principle of the inverse method in a simple manner. If only two, or at the most a few hypotheses, may be made as to the origin of certain phenomena, we may sometimes easily calculate the respective probabilities. It was thus that Bunsen and Kirchhoff established, with a probability little short of certainty, that iron exists in the sun. On comparing the spectra of sunlight and of the light proceed-

[1] Poisson, *Recherches sur la Probabilité des Jugements*, Paris, 1837, pp 82, 83.

ing from the incandescent vapour of iron, it became apparent that at least sixty bright lines in the spectrum of iron
coincided with dark lines in the sun's spectrum. Such coincidences could never be observed with certainty, because,
even if the lines only closely approached, the instrumental
imperfections of the spectroscope would make them apparently coincident, and if one line came within half a millimetre of another, on the map of the spectra, they could not
be pronounced distinct. Now the average distance of the
solar lines on Kirchhoff's map is 2 mm., and if we throw
down a line, as it were, by pure chance on such a map,
the probability is about one-half that the new line will fall
within $\frac{1}{2}$ mm. on one side or the other of some one of the
solar lines. To put it in another way, we may suppose
that each solar line, either on account of its real breadth,
or the defects of the instrument, possesses a breadth of
$\frac{1}{2}$ mm., and that each line in the iron spectrum has a like
breadth. The probability then is just one-half that the
centre of each iron line will come by chance within 1 mm.
of the centre of a solar line, so as to appear to coincide
with it. The probability of casual coincidence of each
iron line with a solar line is in like manner $\frac{1}{2}$. Coincidence in the case of each of the sixty iron lines is a very
unlikely event if it arises casually, for it would have a
probability of only $(\frac{1}{2})^{60}$ or less than 1 in a trillion. The
odds, in short, are more than a million million millions
to unity against such casual coincidence.[1] But on the
other hypothesis, that iron exists in the sun, it is highly
probable that such coincidences would be observed ; it is
immensely more probable that sixty coincidences would be
observed if iron existed in the sun, than that they should
arise from chance. Hence by our principle it is immensely
probable that iron does exist in the sun.

All the other interesting results, given by the comparison
of spectra, rest upon the same principle of probability.
The almost complete coincidence between the spectra of
solar, lunar, and planetary light renders it practically
certain that the light is all of solar origin, and is reflected
from the surfaces of the moon and planets, suffering only

---

[1] Kirchhoff's *Researches on the Solar Spectrum*. First part, translated by Roscoe, pp. 18, 19.

slight alteration from the atmospheres of some of the planets. A fresh confirmation of the truth of the Copernican theory is thus furnished.

Herschel proved in this way the connection between the direction of the oblique faces of quartz crystals, and the direction in which the same crystals rotate the plane of polarisation of light. For if it is found in a second crystal that the relation is the same as in the first, the probability of this happening by chance is $\frac{1}{2}$; the probability that in another crystal also the direction will be the same is $\frac{1}{4}$, and so on. The probability that in $n + 1$ crystals there would be casual agreement of direction is the nth power of $\frac{1}{2}$. Thus, if in examining fourteen crystals the same relation of the two phenomena is discovered in each, the odds that it proceeds from uniform conditions are more than 8000 to 1.[1] Since the first observations on this subject were made in 1820, no exceptions have been observed, so that the probability of invariable connection is incalculably great.

It is exceedingly probable that the ancient Egyptians had exactly recorded the eclipses occurring during long periods of time, for Diogenes Laertius mentions that 373 solar and 832 lunar eclipses had been observed, and the ratio between these numbers exactly expresses that which would hold true of the eclipses of any long period, of say 1200 or 1300 years, as estimated on astronomical grounds. It is evident that an agreement between small numbers, or customary numbers, such as seven, one hundred, a myriad, &c., is much more likely to happen from chance, and therefore gives much less presumption of dependence. If two ancient writers spoke of the sacrifice of oxen, they would in all probability describe it as a hecatomb, and there would be nothing remarkable in the coincidence. But it is impossible to point out any special reason why an old writer should select such numbers as 373 and 832, unless they had been the results of observation.

On similar grounds, we must inevitably believe in the

---

[1] *Edinburgh Review*, No. 185, vol. xcii. July 1850, p. 32 ; Herschel's *Essays*, p. 421 ; *Transactions of the Cambridge Philosophical Society*, vol. i. p. 43.

human origin of the flint flakes so copiously discovered of late years: For though the accidental stroke of one stone against another may often produce flakes, such as are occasionally found on the sea-shore, yet when several flakes are found in close company, and each one bears evidence, not of a single blow only, but of several successive blows, all conducing to form a symmetrical knife-like form, the probability of a natural and accidental origin becomes incredibly small, and the contrary supposition, that they are the work of intelligent beings, approximately certain.[1]

The Theory of Probability in Astronomy.

The science of astronomy, occupied with the simple relations of distance, magnitude, and motion of the heavenly bodies, admits more easily than almost any other science of interesting conclusions founded on the theory of probability. More than a century ago, in 1767, Michell showed the extreme probability of bonds connecting together systems of stars. He was struck by the unexpected number of fixed stars which have companions close to them. Such a conjunction might happen casually by one star, although possibly at a great distance from the other, happening to lie on a straight line passing near the earth. But the probabilities are so greatly against such an optical union happening often in the expanse of the heavens, that Michell asserted the existence of some connection between most of the double stars. It has since been estimated by Struve, that the odds are 9570 to 1 against any two stars of not less than the seventh magnitude falling within the apparent distance of four seconds of each other by chance, and yet ninety-one such cases were known when the estimation was made, and many more cases have since been discovered. There were also four known triple stars, and yet the odds against the appearance of any one such conjunction are 173,524 to 1.[2] The conclusions of Michell have been

---

[1] Evans' *Ancient Stone Implements of Great Britain.* London, 1872 (Longmans).

[2] Herschel, *Outlines of Astronomy,* 1849, p. 565 ; but Todhunter, in his *History of the Theory of Probability,* p. 335, states that the calculations do not agree with those published by Struve.

entirely verified by the discovery that many double stars are connected by gravitation.

Michell also investigated the probability that the six brightest stars in the Pleiades should have come by accidents into such striking proximity. Estimating the number of stars of equal or greater brightness at 1500, he found the odds to be nearly 500,000 to 1 against casual conjunction. Extending the same kind of argument to other clusters, such as that of Præsepe, the nebula in the hilt of Perseus' sword, he says: [1] "We may with the highest probability conclude, the odds against the contrary opinion being many million millions to one, that the stars are really collected together in clusters in some places, where they form a kind of system, while in others there are either few or none of them, to whatever cause this may be owing, whether to their mutual gravitation, or to some other law or appointment of the Creator."

The calculations of Michell have been called in question by the late James D. Forbes,[2] and Mr. Todhunter vaguely countenances his objections,[3] otherwise I should not have thought them of much weight. Certainly Laplace accepts Michell's views,[4] and if Michell be in error it is in the methods of calculation, not in the general validity of his reasoning and conclusions.

Similar calculations might no doubt be applied to the peculiar drifting motions which have been detected by Mr. R. A. Proctor in some of the constellations.[5] The odds are very greatly against any numerous group of stars moving together in any one direction by chance. On like grounds, there can be no doubt that the sun has a considerable proper motion because on the average the fixed stars show a tendency to move apparently from one point of the heavens towards that diametrically opposite. The sun's motion in the contrary direction would explain this tendency, otherwise we must believe that thousands of stars accidentally agree in their direction of motion, or are

[1] *Philosophical Transactions*, 1767, vol. lvii. p. 431.
[2] *Philosophical Magazine*, 3rd Series, vol. xxxvii. p. 401, December 1850 ; also August 1849.
[3] *History*, &c., p. 334.   [4] *Essai Philosophique*, p. 57.
Proceedings of the Royal Society ; 20 January, 1870 ; *Philosophical Magazine*, 4th Series, vol. xxxix. p. 381.

urged by some common force from which the sun is
exempt. It may be said that the rotation of the earth is
proved in like manner, because it is immensely more probable that one body would revolve than that the sun,
moon, planets, comets, and the whole of the stars of the
heavens should be whirled round the earth daily, with a
uniform motion superadded to their own peculiar motions.
This appears to be mainly the reason which led Gilbert,
one of the earliest English Copernicans, and in every way
an admirable physicist, to admit the rotation of the earth,
while Francis Bacon denied it.

In contemplating the planetary system, we are struck
with the similarity in direction of nearly all its movements.
Newton remarked upon the regularity and uniformity of
these motions, and contrasted them with the eccentricity
and irregularity of the cometary orbits.[1] Could we, in
fact, look down upon the system from the northern side,
we should see all the planets moving round from west to
east, the satellites moving round their primaries, and the
sun, planets, and satellites rotating in the same direction,
with some exceptions on the verge of the system. In the
time of Laplace eleven planets were known, and the directions of rotation were known for the sun, six planets, the
satellites of Jupiter, Saturn's ring, and one of his satellites.
Thus there were altogether 43 motions all concurring,
namely :—

Orbital motions of eleven planets	11
Orbital motions of eighteen satellites	18
Axial rotations	14
	43

The probability that 43 motions independent of each
other would coincide by chance is the 42nd power of $\frac{1}{2}$, so
that the odds are about 4,400,000,000,000 to 1 in favour of
some common cause for the uniformity of direction. This
probability, as Laplace observes,[2] is higher than that of
many historical events which we undoubtingly believe. In
the present day, the probability is much increased by the
discovery of additional planets, and the rotation of other

[1] *Principia*, bk. ii. General scholium.
[2] *Essai Philosophique*, p. 55. Laplace appears to count the rings of
Saturn as giving two independent movements.

satellites, and it is only slightly weakened by the fact that some of the outlying satellites are exceptional in direction, there being considerable evidence of an accidental disturbance in the more distant parts of the system.

Hardly less remarkable than the uniform direction of motion is the near approximation of the orbits of the planets to a common plane. Daniel Bernoulli roughly estimated the probability of such an agreement arising from accident as $1 \div (12)^6$ the greatest inclination of any orbit to the sun's equator being 1-12th part of a quadrant. Laplace devoted to this subject some of his most ingenious investigations. He found the probability that the sum of the inclinations of the planetary orbits would not exceed by accident the actual amount ('914187 of a right angle for the ten planets known in 1801) to be $\frac{1}{10}$ ('914187),[10] or about ·0000001235. This probability may be combined with that derived from the direction of motion, and it then becomes immensely probable that the constitution of the planetary system arose out of uniform conditions, or, as we say, from some common cause.[1]

If the same kind of calculation be applied to the orbits of comets, the result is very different.[2] Of the orbits which have been determined 48·9 per cent. only are direct or in the same direction as the planetary motions.[3] Hence it becomes apparent that comets do not properly belong to the solar system, and it is probable that they are stray portions of nebulous matter which have accidentally become attached to the system by the attractive powers of the sun or Jupiter.

The General Inverse Problem.

In the instances described in the preceding sections, we have been occupied in receding from the occurrence of certain similar events to the probability that there

---

[1] Lubbock, *Essay on Probability*, p. 14. De Morgan, *Encyc. Metrop.* art. *Probability*, p. 412. Todhunter's *History of the Theory of Probability*, p. 543. Concerning the objections raised to these conclusions by Boole, see the *Philosophical Magazine*, 4th Series, vol. ii. p. 98. Boole's *Laws of Thought*, pp. 364-375.

[2] Laplace, *Essai Philosophique*, pp. 55, 56.

[3] Chambers' *Astronomy*, 2nd ed. pp. 346-49.

must have been a condition or cause for such events. We
have found that the theory of probability, although never
yielding a certain result, often enables us to establish an
hypothesis beyond the reach of reasonable doubt. There
is, however, another method of applying the theory,
which possesses for us even greater interest, because it
illustrates, in the most complete manner, the theory of
inference adopted in this work, which theory indeed it
suggested. The problem to be solved is as follows :—

*An event having happened a certain number of times,
and failed a certain number of times, required the probability that it will happen any given number of times
in the future under the same circumstances.*

All the *larger* planets hitherto discovered move in one
direction round the sun ; what is the probability that, if a
new planet exterior to Neptune be discovered, it will move
in the same direction ? All known permanent gases, except chlorine, are colourless ; what is the probability that,
if some new permanent gas should be discovered, it will
be colourless ? In the general solution of this problem, we
wish to infer the future happening of any event from the
number of times that it has already been observed to
happen. Now, it is very instructive to find that there is
no known process by which we can pass directly from the
data to the conclusion. It is always requisite to recede
from the data to the probability of some hypothesis, and
to make that hypothesis the ground of our inference
concerning future events. Mathematicians, in fact, make
every hypothesis which is applicable to the question in
hand ; they then calculate, by the inverse method, the
probability of every such hypothesis according to the
data, and the probability that if each hypothesis be true,
the required future event will happen. The total probability that the event will happen is the sum of the
separate probabilities contributed by each distinct hypothesis.

To illustrate more precisely the method of solving the
problem, it is desirable to adopt some concrete mode of
representation, and the ballot-box, so often employed by
mathematicians, will best serve our purpose. Let the
happening of any event be represented by the drawing of
a white ball from a ballot-box, while the failure of an

event is represented by the drawing of a black ball. Now, in the inductive problem we are supposed to be ignorant of the contents of the ballot-box, and are required to ground all our inferences on our experience of those contents as shown in successive drawings. Rude common sense would guide us nearly to a true conclusion. Thus, if we had drawn twenty balls one after another, replacing the ball after each drawing, and the ball had in each case proved to be white, we should believe that there was a considerable preponderance of white balls in the urn, and a probability in favour of drawing a white ball on the next occasion. Though we had drawn white balls for thousands of times without fail, it would still be possible that some black balls lurked in the urn and would at last appear, so that our inferences could never be certain. On the other hand, if black balls came at intervals, we should expect that after a certain number of trials the black balls would appear again from time to time with somewhat the same frequency.

The mathematical solution of the question consists in little more than a close analysis of the mode in which our common sense proceeds. If twenty white balls have been drawn and no black ball, my common sense tells me that any hypothesis which makes the black balls in the urn considerable compared with the white ones is improbable ; a preponderance of white balls is a more probable hypothesis, and as a deduction from this more probable hypothesis, I expect a recurrence of white balls. The mathematician merely reduces this process of thought to exact numbers. Taking, for instance, the hypothesis that there are 99 white and one black ball in the urn, he can calculate the probability that 20 white balls would be drawn in succession in those circumstances ; he thus forms a definite estimate of the probability of this hypothesis, and knowing at the same time the probability of a white ball reappearing if such be the contents of the urn, he combines these probabilities, and obtains an exact estimate that a white ball will recur in consequence of this hypothesis. But as this hypothesis is only one out of many possible ones, since the ratio of white and black balls may be 98 to 2, or 97 to 3, or 96 to 4, and so on, he has to repeat the estimate for every such possible hypothesis.

To make the method of solving the problem perfectly evident, I will describe in the next section a very simple case of the problem, originally devised for the purpose by Condorcet, which was also adopted by Lacroix,[1] and has passed into the works of De Morgan, Lubbock, and others.

Simple Illustration of the Inverse Problem.

Suppose it to be known that a ballot-box contains only four black or white balls, the ratio of black and white balls being unknown. Four drawings having been made with replacement, and a white ball having appeared on each occasion but one, it is required to determine the probability that a white ball will appear next time. Now the hypotheses which can be made as to the contents of the urn are very limited in number, and are at most the following five :—

4	white	and	0	black	balls
3	,,	,,	1	,,	,,
2	,,	,,	2	,,	,,
1	,,	,,	3	,,	,,
0	,,	,,	4	,,	,,

The actual occurrence of black and white balls in the drawings puts the first and last hypothesis out of the question, so that we have only three left to consider.

If the box contains three white and one black, the probability of drawing a white each time is $\frac{3}{4}$, and a black $\frac{1}{4}$; so that the compound event observed, namely, three white and one black, has the probability $\frac{3}{4} \times \frac{3}{4} \times \frac{3}{4} \times \frac{1}{4}$, by the rule already given (p. 204). But as it is indifferent in what order the balls are drawn, and the black ball might come first, second, third, or fourth, we must multiply by four, to obtain the probability of three white and one black in any order, thus getting $\frac{27}{64}$.

Taking the next hypothesis of two white and two black balls in the urn, we obtain for the same probability the quantity $\frac{1}{2} \times \frac{1}{2} \times \frac{1}{2} \times \frac{1}{2} \times 4$, or $\frac{16}{64}$, and from the third hypothesis of one white and three black we deduce likewise $\frac{1}{4} \times \frac{1}{4} \times \frac{1}{4} \times \frac{3}{4} \times 4$, or $\frac{3}{64}$. According, then, as we

[1] *Traité élémentaire du Calcul des Probabilités*, 3rd ed. (1833), p. 148.

adopt the first, second, or third hypothesis, the probability that the result actually noticed would follow is $\frac{27}{64}$, $\frac{16}{64}$, and $\frac{3}{64}$. Now it is certain that one or other of these hypotheses must be the true one, and their absolute probabilities are proportional to the probabilities that the observed events would follow from them (pp. 242, 243). All we have to do, then, in order to obtain the absolute probability of each hypothesis, is to alter these fractions in a uniform ratio, so that their sum shall be unity, the expression of certainty. Now, since $27 + 16 + 3 = 46$, this will be effected by dividing each fraction by 46, and multiplying by 64. Thus the probabilities of the first, second, and third hypotheses are respectively—

$$\frac{27}{46}, \quad \frac{16}{46}, \quad \frac{3}{46}.$$

The inductive part of the problem is completed, since we have found that the urn most likely contains three white and one black ball, and have assigned the exact probability of each possible supposition. But we are now in a position to resume deductive reasoning, and infer the probability that the next drawing will yield, say a white ball. For if the box contains three white and one black ball, the probability of drawing a white one is certainly $\frac{3}{4}$; and as the probability of the box being so constituted is $\frac{27}{46}$, the compound probability that the box will be so filled and will give a white ball at the next trial, is

$$\frac{27}{46} \times \frac{3}{4} \quad \text{or} \quad \frac{81}{184}.$$

Again, the probability is $\frac{16}{46}$ that the box contains two white and two black, and under those conditions the probability is $\frac{1}{2}$ that a white ball will appear; hence the probability that a white ball will appear in consequence of that condition, is

$$\frac{16}{46} \times \frac{1}{2} \quad \text{or} \quad \frac{32}{184}.$$

From the third supposition we get in like manner the probability

$$\frac{3}{46} \times \frac{1}{4} \quad \text{or} \quad \frac{3}{184}.$$

Since one and not more than one hypothesis can be true.

we may add together these separate probabilities, and we find that

$$\frac{81}{184} + \frac{32}{184} + \frac{3}{184} \text{ or } \frac{116}{184}$$

is the complete probability that a white ball will be next drawn under the conditions and data supposed.

General Solution of the Inverse Problem.

In the instance of the inverse method described in the last section, the balls supposed to be in the ballot-box were few, for the purpose of simplifying the calculation. In order that our solution may apply to natural phenomena, we must render our hypotheses as little arbitrary as possible. Having no à priori knowledge of the conditions of the phenomena in question, there is no limit to the variety of hypotheses which might be suggested. Mathematicians have therefore had recourse to the most extensive suppositions which can be made, namely, that the ballot-box contains an infinite number of balls; they have then varied the proportion of white to black balls continuously, from the smallest to the greatest possible proportion, and estimated the aggregate probability which results from this comprehensive supposition.

To explain their procedure, let us imagine that, instead of an infinite number, the ballot-box contains a large finite number of balls, say 1000. Then the number of white balls might be 1 or 2 or 3 or 4, and so on, up to 999. Supposing that three white and one black ball have been drawn from the urn as before, there is a certain very small probability that this would have occurred in the case of a box containing one white and 999 black balls; there is also a small probability that from such a box the next ball would be white. Compound these probabilities, and we have the probability that the next ball really will be white, in consequence of the existence of that proportion of balls. If there be two white and 998 black balls in the box, the probability is greater and will increase until the balls are supposed to be in the proportion of those drawn. Now 999 different hypotheses are possible, and the calculation is to be made for each of these, and their aggregate taken as the final result. It is apparent that as the number of balls in the box is increased, the absolute probability of any one hypothesis concerning the exact proportion of balls is decreased, but the aggregate results of all the hypotheses will assume the character of a wider average.

When we take the step of supposing the balls within the urn to be infinite in number, the possible proportions of white and black balls also become infinite, and the probability of any one proportion actually existing is infinitely small. Hence the final result that the next ball drawn will be white is really the sum of an infinite number of infinitely small quantities. It might seem impossible to calculate out a problem having an infinite number of hypotheses, but the wonderful resources of the integral calculus enable this to be done with far greater facility than if we supposed any large finite number of balls, and then actually computed the results. I will not attempt to describe the processes by which Laplace finally accomplished the complete solution of the problem. They are to be found described in several English works, especially De Morgan's *Treatise on Probabilities*, in the *Encyclopædia Metropolitana*, and Mr. Todhunter's *History of the Theory of Probability*. The abbreviating power of mathematical analysis was never more strikingly shown. But I may add that though the integral calculus is employed as a means of summing infinitely numerous results, we in no way abandon the principles of combinations already treated. We calculate the values of infinitely numerous factorials, not, however, obtaining their actual products, which would lead to an infinite number of figures, but obtaining the final answer to the problem by devices which can only be comprehended after study of the integral calculus.

It must be allowed that the hypothesis adopted by Laplace is in some degree arbitrary, so that there was some opening for the doubt which Boole has cast upon it.[1] But it may be replied, (1) that the supposition of an infinite number of balls treated in the manner of Laplace is less arbitrary and more comprehensive than any other that can be suggested. (2) The result does not differ

---

[1] *Laws of Thought*, pp. 368-375.

much from that which would be obtained on the hypothesis of any large finite number of balls. (3) The supposition leads to a series of simple formulas which can be applied with ease in many cases, and which bear all the appearance of truth so far as it can be independently judged by a sound and practiced understanding.

Rules of the Inverse Method.

By the solution of the problem, as described in the last section, we obtain the following series of simple rules.

1. *To find the probability that an event which has not hitherto been observed to fail will happen once more, divide the number of times the event has been observed increased by one, by the same number increased by two.*

If there have been m occasions on which a certain event might have been observed to happen, and it has happened on all those occasions, then the probability that it will happen on the next occasion of the same kind is $\frac{m+1}{m+2}$. For instance, we may say that there are nine places in the planetary system where planets might exist obeying Bode's law of distance, and in every place there is a planet obeying the law more or less exactly, although no reason is known for the coincidence. Hence the probability that the next planet beyond Neptune will conform to the law is $\frac{10}{11}$.

2. *To find the probability that an event which has not hitherto failed will not fail for a certain number of new occasions, divide the number of times the event has happened increased by one, by the same number increased by one and the number of times it is to happen.*

An event having happened m times without fail, the probability that it will happen n more times is $\frac{m+1}{m+n+1}$. Thus the probability that three new planets would obey Bode's law is $\frac{10}{13}$; but it must be allowed that this, as well as the previous result, would be much weakened by the fact that Neptune can barely be said to obey the law.

3. *An event having happened and failed a certain number of times, to find the probability that it will happen the next time, divide the number of times the event has*

happened increased by one, by the whole number of times the event has happened or failed increased by two.

If an event has happened m times and failed n times, the probability that it will happen on the next occasion is $\dfrac{m+1}{m+n+2}$. Thus, if we assume that of the elements discovered up to the year 1873, 50 are metallic and 14 non-metallic, then the probability that the next element discovered will be metallic is $\frac{51}{66}$. Again, since of 37 metals which have been sufficiently examined only four, namely, sodium, potassium, lanthanum, and lithium, are of less density than water, the probability that the next metal examined or discovered will be less dense than water is $\dfrac{4+1}{37+2}$ or $\dfrac{5}{39}$.

We may state the results of the method in a more general manner thus,[1]—If under given circumstances certain events A, B, C, &c., have happened respectively m, n, p, &c., times, and one or other of these events must happen, then the probabilities of these events are proportional to $m+1$, $n+1$, $p+1$, &c., so that the probability of A will be $\dfrac{m+1}{m+1+n+1+p+1+\&c.}$ But if new events may happen in addition to those which have been observed, we must assign unity for the probability of such new event. The odds then become 1 for a new event, $m+1$ for A, $n+1$ for B, and so on, and the absolute probability of A is $\dfrac{m+1}{1+m+1+n+1+\&c.}$

It is interesting to trace out the variations of probability according to these rules. The first time a casual event happens it is 2 to 1 that it will happen again; if it does happen it is 3 to 1 that it will happen a third time; and on successive occasions of the like kind the odds become 4, 5, 6, &c., to 1. The odds of course will be discriminated from the probabilities which are successively $\frac{2}{3}$, $\frac{3}{4}$, $\frac{4}{5}$, &c. Thus on the first occasion on which a person sees a shark, and notices that it is accompanied by a little pilot fish, the odds are 2 to 1, or the probability $\frac{2}{3}$, that the next shark will be so accompanied.

---

[1] De Morgan's *Essay on Probabilities*, Cabinet Cyclopædia, p. 67.

When an event has happened a very great number of times, its happening once again approaches nearly to certainty. If we suppose the sun to have risen one thousand million times, the probability that it will rise again, on the ground of this knowledge merely, is $\dfrac{1,000,000,000 + 1}{1,000,000,000 + 1 + 1}$. But then the probability that it will continue to rise for as long a period in the future is only $\dfrac{1,000,000,000 + 1}{2,000,000,000 + 1}$, or almost exactly $\frac{1}{2}$. The probability that it will continue so rising a thousand times as long is only about $\frac{1}{1001}$. The lesson which we may draw from these figures is quite that which we should adopt on other grounds, namely, that experience never affords certain knowledge, and that it is exceedingly improbable that events will always happen as we observe them. Inferences pushed far beyond their data soon lose any considerable probability. De Morgan has said,[1] " No finite experience whatsoever can justify us in saying that the future shall coincide with the past in all time to come, or that there is any probability for such a conclusion." On the other hand, we gain the assurance that experience sufficiently extended and prolonged will give us the knowledge of future events with an unlimited degree of probability, provided indeed that those events are not subject to arbitrary interference.

It must be clearly understood that these probabilities are only such as arise from the mere happening of the events, irrespective of any knowledge derived from other sources concerning those events or the general laws of nature. All our knowledge of nature is indeed founded in like manner upon observation, and is therefore only probable. The law of gravitation itself is only probably true. But when a number of different facts, observed under the most diverse circumstances, are found to be harmonized under a supposed law of nature, the probability of the law approximates closely to certainty. Each science rests upon so many observed facts, and derives so much support from analogies or connections with other sciences, that there are comparatively few cases where our judgment of the probability of an event depends entirely upon a few ante-

[1] *Essay on Probabilities*, p. 128.

cedent events, disconnected from the general body of physical science.

Events, again, may often exhibit a regularity of succession or preponderance of character, which the simple formula will not take into account. For instance, the majority of the elements recently discovered are metals, so that the probability of the next discovery being that of a metal, is doubtless greater than we calculated (p. 258). At the more distant parts of the planetary system, there are symptoms of disturbance which would prevent our placing much reliance on any inference from the prevailing order of the known planets to those undiscovered ones which may possibly exist at great distances. These and all like complications in no way invalidate the theoretic truth of the formulas, but render their sound application much more difficult.

Erroneous objections have been raised to the theory of probability, on the ground that we ought not to trust to our à priori conceptions of what is likely to happen, but should always endeavour to obtain precise experimental data to guide us.[1] This course, however, is perfectly in accordance with the theory, which is our best and only guide, whatever data we possess. We ought to be always applying the inverse method of probabilities so as to take into account all additional information. When we throw up a coin for the first time, we are probably quite ignorant whether it tends more to fall head or tail upwards, and we must therefore assume the probability of each event as $\frac{1}{2}$. But if it shows head in the first throw, we now have very slight experimental evidence in favour of a tendency to show head. The chance of two heads is now slightly greater than $\frac{1}{4}$, which it appeared to be at first,[2] and as we go on throwing the coin time after time, the probability of head appearing next time constantly varies in a slight degree according to the character of our previous experience. As Laplace remarks, we ought always to have regard to such considerations in common life. Events when closely scrutinized will hardly ever prove to be quite independent, and the slightest pre-

[1] J. S. Mill, *System of Logic*, 5th edition, bk. iii. chap. xviii. § 3.
[2] Todhunter's *History*, pp. 472, 598.

ponderance one way or the other is some evidence of
connection, and in the absence of better evidence should
be taken into account.

The grand object of seeking to estimate the probability
of future events from past experience, seems to have been
entertained by James Bernoulli and De Moivre, at least
such was the opinion of Condorcet ; and Bernoulli may be
said to have solved one case of the problem.[1] The English
writers Bayes and Price are, however, undoubtedly the
first who put forward any distinct rules on the subject.[2]
Condorcet and several other eminent mathematicians advanced the mathematical theory of the subject ; but it was
reserved to the immortal Laplace to bring to the subject
the full power of his genius, and carry the solution of the
problem almost to perfection. It is instructive to observe
that a theory which arose from petty games of chance, the
rules and the very names of which are forgotten, gradually
advanced, until it embraced the most sublime problems of
science, and finally undertook to measure the value and
certainty of all our inductions.

Fortuitous Coincidences.

We should have studied the theory of probability to
very little purpose, if we thought that it would furnish
us with an infallible guide. The theory itself points
out the approximate certainty, that we shall sometimes
be deceived by extraordinary fortuitous coincidences.
There is no run of luck so extreme that it may not
happen, and it may happen to us, or in our time, as
well as to other persons or in other times. We may be
forced by correct calculation to refer such coincidences
to a necessary cause, and yet we may be deceived. All
that the calculus of probability pretends to give, is *the
result in the long run*, as it is called, and this really means
in *an infinity of cases*. During any finite experience,
however long, chances may be against us. Nevertheless
the theory is the best guide we can have. If we always
think and act according to its well-interpreted indications,

---

[1] Todhunter's *History*, pp. 378, 379.
[2] *Philosophical Transactions*, [1763], vol. liii. p. 370, and [1764],
vol. liv. p. 296. Todhunter, pp. 294-300

we shall have the best chance of escaping error ; and if all persons, throughout all time to come, obey the theory in like manner, they will undoubtedly thereby reap the greatest advantage.

No rule can be given for 'discriminating between coincidences which are casual and those which are the effects of law. By a fortuitous or casual coincidence, we mean an agreement between events, which nevertheless arise from wholly independent and different causes or conditions, and which will not always so agree. It is a fortuitous coincidence, if a penny thrown up repeatedly in various ways always falls on the same side ; but it would not be fortuitous if there were any similarity in the motions of the hand, and the height of the throw, so as to cause or tend to cause a uniform result. Now among the infinitely numerous events, objects, or relations in the universe, it is quite likely that we shall occasionally notice casual coincidences. There are seven intervals in the octave, and there is nothing very improbable in the colours of the spectrum happening to be apparently divisible into the same or similar series of seven intervals. It is hardly yet decided whether this apparent coincidence, with which Newton was much struck, is well founded or not,[1] but the question will probably be decided in the negative.

It is certainly a casual coincidence which the ancients noticed between the seven vowels, the seven strings of the lyre, the seven Pleiades, and the seven chiefs at Thebes.[2] The accidents connected with the number seven have misled the human intellect throughout the historical period. Pythagoras imagined a connection between the seven planets and the seven intervals of the monochord. The alchemists were never tired of drawing inferences from the coincidence in numbers of the seven planets and the seven metals, not to speak of the seven days of the week.

A singular circumstance was pointed out concerning the dimensions of the earth, sun, and moon ; the sun's diameter was almost exactly 110 times as great as the

---

[1] Newton's *Opticks*, Bk. I., Part ii. Prop. 3 ; *Nature*, vol. i. p 286
[2] Aristotle's *Metaphysics*, xiii. 6. 3.

earth's diameter, while in almost exactly the same ratio the mean distance of the earth was greater than the sun's diameter, and the mean distance of the moon from the earth was greater than the moon's diameter.   The agreement was so close that it might have proved more than casual, but its fortuitous character is now sufficiently shown by the fact, that the coincidence ceases to be remarkable when we adopt the amended dimensions of the planetary system.

A considerable number of the elements have atomic weights, which are apparently exact multiples of that of hydrogen.   If this be not a law to be ultimately extended to all the elements, as supposed by Prout, it is a most remarkable coincidence.   But, as I have observed, we have no means of absolutely discriminating accidental coincidences from those which imply a deep producing cause.   A coincidence must either be very strong in itself, or it must be corroborated by some explanation or connection with other laws of nature.   Little attention was ever given to the coincidence concerning the dimensions of the sun, earth, and moon, because it was not very strong in itself, and had no apparent connection with the principles of physical astronomy.   Prout's Law bears more probability because it would bring the constitution of the elements themselves in close connection with the atomic theory, representing them as built up out of a simpler substance.

In historical and social matters, coincidences are frequently pointed out which are due to chance, although there is always a strong popular tendency to regard them as the work of design, or as having some hidden meaning. If to 1794, the number of the year in which Robespierre fell, we add the sum of its digits, the result is 1815, the year in which Napoleon fell; the repetition of the process gives 1830 the year in which Charles the Tenth abdicated. Again, the French Chamber of Deputies, in 1830, consisted of 402 members, of whom 221 formed the party called " La queue de Robespierre," while the remainder, 181 in number, were named " Les honnêtes gens."   If we give to each letter a numerical value corresponding to its place in the alphabet, it will be found that the sum of the values of the letters in each name exactly indicates the number of the party.

A number of such coincidences, often of a very curious character, might be adduced, and the probability against the occurrence of each is enormously great. They must be attributed to chance, because they cannot be shown to have the slightest connection with the general laws of nature ; but persons are often found to be greatly influenced by such coincidences, regarding them as evidence of fatality, that is of a system of causation governing human affairs independently of the ordinary laws of nature. Let it be remembered that there are an infinite number of opportunities in life for some strange coincidence to present itself, so that it is quite to be expected that remarkable conjunctions will sometimes happen.

In all matters of judicial evidence, we must bear in mind the probable occurrence from time to time of unaccountable coincidences. The Roman jurists refused for this reason to invalidate a testamentary deed, the witnesses of which had sealed it with the same seal. For witnesses independently using their own seals might be found to possess identical ones by accident.[1] It is well known that circumstantial evidence of apparently overwhelming completeness will sometimes lead to a mistaken judgment, and as absolute certainty is never really attainable, every court must act upon probabilities of a high amount, and in a certain small proportion of cases they must almost of necessity condemn the innocent victims of a remarkable conjuncture of circumstances.[2] Popular judgments usually turn upon probabilities of far less amount, as when the palace of Nicomedia, and even the bedchamber of Diocletian, having been on fire twice within fifteen days, the people entirely refused to believe that it could be the result of accident. The Romans believed that there was fatality connected with the name of Sextus.

"Semper sub Sextis perdita Roma fuit."

The utmost precautions will not provide against all contingencies. To avoid errors in important calculations,

[1] Possunt autem omnes testes et uno annulo signare testamentum Quid enim si septem annuli una sculptura fuerint, secundum quod Pomponio visum est ?—*Justinian*, ii. tit. x. 5.

[2] See Wills on *Circumstantial Evidence* n. 148.

it is usual to have them repeated by different computers ; but a case is on record in which three computers made exactly the same calculations of the place of a star, and yet all did it wrong in precisely the same manner, for no apparent reason.[1]

Summary of the Theory of Inductive Inference.

The theory of inductive inference stated in this and the previous chapters, was suggested by the study of the Inverse Method of Probability, but it also bears much resemblance to the so-called Deductive Method described by Mill, in his celebrated *System of Logic*. Mill's views concerning the Deductive Method, probably form the most original and valuable part of his treatise, and I should have ascribed the doctrine entirely to him, had I not found that the opinions put forward in other parts of his work are entirely inconsistent with the theory here upheld. As this subject is the most important and difficult one with which we have to deal, I will try to remedy the imperfect manner in which I have treated it, by giving a recapitulation of the views adopted.

All inductive reasoning is but the inverse application of deductive reasoning. Being in possession of certain particular facts or events expressed in propositions, we imagine some more general proposition expressing the existence of a law or cause; and, deducing the particular results of that supposed general proposition, we observe whether they agree with the facts in question. Hypothesis is thus always employed, consciously or unconsciously. The sole conditions to which we need conform in framing any hypothesis is, that we both have and exercise the power of inferring deductively from the hypothesis to the particular results, which are to be compared with the known facts. Thus there are but three steps in the process of induction :—

(1) Framing some hypothesis as to the character of the general law.

(2) Deducing consequences from that law.

---

[1] *Memoirs of the Royal Astronomical Society*, vol. iv. p. 290, quoted by Lardner, *Edinburgh Review*, July 1834, p. 278.

(3) Observing whether the consequences agree with the particular facts under consideration.

In very simple cases of inverse reasoning, hypothesis may seem altogether needless. To take numbers again as a convenient illustration, I have only to look at the series,

1, 2, 4, 8, 16, 32, &c.,

to know at once that the general law is that of geometrical progression; I need no successive trial of various hypotheses, because I am familiar with the series, and have long since learnt from what general formula it proceeds. In the same way a mathematician becomes acquainted with the integrals of a number of common formulas, so that he need not go through any process of discovery. But it is none the less true that whenever previous reasoning does not furnish the knowledge, hypotheses must be framed and tried (p. 124).

There naturally arise two cases, according as the nature of the subject admits of certain or only probable deductive reasoning. Certainty, indeed, is but a singular case of probability, and the general principles of procedure are always the same. Nevertheless, when certainty of inference is possible, the process is simplified. Of several mutually inconsistent hypotheses, the results of which can be certainly compared with fact, but one hypothesis can ultimately be entertained. Thus in the inverse logical problem, two logically distinct conditions could not yield the same series of possible combinations. Accordingly, in the case of two terms we had to choose one of six different kinds of propositions (p. 136), and in the case of three terms, our choice lay among 192 possible distinct hypotheses (p. 140). Natural laws, however, are often quantitative in character, and the possible hypotheses are then infinite in variety.

When deduction is certain, comparison with fact is needed only to assure ourselves that we have rightly selected the hypothetical conditions. The law establishes itself, and no number of particular verifications can add to its probability. Having once deduced from the principles of algebra that the difference of the squares of two numbers is equal to the product of their sum and difference, no number of particular trials of its truth will render it more certain. On the other hand, no finite number of particular verifications of a supposed law will render that law certain. In short, certainty belongs only to the deductive process, and to the teachings of direct intuition; and as the conditions of nature are not given by intuition, we can only be certain that we have got a correct hypothesis when, out of a limited number conceivably possible, we select that one which alone agrees with the facts to be explained.

In geometry and kindred branches of mathematics, deductive reasoning is conspicuously certain, and it would often seem as if the consideration of a single diagram yields us certain knowledge of a general proposition. But in reality all this certainty is of a purely hypothetical character. Doubtless if we could ascertain that a supposed circle was a true and perfect circle, we could be certain concerning a multitude of its geometrical properties. But geometrical figures are physical objects, and the senses can never assure us as to their exact forms. The figures really treated in Euclid's *Elements* are imaginary, and we never can verify in practice the conclusions which we draw with certainty in inference; questions of degree and probability enter.

Passing now to subjects in which deduction is only probable, it ceases to be possible to adopt one hypothesis to the exclusion of the others. We must entertain at the same time all conceivable hypotheses, and regard each with the degree of esteem proportionate to its probability. We go through the same steps as before.

(1) We frame an hypothesis.

(2) We deduce the probability of various series of possible consequences.

(3) We compare the consequences with the particular facts, and observe the probability that such facts would happen under the hypothesis.

The above processes must be performed for every conceivable hypothesis, and then the absolute probability of each will be yielded by the principle of the inverse method (p. 242). As in the case of certainty we accept that hypothesis which certainly gives the required results, so now we accept as most probable that hypothesis which most probably gives the results; but we are obliged to entertain at the same time all other hypotheses with degrees of probability proportionate to the probabilities that they would give the same results.

So far we have treated only of the process by which we pass from special facts to general laws, that inverse application of ˙deduction which constitutes induction. But the direct employment of .deduction is often combined with the inverse. No sooner have we established a general law, than the mind rapidly draws particular consequences from it. In geometry we may almost seem to infer that *because* one equilateral triangle is equiangular, therefore another is so. In reality it is not because one is that another is, but because all are. The geometrical conditions are perfectly general, and by what is sometimes called *parity of reasoning* whatever is true of one equilateral triangle, so far as it is equilateral, is true of all equilateral triangles.

Similarly, in all other cases of inductive inference, where we seem to pass from some particular instances to a new instance, we go through the same process. We form an hypothesis as to the logical conditions under which the given instances might occur; we calculate inversely the probability of that hypothesis, and compounding this with the probability that a new instance would proceed from the same conditions, we gain the absolute probability of occurrence of the new instance in virtue of this hypothesis. But as several, or many, or even an infinite number of mutually inconsistent hypotheses may be possible, we must repeat the calculation for each such conceivable hypothesis, and then the complete probability of the future instance will be the sum of the separate probabilities. The complication of this process is often very much reduced in practice, owing to the fact that one hypothesis may be almost certainly true, and other hypotheses, though conceivable, may be so improbable as to be neglected without appreciable error.

When we possess no knowledge whatever of the conditions from which the events proceed, we may be unable to form any probable hypotheses as to their mode of origin. We have now to fall back upon the general solution of the problem effected by Laplace, which consists in admitting on an equal footing every conceivable ratio of favourable and unfavourable chances for the production

of the event, and then accepting the aggregate result as
the best which can be obtained. This solution is only to
be accepted in the absence of all better means, but like
other results of the calculus of probability, it comes to our
aid where knowledge is at an end and ignorance begins,
and it prevents us from over-estimating the knowledge we
possess. The general results of the solution are in accordance with common sense, namely, that the more often an
event has happened the more probable, as a general rule,
is its subsequent recurrence. With the extension of
experience this probability increases, but at the same time
the probability is slight that events will long continue to
happen as they have previously happened.

We have now pursued the theory of inductive inference,
as far as can be done with regard to simple logical or
numerical relations. The laws of nature deal with time
and space, which are infinitely divisible. As we passed
from pure logic to numerical logic, so we must now pass
from questions of discontinuous, to questions of continuous
quantity, encountering fresh considerations of much difficulty. Before, therefore, we consider how the great inductions and generalisations of physical science illustrate
the views of inductive reasoning just explained, we must
break off for a time, and review the means which we
possess of measuring and comparing magnitudes of time,
space, mass, force, momentum, energy, and the various
manifestations of energy in motion, heat, electricity,
chemical change, and the other phenomena of nature.

BOOK III.

METHODS OF MEASUREMENT.

CHAPTER XIII.

THE EXACT MEASUREMENT OF PHENOMENA

As physical science advances, it becomes more and more accurately quantitative. Questions of simple logical fact after a time resolve themselves into questions of degree, time, distance, or weight. Forces hardly suspected to exist by one generation, are clearly recognised by the next, and precisely measured by the third generation. But one condition of this rapid advance is the invention of suitable instruments of measurement. We need what Francis Bacon called *Instantiæ citantes*, or *evocantes*, methods of rendering minute phenomena perceptible to the senses; and we also require *Instantiæ radii* or *curriculi*, that is measuring instruments. Accordingly, the introduction of a new instrument often forms an epoch in the history of science. As Davy said, "Nothing tends so much to the advancement of knowledge as the application of a new instrument. The native intellectual powers of men in different times are not so much the causes of the different success of their labours, as the peculiar nature of the means and artificial resources in their possession."

In the absence indeed of advanced theory and analytical power, a very precise instrument would be useless. Measuring apparatus and mathematical theory should advance *pari passu*, and with just such precision as the theorist can anticipate results, the experimentalist should be able to compare them with experience. The scrupulously accurate observations of Flamsteed were the proper complement to the intense mathematical powers of Newton.

Every branch of knowledge commences with quantitative notions of a very rude character. After we have far progressed, it is often amusing to look back into the infancy of the science, and contrast present with past methods. At Greenwich Observatory in the present day, the hundredth part of a second is not thought an inconsiderable portion of time. The ancient Chaldæans recorded an eclipse to the nearest hour, and the early Alexandrian astronomers thought it superfluous to distinguish between the edge and centre of the sun. By the introduction of the astrolabe, Ptolemy and the later Alexandrian astronomers could determine the places of the heavenly bodies within about ten minutes of arc. Little progress then ensued for thirteen centuries, until Tycho Brahe made the first great step towards accuracy, not only by employing better instruments, but even more by ceasing to regard an instrument as correct. Tycho, in fact, determined the errors of his instruments, and corrected his observations. He also took notice of the effects of atmospheric refraction, and succeeded in attaining an accuracy often sixty times as great as that of Ptolemy. Yet Tycho and Hevelius often erred several minutes in the determination of a star's place, and it was a great achievement of Rœmer and Flamsteed to reduce this error to seconds. Bradley, the modern Hipparchus, carried on the improvement, his errors in right ascension, according to Bessel, being under one second of time, and those of declination under four seconds of arc. In the present day the average error of a single observation is probably reduced to the half or quarter of what it was in Bradley's time; and further extreme accuracy is attained by the multiplication of observations, and their skilful combination according to the theory of error. Some of the more important constants, for instance that of nutation, have been determined within the tenth part of a second of space.[1]

It would be a matter of great interest to trace out the dependence of this progress upon the introduction of new instruments. The astrolabe of Ptolemy, the telescope of Galileo, the pendulum of Galileo and Huyghens, the micrometer of Horrocks, and the telescopic sights and micrometer of Gascoygne and Picard, Rœmer's transit instrument, Newton's and Hadley's quadrant, Dollond's achromatic lenses, Harrison's chronometer, and Ramsden's dividing engine—such were some of the principal additions to astronomical apparatus. The result is, that we now take note of quantities, 300,000 or 400,000 times as small as in the time of the Chaldæans.

It would be interesting again to compare the scrupulous accuracy of a modern trigonometrical survey with Eratosthenes' rude but ingenious guess at the difference of latitude between Alexandria and Syene—or with Norwood's measurement of a degree of latitude in 1635. "Sometimes I measured, sometimes I paced," said Norwood; "and I believe I am within a scantling of the truth." Such was the germ of those elaborate geodesical measurements which have made the dimensions of the globe known to us within a few hundred yards.

In other branches of science, the invention of an instrument has usually marked, if it has not made, an epoch. The science of heat might be said to commence with the construction of the thermometer, and it has recently been advanced by the introduction of the thermo-electric pile. Chemistry has been created chiefly by the careful use of the balance, which forms a unique instance of an instrument remaining substantially in the form in which it was first applied to scientific purposes by Archimedes. The balance never has been and probably never can be improved, except in details of construction. The torsion balance, introduced by Coulomb towards the end of last century, has rapidly become essential in many branches of investigation. In the hands of Cavendish and Baily, it gave a determination of the earth's density; applied in the galvanometer, it gave a delicate measure of electrical

[1] Baily, *British Association Catalogue of Stars*, pp. 7, 23.

forces, and is indispensable in the thermo-electric pile. This balance is made by simply suspending any light rod by a thin wire or thread attached to the middle point. And we owe to it almost all the more delicate investigations in the theories of heat, electricity, and magnetism.

Though we can now take note of the millionth of an inch in space, and the millionth of a second in time, we must not overlook the fact that in other operations of science we are yet in the position of the Chaldæans. Not many years have elapsed since the magnitudes of the stars, meaning the amounts of light they send to the observer's eye, were guessed at in the rudest manner, and the astronomer adjudged a star to this or that order of magnitude by a rough comparison with other stars of the same order. To Sir John Herschel we owe an attempt to introduce a uniform method of measurement and expression, bearing some relation to the real photometric magnitudes of the stars.[1] Previous to the researches of Bunsen and Roscoe on the chemical action of light, we were devoid of any mode of measuring the energy of light; even now the methods are tedious, and it is not clear that they give the energy of light so much as one of its special effects. Many natural phenomena have hardly yet been made the subject of measurement at all, such as the intensity of sound, the phenomena of taste and smell, the magnitude of atoms, the temperature of the electric spark or of the sun's photosphere.

To suppose, then, that quantitative science treats only of exactly measurable quantities, is a gross if it be a common mistake. Whenever we are treating of an event which either happens altogether or does not happen at all, we are engaged with a non-quantitative phenomenon, a matter of fact, not of degree; but whenever a thing may be greater or less, or twice or thrice as great as another, whenever, in short, ratio enters even in the rudest manner, there science will have a quantitative character. There can be little doubt, indeed, that every science as it progresses will become gradually more and more quantitative. Numerical precision is the soul of science, as

---

[1] *Outlines of Astronomy*, 4th ed. sect. 781, p. 522. *Results of Observations at the Cape of Good Hope*, &c., p. 37:

Herschel said, and as all natural objects exist in space, and involve molecular movements, measurable in velocity and extent, there is no apparent limit to the ultimate extension of quantitative science. But the reader must not for a moment suppose that, because we depend more and more upon mathematical methods, we leave logical methods behind us. Number, as I have endeavoured to show, is logical in its origin, and quantity is but a development of number, or analogous thereto.

Division of the Subject.

The general subject of quantitative investigation will have to be divided into several parts. We shall firstly consider the means at our disposal for measuring phenomena, and thus rendering them more or less amenable to mathematical treatment. This task will involve an analysis of the principles on which accurate methods of measurement are founded, forming the subject of the remainder of the present chapter. As measurement, however, only yields ratios, we have in the next chapter to consider the establishment of unit magnitudes, in terms of which our results may be expressed. As every phenomenon is usually the sum of several distinct quantities depending upon different causes, we have next to investigate in Chapter XV. the methods by which we may disentangle complicated effects, and refer each part of the joint effect to its separate cause.

It yet remains for us in subsequent chapters to treat of quantitative induction, properly so called. We must follow out the inverse logical method, as it presents itself in problems of a far higher degree of difficulty than those which treat of objects related in a simple logical manner, and incapable of merging into each other by addition and subtraction.

Continuous Quantity.

The phenomena of nature are for the most part manifested in quantities which increase or decrease continuously. When we inquire into the precise meaning of continuous quantity, we find that it can only be described

as that which is divisible without limit. We can divide
a millimetre into ten, or a hundred, or a thousand, or ten
thousand parts, and mentally at any rate we can carry
on the division *ad infinitum.* Any finite space, then,
must be conceived as made up of an infinite number of
parts each infinitely small. We cannot entertain the
simplest geometrical notions without allowing this. The
conception of a square involves the conception of a side
and diagonal, which, as Euclid beautifully proves in the
117th proposition of his tenth book, have no common
measure,[1] meaning no finite common measure. Incommensurable quantities are, in fact, those which have for their
only common measure an infinitely small quantity. It is
somewhat startling to find, too, that in theory incommensurable quantities will be infinitely more frequent than
commensurable. Let any two lines be drawn haphazard ;
it is infinitely unlikely that they will be commensurable,
so that the commensurable quantities, which we are supposed to deal with in practice, are but singular cases
among an infinitely greater number of incommensurable
cases.

Practically, however, we treat all quantities as made up
of the least quantities which our senses, assisted by the
best measuring instruments, can perceive. So long as
microscopes were uninvented, it was sufficient to regard
an inch as made up of a thousand thousandths of an
inch ; now we must treat it as composed of a million
millionths. We might apparently avoid all mention of
infinitely small quantities, by never carrying our approximations beyond quantities which the senses can appreciate.
In geometry, as thus treated, we should never assert two
quantities to be equal, but only to be *apparently* equal.
Legendre really adopts this mode of treatment in the
twentieth proposition of the first book of his Geometry ;
and it is practically adopted throughout the physical
sciences, as we shall afterwards see. But though our
fingers, and senses, and instruments must stop somewhere,
there is no reason why the mind should not go on. We
can see that a proof which is only carried through a few
steps in fact, might be carried on without limit, and it is

---

[1] See De Morgan, *Study of Mathematics,* in U.K.S. Library, p. 81.

this consciousness of no stopping-place, which renders Euclid's proof of his 117th proposition so impressive. Try how we will to circumvent the matter, we cannot really avoid the consideration of the infinitely small and the infinitely great. The same methods of approximation which seem confined to the finite, mentally extend themselves to the infinite.

One result of these considerations is, that we cannot possibly adjust two quantities in absolute equality. The suspension of Mahomet's coffin between two precisely equal magnets is theoretically conceivable but practically impossible. The story of the *Merchant of Venice* turns upon the infinite improbability that an exact quantity of flesh could be cut. Unstable equilibrium cannot exist in nature, for it is that which is destroyed by an infinitely small displacement. It might be possible to balance an egg on its end practically, because no egg has a surface of perfect curvature. Suppose the egg shell to be perfectly smooth, and the feat would become impossible.

The Fallacious Indications of the Senses.

I may briefly remind the reader how little we can trust to our unassisted senses in estimating the degree or magnitude of any phenomenon. The eye cannot correctly estimate the comparative brightness of two luminous bodies which differ much in brilliancy; for we know that the iris is constantly adjusting itself to the intensity of the light received, and thus admits more or less light according to circumstances. The moon which shines with almost dazzling brightness by night, is pale and nearly imperceptible while the eye is yet affected by the vastly more powerful light of day. Much has been recorded concerning the comparative brightness of the zodiacal light at different times, but it would be difficult to prove that these changes are not due to the varying darkness at the time, or the different acuteness of the observer's eye. For a like reason it is exceedingly difficult to establish the existence of any change in the form or comparative brightness of nebulæ; the appearance of a nebula greatly depends upon the keenness of sight of the observer, or the accidental condition of freshness or

fatigue of his eye. The same is true of lunar observations; and even the use of the best telescope fails
to remove this difficulty. In judging of colours, again,
we must remember that light of any given colour tends
to dull the sensibility of the eye for light of the same
colour.

Nor is the eye when unassisted by instruments a much
better judge of magnitude. Our estimates of the size of
minute bright points, such as the fixed stars, are completely falsified by the effects of irradiation. Tycho
calculated from the apparent size of the star-discs, that
no one of the principal fixed stars could be contained
within the area of the earth's orbit. Apart, however, from
irradiation or other distinct causes of error our visual
estimates of sizes and shapes are often astonishingly
incorrect. Artists almost invariably draw distant mountains in ludicrous disproportion to nearer objects, as a
comparison of a sketch with a photograph at once shows.
The extraordinary apparent difference of size of the sun
or moon, according as it is high in the heavens or near
the horizon, should be sufficient to make us cautious in
accepting the plainest indications of our senses, unassisted
by instrumental measurement. As to statements concerning the height of the aurora and the distance of meteors,
they are to be utterly distrusted. When Captain Parry
says that a ray of the aurora shot suddenly downwards
between him and the land which was only 3,000 yards
distant, we must consider him subject to an illusion of
sense.[1]

It is true that errors of observation are more often
errors of judgment than of sense. That which is actually
seen must be so far truly seen ; and if we correctly interpret
the meaning of the phenomenon, there would be no error
at all. But the weakness of the bare senses as measuring
instruments, arises from the fact that they import varying
conditions of unknown amount, and we cannot make the
requisite corrections and allowances as in the case of a
solid and invariable instrument.

Bacon has excellently stated the insufficiency of the

[1] Loomis, *On the Aurora Borealis.* Smithsonian Transactions,
quoting Parry's Third Voyage, p. 61.

senses for estimating the magnitudes of objects, or detecting the degrees in which phenomena present themselves. " Things escape the senses," he says, " because the
object is not sufficient in quantity to strike the sense : as
all minute bodies ; because the percussion of the object is
too great to be endured by the senses : as the form of the
sun when looking directly at it in mid-day ; because the
time is not proportionate to actuate the sense : as the
motion of a bullet in the air, or the quick circular motion
of a firebrand, which are too fast, or the hour-hand of
a common clock, which is too slow ; from the distance
of the object as to place : as the size of the celestial
bodies, and the size and nature of all distant bodies ;
from prepossession by another object : as one powerful
smell renders other smells in the same room imperceptible ; from the interruption of interposing bodies :
as the internal parts of animals ; and because the object
is unfit to make an impression upon the sense : as the
air or the invisible and untangible spirit which is included in every living body."

Complexity of Quantitative Questions.

One remark which we may well make in entering
upon quantitative questions, has regard to the great variety
and extent of phenomena presented to our notice. So
long as we deal only with a simply logical question, that
question is merely, Does a certain event happen ? or, Does
a certain object exist ?   No sooner do we regard the event
or object as capable of more and less, than the question
branches out into many. We must now ask, How much
is it compared with its cause ? Does it change when the
amount of the cause changes ? If so, does it change in
the same or opposite direction ? Is the change in simple
proportion to that of the cause ? If not, what more complex law of connection holds true? This law determined
satisfactorily in one series of circumstances may be varied
under new conditions, and the most complex relations of
several quantities may ultimately be established.

In every question of physical science there is thus a
series of steps the first one or two of which are usually
made with ease while the succeeding ones demand more

and more careful measurement. We cannot lay down any invariable series of questions which must be asked from nature. The exact character of the questions will vary according to the nature of the case, but they will usually be of an evident kind, and we may readily illustrate them by examples. Suppose that we are investigating the solution of some salt in water. The first is a purely logical question : Is there solution, or is there not ? Assuming the answer to be in the affirmative, we next inquire, Does the solubility vary with the temperature, or not ? In all probability some variation will exist, and we must have an answer to the further question, Does the quantity dissolved increase, or does it diminish with the temperature ? In by far the greatest number of cases salts and substances of all kinds dissolve more freely the higher the temperature of the water ; but there are a few salts, such as calcium sulphate, which follow the opposite rule. A considerable number of salts resemble sodium sulphate in becoming more soluble up to a certain temperature, and then varying in the opposite direction. We next require to assign the amount of variation as compared with that of the temperature, assuming at first that the increase of solubility is proportional to the increase of temperature. Common salt is an instance of very slight variation, and potassium nitrate of very considerable increase with temperature. Accurate observations will probably show, however, that the simple law of proportionate variation is only approximately true, and some more complicated law involving the second, third, or higher powers of the temperature may ultimately be established. All these investigations have to be carried out for each salt separately, since no distinct principles by which we may infer from one substance to another have yet been detected. There is still an indefinite field for further research open; for the solubility of salts will probably vary with the pressure under which the medium is placed; the presence of other salts already dissolved may have effects yet unknown. The researches already effected as regards the solvent power of water must be repeated with alcohol, ether, carbon bisulphide, and other media, so that unless general laws can be detected, this one phenomenon of solution can never be exhaustively treated. The same kind of questions recur as regards the solution or absorption of gases in liquids, the pressure as well as the temperature having then a most decided effect, and Professor Roscoe's researches on the subject present an excellent example of the successive determination of various complicated laws.[1]

There is hardly a branch of physical science in which similar complications are not ultimately encountered. In the case of gravity, indeed, we arrive at the final law, that the force is the same for all kinds of matter, and varies only with the distance of action. But in other subjects the laws, if simple in their ultimate nature, are disguised and complicated in their apparent results. Thus the effect of heat in expanding solids, and the reverse effect of forcible extension or compression upon the temperature of a body, will vary from one substance to another, will vary as the temperature is already higher or lower, and will probably follow a highly complex law, which in some cases gives negative or exceptional results. In crystalline substances the same researches have to be repeated in each distinct axial direction.

In the sciences of pure observation, such as those of astronomy, meteorology, and terrestrial magnetism, we meet with many interesting series of quantitative determinations. The so-called fixed stars, as Giordano Bruno divined, are not really fixed, and may be more truly described as vast wandering orbs, each pursuing its own path through space. We must then determine separately for each star the following questions :—

1. Does it move ?
2. In what direction ?
3. At what velocity ?
4. Is this velocity variable or uniform ?
5. If variable, according to what law ?
6. Is the direction uniform ?
7. If not, what is the form of the apparent path ?
8. Does it approach or recede ?
9. What is the form of the real path ?

The successive answers to such questions in the case of certain binary stars, have afforded a proof that the

[1] Watts' *Dictionary of Chemistry*, vol. ii. p. 790.

motions are due to a central force coinciding in law with
gravity, and doubtless identical with it. In other cases
the motions are usually so small that it is exceedingly
difficult to distinguish them with certainty. And the time
is yet far off when any general results as regards stellar
motions can be established.

The variation in the brightness of stars opens an unlimited field for curious observation. There is not a star
in the heavens concerning which we might not have to
determine :—

1. Does it vary in brightness ?
2. Is the brightness increasing or decreasing ?
3. Is the variation uniform ?
4. If not, acording to what law does it vary ?

In a majority of cases the change will probably be
found to have a periodic character, in which case several
other questions will arise, such as—

5. What is the length of the period ?
6. Are there minor periods ?
7. What is the law of variation within the period ?
8. Is there any change in the amount of variation ?
9. If so, is it a secular, *i.e.* a continually growing
change, or does it give evidence of a greater period ?

Already the periodic changes of a certain number of
stars have been determined with accuracy, and the lengths
of the periods vary from less than three days up to
intervals of time at least 250 times as great. Periods
within periods have also been detected.

There is, perhaps, no subject in which more complicated
quantitative conditions have to be determined than terrestrial magnetism. Since the time when the declination
of the compass was first noticed, as some suppose by
Columbus, we have had successive discoveries from time
to time of the progressive change of declination from
century to century ; of the periodic character of this
change ; of the difference of the declination in various
parts of the earth's surface ; of the varying laws of
the change of declination ; of the dip or inclination of
the needle, and the corresponding laws of its periodic
changes ; the horizontal and perpendicular intensities have
also been the subject of exact measurement, and have been
found to vary with place and time, like the directions of

the needle ; daily and yearly periodic changes have also
been detected, and all the elements are found to be subject
to occasional storms or abnormal perturbations, in which
the eleven year period, now known to be common to many
planetary relations, is apparent. The complete solution
of these motions of the compass needle involves nothing
less than a determination of its position and oscillations in
every part of the world at any epoch, the like determination for another epoch, and so on, time after time, until
the periods of all changes are ascertained. This one subject offers to men of science an almost inexhaustible field
for interesting quantitative research, in which we shall
doubtless at some future time discover the operation of
causes now most mysterious and unaccountable.

The Methods of Accurate Measurement.

In studying the modes by which physicists have accomplished very exact measurements, we find that they
are very various, but that they may perhaps be reduced
under the following three classes :—

1. The increase or decrease, in some determinate ratio,
of the quantity to be measured, so as to bring it within
the scope of our senses, and to equate it with the standard
unit, or some determinate multiple or sub-multiple of this
unit.

2. The discovery of some natural conjunction of events
which will enable us to compare directly the multiples of
the quantity with those of the unit, or a quantity related
in a definite ratio to that unit.

3. Indirect measurement, which gives us not the quantity itself, but some other quantity connected with it by
known mathematical relations.

Conditions of Accurate Measurement.

Several conditions are requisite in order that a measurement may be made with great accuracy, and that
the results may be closely accordant when several independent measurements are made.

In the first place the magnitude must be exactly defined
by sharp terminations, or precise marks of inconsiderable

thickness. When a boundary is vague and graduated, like the penumbra in a lunar eclipse, it is impossible to say where the end really is, and different people will come to different results. We may sometimes overcome this difficulty to a certain extent, by observations repeated in a special manner, as we shall afterwards see; but when possible, we should choose opportunities for measurement when precise definition is easy. The moment of occultation of a star by the moon can be observed with great accuracy, because the star disappears with perfect suddenness; but there are other astronomical conjunctions, eclipses, transits, &c., which occupy a certain length of time in happening, and thus open the way to differences of opinion. It would be impossible to observe with precision the movements of a body possessing no definite points of reference. The colours of the complete spectrum shade into each other so continuously that exact determinations of refractive indices would have been impossible, had we not the dark lines of the solar spectrum as precise points for measurement, or various kinds of homogeneous light, such as that of sodium, possessing a nearly uniform length of vibration.

In the second place, we cannot measure accurately unless we have the means of multiplying or dividing a quantity without considerable error, so that we may correctly equate one magnitude with the multiple or sub-multiple of the other. In some cases we operate upon the quantity to be measured, and bring it into accurate coincidence with the actual standard, as when in photometry we vary the distance of our luminous body, until its illuminating power at a certain point is equal to that of a standard lamp. In other cases we repeat the unit until it equals the object, as in surveying land, or determining a weight by the balance. The requisites of accuracy now are :—(1) That we can repeat unit after unit of exactly equal magnitude; (2) That these can be joined together so that the aggregate shall really be the sum of the parts. The same conditions apply to subdivision, which may be regarded as a multiplication of subordinate units. In order to measure to the thousandth of an inch, we must be able to add thousandth after thousandth without error in the magnitude of these spaces, or in their conjunction.

Measuring Instruments.

To consider the mechanical construction of scientific
instruments, is no part of my purpose in this book. I
wish to point out merely the general purpose of such
instruments, and the methods adopted to carry out that
purpose with great precision. In the first place we must
distinguish between the instrument which effects a comparison between two quantities, and the standard magnitude which often forms one of the quantities compared.
The astronomer's clock, for instance, is no standard of the
efflux of time; it serves but to subdivide, with approximate accuracy, the interval of successive passages of a
star across the meridian, which it may effect perhaps to
the tenth part of a second, or $\frac{1}{864000}$ part of the whole.
The moving globe itself is the real standard clock, and the
transit instrument the finger of the clock, while the stars
are the hour, minute, and second marks, none the less
accurate because they are disposed at unequal intervals.
The photometer is a simple instrument, by which we compare the relative intensity of rays of light falling upon a
given spot. The galvanometer shows the comparative
intensity of electric currents passing through a wire.
The calorimeter gauges the quantity of heat passing from
a given object. But no such instruments furnish the
standard unit in terms of which our results are to be expressed. In one peculiar case alone does the same instrument combine the unit of measurement and the means of
comparison. A theodolite, mural circle, sextant, or other
instrument for the measurement of angular magnitudes
has no need of an additional physical unit; for the circle
itself, or complete revolution, is the natural unit to which
all greater or lesser amounts of angular magnitude are
referred.

The result of every measurement is to make known the
purely numerical ratio existing between the magnitude
to be measured, and a certain other magnitude, which
should, when possible, be a fixed unit or standard magnitude, or at least an intermediate unit of which the value
can be ascertained in terms of the ultimate standard. But
though a ratio is the required result, an equation is the
mode in which the ratio is determined and expressed. In

every measurement we equate some multiple or submultiple of one quantity, with some multiple or submultiple of another, and equality is always the fact which we ascertain by the senses. By the eye, the ear, or the touch, we judge whether there is a discrepancy or not between two lights, two sounds, two intervals of time, two bars of metal. Often indeed we substitute one sense for the other, as when the efflux of time is judged by the marks upon a moving slip of paper, so that equal intervals of time are represented by equal lengths. There is a tendency to reduce all comparisons to the comparison of space magnitudes, but in every case one of the senses must be the ultimate judge of coincidence or non-coincidence.

Since the equation to be established may exist between any multiples or submultiples of the quantities compared, there naturally arise several different modes of comparison adapted to different cases. Let p be the magnitude to be measured, and q that in terms of which it is to be expressed. Then we wish to find such numbers x and y, that the equation $p = \frac{x}{y} q$ may be true. This equation may be presented in four forms, namely :—

First Form.	Second Form.	Third Form.	Fourth Form.
$p = \frac{x}{y} q$	$p \frac{y}{x} = q$	$py = qx$	$\frac{p}{x} = \frac{q}{y}$

Each of these modes of expressing the same equation corresponds to one mode of effecting a measurement.

When the standard quantity is greater than that to be measured, we often adopt the first mode, and subdivide the unit until we get a magnitude equal to that measured. The angles observed in surveying, in astronomy, or in goniometry are usually smaller than a whole revolution, and the measuring circle is divided by the use of the screw and microscope, until we obtain an angle undistinguishable from that observed. The dimensions of minute objects are determined by subdividing the inch or centimetre, the screw micrometer being the most accurate means of subdivision. Ordinary temperatures are estimated by division of the standard interval between the freezing and boiling points of water, as marked on a thermometer tube.

In a still greater number of cases, perhaps, we multiply the standard unit until we get a magnitude equal to that to be measured. Ordinary measurement by a foot rule, a surveyor's chain, or the excessively careful measurements of the base line of a trigonometrical survey by standard bars, are sufficient instances of this procedure.

In the second case, where $p \frac{y}{x} = q$, we multiply or divide a magnitude until we get what is equal to the unit, or to some magnitude easily comparable with it. As a general rule the quantities which we desire to measure in physical science are too small rather than too great for easy determination, and the problem consists in multiplying them without introducing error. Thus the expansion of a metallic bar when heated from $0°$ C to $100°$ may be multiplied by a train of levers or cog wheels. In the common thermometer the expansion of the mercury, though slight, is rendered very apparent, and easily measurable by the fineness of the tube, and many other cases might be quoted. There are some phenomena, on the contrary, which are too great or rapid to come within the easy range of our senses, and our task is then the opposite one of diminution. Galileo found it difficult to measure the velocity of a falling body, owing to the considerable velocity acquired in a single second. He adopted the elegant device, therefore, of lessening the rapidity by letting the body roll down an inclined plane, which enables us to reduce the accelerating force in any required ratio. The same purpose is effected in the well-known experiments performed on Attwood's machine, and the measurement of gravity by the pendulum really depends on the same principle applied in a far more advantageous manner. Wheatstone invented a beautiful method of galvanometry for strong currents, which consists in drawing off from the main current a certain determinate portion, which is equated by the galvanometer to a standard current. In short, he measures not the current itself but a known fraction of it.

In many electrical and other experiments, we wish to measure the movements of a needle or other body, which are not only very slight in themselves, but the manifestations of exceedingly small forces. We cannot even

approach a delicately balanced needle without disturbing
it. Under these circumstances the only mode of proceeding with accuracy, is to attach a very small mirror to the
moving body, and employ a ray of light reflected from
the mirror as an index of its movements. The ray may
be considered quite incapable of affecting the body, and
yet by allowing the ray to pass to a sufficient distance,
the motions of the mirror may be increased to almost any
extent. A ray of light is in fact a perfectly weightless
finger or index of indefinite length, with the additional
advantage that the angular deviation is by the law of
reflection double that of the mirror. This method was
introduced by Gauss, and is now of great importance;
but in Wollaston's reflecting goniometer a ray of light
had previously been employed as an index. Lavoisier
and Laplace had also used a telescope in connection with
the pyrometer.

It is a great advantage in some instruments that they
can be readily made to manifest a phenomenon in a greater
or less degree, by a very slight change in the construction.
Thus either by enlarging the bulb or contracting the tube
of the thermometer, we can make it give more conspicuous
indications of change of temperature. The ordinary barometer, on the other hand, always gives the variations of
pressure on one scale. The torsion balance is remarkable for the extreme delicacy which may be attained
by increasing the length and lightness of the rod, and the
length and thinness of the supporting thread. Forces so
minute as the attraction of gravitation between two balls,
or the magnetic and diamagnetic attraction of common
liquids and gases, may thus be made apparent, and even
measured. The common chemical balance, too, is capable
theoretically of unlimited sensibility.

The third mode of measurement, which may be called
the Method of Repetition, is of such great importance and
interest that we must consider it in a separate section. It
consists in multiplying both magnitudes to be compared
until some multiple of the first is found to coincide very
nearly with some multiple of the second. If the multiplication can be effected to an unlimited extent, without the
introduction of countervailing errors, the accuracy with
which the required ratio can be determined is unlimited,

and we thus account for the extraordinary precision with which intervals of time in astronomy are compared together.

The fourth mode of measurement, in which we equate submultiples of two magnitudes, is comparatively seldom employed, because it does not conduce to accuracy. In the photometer, perhaps, we may be said to use it; we compare the intensity of two sources of light, by placing them both at such distances from a given surface, that the light falling on the surface is tolerable to the eye, and equally intense from each source. Since the intensity of light varies inversely as the square of the distance, the relative intensities of the luminous bodies are proportional to the squares of their distances. The equal intensity of two rays of similarly coloured light may be most accurately ascertained in the mode suggested by Arago, namely, by causing the rays to pass in opposite directions through two nearly flat lenses pressed together. There is an exact equation between the intensities of the beams when Newton's rings disappear, the ring created by one ray being exactly the complement of that created by the other.

The Method of Repetition.

The ratio of two quantities can be determined with unlimited accuracy, if we can multiply both the object of measurement and the standard unit without error, and then observe what multiple of the one coincides or nearly coincides with some multiple of the other. Although perfect coincidence can never be really attained, the error thus arising may be indefinitely reduced. For if the equation $py = qx$ be uncertain to the amount e, so that $py = qx \pm e$, then we have $p = q\frac{x}{y} \pm \frac{e}{y}$, and as we are supposed to be able to make y as great as we like without increasing the error e, it follows that we can make $e \div y$ as small as we like, and thus approximate within an inconsiderable quantity to the required ratio $x \div y$.

This method of repetition is naturally employed whenever quantities can be repeated, or repeat themselves

without error of juxtaposition, which is especially the
case with the motions of the earth and heavenly bodies.
In determining the length of the sidereal day, we determine the ratio between the earth's revolution round the
sun, and its rotation on its own axis. We might ascertain
the ratio by observing the successive passages of a star
across the zenith, and comparing the interval by a good
clock with that between two passages of the sun, the
difference being due to the angular movement of the
earth round the sun. In such observations we should
have an error of a considerable part of a second at each
observation, in addition to the irregularities of the clock.
But the revolutions of the earth repeat themselves day
after day, and year after year, without the slightest interval between the end of one period and the beginning
of another. The operation of multiplication is perfectly
performed for us by nature. If, then, we can find an observation of the passage of a star across the meridian a hundred years ago, that is of the interval of time between
the passage of the sun and the star, the instrumental
errors in measuring this interval by a clock and telescope
may be greater than in the present day, but will be
divided by about 36,524 days, and rendered excessively
small. It is thus that astronomers have been able to
ascertain the ratio of the mean solar to the sidereal day
to the 8th place of decimals ($1 \cdot 00273791$ to 1), or to the
hundred millionth part, probably the most accurate result
of measurement in the whole range of science.

The antiquity of this mode of comparison is almost as
great as that of astronomy itself. Hipparchus made the
first clear application of it, when he compared his own
observations with those of Aristarchus, made 145 years
previously, and thus ascertained the length of the year.
This calculation may in fact be regarded as the earliest
attempt at an exact determination of the constants of
nature. The method is the main resource of astronomers; Tycho, for instance, detected the slow diminution
of the obliquity of the earth's axis, by the comparison
of observations at long intervals. Living astronomers
use the method as much as earlier ones; but so superior
in accuracy are all observations taken during the last
hundred years to all previous ones, that it is often

found preferable to take a shorter interval, rather than incur the risk of greater instrumental errors in the earlier observations.

It is obvious that many of the slower changes of the heavenly bodies must require the lapse of large intervals of time to render their amount perceptible. Hipparchus could not possibly have discovered the smaller inequalities of the heavenly motions, because there were no previous observations of sufficient age or exactness to exhibit them. And just as the observations of Hipparchus formed the starting-point for subsequent comparisons, so a large part of the labour of present astronomers is directed to recording the present state of the heavens so exactly, that future generations of astronomers may detect changes, which cannot possibly become known in the present age.

The principle of repetition was very ingeniously employed in an instrument first proposed by Mayer in 1767, and carried into practice in the Repeating Circle of Borda. The exact measurement of angles is indispensable, not only in astronomy but also in trigonometrical surveys, and the highest skill in the mechanical execution of the graduated circle and telescope will not prevent terminal errors of considerable amount. If instead of one telescope, the circle be provided with two similar telescopes, these may be alternately directed to two distant points, say the marks in a trigonometrical survey, so that the circle shall be turned through any multiple of the angle subtended by those marks, before the amount of the angular revolution is read off upon the graduated circle. Theoretically speaking, all error arising from imperfect graduation might thus be indefinitely reduced, being divided by the number of repetitions. In practice, the advantage of the invention is not found to be very great, probably because a certain error is introduced at each observation in the changing and fixing of the telescopes. It is moreover inapplicable to moving objects like the heavenly bodies, so that its use is confined to important trigonometrical surveys.

The pendulum is the most perfect of all instruments, chiefly because it admits of almost endless repetition. Since the force of gravity never ceases, one swing of the pendulum is no sooner ended than the other is begun, so that the juxtaposition of successive units is absolutely perfect. Provided that the oscillations be equal, one thousand oscillations will occupy exactly one thousand times as great an interval of time as one oscillation. Not only is the subdivision of time entirely dependent on this fact, but in the accurate measurement of gravity, and many other important determinations, it is of the greatest service. In the deepest mine, we could not observe the rapidity of fall of a body for more than a quarter of a minute, and the measurement of its velocity would be difficult, and subject to uncertain errors from resistance of air, &c. In the pendulum, we have a body which can be kept rising and falling for many hours, in a medium entirely under our command or if desirable in a vacuum. Moreover, the comparative force of gravity at different points, at the top and bottom of a mine for instance, can be determined with wonderful precision, by comparing the oscillations of two exactly similar pendulums, with the aid of electric clock signals.

To ascertain the comparative times of vibration of two pendulums, it is only requisite to swing them one in front of the other, to record by a clock the moment when they coincide in swing, so that one hides the other, and then count the number of vibrations until they again come to coincidence. If one pendulum makes m vibrations and the other n, we at once have our equation $pn = qm$; which gives the length of vibration of either pendulum in terms of the other. This method of coincidence, embodying the principle of repetition in perfection, was employed with wonderful skill by Sir George Airy, in his experiments on the Density of the Earth at the Harton Colliery, the pendulums above and below being compared with clocks, which again were compared with each other by electric signals. So exceedingly accurate was this method of observation, as carried out by Sir George Airy, that he was able to measure a total difference in the vibrations at the top and bottom of the shaft, amounting to only 2·24 seconds in the twenty-four hours, with an error of less than one hundredth part of a second, or one part in 8,640,000 of the whole day.[1]

The principle of repetition has been elegantly applied

---

[1] *Philosophical Transactions*, (1856) vol. 146, Part i. p. 297.

in observing the motion of waves in water. If the canal in which the experiments are made be short, say twenty feet long, the waves will pass through it so rapidly that an observation of one length, as practised by Walker, will be subject to much terminal error, even when the observer is very skilful. But it is a result of the undulatory theory that a wave is unaltered, and loses no time by complete reflection, so that it may be allowed to travel backwards and forwards in the same canal, and its motion, say through sixty lengths, or 1200 feet, may be observed with the same accuracy as in a canal 1200 feet long, with the advantage of greater uniformity in the condition of the canal and water.[1] It is always desirable, if possible, to bring an experiment into a small compass, so that it may be well under command, and yet we may often by repetition enjoy at the same time the advantage of extensive trial.

One reason of the great accuracy of weighing with a good balance is the fact, that weights placed in the same scale are naturally added together without the slightest error. There is no difficulty in the precise juxtaposition of two grams, but the juxtaposition of two metre measures can only be effected with tolerable accuracy, by the use of microscopes and many precautions. Hence, the extreme trouble and cost attaching to the exact measurement of a base line for a survey, the risk of error entering at every juxtaposition of the measuring bars, and indefatigable attention to all the requisite precautions being necessary throughout the operation.

Measurements by Natural Coincidence.

In certain cases a peculiar conjunction of circumstances enables us to dispense more or less with instrumental aids, and to obtain very exact numerical results in the simplest manner. The mere fact, for instance, that no human being has ever seen a different face of the moon from that familiar to us, conclusively proves that the period of rotation of the moon on its own axis is equal

---

[1] Airy, *On Tides and Waves*, Encyclopædia Metropolitana, p. 345. Scott Russell, *British Association Report*, 1837, p. 432.

to that of its revolution round the earth.   Not only have
we the repetition of these movements during 1000 or
2000 years at least, but we have observations made for
us at very remote periods, free from instrumental error,
no instrument being needed.   We learn that the seventh
satellite of Saturn is subject to a similar law, because its
light undergoes a variation in each revolution, owing to
the existence of some dark tract of land; now this failure
of light always occurs while it is in the same position
relative to Saturn, clearly proving the equality of the
axial and revolutional periods, as Huygens perceived.[1]
A like peculiarity in the motions of Jupiter's fourth satellite was similarly detected by Maraldi in 1713.

Remarkable conjunctions of the planets may sometimes
allow us to compare their periods of revolution, through
great intervals of time, with much accuracy.   Laplace in
explaining the long inequality in the motions of Jupiter
and Saturn, was assisted by a conjunction of these
planets, observed at Cairo, towards the close of the
eleventh century.   Laplace calculated that such a con- ,
junction must have happened on the 31st of October, A.D.
1087; and the discordance between the distances of the
planets as recorded, and as assigned by theory, was less
than one-fifth part of the apparent diameter of the sun.
This difference being less than the probable ·error of the
early record, the theory was confirmed as far as facts
were available.[2]

Ancient astronomers often showed the highest ingenuity in turning any opportunities of measurement which
occurred to good account.   Eratosthenes, as early as
250 B.C., happening to hear that the sun at Syene, in
Upper Egypt, was visible at the summer solstice at the
bottom of a well, proving that it was in the zenith, proposed to determine the dimensions of the earth, by measuring the length of the shadow of a rod at Alexandria on
the same day of the year.   He thus learnt in a rude
manner the difference of latitude between Alexandria and
Syene and finding it to be about one fiftieth part of the
whole circumference, he ascertained the dimensions of the

[1] *Hugenii Cosmotheoros*, pp. 117, 118.   Laplace's *Système*, translated, vol. i. p. 67.
[2] Grant's *History of Physical Astronomy*, p. 129.

earth within about one sixth part of the truth. The use of wells in astronomical observation appears to have been occasionally practised in comparatively recent times as by Flamsteed in 1679.[1] The Alexandrian astronomers employed the moon as an instrument of measurement in several sagacious modes. When the moon is exactly half full, the moon, sun, and earth, are at the angles of a right-angled triangle. Aristarchus measured at such a time the moon's elongation from the sun, which gave him the two other angles of the triangle, and enabled him to judge of the comparative distances of the moon and sun from the earth. His result, though very rude, was far more accurate than any notions previously entertained, and enabled him to form some estimate of the comparative magnitudes of the bodies. Eclipses of the moon were very useful to Hipparchus in ascertaining the longtitude of the stars, which are invisible when the sun is above the horizon. For the moon when eclipsed must be 180° distant from the sun ; hence it is only requisite to measure the distance of a fixed star in longitude from the eclipsed moon to obtain with ease its angular distance from the sun.

In later times the eclipses of Jupiter have served to measure an angle ; for at the middle moment of the eclipse the satellite must be in the same straight line with the planet and sun, so that we can learn from the known laws of movement of the satellite the longitude of Jupiter as seen from the sun. If at the same time we measure the elongation or apparent angular distance of Jupiter from the sun, as seen from the earth, we have all the angles of the triangle between Jupiter, the sun, and the earth, and can calculate the comparative magnitudes of the sides of the triangle by trigonometry.

The transits of Venus over the sun's face are other natural events which give most accurate measurements of the sun's parallax, or apparent difference of position as seen from distant points of the earth's surface. The sun forms a kind of background on which the place of the planet is marked, and serves as a measuring instrument free from all the errors of construction which affect

---

[1] Baily's *Account of Flamsteed*, p. lix.

human instruments. The rotation of the earth, too, by
variously affecting the apparent velocity of ingress or
egress of Venus, as seen from different places, discloses
the amount of the parallax. It has been sufficiently
shown that by rightly choosing the moments of observation, the planetary bodies may often be made to reveal
their relative distance, to measure their own position, to
record their own movements with a high degree of
accuracy. With the improvement of astronomical instruments, such conjunctions become less necessary to the
progress of the science, but it will always remain advantageous to choose those moments for observation when
instrumental errors enter with the least effect.

In other sciences, exact quantitative laws can occasionally be obtained without instrumental measurement, as
when we learn the exactly equal velocity of sounds of
different pitch, by observing that a peal of bells or a
musical performance is heard harmoniously at any distance to which the sound penetrates; this could not be
the case, as Newton remarked, if one sound overtook
the other. One of the most important principles of the
atomic theory, was proved by implication before the use
of the balance was introduced into chemistry. Wenzel
observed, before 1777, that when two neutral substances
decompose each other, the resulting salts are also neutral.
In mixing sodium sulphate and barium nitrate, we
obtain insoluble barium sulphate and neutral sodium
nitrate. This result could not follow unless the nitric
acid, requisite to saturate one atom of sodium, were
exactly equal to that required by one atom of barium,
so that an exchange could take place without leaving
either acid or base in excess.

An important principle of mechanics may also be
established by a simple acoustical observation. When
a rod or tongue of metal fixed at one end is set in
vibration, the pitch of the sound may be observed to
be exactly the same, whether the vibrations be small or
great; hence the oscillations are isochronous, or equally
rapid, independently of their magnitude. On the ground
of theory, it can be shown that such a result only
happens when the flexure is proportional to the deflecting
force. Thus the simple observation that the pitch of

the sound of a harmonium, for instance, does not change with its loudness establishes an exact law of nature.[1]

A closely similar instance is found in the proof that the intensity of light or heat rays varies inversely as the square of the distance increases. For the apparent magnitude certainly varies according to this law ; hence, if the intensity of light varied according to any other law, the brightness of an object would be different at different distances, which is not observed to be the case. Melloni applied the same kind of reasoning, in a somewhat different form, to the radiation of heat-rays.

Modes of Indirect Measurement.

Some of the most conspicuously beautiful experiments in the whole range of science, have been devised for the purpose of indirectly measuring quantities, which in their extreme greatness or smallness surpass the powers of sense. All that we need to do, is to discover some other conveniently measurable phenomenon, which is related in a known ratio or according to a known law, however complicated, with that to be measured. Having once obtained experimental data, there is no further difficulty beyond that of arithmetic or algebraic calculation.

Gold is reduced by the gold-beater to leaves so thin, that the most powerful microscope would not detect any measurable thickness. If we laid several hundred leaves upon each other to multiply the thickness, we should still have no more than $\frac{1}{100}$th of an inch at the most to measure, and the errors arising in the superposition and measurement would be considerable. But we can readily obtain an exact result through the connected amount of weight. Faraday weighed 2000 leaves of gold, each $3\frac{3}{8}$ inch square, and found them equal to 384 grains. From the known specific gravity of gold it was easy to calculate that the average thickness of the leaves was $\frac{1}{282,000}$ of an inch.[2]

We must ascribe to Newton the honour of leading the

[1] Jamin, *Cours de Physique*, vol. i. p. 152.

[2] Faraday. *Chemical Researches*, p. 393.

way in methods of minute measurement. He did not call waves of light by their right name, and did not understand their nature; yet he measured their length, though it did not exceed the 2,000,000th part of a metre or the one fifty-thousandth part of an inch. He pressed together two lenses of large but known radii. It is easy to calculate the interval between the lenses at any point, by measuring the distance from the central point of contact. Now, with homogeneous rays the successive rings of light and darkness mark the points at which the interval between the lenses is equal to one half, or any multiple of half a vibration of the light, so that the length of the vibration became known. In a similar manner many phenomena of interference of rays of light admit of the measurement of the wave lengths. Fringes of interference arise from rays of light which cross each other at a small angle, and an excessively minute difference in the lengths of the waves makes a very perceptible difference in the position of the point at which two rays will interfere and produce darkness.

Fizeau has recently employed Newton's rings to measure small amounts of motion. By merely counting the number of rings of sodium monochromatic light passing a certain point where two glass plates are in close proximity, he is able to ascertain with the greatest accuracy and ease the change of distance between these glasses, produced, for instance, by the expansion of a metallic bar, connected with one of the glass plates.[1]

Nothing excites more admiration than the mode in which scientific observers can occasionally measure quantities, which seem beyond the bounds of human observation. We know the *average* depth of the Pacific Ocean to be 14,190 feet, not by actual sounding, which would be impracticable in sufficient detail, but by noticing the rate of transmission of earthquake waves from the South American to the opposite coasts, the rate of movement being connected by theory with the depth of the water.[2] In the same way the average depth of the Atlantic Ocean is inferred to be no less than 22,157 feet, from the velocity

[1] *Proceedings of the Royal Society,* 30th November, 1866.
[2] Herschel, *Physical Geography,* § 40.

of the ordinary tidal waves. A tidal wave again gives beautiful evidence of an effect of the law of gravity, which we could never in any other way detect. Newton estimated that the moon's force in moving the ocean is only one part in 2,871,400 of the whole force of gravity, so that even the pendulum, used with the utmost skill, would fail to render it apparent. Yet, the immense extent of the ocean allows the accumulation of the effect into a very palpable amount; and from the comparative heights of the lunar and solar tides, Newton roughly estimated the comparative forces of the moon's and sun's gravity at the earth.[1]

A few years ago it might have seemed impossible that we should ever measure the velocity with which a star approaches or recedes from the earth, since the apparent position of the star is thereby unaltered. But the spectroscope now enables us to detect and even measure such motions with considerable accuracy, by the alteration which it causes in the apparent rapidity of vibration, and consequently in the refrangibility of rays of light of definite colour. And while our estimates of the lateral movements of stars depend upon our very uncertain knowledge of their distances, the spectroscope gives the motions of approach and recess irrespective of other motions excepting that of the earth. It gives in short the motions of approach and recess of the stars relatively to the earth.[2]

The rapidity of vibration for each musical tone, having been accurately determined by comparison with the Syren (p. 10), we can use sounds as indirect indications of rapid vibrations. It is now known that the contraction of a muscle arises from the periodical contractions of each separate fibre, and from a faint sound or susurrus which accompanies the action of a muscle, it is inferred that each contraction lasts for about one 300th part of a second. Minute quantities of radiant heat are now always measured indirectly by the electricity which they produce when falling upon a thermopile. The extreme delicacy of the method seems to be due to the power of multiplication at several points in the apparatus. The number of elements or junc-

[1] *Principia*, bk. iii. Prop. 37, *Corollaries*, 2 and 3. Motte's translation, vol. ii. p. 310.
[2] Roscoe's *Spectrum Analysis*, 1st ed. p. 296.

tions of different metals in the thermopile can be increased
so that the tension of the electric current derived from the
same intensity of radiation is multiplied; the effect of the
current upon the magnetic needle can be multiplied within
certain bounds, by passing the current many times round
it in a coil; the excursions of the needle can be increased
by rendering it astatic and increasing the delicacy of its
suspension; lastly, the angular divergence can be observed,
with any required accuracy, by the use of an attached
mirror and distant scale viewed through a telecope (p. 287).
Such is the delicacy of this method of measuring heat, that
Dr. Joule succeeded in making a thermopile which would
indicate a difference of $0°·000114$ Cent.[1]

A striking case of indirect measurement is furnished by
the revolving mirror of Wheatstone and Foucault, whereby
a minute interval of time is estimated in the form of an
angular deviation. Wheatstone viewed an electric spark
in a mirror rotating so rapidly, that if the duration of the
spark had been more than one 72,000th part of a second,
the point of light would have appeared elongated to an
angular extent of one-half degree. In the spark, as drawn
directly from a Leyden jar, no elongation was apparent, so
that the duration of the spark was immeasurably small; but
when the discharge took place through a bad conductor,
the elongation of the spark denoted a sensible duration.[2]
In the hands of Foucault the rotating mirror gave a
measure of the time occupied by light in passing through
a few metres of space.

Comparative Use of Measuring Instruments.

In almost every case a measuring instrument serves,
and should serve only as a means of comparison between
two or more magnitudes. As a general rule, we should
not attempt to make the divisions of the measuring scale
exact multiples or submultiples of the unit, but, regarding
them as arbitrary marks, should determine their values by
comparison with the standard itself. The perpendicular
wires in the field of a transit telescope, are fixed at nearly

---

[1] *Philosophical Transactions* (1859), vol. cxlix. p. 94.
[2] Watts' *Dictionary of Chemistry*, vol. ii. p. 393.

equal but arbitrary distances, and those distances are afterwards determined, as first suggested by Malvasia, by watching the passage of star after star across them, and noting
the intervals of time by the clock. Owing to the perfectly
regular motion of the earth, these time intervals give exact
determinations of the angular intervals. In the same way,
the angular value of each turn of the screw micrometer
attached to a telescope, can be easily and accurately
ascertained.

When a thermopile is used to observe radiant heat, it
would be almost impossible to calculate on à priori grounds
what is the value of each division of the galvanometer
circle, and still more difficult to construct a galvanometer,
so that each division should have a given value. But this
is quite unnecessary, because by placing the thermopile
before a body of known dimensions, at a known distance,
with a known temperature and radiating power, we measure
a known amount of radiant heat, and inversely measure
the value of the indications of the thermopile. In a
similar way Dr. Joule ascertained the actual temperature
produced by the compression of bars of metal. For having
inserted a small thermopile composed of a single junction
of copper and iron wire, and noted the deflections of the
galvanometer, he had only to dip the bars into water of
different temperatures, until he produced a like deflection, in order to ascertain the temperature developed by
pressure.[1]

In some cases we are obliged to accept a very carefully
constructed instrument as a standard, as in the case of a
standard barometer or thermometer. But it is then best
to treat all inferior instruments comparatively only, and
determine the values of their scales by comparison with
the assumed standard.

Systematic Performance of Measurements.

When a large number of accurate measurements have
to be effected, it is usually desirable to make a certain
number of determinations with scrupulous care, and afterwards use them as points of reference for the remaining

---

[1] *Philosophical Transactions* (1859), vol. cxlix. p. 119, &c.

determinations. In the trigonometrical survey of a country, the principal triangulation fixes the relative positions
and distances of a few points with rigid accuracy. A
minor triangulation refers every prominent hill or village
to one of the principal points, and then the details are
filled in by reference to the secondary points. The survey
of the heavens is effected in a like manner. The ancient
astronomers compared the right ascensions of a few principal stars with the moon, and thus ascertained their positions with regard to the sun; the minor stars were afterwards
referred to the principal stars. Tycho followed the same
method, except that he used the more slowly moving
planet Venus instead of the moon. Flamsteed was in the
habit of using about seven stars, favourably situated at
points all round the heavens. In his early observations
the distances of the other stars from these standard points
were determined by the use of the quadrant.[1] Even since
the introduction of the transit telescope and the mural
circle, tables of standard stars are formed at Greenwich,
the positions being determined with all possible accuracy,
so that they can be employed for purposes of reference by
astronomers.

In ascertaining the specific gravities of substances, all
gases are referred to atmospheric air at a given temperature and pressure; all liquids and solids are referred to
water. We require to compare the densities of water and
air with great care, and the comparative densities of any
two substances whatever can then be ascertained.

In comparing a very great with a very small magnitude,
it is usually desirable to break up the process into several
steps, using intermediate terms of comparison. We should
never think of measuring the distance from London to
Edinburgh by laying down measuring rods, throughout the
whole length. A base of several miles is selected on level
ground, and compared on the one hand with the standard
yard, and on the other with the distance of London and
Edinburgh, or any other two points, by trigonometrical
survey. Again, it would be exceedingly difficult to compare the light of a star with that of the sun, which would
be about thirty thousand million times greater; but Her-

[1] Baily's *Account of Flamsteed*, pp. 378—380.

schel [1] effected the comparison by using the full moon as
an intermediate unit.   Wollaston ascertained that the sun
gave 801,072 times as much light as the full moon, and
Herschel determined that the light of the latter exceeded
that of *a* Centauri 27,408 times, so that we find the ratio
between the light of the sun and star to be that of about
22,000,000,000 to 1.

The Pendulum.

By far the most perfect and beautiful of all instruments
of measurement is the pendulum.   Consisting merely of a
heavy body suspended freely at an invariable distance from
a fixed point, it is most simple in construction ; yet all the
highest problems of physical measurement depend upon its
careful use.   Its excessive value arises from two circumstances.

(1) The method of repetition is eminently applicable
to it, as already described (p. 290).

(2) Unlike other instruments, it connects together three
different quantities, those of space, time and force.

In most works on natural philosophy it is shown, that
when the oscillations of the pendulum are infinitely small,
the square of the time occupied by an oscillation is directly
proportional to the length of the pendulum, and indirectly
proportional to the force affecting it, of whatever kind.
The whole theory of the pendulum is contained in the
formula, first given by Huygens in his *Horologium Oscil-
latorium.*

$$\text{Time of oscillation} = 3\text{·}14159 \times \sqrt{\frac{\text{length of pendulum}}{\text{force.}}}$$

The quantity 3·14159 is the constant ratio of the circumference and radius of a circle, and is of course known with
accuracy.   Hence, any two of the three quantities concerned being given, the third may be found ; or any two
being maintained invariable, the third will be invariable.
Thus a pendulum of invariable length suspended at the
same place, where the force of gravity may be considered
constant, furnishes a measure of time.   The same invariable pendulum being made to vibrate at different points of

---

[1] Herschel's *Astronomy,* § 817, 4th. ed. p. 553

the earth's surface, and the times of vibration being astronomically determined, the force of gravity becomes accurately known. Finally, with a known force of gravity, and time of vibration ascertained by reference to the stars, the length is determinate.

All astronomical observations depend upon the first manner of using the pendulum, namely, in the astronomical clock. In the second employment it has been almost equally indispensable. The primary principle that gravity is equal in all matter was proved by Newton's and Gauss' pendulum experiments. The torsion pendulum of Michell, Cavendish, and Baily, depending upon exactly the same principles as the ordinary pendulum, gave the density of the earth, one of the foremost natural constants. Kater and Sabine, by pendulum observations in different parts of the earth, ascertained the variation of gravity, whence comes a determination of the earth's ellipticity. The laws of electric and magnetic attraction have also been determined by the method of vibrations, which is in constant use in the measurement of the horizontal force of terrestrial magnetism.

We must not confuse with the ordinary use of the pendulum its application by Newton, to show the absence of internal friction against space,[1] or to ascertain the laws of motion and elasticity.[2] In these cases the extent of vibration is the quantity measured, and the principles of the instrument are different.

Attainable Accuracy of Measurement.

It is a matter of some interest to compare the degrees of accuracy which can be attained in the measurement of different kinds of magnitude. Few measurements of any kind are exact to more than six significant figures,[3] but it is seldom that such accuracy can be hoped for. Time is the magnitude which seems to be capable of the most exact estimation, owing to the properties of the pendulum, and the principle of repetition described in previous sections.

[1] *Principia*, bk. ii. Sect. 6. Prop. 31. Motte's Translation, vol. ii. p. 107.

[2] Ibid. bk. i. Law iii. Corollary 6. Motte's Translation, vol. i. p. 33.

[3] Thomson and Tait's *Natural Philosophy*, vol. i. p. 333.

As regards short intervals of time, it has already been stated that Sir George Airy was able to estimate one part in 8,640,000, an exactness, as he truly remarks, " almost beyond conception." [1] The ratio between the mean solar and the sidereal day is known to be about one part in one hundred millions, or to the eighth place of decimals, (p. 289).

Determinations of weight seem to come next in exactness, owing to the fact that repetition without error is applicable to them. An ordinary good balance should show about one part in 500,000 of the load. The finest balance employed by M. Stas, turned with one part in 825,000 of the load.[2] But balances have certainly been constructed to show one part in a million,[3] and Ramsden is said to have constructed a balance for the Royal Society, to indicate one part in seven millions, though this is hardly credible. Professor Clerk Maxwell takes it for granted that one part in five millions can be detected, but we ought to discriminate between what a balance can do when first constructed, and when in continuous use.

Determinations of length, unless performed with extraordinary care, are open to much error in the junction of the measuring bars. Even in measuring the base line of a trigonometrical survey, the accuracy generally attained is only that of about one part in 60,000, or an inch in the mile; but it is said that in four measurements of a base line carried out very recently at Cape Comorin, the greatest error was 0·077 inch in 1·68 mile, or one part in 1,382,400, an almost incredible degree of accuracy. Sir J. Whitworth has shown that touch is even a more delicate mode of measuring lengths than sight, and by means of a splendidly executed screw, and a small cube of iron placed between two flat-ended iron bars, so as to be suspended when touching them, he can detect a change of dimension in a bar, amounting to no more than one-millionth of an inch.[4]

[1] *Philosophical Transactions*, (1856), vol. cxlvi. pp. 330, 331.
[2] *First Annual Report of the Mint*, p. 106.
[3] Jevons, in Watts' *Dictionary of Chemistry*, vol. i. p. 483.
[4] British Association, Glasgow, 1856. *Address of the President of the Mechanical Section.*

CHAPTER XIV.

UNITS AND STANDARDS OF MEASUREMENT.

As we have seen, instruments of measurement are only means of comparison between one magnitude and another, and as a general rule we must assume some one arbitrary magnitude, in terms of which all results of measurement are to be expressed. Mere ratios between any series of objects will never tell us their absolute magnitudes; we must have at least one ratio for each, and we must have one absolute magnitude. The number of ratios n are expressible in n equations, which will contain at least $n + 1$ quantities, so that if we employ them to make known n magnitudes, we must have one magnitude known. Hence, whether we are measuring time, space, density, mass, weight, energy, or any other physical quantity, we must refer to some concrete standard, some actual object, which if once lost and irrecoverable, all our measures lose their absolute meaning. This concrete standard is in all cases arbitrary in point of theory, and its selection a question of practical convenience.

There are two kinds of magnitude, indeed, which do not need to be expressed in terms of arbitrary concrete units, since they pre-suppose the existence of natural standard units. One case is that of abstract number itself, which needs no special unit, because any object which exists or is thought of as separate from other objects (p. 157) furnishes us with a unit, and is the only standard required.

Angular magnitude is the second case in which we have a natural unit of reference, namely the whole

revolution or *perigon*, as it has been called by Mr. Sandeman.[1] It is a necessary result of the uniform properties
of space, that all complete revolutions are equal to each
other, so that we need not select any one revolution, but
can always refer anew to space itself. Whether we take
the whole perigon, its half, or its quarter, is really immaterial ; Euclid took the right angle, because the Greek geometers had never generalised their notions of angular
magnitude sufficiently to treat angles of all magnitudes, or
of unlimited *quantity of revolution*. Euclid defines a right
angle as half that made by a line with its own continuation,
which is of course equal to half a revolution, but which
was not treated as an angle by him. In mathematical
analysis a different fraction of the perigon is taken, namely,
such a fraction that the arc or portion of the circumference
included within it is equal to the radius of the circle. In
this point of view angular magnitude is an abstract ratio,
namely, the ratio between the length of arc subtended and
the length of the radius. The geometrical unit is then
necessarily the angle corresponding to the ratio unity.
This angle is equal to about $57°$, $17'$, $44''\cdot8$, or decimally
$57°\cdot295779513\ldots$.[2] It was called by De Morgan the *arcual
unit*, but a more convenient name for common use would
be *radian*, as suggested by Professor Everett. Though this
standard angle is naturally employed in mathematical
analysis, and any other unit would introduce great complexity, we must not look upon it as a distinct unit, since
its amount is connected with that of the half perigon,
by the natural constant $3\cdot14159\ldots$ usually denoted by
the letter π.

When we pass to other species of quantity, the choice
of unit is found to be entirely arbitrary. There is absolutely no mode of defining a length, but by selecting some
physical object exhibiting that length between certain
obvious points—as, for instance, the extremities of a bar,
or marks made upon its surface.

---

[1] *Pelicotetics, or the Science of Quantity ; an Elementary Treatise on
Algebra, and its groundwork Arithmetic.* By Archibald Sandeman,
M.A. Cambridge (Deighton, Bell, and Co.), 1868, p. 304.
[2] De Morgan's *Trigonometry and Double Algebra*, p. 5.

Standard Unit of Time.

Time is the great independent variable of all change—that which itself flows on uninterruptedly, and brings the variety which we call motion and life. When we reflect upon its intimate nature, Time, like every other element of existence, proves to be an inscrutable mystery. We can only say with St. Augustin, to one who asks us what is time, " I know when you do not ask me." The mind of man will ask what can never be answered, but one result of a true and rigorous logical philosophy must be to convince us that scientific explanation can only take place between phenomena which have something in common, and that when we get down to primary notions, like those of time and space, the mind must meet a point of mystery beyond which it cannot penetrate. A definition of time must not be looked for ; if we say with Hobbes,[1] that it is " the phantasm of before and after in motion," or with Aristotle that it is " the number of motion according to former and latter," we obviously gain nothing, because the notion of time is involved in the expressions *before and after, former and latter*. Time is undoubtedly one of those primary notions which can only be defined physically, or by observation of phenomena which proceed in time.

If we have not advanced a step beyond Augustin's acute reflections on this subject,[2] it is curious to observe the wonderful advances which have been made in the practical measurement of its efflux. In earlier centuries the rude sun-dial or the rising of a conspicuous star gave points of reference, while the flow of water from the clepsydra, the burning of a candle, or, in the monastic ages, even the continuous chanting of psalms, were the means of roughly subdividing periods, and marking the hours of the day and night.[3] The sun and stars still furnish the standard of time, but means of accurate subdivision have become requisite, and this has been furnished by the pendulum

[1] *English Works of Thos. Hobbes*, Edit. by Molesworth, vol. i. p. 95.
[2] *Confessions*, bk. xi. chapters 20—28.
[3] Sir G. C. Lewis gives many curious particulars concerning the measurement of time in his *Astronomy of the Ancients*, pp. 241, &c.

and the chronograph. By the pendulum we can accurately
divide the day into seconds of time. By the chronograph
we can subdivide the second into a hundred, a thousand,
or even a million parts. Wheatstone measured the duration of an electric spark, and found it to be no more than
one 115,200th part of a second, while more recently
Captain Noble has been able to appreciate intervals of
time not exceeding the millionth part of a second.

When we come to inquire precisely what phenomenon
it is that we thus so minutely measure, we meet insur-
mountable difficulties. Newton distinguished time according as it was *absolute* or *apparent* time, in the following
words :—" Absolute, true, and mathematical time, of itself
and from its own nature, flows equably without regard to
anything external, and by another name is called *duration;*
relative, apparent and common time, is some sensible and
external measure of duration by the means of motion."[1]
Though we are perhaps obliged to assume the existence
of a uniformly increasing quantity which we call time,
yet we cannot feel or know abstract and absolute time.
Duration must be made manifest to us by the recurrence
of some phenomenon. The succession of our own thoughts
is no doubt the first and simplest measure of time, but a
very rude one, because in some persons and circumstances
the thoughts evidently flow with much greater rapidity
than in other persons and circumstances. In the absence
of all other phenomena, the interval between one thought
and another would necessarily become the unit of time,
but the most cursory observations show that there are
changes in the outward world much better fitted by their
constancy to measure time than the change of thoughts
within us.

The earth, as I have already said, is the real clock of the
astronomer, and is practically assumed as invariable in
its movements. But on what ground is it so assumed ?
According to the first law of motion, every body perseveres
in its state of rest or of uniform motion in a right line,
unless it is compelled to change that state by forces impressed thereon. Rotatory motion is subject to a like

---

[1] *Principia*, bk. i. *Scholium to Definitions.* Translated by Motte,
vol. i. p. 9. See also p. 11.

condition, namely, that it perseveres uniformly unless disturbed by extrinsic forces. Now uniform motion means motion through equal spaces in equal times, so that if we have a body entirely free from all resistance or perturbation, and can measure equal spaces of its path, we have a perfect measure of time. But let it be remembered that this law has never been absolutely proved by experience ; for we cannot point to any body, and say that it is wholly unresisted or undisturbed ; and even if we had such a body, we should need some independent standard of time to ascertain whether its motion was really uniform. As it is in moving bodies that we find the best standard of time, we cannot use them to prove the uniformity of their own movements, which would amount to a *petitio principii*. Our experience comes to this, that when we examine and compare the movements of bodies which seem to us nearly free from disturbance, we find them giving nearly harmonious measures of time. If any one body which seems to us to move uniformly is not doing so, but is subject to fits and starts unknown to us, because we have no absolute standard of time, then all other bodies must be subject to the same arbitrary fits and starts, otherwise there would be discrepancy disclosing the irregularities. Just as in comparing together a number of chronometers, we should soon detect bad ones by their going irregularly, as compared with the others, so in nature we detect disturbed movement by its discrepancy from that of other bodies which we believe to be undisturbed, and which agree nearly among themselves. But inasmuch as the measure of motion involves time, and the measure of time involves motion, there must be ultimately an assumption. We may define equal times, as times during which a moving body under the influence of no force describes equal spaces ; [1] but all we can say in support of this definition is, that it leads us into no known difficulties, and that to the best of our experience one freely moving body gives the same results as any other.

When we inquire where the freely moving body is, no perfectly satisfactory answer can be given. Practically the rotating globe is sufficiently accurate, and Thomson

[1] Rankine, *Philosophical Magazine*, Feb. 1867, vol. xxxiii p. 91.

and Tait say : "Equal times are times during which the earth turns through equal angles."[1] No long time has passed since astronomers thought it impossible to detect any inequality in its movement. Poisson was supposed to have proved that a change in the length of the sidereal day amounting to one ten-millionth part in 2,500 years was incompatible with an ancient eclipse recorded by the Chaldæans, and similar calculations were made by Laplace. But it is now known that these calculations were somewhat in error, and that the dissipation of energy arising out of the friction of tidal waves, and the radiation of the heat into space, has slightly decreased the rapidity of the earth's rotatory motion. The sidereal day is now longer by one part in 2,700,000, than it was in 720 B.C. Even before this discovery, it was known that invariability of rotation depended upon the perfect maintenance of the earth's internal heat, which is requisite in order that the earth's dimensions shall be unaltered. Now the earth being superior in temperature to empty space, must cool more or less rapidly, so that it cannot furnish an absolute measure of time. Similar objections could be raised to all other rotating bodies within our cognisance.

The moon's motion round the earth, and the earth's motion round the sun, form the next best measure of time. They are subject, indeed, to disturbance from other planets, but it is believed that these perturbations must in the course of time run through their rhythmical courses, leaving the mean distances unaffected, and consequently, by the third Law of Kepler, the periodic times unchanged. But there is more reason than not to believe that the earth encounters a slight resistance in passing through space, like that which is so apparent in Encke's comet. There may also be dissipation of energy in the electrical relations of the earth to the sun, possibly identical with that which is manifested in the retardation of comets.[2] It is probably an untrue assumption then, that the earth's orbit remains quite invariable. It is just possible that some other body may be found in the course of time to furnish a better

---

[1] *Treatise on Natural Philosophy,* vol. i. p. 179.
[2] *Proceedings of the Manchester Philosophical Society,* 28th Nov. 1871, vol. xi. p. 33.

standard of time than the earth in its annual motion. The greatly superior mass of Jupiter and its satellites, and their greater distance from the sun, may render the electrical dissipation of energy less considerable than in the case of the earth. But the choice of the best measure will always be an open one, and whatever moving body we choose may ultimately be shown to be subject to disturbing forces.

The pendulum, although so admirable an instrument for subdivision of time, fails as a standard; for though the same pendulum affected by the same force of gravity performs equal vibrations in equal times, yet the slightest change in the form or weight of the pendulum, the least corrosion of any part, or the most minute displacement of the point of suspension, falsifies the results, and there enter many other difficult questions of temperature, friction, resistance, length of vibration, &c.

Thomson and Tait are of opinion [1] that the ultimate standard of chronometry must be founded on the physical properties of some body of more constant character than the earth; for instance, a carefully arranged metallic spring, hermetically sealed in an exhausted glass vessel. But it is hard to see how we can be sure that the dimensions and elasticity of a piece of wrought metal will remain perfectly unchanged for the few millions of years contemplated by them. A nearly perfect gas, like hydrogen, is perhaps the only kind of substance in the unchanged elasticity of which we could have confidence. Moreover, it is difficult to perceive how the undulations of such a spring could be observed with the requisite accuracy. More recently Professor Clerk Maxwell has made the novel suggestion, discussed in a subsequent section, that undulations of light *in vacuo* would form the most universal standard of reference, both as regards time and space. According to this system the unit of time would be the time occupied by one vibration of the particular kind of light whose wave length is taken as the unit of length.

[1] *The Elements of Natural Philosophy*, part i. p. 119.

The Unit of Space and the Bar Standard.

Next in importance after the measurement of time is that of space. Time comes first in theory, because phenomena, our internal thoughts for instance, may change in time without regard to space. As to the phenomena of outward nature, they tend more and more to resolve themselves into motions of molecules, and motion cannot be conceived or measured without reference both to time and space.

Turning now to space measurement, we find it almost equally difficult to fix and define once and for ever, a unit magnitude. There are three different modes in which it has been proposed to attempt the perpetuation of a standard length.

(1) By constructing an actual specimen of the standard yard or metre, in the form of a bar.

(2) By assuming the globe itself to be the ultimate standard of magnitude, the practical unit being a submultiple of some dimension of the globe.

(3) By adopting the length of the simple seconds pendulum, as a standard of reference.

At first sight it might seem that there was no great difficulty in this matter, and that any one of these methods might serve well enough; but the more minutely we inquire into the details, the more hopeless appears to be the attempt to establish an invariable standard. We must in the first place point out a principle not of an obvious character, namely, that *the standard length must be defined by one single object.*[1] To make two bars of exactly the same length, or even two bars bearing a perfectly defined ratio to each other, is beyond the power of human art. If two copies of the standard metre be made and declared equally correct, future investigators will certainly discover some discrepancy between them, proving of course that they cannot both be the standard, and giving cause for dispute as to what magnitude should then be taken as correct.

If one invariable bar could be constructed and maintained as the absolute standard, no such inconvenience could arise. Each successive generation as it acquired

---

[1] See Harris' *Essay upon Money and Coins*, part. ii. [1758] p. 127.

higher powers of measurement, would detect errors in
the copies of the standard, but the standard itself would
be unimpeached, and would, as it were, become by degrees
more and more accurately known. Unfortunately to construct and preserve a metre or yard is also a task which
is either impossible, or what comes nearly to the same
thing, cannot be shown to be possible. Passing over the
practical difficulty of defining the ends of the standard
length with complete accuracy, whether by dots or lines
on the surface, or by the terminal points of the bar, we
have no means of proving that substances remain of invariable dimensions. Just as we cannot tell whether the
rotation of the earth is uniform, except by comparing it
with other moving bodies, believed to be more uniform
in motion, so we cannot detect the change of length in a
bar, except by comparing it with some other bar supposed to be invariable. But how are we to know which
is the invariable bar? It is certain that many rigid
and apparently invariable substances do change in dimensions. The bulb of a thermometer certainly contracts
by age, besides undergoing rapid changes of dimensions
when warmed or cooled through 100° Cent. Can we
be sure that even the most solid metallic bars do not
slightly contract by age, or undergo variations in their
structure by change of temperature. Fizeau was induced
to try whether a quartz crystal, subjected to several
hundred alternations of temperature, would be modified in
its physical properties, and he was unable to detect any
change in the coefficient of expansion.[1] It does not
follow, however, that, because no apparent change was
discovered in a quartz crystal, newly-constructed bars of
metal would undergo no change.

The best principle, as it seems to me, upon which the
perpetuation of a standard of length can be rested, is that,
if a variation of length occurs, it will in all probability be
of different amount in different substances. If then a
great number of standard metres were constructed of all
kinds of different metals and alloys ; hard rocks, such as
granite, serpentine, slate, quartz, limestone ; artificial
substances, such as porcelain, glass, &c., &c., careful

---

[1] *Philosophical Magazine*, (1868), 4th Series, vol. xxxvi. p. 32.

comparison would show from time to time the comparative variations of length of these different substances. The most variable substances would be the most divergent, and the standard would be furnished by the mean length of those which agreed most closely with each other just as uniform motion is that of those bodies which agree most closely in indicating the efflux of time.

The Terrestrial Standard.

The second method assumes that the globe itself is a body of invariable dimensions and the founders of the metrical system selected the ten-millionth part of the distance from the equator to the pole as the definition of the metre. The first imperfection in such a method is that the earth is certainly not invariable in size; for we know that it is superior in temperature to surrounding space, and must be slowly cooling and contracting. There is much reason to believe that all earthquakes, volcanoes, mountain elevations, and changes of sea level are evidences of this contraction as asserted by Mr. Mallet.[1] But such is the vast bulk of the earth and the duration of its past existence, that this contraction is perhaps less rapid in proportion than that of any bar or other material standard which we can construct.

The second and chief difficulty of this method arises from the vast size of the earth, which prevents us from making any comparison with the ultimate standard, except by a trigonometrical survey of a most elaborate and costly kind. The French physicists, who first proposed the method, attempted to obviate this inconvenience by carrying out the survey once for all, and then constructing a standard metre, which should be exactly the one ten millionth part of the distance from the pole to the equator. But since all measuring operations are merely approximate, it was impossible that this operation could be perfectly achieved. Accordingly, it was shown in 1838 that the supposed French metre was erroneous to the considerable extent of one part in 5527. It then became necessary either to alter the length of the assumed metre,

---

[1] *Proceedings of the Royal Society*, 20th June, 1872, vol. xx. p. 438.

or to abandon its supposed relation to the earth's dimensions. The French Government and the International Metrical Commission have for obvious reasons decided in favour of the latter course, and have thus reverted to the first method of defining the metre by a given bar. As from time to time the ratio between this assumed standard metre and the quadrant of the earth becomes more accurately known, we have better means of restoring that metre by reference to the globe if required. But until lost, destroyed, or for some clear reason discredited, the bar metre and not the globe is the standard. Thomson and Tait remark that any of the more accurate measurements of the English trigonometrical survey might in like manner be employed to restore our standard yard, in terms of which the results are recorded.

The Pendulum Standard.

The third method of defining a standard length, by reference to the seconds pendulum, was first proposed by Huyghens, and was at one time adopted by the English Government. From the principle of the pendulum (p. 302) it clearly appears that if the time of oscillation and the force actuating the pendulum be the same, the length of the pendulum must be the same. We do not get rid of theoretical difficulties, for we must assume the attraction of gravity at some point of the earth's surface, say London, to be unchanged from time to time, and the sidereal day to be invariable, neither assumption being absolutely correct so far as we can judge. The pendulum, in short, is only an indirect means of making one physical quantity of space depend upon two other physical quantities of time and force.

The practical difficulties are, however, of a far more serious character than the theoretical ones. The length of a pendulum is not the ordinary length of the instrument, which might be greatly varied without affecting the duration of a vibration, but the distance from the centre of suspension to the centre of oscillation. There are no direct means of determining this latter centre, which depends upon the average momentum of all the particles of the pendulum as regards the centre of suspension. Huyghens discovered that the centres of suspension and oscillation are interchangeable, and Kater pointed out that if a pendulum vibrates with exactly the same rapidity when suspended from two different points, the distance between these points is the true length of the equivalent simple pendulum.[1] But the practical difficulties in em-- ploying Kater's reversible pendulum are considerable, and questions regarding the disturbance of the air, the force of gravity, or even the interference of electrical attractions have to be entertained. It has been shown that all the experiments made under the authority of Government for determining the ratio between the standard yard and the seconds pendulum, were vitiated by an error in the corrections for the resisting, adherent, or buoyant power of the air in which the pendulums were swung. Even if such corrections were rendered unnecessary by operating in a vacuum, other difficult questions remain.[2] Gauss' mode of comparing the vibrations of a wire pendulum when suspended at two different lengths is open to equal or greater practical difficulties. Thus it is found that the pendulum standard cannot compete in accuracy and certainty with the simple bar standard, and the method would only be useful as an accessory mode of restoring the bar standard if at any time again destroyed.

Unit of Density.

Before we can measure the phenomena of nature, we require a third independent unit, which shall enable us to define the quantity of matter occupying any given space. All the changes of nature, as we shall see, are probably so many manifestations of energy; but energy requires some substratum or material machinery of molecules, in and by which it may be manifested. Observation shows that, as regards force, there may be two modes of variation of matter. As Newton says in the first definition of the Principia, "the quantity of matter is the measure of the same, arising from its density and bulk conjunctly."

---

[1] Kater's *Treatise on Mechanics*, Cabinet Cyclopædia, p. 154.
[2] Grant's *History of Physical Astronomy*, p. 156.

Thus the force required to set a body in motion varies both according to the bulk of the matter, and also according to its quality. Two cubic inches of iron of uniform quality, will require twice as much force as one cubic inch to produce a certain velocity in a given time ; but one cubic inch of gold will require more force than one cubic inch of iron. There is then some new measurable quality in matter apart from its bulk, which we may call *density*, and which is, strictly speaking, indicated by its capacity to resist and absorb the action of force. For the unit of density we may assume that of any substance which is uniform in quality, and can readily be referred to from time to time. Pure water at any definite temperature, for instance that of snow melting under inappreciable pressure, furnishes an invariable standard of density, and by comparing equal bulks of various substances with a like bulk of ice-cold water, as regards the velocity produced in a unit of time by the same force, we should ascertain the densities of those substances as expressed in that of water. Practically the force of gravity is used to measure density ; for a beautiful experiment with the pendulum, performed by Newton and repeated by Gauss, shows that all kinds of matter gravitate equally. Two portions of matter then which are in equilibrium in the balance, may be assumed to possess equal inertia, and their densities will therefore be inversely as their cubic dimensions.

Unit of Mass.

Multiplying the number of units of density of a portion of matter, by the number of units of space occupied by it, we arrive at the quantity of matter, or, as it is usually called, the *unit of mass*, as indicated by the inertia and gravity it possesses. To proceed in the most simple manner, the unit of mass ought to be that of a cubic unit of matter of the standard density ; but the founders of the metrical system took as their unit of mass, the cubic centimetre of water, at the temperature of maximum density (about 4° Cent.). They called this unit of mass the *gramme*, and constructed standard specimens of the kilogram, which might be readily referred to by all who required to employ accurate weights. Unfortunately the determination of the bulk of a given weight of water at a certain temperature is an operation involving many dif ficulties, and it cannot be performed in the present day with a greater exactness than that of about one part in 5000, the results of careful observers being sometimes found to differ as much as one part in 1000.[1]

Weights, on the other hand, can be compared with each other to at least one part in a million. Hence if different specimens of the kilogram be prepared by direct weighing against water, they will not agree closely with each other; the two principal standard kilograms agree neither with each other, nor with their definition. According to Professor Miller the so-called Kilogramme des Archives weighs 15432·34874 grains, while the kilogram deposited at the Ministry of the Interior in Paris, as the standard for commercial purposes, weighs 15432·344 grains. Since a standard weight constructed of platinum, or platinum and iridium, can be preserved free from any appreciable alteration, and since it can be very accurately compared with other weights, we shall ultimately attain the greatest exactness in our measurements of mass, by assuming some single kilogram as a *provisional standard*, leaving the determination of its actual mass in units of space and density for future investigation. This is what is practically done at the present day, and thus a unit of mass takes the place of the unit of density, both in the French and English systems. The English pound is defined by a certain lump of platinum, preserved at Westminster, and is an arbitrary mass, chosen merely that it may agree as nearly as possible with old English pounds. The gallon, the old English unit of cubic measurement, is defined by the condition that it shall contain exactly ten pounds weight of water at 62° Fahr.; and although it is stated that it has the capacity of about 277·274 cubic inches, this ratio between the cubic and linear systems of measurement is not legally enacted, but left open to investigation. While the French metric system as originally designed was theoretically perfect, it does not differ practically in this point from the English system.

---

[1] Clerk Maxwell's *Theory of Heat*, p. 79.

Natural System of Standards.

Quite recently Professor Clerk Maxwell has suggested that the vibrations of light and the atoms of matter might conceivably be employed as the ultimate standards of length, time, and mass. We should thus arrive at a *natural system of standards,* which, though possessing no present practical importance, has considerable theoretical interest. " In the present state of science," he says, " the most universal standard of length which we could assume would be the wave-length in vacuum of a particular kind of light, emitted by some widely diffused substance such as sodium, which has well-defined lines in its spectrum. Such a standard would be independent of any changes in the dimensions of the earth, and should be adopted by those who expect their writings to be more permanent than that body." [1] In the same way we should get a universal standard unit of time, independent of all questions about the motion of material bodies, by taking as the unit the periodic time of vibration of that particular kind of light whose wave-length is the unit of length. It would follow that with these units of length and time the unit of velocity would coincide with the velocity of light in empty space. As regards the unit of mass, Professor Maxwell, humorously as I should think, remarks that if we expect soon to be able to determine the mass of a single molecule of some standard substance, we may wait for this determination before fixing a universal standard of mass.

In a theoretical point of view there can be no reasonable doubt that vibrations of light are, as far as we can tell, the most fixed in magnitude of all phenomena. There is as usual no certainty in the matter, for the properties of the basis of light may vary to some extent in different parts of space. But no differences could ever be established in the velocity of light in different parts of the solar system, and the spectra of the stars show that the times of vibration there do not differ perceptibly from those in this part of the universe. Thus all presumption is in favour of the absolute constancy of the vibrations of light—absolute, that is, so far as regards any means of investigation we are

[1] *Treatise on Electricity and Magnetism,* vol. i. p. 3.

likely to possess. Nearly the same considerations apply
to the atomic weight as the standard of mass. It is impossible to prove that all atoms of the same substance are
of equal mass, and some physicists think that they differ, so
that the fixity of combining proportions may be due only
to the approximate constancy of the mean of countless
millions of discrepant weights. But in any case the de
tection of difference is probably beyond our powers. In a
theoretical point of view, then, the magnitudes suggested
by Professor Maxwell seem to be the most fixed ones of
which we have any knowledge, so that they necessarily
become the natural units.

In a practical point of view, as Professor Maxwell would
be the first to point out, they are of little or no value, because in the present state of science we cannot measure a
vibration or weigh an atom with any approach to the
accuracy which is attainable in the comparison of standard
metres and kilograms. The velocity of light is not known
probably within a thousandth part, and as we progress in
the knowledge of light, so we shall progress in the accurate fixation of other standards. All that can be said then,
is that it is very desirable to determine the wave-lengths
and periods of the principal lines of the solar spectrum,
and the absolute atomic weights of the elements, with all
attainable accuracy, in terms of our existing standards.
The numbers thus obtained would admit of the reproduction of our standards in some future age of the world to a
corresponding degree of accuracy, were there need of such
reference; but so far as we can see at present, there is no
considerable probability that this mode of reproduction
would ever be the best mode.

Subsidiary Units.

Having once established the standard units of time,
space, and density or mass, we might employ them for the
expression of all quantities of such nature. But it is often
convenient in particular branches of science to use multiples or submultiples of the original units, for the expression of quantities in a simple manner. We use the
mile rather than the yard when treating of the magnitude
of the globe, and the mean distance of the earth and

sun is not too large a unit when we have to describe the distances of the stars. On the other hand, when we are occupied with microscopic objects, the inch, the line or the millimetre, become the most convenient terms of expression.

It is allowable for a scientific man to introduce a new unit in any branch of knowledge, provided that it assists precise expression, and is carefully brought into relation with the primary units. Thus Professor A. W. Williamson has proposed as a convenient unit of volume in chemical science, an absolute volume equal to about 11·2 litres representing the bulk of one gram of hydrogen gas at standard temperature and pressure, or the *equivalent* weight of any other gas, such as 16 grams of oxygen, 14 grams of nitrogen, &c.; in short, the bulk of that quantity of any one of those gases which weighs as many grams as there are units in the number expressing its atomic weight.[1] Hofmann has proposed a new unit of weight for chemists, called a *crith*, to be defined by the weight of one litre of hydrogen gas at 0° C. and 0°·76 mm., weighing about 0·0896 gram.[2] Both of these units must be regarded as purely subordinate units, ultimately defined by reference to the primary units, and not involving any new assumption.

Derived Units.

The standard units of time, space, and mass having been once fixed, many kinds of magnitude are naturally measured by units derived from them. From the metre, the unit of linear magnitude follows in the most obvious manner the centiare or square metre, the unit of superficial magnitude, and the litre that is the cube of the tenth part of a metre, the unit of capacity or volume. Velocity of motion is expressed by the ratio of the space passed over, when the motion is uniform, to the time occupied; hence the unit of velocity is that of a body which passes over a unit of space in a unit of time. In physical science the unit of velocity might be taken as one metre per second.

[1] *Chemistry for Students*, by A. W. Williamson. Clarendon Press Series, 2nd ed. Preface p. vi. [2] *Introduction to Chemistry*, p. 131.

Momentum is measured by the mass moving, regard being paid both to the amount of matter and the velocity at which it is moving.   Hence the unit of momentum will be that of a unit volume of matter of the unit density moving with the unit velocity, or in the French system, a cubic centimetre of water of the maximum density moving one metre per second.

An accelerating force is measured by the ratio of the momentum generated to the time occupied, the force being supposed to act uniformly.   The unit of force will therefore be that which generates a unit of momentum in a unit of time, or which causes, in the French system, one cubic centimetre of water at maximum density to acquire in one second a velocity of one metre per second. The force of gravity is the most familiar kind of force, and as, when acting unimpeded upon any substance, it produces in a second a velocity of $9^{.}80868$ . . metres per second in Paris, it follows that the absolute unit of force is about the tenth part of the force of gravity. If we employ British weights and measures, the absolute unit of force is represented by the gravity of about half an ounce, since the force of gravity of any portion of matter acting upon that matter during one second, produces a final velocity of $32^{.}1889$ feet per second or about 32 units of velocity.   Although from its perpetual action and approximate uniformity we find in gravity the most convenient force for reference, and thus habitually employ it to estimate quantities of matter, we must remember that it is only one of many instances of force.   Strictly speaking, we should express weight in terms of force, but practically we express other forces in terms of weight.

We still require the unit of energy, a more complex notion.   The momentum of a body expresses the quantity of motion which belongs or would belong to the aggregate of the particles; but when we consider how this motion is related to the action of a force producing or removing it, we find that the effect of a force is proportional to the mass multiplied by the square of the velocity and it is convenient to take half this product as the expression required.   But it is shown in books upon dynamics that it will be exactly the same thing if we define energy by a force acting through a space.   The natural unit of energy will then be that which overcomes a unit of force acting through a unit of space; when we lift one kilogram through one metre, against gravity, we therefore accomplish 9˙80868 . . units of work, that is, we turn so many units of potential energy existing in the muscles, into potential energy of gravitation. In lifting one pound through one foot there is in like manner a conversion of 32˙1889 units of energy. Accordingly the unit of energy will be in the English system, that required to lift one pound through about the thirty-second part of a foot; in terms of metric units, it will be that required to lift a kilogram through about one tenth part of a metre.

Every person is at liberty to measure and record quantities in terms of any unit which he likes. He may use the yard for linear measurement and the litre for cubic measurement, only there will then be a complicated relation between his different results. The system of derived units which we have been briefly considering, is that which gives the most simple and natural relations between quantitative expressions of different kinds, and therefore conduces to ease of comprehension and saving of laborious calculation.

It would evidently be a source of great convenience if scientific men could agree upon some single system of units, original and derived, in terms of which all quantities could be expressed. Statements would thus be rendered easily comparable, a large part of scientific literature would be made intelligible to all, and the saving of mental labour would be immense. It seems to be generally allowed, too, that the metric system of weights and measures presents the best basis for the ultimate system; it is thoroughly established in Western Europe; it is legalised in England; it is already commonly employed by scientific men; it is in itself the most simple and scientific of systems. There is every reason then why the metric system should be accepted at least in its main features.

Provisional Units.

Ultimately, as we can hardly doubt, all phenomena will be recognised as so many manifestations of energy; and, being expressed in terms of the unit of energy, will be referable to the primary units of space, time, and density. To effect this reduction, however, in any particular case, we must not only be able to compare different quantities of the phenomenon, but to trace the whole series of steps by which it is connected with the primary notions. We can readily observe that the intensity of one source of light is greater than that of another ; and, knowing that the intensity of light decreases as the square of the distance increases, we can easily determine their comparative brilliance. Hence we can express the intensity of light falling upon any surface, if we have a unit in which to make the expression. Light is undoubtedly one form of energy, and the unit ought therefore to be the unit of energy. But at present it is quite impossible to say how much energy there is in any particular amount of light. The question then arises,—Are we to defer the measurement of light until we can assign its relation to other forms of energy ? If we answer Yes, it is equivalent to saying that the science of light must stand still perhaps for a generation ; and not only this science but many others. The true course evidently is to select, as the provisional unit of light, some light of convenient intensity, which can be reproduced from time to time in the same intensity, and which is defined by physical circumstances. All the phenomena of light may be experimentally investigated relatively to this unit, for instance that obtained after much labour by Bunsen and Roscoe.[1] In after years it will become a matter of inquiry what is the energy exerted in such unit of light; but it may be long before the relation is exactly determined.

A provisional unit, then, means one which is assumed and physically defined in a safe and reproducible manner, in order that particular quantities may be compared *inter se* more accurately than they can yet be referred to the primary units. In reality the great majority of our measurements are expressed in terms of such provisionally independent units, and even the unit of mass, as we have seen, ought to be considered as provisional.

The unit of heat ought to be simply the unit of energy, already described. But a weight can be measured to the

---

[1] *Philosophical Transactions* (1859), vol. cxlix. p. 884, &c.

one-millionth part, and temperature to less than the
thousandth part of a degree Fahrenheit, and to less therefore than the five-hundred thousandth part of the absolute
temperature, whereas the mechanical equivalent of heat is
probably not known to the thousandth part. Hence the
need of a provisional unit of heat, which is often taken as
that requisite to raise one gram of water through one degree
Centigrade, that is from 0° to 1°. This quantity of heat is
capable of approximate expression in terms of time, space,
and mass; for by the natural constant, determined by Dr.
Joule, and called the mechanical equivalent of heat, we
know that the assumed unit of heat is equal to the energy
of 423·55 gram-metres, or that energy which will raise
the mass of 423·55 grams through one metre against 9·8...
absolute units of force. Heat may also be expressed in
terms of the quantity of ice at 0° Cent., which it is capable
of converting into water under inappreciable pressure.

Theory of Dimensions.

In order to understand the relations between the quantities dealt with in physical science, it is necessary to pay
attention to the Theory of Dimensions, first clearly stated
by Joseph Fourier,[1] but in later years developed by several
physicists. This theory investigates the manner in which
each derived unit depends upon or involves one or more of
the fundamental units. The number of units in a rectangular area is found by multiplying together the numbers
of units in the sides; thus the unit of length enters twice
into the unit of area, which is therefore said to have two
dimensions with respect to length. Denoting length by L,
we may say that the dimensions of area are $L \times L$ or
L^2. It is obvious in the same way that the dimensions of
volume or bulk will be L^3.

The number of units of mass in a body is found by multiplying the number of units of volume, by those of density.
Hence mass is of three dimensions as regards length,
and one as regards density. Calling density D, the dimensions of mass are L^3D. As already explained, however,
it is usual to substitute an arbitrary provisional unit of

[1] *Théorie Analytique de la Chaleur*, Paris; 1822, §§ 157—162.

mass, symbolised by M ; according to the view here taken
we may say that the dimensions of M are L^3D.

Introducing time, denoted by T, it is easy to see that
the dimensions of velocity will be $\dfrac{L}{T}$ or LT^{-1}, because
the number of units in the velocity of a body is found
by *dividing* the units of length passed over by the units
of time occupied in passing. The acceleration of a body
is measured by the increase of velocity in relation to
the time, that is, we must divide the units of velocity
gained by the units of time occupied in gaining it ; hence
its dimensions will be LT^{-2}. Momentum is the product
of mass and velocity, so that its dimensions are MLT^{-1}.
The effect of a force is measured by the acceleration
produced in a unit of mass in a unit of time ; hence the
dimensions of force are MLT^{-2}. Work done is proportional to the force acting and to the space through
which it acts ; so that it has the dimensions of force with
that of length added, giving ML^2T^{-2}.

It should be particularly noticed that angular magnitude has no dimensions at all, being measured by the
ratio of the arc to the radius (p. 305). Thus we have the
dimensions LL^{-1} or L^0. This agrees with the statement
previously made, that no arbitrary unit of angular magnitude is needed. Similarly, all pure numbers expressing
ratios only, such as sines and other trigonometrical functions, logarithms, exponents, &c., are devoid of dimensions.
They are absolute numbers necessarily expressed in terms
of unity itself, and are quite unaffected by the selection of
the arbitrary physical units. Angular magnitude, however,
enters into other quantities, such as angular velocity, which
has the dimensions $\dfrac{1}{T}$ or T^{-1}, the units of angle being
divided by the units of time occupied. The dimensions of
angular acceleration are denoted by T^{-2}.

The quantities treated in the theories of heat and
electricity are numerous and complicated as regards
their dimensions. Thermal capacity has the dimensions
ML^{-3}, thermal conductivity, $ML^{-1}T^{-1}$. In Magnetism
the dimensions of the strength of pole are $M^{\frac{1}{2}}L^{\frac{3}{2}}T^{-1}$,
the dimensions of field-intensity are $M^{\frac{1}{2}}L^{-\frac{1}{2}}T^{-1}$, and the

intensity of magnetisation has the same dimensions. In the science of electricity physicists have to deal with numerous kinds of quantity, and their dimensions are different too in the electro-static and the electro-magnetic systems. Thus electro - motive force has the dimensions $M^{\frac{1}{2}}L^{\frac{1}{2}}T^{-1}$, in the former, and $M^{\frac{1}{2}}L^{\frac{1}{2}}T^{-2}$ in the latter system. Capacity simply depends upon length in electro-statics, but upon $L^{-1}T^2$ in electro-magnetics. It is worthy of particular notice that electrical quantities have simple dimensions when expressed in terms of density instead of mass. The instances now given are sufficient to show the difficulty of conceiving and following out the relations of the quantities treated in physical science without a systematic method of calculating and exhibiting their dimensions. It is only in quite recent years that clear ideas about these quantities have been attained. Half a century ago probably no one but Fourier could have explained what he meant by temperature or capacity for heat. The notion of measuring electricity had hardly been entertained.

Besides affording us a clear view of the complex relations of physical quantities, this theory is specially useful in two ways. Firstly, it affords a test of the correctness of mathematical reasoning. According to the *Principle of Homogeneity*, all the quantities *added* together, and equated in any equation, must have the same dimensions. Hence if, on estimating the dimensions of the terms in any equation, they be not homogeneous, some blunder must have been committed. It is impossible to add a force to a velocity, or a mass to a momentum. Even if the numerical values of the two members of a non-homogeneous equation were equal, this would be accidental, and any alteration in the physical units would produce inequality and disclose the falsity of the law expressed in the equation.

Secondly, the theory of units enables us readily and infallibly to deduce the change in the numerical expression of any physical quantity, produced by a change in the fundamental units. It is of course obvious that in order to represent the same absolute quantity, a number must vary inversely as the magnitude of the units which are numbered. The yard expressed in feet is 3 ; taking the inch as the unit instead of the foot it becomes 36. Every quantity into which the dimension length enters positively must be altered in like manner. Changing the unit from the foot to the inch, numerical expressions of volume must be multiplied by $12 \times 12 \times 12$. When a dimension enters negatively the opposite rule will hold. If for the minute we substitute the second as unit of time, then we must divide all numbers expressing angular velocities by 60, and numbers expressing angular acceleration by 60×60. The rule is that a numerical expression varies inversely as the magnitude of the unit as regards each whole dimension entering positively, and it varies directly as the magnitude of the unit for each whole dimension entering negatively. In the case of fractional exponents, the proper root of the ratio of change has to be taken.

The study of this subject may be continued in Professor J. D. Everett's " Illustrations of the Centimetre-gramme-second System of Units," published by Taylor and Francis, 1875 ; in Professor Maxwell's " Theory of Heat ; " or Professor Fleeming Jenkin's "Text Book of Electricity."

Natural Constants.

Having acquired accurate measuring instruments, and decided upon the units in which the results shall be expressed, there remains the question, What use shall be made of our powers of measurement ? Our principal object must be to discover general quantitative laws of nature ; but a very large amount of preliminary labour is employed in the accurate determination of the dimensions of existing objects, and the numerical relations between diverse forces and phenomena. Step by step every part of the material universe is surveyed and brought into known relations with other parts. Each manifestation of energy is correlated with each other kind of manifestation. Professor Tyndall has described the care with which such operations are conducted.[1]

" Those who are unacquainted with the details of scientific investigation, have no idea of the amount of labour expended on the determination of those numbers on which important calculations or inferences depend. They have no idea of the patience shown by a Berzelius in determining atomic weights ; by a Regnault in deter-

[1] Tyndall's *Sound*, 1st ed. p. 26.

mining coefficients of expansion; or by a Joule in determining the mechanical equivalent of heat. There is a
morality brought to bear upon such matters which, in
point of severity, is probably without a parallel in any other
domain of intellectual action."

Every new natural constant which is recorded brings
many fresh inferences within our power. For if n be the
number of such constants known, then $\frac{1}{2}$ (n^2-n) is the
number of ratios which are within our powers of calculation, and this increases with the square of n. We thus
gradually piece together a map of nature, in which the
lines of inference from one phenomenon to another rapidly
grow in complexity, and the powers of scientific prediction
are correspondingly augmented.

Babbage [1] proposed the formation of a collection of the
constant numbers of nature, a work which has at last
been taken in hand by the Smithsonian Institution.[2] It
is true that a complete collection of such numbers would
be almost co-extensive with scientific literature, since
almost all the numbers occurring in works on chemistry,
mineralogy, physics, astronomy, &c., would have to be
included. Still a handy volume giving all the more
important numbers and their logarithms, referred when
requisite to the different units in common use, would be
very useful. A small collection of constant numbers will
be found at the end of Babbage's, Hutton's, and many
other tables of logarithms, and a somewhat larger collection is given in Templeton's *Millwright and Engineer's
Pocket Companion.*

Our present object will be to classify these constant
numbers roughly, according to their comparative generality
and importance, under the following heads :—

       (1) Mathematical constants.
       (2) Physical constants.
       (3) Astronomical constants.
       (4) Terrestrial numbers.
       (5) Organic numbers.
       (6) Social numbers.

[1] British Association, Cambridge, 1833. Report, pp. 484—490.
[2] *Smithsonian Miscellaneous Collections*, vol. xii., the Constants of
Nature, part. i. Specific gravities compiled by F. W. Clarke. 8vo.
Washington, 1873.

Mathematical Constants.

At the head of the list of natural constants must come those which express the necessary relations of numbers to each other. The ordinary Multiplication Table is the most familiar and the most important of such series of constants, and is, theoretically speaking, infinite in extent. Next we must place the Arithmetical Triangle, the significance of which has already been pointed out (p. 182). Tables of logarithms also contain vast series of natural constants, arising out of the relations of pure numbers. At the base of all logarithmic theory is the mysterious natural constant commonly denoted by e, or ϵ, being equal to the infinite series $1 + \dfrac{1}{1} + \dfrac{1}{1.2} + \dfrac{1}{1.2.3} + \dfrac{1}{1.2.3.4} + \dots$, and thus consisting of the sum of the ratios between the numbers of permutations and combinations of 0, 1, 2, 3, 4, &c. things. Tables of prime numbers and of the factors of composite numbers must not be forgotten.

Another vast and in fact infinite series of numerical constants contains those connected with the measurement of angles, and embodied in trigonometrical tables, whether as natural or logarithmic sines, cosines, and tangents. It should never be forgotten that though these numbers find their chief employment in connection with trigonometry, or the measurement of the sides of a right-angled triangle, yet the numbers themselves arise out of numerical relations bearing no special relation to space. Foremost among trigonometrical constants is the well known number π, usually employed as expressing the ratio of the circumference and the diameter of a circle; from π follows the value of the arcual or natural unit of angular value as expressed in ordinary degrees (p. 306).

Among other mathematical constants not uncommonly used may be mentioned tables of factorials (p. 179), tables of Bernouilli's numbers, tables of the error function,[1] which latter are indispensable not only in the theory of probability but also in several other branches of science.

[1] J. W. L. Glaisher, *Philosophical Magazine*, 4th Series, vol. xlii. p. 421.

It should be clearly understood that the mathematical constants and tables of reference already in our possession, although very extensive, are only an infinitely small part of what might be formed. With the progress of science the tabulation of new functions will be continually demanded, and it is worthy of consideration whether public money should not be available to reward the severe, long continued, and generally thankless labour which must be gone through in calculating tables. Such labours are a benefit to the whole human race as long as it shall exist, though there are few who can appreciate the extent of this benefit. A most interesting and excellent description of many mathematical tables will be found in De Morgan's article on *Tables*, in the *English Cyclopædia*, Division of Arts and Sciences, vol. vii. p. 976. An almost exhaustive critical catalogue of extant tables is being published by a Committee of the British Association, two portions, drawn up chiefly by Mr. J. W. L. Glaisher and Professor Cayley, having appeared in the Reports of the Association for 1873 and 1875.

Physical Constants.

The second class of constants contains those which refer to the actual constitution of matter. For the most part they depend upon the peculiarities of the chemical substance in question, but we may begin with those which are of the most general character. In a first subclass we may place the velocity of light or heat undulations, the numbers expressing the relation between the lengths of the undulations, and the rapidity of the undulations, these numbers depending only on the properties of the ethereal medium, and being probably the same in all parts of the universe. The theory of heat gives rise to several numbers of the highest importance, especially Joule's mechanical equivalent of heat, the absolute zero of temperature, the mean temperature of empty space, &c.

Taking into account the diverse properties of the elements we must have tables of the atomic weights, the specific heats, the specific gravities, the refractive powers, not only of the elements, but their almost infinitely numerous compounds. The properties of hardness, elasticity, viscosity, expansion by heat, conducting powers for heat and electricity, must also be determined in immense detail. There are, however, certain of these numbers which stand out prominently because they serve as intermediate units or terms of comparison. Such are, for instance, the absolute coefficients of expansion of air, water and mercury, the temperature of the maximum density of water, the latent heats of water and steam, the boiling-point of water under standard pressure, the melting and boiling-points of mercury, and so forth.

Astronomical Constants.

The third great class consists of numbers possessing far less generality because they refer not to the properties of matter, but to the special forms and distances in which matter has been disposed in the part of the universe open to our examination. We have, first of all, to define the magnitude and form of the earth, its mean density, the constant of aberration of light expressing the relation between the earth's mean velocity in space and the velocity of light. From the earth, as our observatory, we then proceed to lay down the mean distances of the sun, and of the planets from the same centre; all the elements of the planetary orbits, the magnitudes, densities, masses, periods of axial rotation of the several planets are by degrees determined with growing accuracy. The same labours must be gone through for the satellites. Catalogues of comets with the elements of their orbits, as far as ascertainable, must not be omitted.

From the earth's orbit as a new base of observations, we next proceed to survey the heavens and lay down the apparent positions, magnitudes, motions, distances, periods of variation, &c. of the stars. All catalogues of stars from those of Hipparchus and Tycho, are full of numbers expressing rudely the conformation of the visible universe. But there is obviously no limit to the labours of astronomers; not only are millions of distant stars awaiting their first measurements, but those already registered require endless scrutiny as regards their movements in the three dimensions of space, their periods of revolution, their

changes of brilliance and colour. It is obvious that
though astronomical numbers are conventionally called
constant, they are probably in all cases subject to more
or less rapid variation.

Terrestrial Numbers.

Our knowledge of the globe we inhabit involves many
numerical determinations, which have little or no connection with astronomical theory. The extreme heights
of the principal mountains, the mean elevations of
continents, the mean or extreme depths of the oceans,
the specific gravities of rocks, the temperature of mines,
the host of numbers expressing the meteorological or
magnetic conditions of every part of the surface, must
fall into this class. Many such numbers are not to be
called constant, being subject to periodic or secular
changes, but they are hardly more variable in fact than
some which in astronomical science are set down as
constant. In many cases quantities which seem most
variable may go through rhythmical changes resulting
in a nearly uniform average, and it is only in the long
progress of physical investigation that we can hope to
discriminate successfully between those elemental numbers which are fixed and those which vary. In the latter
case the law of variation becomes the constant relation
which is the object of our search.

Organic Numbers.

The forms and properties of brute nature having been
sufficiently defined by the previous classes of numbers,
the organic world, both vegetable and animal, remains
outstanding, and offers a higher series of phenomena for
our investigation. All exact knowledge relating to the
forms and sizes of living things, their numbers, the
quantities of various compounds which they consume,
contain, or excrete, their muscular or nervous energy, &c.
must be placed apart in a class by themselves. All such
numbers are doubtless more or less subject to variation,
and but in a minor degree capable of exact determination.
Man, so far as he is an animal, and as regards his physical
form, must also be treated in this class.

Social Numbers.

Little allusion need be made in this work to the fact that man in his economic, sanitary, intellectual, æsthetic, or moral relations may become the subject of sciences, the highest and most useful of all sciences. Every one who is engaged in statistical inquiry must acknowledge the possibility of natural laws governing such statistical facts. Hence we must allot a distinct place to numerical information relating to the numbers, ages, physical and sanitary condition, mortality, &c., of different peoples, in short, to vital statistics. Economic statistics, comprehending the quantities of commodities produced, existing, exchanged and consumed, constitute another extensive body of science. In the progress of time exact investigation may possibly subdue regions of phenomena which at present defy all scientific treatment. That scientific method can ever exhaust the phenomena of the human mind is incredible.

CHAPTER XV.

ANALYSIS OF QUANTITATIVE PHENOMENA.

In the two preceding chapters we have been engaged in considering how a phenomenon may be accurately measured and expressed. So delicate and complex an operation is a measurement which pretends to any con siderable degree of exactness, that no small part of the skill and patience of physicists is usually spent upon this work. Much of this difficulty arises from the fact that it is scarcely ever possible to measure a single effect at a time. The ultimate object must be to discover the mathematical equation or law connecting a quantitative cause with its quantitative effect; this purpose usually involves, as we shall see, the varying of one condition at a time, the other conditions being maintained constant. The labours of the experimentalist would be comparatively light if he could carry out this rule of varying one circumstance at a time. He would then obtain a series of corresponding values of the variable quantities concerned, from which he might by proper hypothetical treatment obtain the required law of connection. But in reality it is seldom possible to carry out this direction except in an approximate manner. Before then we proceed to the consideration of the actual process of quantitative induction, it is necessary to review the several devices by which a complicated series of effects can be disentangled. Every phenomenon measured will usually be the sum, difference, or it may be the product or quotient, of two or more different effects, and these must be in some

way analysed and separately measured before we possess
the materials for inductive treatment.

Illustrations of the Complication of Effects.

It is easy to bring forward a multitude of instances to
show that a phenomenon is seldom to be observed simple
and alone. A more or less elaborate process of analysis
is almost always necessary. Thus if an experimentalist
wishes to observe and measure the expansion of a liquid
by heat, he places it in a thermometer tube and registers
the rise of the column of liquid in the narrow tube. But
he cannot heat the liquid without also heating the glass,
so that the change observed is really the difference between
the expansions of the liquid and the glass. More minute
investigation will show the necessity perhaps of allowing
for further minute effects, namely the compression of the
liquid and the expansion of the bulb due to the increased
pressure of the column as it becomes lengthened.

In a great many cases an observed effect will be
apparently at least the simple sum of two separate and
independent effects. The heat evolved in the combustion
of oil is partly due to the carbon and partly to the
hydrogen. A measurement of the heat yielded by the two
jointly, cannot inform us how much proceeds from the
one and how much from the other. If by some separate
determination we can ascertain how much the hydrogen
yields, then by mere subtraction we learn what is due
to the carbon; and *vice versâ*. The heat conveyed by a
liquid, may be partly conveyed by true conduction, partly
by convection. The light dispersed in the interior of a
liquid consists both of what is reflected by floating
particles and what is due to true fluorescence;[1] and we
must find some mode of determining one portion before
we can learn the other. The apparent motion of the spots
on the sun, is the algebraic sum of the sun's axial
rotation, and of the proper motion of the spots upon the
sun's surface; hence the difficulty of ascertaining by
direct observations the period of the sun's rotation.

We cannot obtain the weight of a portion of liquid

---

[1] Stokes, *Philosophical Transactions* (1852), vol. cxlii. p. 529.

in a chemical balance without weighing it with the containing vessel. Hence to have the real weight of the liquid operated upon in an experiment, we must make a separate weighing of the vessel, with or without the adhering film of liquid according to circumstances. This is likewise the mode in which a cart and its load are weighed together, the *tare* of the cart previously ascertained being deducted. The variation in the height of the barometer is a joint effect, partly due to the real variation of the atmospheric pressure, partly to the expansion of the mercurial column by heat. The effects may be discriminated, if, instead of one barometer tube we have two tubes containing mercury placed closely side by side, so as to have the same temperature. If one of them be closed at the bottom so as to be unaffected by the atmospheric pressure, it will show the changes due to temperature only, and, by subtracting these changes from those shown in the other tube, employed as a barometer, we get the real oscillations of atmospheric pressure. But this correction, as it is called, of the barometric reading, is better effected by calculation from the readings of an ordinary thermometer.

In other cases a quantitative effect will be the difference of two causes acting in opposite directions. Sir John Herschel invented an instrument like a large thermometer, which he called the Actinometer,[1] and Pouillet constructed a somewhat similar instrument called the Pyrheliometer, for ascertaining the heating power of the sun's rays. In both instruments the heat of the sun was absorbed by a reservoir containing water, and the rise of temperature of the water was exactly observed, either by its own expansion, or by the readings of a delicate thermometer immersed in it. But in exposing the actinometer to the sun, we do not obtain the full effect of the heat absorbed, because the receiving surface is at the same time radiating heat into empty space. The observed increment of temperature is in short the difference between what is received from the sun and lost by radiation. The latter quantity is capable of ready determination ; we have only to shade the instrument from the direct rays of the sun, leaving it

---

[1] *Admiralty Manual of Scientific Enquiry*, 2nd ed. p. 299.

exposed to the sky, and we can observe how much it cools in a certain time. The total effect of the sun's rays will obviously be the apparent effect *plus* the cooling effect in an equal time. By alternate exposure in sun and shade during equal intervals the desired result may be obtained with considerable accuracy.[1]

Two quantitative effects were beautifully distinguished in an experiment of John Canton, devised in 1761 for the purpose of demonstrating the compressibility of water. He constructed a thermometer with a large bulb full of water and a short capillary tube, the part of which above the water was freed from air. Under these circumstances the water was relieved from the pressure of the atmosphere, but the glass bulb in bearing that pressure was somewhat contracted. He next placed the instrument under the receiver of an air-pump, and on exhausting the air, the water sank in the tube. Having thus obtained a measure of the effect of atmospheric pressure on the bulb, he opened the top of the thermometer tube and admitted the air. .The level of the water now sank still more, partly from the pressure on the bulb being now compensated, and partly from the compression of the water by the atmospheric pressure. It is obvious that the amount of the latter effect was approximately the difference of the two observed depressions.

Not uncommonly the actual phenomenon which we wish to measure is considerably less than various disturbing effects which enter into the question. Thus the compressibility of mercury is considerably less than the expansion of the vessels in which it is measured under pressure, so that the attention of the experimentalist has chiefly to be concentrated on the change of magnitude of the vessels. Many astronomical phenomena, such as the parallax or the proper motions of the fixed stars, are far less than the errors caused by instrumental imperfections, or motions arising from precession, nutation, and aberration. We need not be surprised that astronomers have from time to time mistaken one phenomenon for another, as when Flamsteed imagined that he had discovered the parallax of the Pole star.[2]

[1] Pouillet, *Taylor's Scientific Memoirs*, vol. iv. p. 45.
[2] Baily's *Account of the Rev. John Flamsteed*, p. 58.

Methods of Eliminating Error.

In any particular experiment it is the object of the experimentalist to measure a single effect only, and he endeavours to obtain that effect free from interfering effects. If this cannot be, as it seldom or never can really be, he makes the effect as considerable as possible compared with the other effects, which he reduces to a minimum, and treats as noxious errors. Those quantities, which are called *errors* in one case, may really be most important and interesting phenomena in another investigation. When we speak of eliminating error we really mean·disentangling the complicated phenomena of nature. The physicist rightly wishes to treat one thing at a time, but as this object can seldom be rigorously carried into practice, he has to seek some mode of counteracting the irrelevant and interfering causes.

The general principle is that a single observation can render known only a single quantity. Hence, if several different quantitative effects are known to enter into any investigation, we must have at least as many distinct observations as there are quantities to be determined. Every complete experiment will therefore consist in general of several operations. Guided if possible by previous knowledge of the causes in action, we must arrange the determinations, so that by a simple mathematical process we may distinguish the separate quantities. There appear to be five principal methods by which we may accomplish this object ; these methods are specified below and illustrated in the succeeding sections.

(1) *The Method of Avoidance.* The physicist may seek for some special mode of experiment or opportunity of observation, in which the error is non-existent or inappreciable.

(2) *The Differential Method.* He may find opportunities of observation when all interfering phenomena remain constant, and only the subject of observation is at one time present and another time absent ; the difference between two observations then gives its amount.

(3) *The Method of Correction.* He may endeavour to estimate the amount of the interfering effect by the best available mode, and then make a corresponding correction in the results of observation.

(4) *The Method of Compensation.* He may invent some mode of neutralising the interfering cause by balancing against it an exactly equal and opposite cause of unknown amount.

(5) *The Method of Reversal.* He may so conduct the experiment that the interfering cause may act in opposite directions, in alternate observations, the mean result being free from interference.

1. *Method of Avoidance of Error.*

Astronomers seek opportunities of observation when errors will be as small as possible. In spite of elaborate observations and long-continued theoretical investigation, it is not practicable to assign any satisfactory law to the refractive power of the atmosphere. Although the apparent change of place of a heavenly body produced by refraction may be more or less accurately calculated yet the error depends upon the temperature and pressure of the atmosphere, and, when a ray is highly inclined to the perpendicular, the uncertainty in the refraction becomes very considerable. Hence astronomers always make their observations, if possible, when the object is at the highest point of its daily course, *i.e.* on the meridian. In some kinds of investigation, as, for instance, in the determination of the latitude of an observatory, the astronomer is at liberty to select one or more stars out of the countless number visible. There is an evident advantage in such a case, in selecting a star which passes close to the zenith, so that it may be observed almost entirely free from atmospheric refraction, as was done by Hooke.

Astronomers endeavour to render their clocks as accurate as possible, by removing the source of variation. The pendulum is perfectly isochronous so long as its length remains invariable, and the vibrations are exactly of equal length. They render it nearly invariable in length, that is in the distance between the centres of suspension and oscillation, by a compensatory arrangement for the change of temperature. But as this compensation may not be perfectly accomplished, some astronomers place their chief controlling clock in a cellar, or other apartment, where the changes of temperature may be as slight as possible.

At the Paris Observatory a clock has been placed in the caves beneath the building, where there is no appreciable difference between the summer and winter temperature.

To avoid the effect of unequal oscillations Huyghens made his beautiful investigations, which resulted in the discovery that a pendulum, of which the centre of oscillation moved upon a cycloidal path, would be perfectly isochronous, whatever the variation in the length of oscillations. But though a pendulum may be easily rendered in some degree cycloidal by the use of a steel suspension spring, it is found that the mechanical arrangements requisite to produce a truly cycloidal motion introduce more error than they remove. Hence astronomers seek to reduce the error to the smallest amount by maintaining their clock pendulums in uniform movement; in fact, while a clock is in good order and has the same weights, there need be little change in the length of oscillation. When a pendulum cannot be made to swing uniformly, as in experiments upon the force of gravity, it becomes requisite to resort to the third method, and a correction is introduced, calculated on theoretical grounds from the amount of the observed change in the length of vibration.

It has been mentioned that the apparent expansion of a liquid by heat, when contained in a thermometer tube or other vessel, is the difference between the real expansion of the liquid and that of the containing vessel. The effects can be accurately distinguished provided that we can learn the real expansion by heat of any one convenient liquid; for by observing the apparent expansion of the same liquid in any required vessel we can by difference learn the amount of expansion of the vessel due to any given change of temperature. When we once know the change of dimensions of the vessel, we can of course determine the absolute expansion of any other liquid tested in it. Thus it became an all-important object in scientific research to measure with accuracy the absolute dilatation by heat of some one liquid, and mercury owing to several circumstances was by far the most suitable. Dulong and Petit devised a beautiful mode of effecting this by simply avoiding altogether the effect of the change of size of the vessel. Two upright tubes full of mercury were connected by a fine tube at the bottom, and were maintained at two different temperatures. As mercury was free to flow from one tube to the other by the connecting tube, the two columns necessarily exerted equal pressures by the principles of hydrostatics. Hence it was only necessary to measure very accurately by a cathetometer the difference of level of the surfaces of the two columns of mercury, to learn the difference of length of columns of equal hydrostatic pressure, which at once gives the difference of density of the mercury, and the dilatation by heat. The changes of dimension in the containing tubes became a matter of entire indifference, and the length of a column of mercury at different temperatures was measured as easily as if it had formed a solid bar. The experiment was carried out by Regnault with many improvements of detail, and the absolute dilatation of mercury, at temperatures between 0° Cent. and 350°, was determined almost as accurately as was needful.[1]

The presence of a large and uncertain amount of error may render a method of experiment valueless. Foucault devised a beautiful experiment with the pendulum for demonstrating popularly the rotation of the earth, but it could be of no use for measuring the rotation exactly. It is impossible to make the pendulum swing in a perfect plane, and the slightest lateral motion gives it an elliptic path with a progressive motion of the axis of the ellipse, which disguises and often entirely overpowers that due to the rotation of the earth.[2]

Faraday's laborious experiments on the relation of gravity and electricity were much obstructed by the fact that it is impossible to move a large weight of metal without generating currents of electricity, either by friction or induction. To distinguish the electricity, if any, directly due to the action of gravity from the greater quantities indirectly produced was a problem of excessive difficulty. Baily in his experiments on the density of the earth was aware of the existence of inexplicable disturbances which have since been referred with much probability to the action of electricity.[3] The skill and ingenuity of the experimentalist

---

[1] Jamin, *Cours de Physique*, vol. ii. pp. 15—28.
[2] *Philosophical Magazine*, 1851, 4th Series, vol. ii. *passim*.
[3] Hearn, *Philosophical Transactions*, 1847, vol. cxxxvii. pp. 217 221.

are often exhausted in trying to devise a form of apparatus in which such causes of error shall be reduced to a minimum.

In some rudimentary experiments we wish merely to establish the existence of a quantitative effect without precisely measuring its amount ; if there exist causes of error of which we can neither render the amount known or inappreciable, the best way is to make them all negative so that the quantitative effects will be less than the truth rather than greater. Grove, for instance, in proving that the magnetisation or demagnetisation of a piece of iron raises its temperature, took care to maintain the electro-magnet by which the iron was magnetised at a lower temperature than the iron, so that it would cool rather than warm the iron by radiation or conduction.[1]

Rumford's celebrated experiment to prove that heat was generated out of mechanical force in the boring of a cannon was subject to the difficulty that heat might be brought to the cannon by conduction from neighbouring bodies. It was an ingenious device of Davy to produce friction by a piece of clock-work resting upon a block of ice in an exhausted receiver; as the machine rose in temperature above 32°, it was certain that no heat was received by conduction from the support.[2] In many other experiments ice may be employed to prevent the access of heat by conduction, and this device, first put in practice by Murray,[3] is beautifully employed in Bunsen's calorimeter.

To observe the true temperature of the air, though apparently so easy, is really a very difficult matter, because the thermometer is sure to be affected either by the sun's rays, the radiation from neighbouring objects, or the escape of heat into space. These sources of error are too fluctuating to allow of correction, so that the only accurate mode of procedure is that devised by Dr. Joule, of surrounding the thermometer with a copper cylinder ingeniously

[1] *The Correlation of Physical Forces*, 3rd ed. p. 159.
[2] *Collected Works of Sir H. Davy*, vol. ii. pp. 12—14. *Elements of Chemical Philosophy*, p. 94.
[3] *Nicholson's Journal*, vol. i. p. 241 ; quoted in *Treatise on Heat* Useful Knowledge Society. p. 24.

adjusted to the temperature of the air, as described by him, so that the effect of radiation shall be nullified.[1]

When the avoidance of error is not practicable, it will yet be desirable to reduce the absolute amount of the interfering error as much as possible before employing the succeeding methods to correct the result. As a general rule we can determine a quantity with less inaccuracy as it is smaller, so that if the error itself be small the error in determining that error will be of a still lower order of magnitude. But in some cases the absolute amount of an error is of no consequence, as in the index error of a divided circle, or the difference between a chronometer and astronomical time. Even the rate at which a clock gains or loses is a matter of little importance provided it remain constant, so that a sure calculation of its amount can be made.

2. *Differential Method.*

When we cannot avoid the existence of error, we can often resort with success to the second mode by measuring phenomena under such circumstances that the error shall remain very nearly the same in all the observations, and neutralise itself as regards the purposes in view. This mode is available whenever we want a difference between quantities and not the absolute quantity of either. The determination of the parallax of the fixed stars is exceedingly difficult, because the amount of parallax is far less than most of the corrections for atmospheric refraction, nutation, aberration, precession, instrumental irregularities, &c., and can with difficulty be detected among these phenomena of various magnitude. But, as Galileo long ago suggested, all such difficulties would be avoided by the differential observation of stars, which, though apparently close together, are really far separated on the line of sight. Two such stars in close apparent proximity will be subject to almost exactly equal errors, so that all we need do is to observe the apparent change of place of the nearer star as referred to the more distant one.

---

[1] Clerk Maxwell, *Theory of Heat*, p. 228. *Proceedings of the Manchester Philosophical Society*, Nov. 26. 1867, vol. vii. p. 35.

A good telescope furnished with an accurate micrometer is alone needed for the application of the method. Huyghens appears to have been the first observer who actually tried to employ the method practically, but it was not until 1835 that the improvement of telescopes and micrometers enabled Struve to detect in this way the parallax of the star *a* Lyræ. It is one of the many advantages of the observation of transits of Venus for the determination of the solar parallax that the refraction of the atmosphere affects in an exactly equal degree the planet and the portion of the sun's face over which it is passing. Thus the observations are strictly of a differential nature.

By the process of substitutive weighing it is possible to ascertain the equality or inequality of two weights with almost perfect freedom from error. If two weights A and B be placed in the scales of the best balance we cannot be sure that the equilibrium of the beam indicates exact equality, because the arms of the beam may be unequal or unbalanced. But if we take B out and put another weight C in, and equilibrium still exists, it is apparent that the same causes of erroneous weighing exist in both cases, supposing that the balance has not been disarranged ; B then must be exactly equal to C, since it has exactly the same effect under the same circumstances. In like manner it is a general rule that, if by any uniform mechanical process we get a copy of an object, it is unlikely that this copy will be precisely the same as the original in magnitude and form, but two copies will equally diverge from the original, and will therefore almost exactly resemble each other.

Leslie's Differential Thermometer[1] was well adapted to the experiments for which it was invented. Having two equal bulbs any alteration in the temperature of the air will act equally by conduction on each and produce no change in the indications of the instrument. Only that radiant heat which is purposely thrown upon one of the bulbs will produce any effect. This thermometer in short carries out the principle of the differential method in a mechanical manner.

---

[1] Leslie, *Inquiry into the Nature of Heat*, p. 10.

3. *Method of Correction.*

Whenever the result of an experiment is affected by an interfering cause to a calculable amount, it is sufficient to add or subtract this amount. We are said to correct observations when we thus eliminate what is due to extraneous causes, although of course we are only separating the correct effects of several agents. The variation in the height of the barometer is partly due to the change of temperature, but since the coefficient of absolute dilatation of mercury has been exactly determined, as already described (p. 341), we have only to make calculations of a simple character, or, what is better still, tabulate a series of such calculations for general use, and the correction for temperature can be made with all desired accuracy. The height of the mercury in the barometer is also affected by capillary attraction, which depresses it by a constant amount depending mainly on the diameter of the tube. The requisite corrections can be estimated with accuracy sufficient for most purposes, more especially as we can check the correctness of the reading of a barometer by comparison with a standard barometer, and introduce if need be an index error including both the error in the affixing of the scale and the effect due to capillarity. But in constructing the standard barometer itself we must take greater precautions ; the capillary depression depends somewhat upon the quality of the glass, the absence of air, and the perfect cleanliness of the mercury, so that we cannot assign the exact amount of the effect. Hence a standard barometer is constructed with a wide tube, sometimes even an inch in diameter, so that the capillary effect may be rendered almost zero.[1] Gay-Lussac made barometers in the form of a uniform siphon tube, so that the capillary forces acting at the upper and lower surfaces should balance and destroy each other ; but the method fails in practice because the lower surface, being open to the air, becomes sullied and subject to a different force of capillarity.

In mechanical experiments friction is an interfering condition, and drains away a portion of the energy in-

[1] Jevons, Watts' *Dictionary of Chemistry*, vol. i. pp. 513—515.

tended to be operated upon in a definite manner. We
should of course reduce the friction in the first place to the
lowest possible amount, but as it cannot be altogether prevented, and is not calculable with certainty from any
general laws, we must determine it separately for each
apparatus by suitable experiments. Thus Smeaton, in
his admirable but almost forgotten researches concerning
water-wheels, eliminated friction in the most simple
manner by determining by trial what weight, acting by a
cord and roller upon his model water-wheel, would make
it turn without water as rapidly as the water made it turn.
In short, he ascertained what weight concurring with the
water would exactly compensate for the friction.[1] In Dr.
Joule's experiments to determine the mechanical equivalent of heat by the condensation of air, a considerable
amount of heat was produced by friction of the condensing
pump, and a small portion by stirring the water employed
to absorb the heat. This heat of friction was measured by
simply repeating the experiment in an exactly similar
manner except that no condensation was effected, and observing the change of temperature then produced.[2]

We may describe as *test experiments* any in which we
perform operations not intended to give the quantity of
the principal phenomenon, but some quantity which would
otherwise remain as an error in the result. Thus in
astronomical observations almost every instrumental error
may be avoided by increasing the number of observations
and distributing them in such a manner as to produce
in the final mean as much error in one way as in the
other. But there is one source of error, first discovered
by Maskelyne, which cannot be thus avoided, because it
affects all observations in the same direction and to the
same average amount, namely the Personal Error of the
observer or the inclination to record the passage of a star
across the wires of the telescope a little too soon or a
little too late. This personal error was first carefully
described in the. *Edinburgh Journal of Science*, vol. i.
p. 178. The difference between the judgment of observers
at the Greenwich Observatory usually varies from $\frac{1}{100}$ to $\frac{1}{3}$

[1] *Philosophical Transactions*, vol. li. p. 100.
[2] *Philosophical Magazine*, 3rd Series, vol. xxvi. p. 372.

of a second, and remains pretty constant for the same observers.[1] One practised observer in Sir George Airy's pendulum experiments recorded all his time observations half a second too early on the average as compared with the chief observer.[2] In some observers it has amounted to seven or eight-tenths of a second.[3] De Morgan appears to have entertained the opinion that this source of error was essentially incapable of elimination or correction.[4] But it seems clear, as I suggested without knowing what had been done,[5] that this personal error might be determined absolutely with any desirable degree of accuracy by test experiments, consisting in making an artificial star move at a considerable distance and recording by electricity the exact moment of its passage over the wire. This method has in fact been successfully employed in Leyden, Paris, and Neuchatel.[6] More recently, observers were trained for the Transit of Venus Expeditions by means of a mechanical model representing the motion of Venus over the sun, this model being placed at a little distance and viewed through a telescope, so that differences in the judgments of different observers would become apparent. It seems likely that tests of this nature might be employed with advantage in other cases.

Newton employed the pendulum for making experiments on the impact of balls. Two balls were hung in contact, and one of them, being drawn aside through a measured arc, was then allowed to strike the other, the arcs of vibration giving sufficient data for calculating the distribution of energy at the moment of impact. The resistance of the air was an interfering cause which he estimated very simply by causing one of the balls to make several complete vibrations without impact and then marking the reduction in the lengths of the arcs, a proper fraction of which reduction was added to each of the other arcs of vibration when impact took place.[7]

[1] *Greenwich Observations for* 1866, p. xlix.
[2] *Philosophical Transactions*, 1856, p. 309.
[3] *Penny Cyclopædia*, art. *Transit*, vol. xxv. pp. 129, 130.
[4] Ibid. art. *Observation*, p. 390.   [5] *Nature*, vol. i. p. 85.
[6] *Nature*, vol. i. p. 337. See references to the Memoirs describing the method.
[7] *Principia*, Book I. Law III. Corollary VI. Scholium. Motte's translation, vol. i. p. 33.

The exact definition of the standard of length is one of the most important, as it is one of the most difficult questions in physical science, and the different practice of different nations introduces needless confusion. Were all standards constructed so as to give the true length at a fixed uniform temperature, for instance the freezing-point, then any two standards could be compared without the interference of temperature by bringing them both to exactly the same fixed temperature. Unfortunately the French metre was defined by a bar of platinum at o°C, while our yard was defined by a bronze bar at 62°F. It is quite impossible, then, to make a comparison of the yard and metre without the introduction of a correction, either for the expansion of platinum or bronze, or both. Bars of metal differ too so much in their rates of expansion according to their molecular condition that it is dangerous to infer from one bar to another.

When we come to use instruments with great accuracy there are many minute sources of error which must be guarded against. If a thermometer has been graduated when perpendicular, it will read somewhat differently when laid flat, as the pressure of a column of mercury is removed from the bulb. The reading may also be somewhat altered if it has recently been raised to a higher temperature than usual, if it be placed under a vacuous receiver, or if the tube be unequally heated as compared with the bulb. For these minute causes of error we may have to introduce troublesome corrections, unless we adopt the simple precaution of using the thermo-meter in circumstances of position, &c., exactly similar to those in which it was graduated. There is no end to the number of minute corrections which may ultimately be required. A large number of experiments on gases, standard weights and measures, &c., depend upon the height of the barometer; but when experiments in dif-ferent parts of the world are compared together we ought as a further refinement to take into account the varying force of gravity, which even between London and Paris makes a difference of ·008 inch of mercury.

The measurement of quantities of heat is a matter of great difficulty, because there is no known substance impervious to heat. and the problem is therefore as

difficult as to measure liquids in porous vessels. To
determine the latent heat of steam we must condense a
certain amount of the steam in a known weight of water,
and then observe the rise of temperature of the water.
But while we are carrying out the experiment, part of
the heat will escape by radiation and conduction from
the condensing vessel or calorimeter. We may indeed
reduce the loss of heat by using vessels with double sides
and bright surfaces, surrounded with swans-down wool or
other non-conducting materials; and we may also avoid
raising the temperature of the water much above that of
the surrounding air. Yet we cannot by any such means
render the loss of heat inconsiderable. Rumford ingeniously proposed to reduce the loss to zero by commencing
the experiment when the temperature of the calorimeter
is as much below that of the air as it is at the end of the
experiment above it. Thus the vessel will first gain and
then lose by radiation and conduction, and these opposite
errors will approximately balance each other. But Regnault has shown that the loss and gain do not proceed by
exactly the same laws, so that in very accurate investigations Rumford's method is not sufficient. There
remains the method of correction which was beautifully
carried out by Regnault in his determination of the latent
heat of steam. He employed two calorimeters, made in
exactly the same way and alternately used to condense a
certain amount of steam, so that while one was measuring
the latent heat, the other calorimeter was engaged in
determining the corrections to be applied, whether on
account of radiation and conduction from the vessel or
on account of heat reaching the vessel by means of the
connecting pipes.[1]

4. *Method of Compensation.*

There are many cases in which a cause of error cannot
conveniently be rendered null, and is yet beyond the
reach of the third method, that of calculating the requisite
correction from independent observations. The magnitude

---

[1] Graham's *Chemical Reports and Memoirs*, Cavendish Society,
pp. 247, 268, &c.

of an error may be subject to continual variations, on account of change of weather, or other fickle cirumstances beyond our control. It may either be impracticable to observe the variation of those circumstances in sufficient detail, or, if observed, the calculation of the amount of error' may be subject to doubt. In these cases, and only in these cases, it will be desirable to invent some artificial mode of counterpoising the variable error against an equal error subjéct to exactly the same variation.

We cannot weigh an object with great accuracy unless we make a correction for the weight of the air displaced by the object, and add this to the apparent weight. In very accurate investigations relating to standard weights, it is usual to note the barometer and thermometer at the time of making a weighing, and, from the measured bulks of the objects compared, to calculate the weight of air displaced ; the third method in fact is adopted. To make these calculations in the frequent weighings requisite in chemical analysis would be exceedingly laborious, hence the correction is usually neglected. But when the chemist wishes to weigh gas contained in a large glass globe for the purpose of determining its specific gravity, the correction becomes of much importance. Hence chemists avoid at once the error, and the labour of correcting it, by attaching to the opposite scale of the balance a dummy sealed glass globe of equal capacity to that containing the gas to be weighed, noting only the difference of weight when the operating globe is full and empty. The correction, being the same for both globes, may be entirely neglected.[1]

A device of nearly the same kind is employed in the construction of galvanometers which measure the force of an electric current by the deflection of a suspended magnetic needle. The resistance of the needle is partly due to the directive influence of the earth's magnetism, and partly to the torsion of the thread. But the former force may often be inconveniently great as well as troublesome to determine for different inclinations. Hence it is customary to connect together two equally magnetised needles, with their poles pointing in opposite directions,

[1] Regnault's *Cours Élémentaire de Chimie*, 1851, vol i. p. 141.

one needle being within and another without the coil of
wire. As regards the earth's magnetism, the needles are
now *astatic* or indifferent, the tendency of one needle
towards the pole being balanced by that of the other.

An elegant instance of the elimination of a disturbing
force by compensation is found in Faraday's researches
upon the magnetism of gases. To observe the magnetic
attraction or repulsion of a gas seems impossible unless we
enclose the gas in an envelope, probably best made of
glass. But any such envelope is sure to be more or less
affected by the magnet, so that it becomes difficult to
distinguish between three forces which enter into the
problem, namely, the magnetism of the gas in question,
that of the envelope, and that of the surrounding atmospheric air. Faraday avoided all difficulties by employing
two equal and similar glass tubes connected together, and
so suspended from the arm of a torsion balance that the
tubes were in similar parts of the magnetic field. One
tube being filled with nitrogen and the other with oxygen,
it was found that the oxygen seemed to be attracted and
the nitrogen repelled. The suspending thread of the
balance was then turned until the force of torsion restored
the tubes to their original places, where the magnetism of
the tubes as well as that of the surrounding air, being
the same and in the opposite directions upon the two tubes,
could not produce any interference. The force required
to restore the tubes was measured by the amount of
torsion of the thread, and it indicated correctly the difference between the attractive powers of oxygen and
nitrogen. The oxygen was then withdrawn from one of
the tubes, and a second experiment made, so as to compare
a vacuum with nitrogen. No force was now required to
maintain the tubes in their places, so that nitrogen was
found to be, approximately speaking, indifferent to the
magnet, that is, neither magnetic nor diamagnetic, while
oxygen was proved to be positively magnetic.[1] It required
the highest experimental skill on the part of Faraday
and Tyndall, to distinguish between what is apparent and
real in magnetic attraction and repulsion.

Experience alone can finally decide when a com-

---

[1] Tyndall's *Faraday*, pp. 114, 115.

pensating arrangement is conducive to accuracy. As a general rule mechanical compensation is the last resource, and in the more accurate observations it is likely to introduce more uncertainty than it removes. A multitude of instruments involving mechanical compensation have been devised, but they are usually of an unscientific character,[1] because the errors compensated can be more accurately determined and allowed for. But there are exceptions to this rule, and it seems to be proved that in the delicate and tiresome operation of measuring a base line, invariable bars, compensated for expansion by heat, give the most accurate results. This arises from the fact that it is very difficult to determine accurately the temperature of the measuring bars under varying conditions of weather and manipulation.[2] Again, the last refinement in the measurement of time at Greenwich Observatory depends upon mechanical compensation. Sir George Airy, observing that the standard clock increased its losing rate 0·30 second for an increase of one inch in atmospheric pressure, placed a magnet moved by a barometer in such a position below the pendulum, as almost entirely to neutralise this cause of irregularity. The thorough remedy, however, would be to remove the cause of error altogether by placing the clock in a vacuous case.

We thus see that the choice of one or other mode of eliminating an error depends entirely upon circumstances and the object in view ; but we may safely lay down the following conclusions. First of all, seek to avoid the source of error altogether if it can be conveniently done ; if not, make the experiment so that the error may be as small, but more especially as constant, as possible. If the means are at hand for determining its amount by calculation from other experiments and principles of science, allow the error to exist and make a correction in the result. If this cannot be accurately done or involves too much labour for the purposes in view, then throw in a counteracting error which shall as nearly as possible be of equal amount in all circumstances with that to be eliminated. There yet remains, however, one important method, that of Reversal,

[1] See, for instance, the Compensated Sympiesometer, *Philosophical Magazine*, 4th Series, vol. xxxix. p. 371.
[2] Grant, *History of Physical Astronomy*, pp. 146, 147.

which will form an appropriate transition to the succeeding chapters on the Method of Mean Results and the Law of Error.

5. *Method of Reversal.*

The fifth method of eliminating error is most potent and satisfactory when it can be applied, but it requires that we shall. be able to reverse the apparatus and mode of procedure, so as to make the interfering cause act alternately in opposite directions. If we can get two experimental results, one of which is as much too great as the other is too small, the error is equal to half the difference, and the true result is the mean of the two apparent results. It is an unavoidable defect of the chemical balance, for instance, that the points of suspension of the pans cannot be fixed at exactly equal distances from the centre of suspension of the beam. Hence two weights which seem to balance each other will never be quite equal in reality. The difference is detected by reversing the weights, and it may be estimated by adding small weights to the deficient side to restore equilibrium, and then taking as the true weight the geometric mean of the two apparent weights of the same object. If the difference is small, the arithmetic mean, that is half the sum, may be substituted for the geometric mean, from which it will not appreciably differ.

This method of reversal is most extensively employed in practical astronomy. The apparent elevation of a heavenly body is observed by a telescope moving upon a divided circle, upon which the inclination of the telescope is read off. Now this reading will be erroneous if the circle and the telescope have not accurately the same centre. But if we read off at the same time both ends of the telescope, the one reading will be about as much too small as the other is too great, and the mean will be nearly free from error. In practice the observation is differently conducted, but the principle is the same ; the telescope is fixed to the circle, which moves with it, and the angle through which it moves is read off at three, six, or more points, disposed at equal intervals round the circle. The older astronomers, down even to the time of

Flamsteed, were accustomed to use portions only of a divided circle, generally quadrants, and Römer made a vast improvement when he introduced the complete circle.

The transit circle, employed to determine the meridian passage of heavenly bodies, is so constructed that the telescope and the axis bearing it, in fact the whole moving part of the instrument, can be taken out of the bearing sockets and turned over, so that what was formerly the western pivot becomes the eastern one, and *vice versâ*. It is impossible that the instrument could have been so perfectly constructed, mounted, and adjusted that the telescope should point exactly to the meridian, but the effect of the reversal is that it will point as much to the west in one position as it does to the east in the other, and the mean result of observations in the two positions must be free from such cause of error.

The accuracy with which the inclination of the compass needle can be determined depends almost entirely on the method of reversal. The dip needle consists of a bar of magnetised steel, suspended somewhat like the beam of a delicate balance on a slender axis passing through the centre of gravity of the bar, so that it is at liberty to rest in that exact degree of inclination in the magnetic meridian which the magnetism of the earth induces. The inclination is read off upon a vertical divided circle, but to avoid error arising from the centring of the needle and circle, both ends are read, and the mean of the results is taken. The whole instrument is now turned carefully round through 180°, which causes the needle to assume a new position relatively to the circle and gives two new readings, in which any error due to the wrong position of the zero of the division will be reversed. As the axis of the needle may not be exactly horizontal, it is now reversed in the same manner as the transit instrument, the end of the axis which formerly pointed east being made to point west, and a new set of four readings is taken.

Finally, error may arise from the axis not passing accurately through the centre of gravity of the bar, and this error can only be detected and eliminated on changing the magnetic poles of the bar by the application of a strong magnet. The error is thus made to act in opposite directions. To ensure all possible accuracy each reversal ought to be combined with each other reversal, so that the needle will be observed in eight different positions by sixteen readings, the mean of the whole of which will give the required inclination free from all eliminable errors.[1]

There are certain cases in which a disturbing cause can with ease be made to act in opposite directions, in alternate observations, so that the mean of the results will be free from disturbance. Thus in direct experiments upon the velocity of sound in passing through the air between stations two or three miles apart, the wind is a cause of error. It will be well, in the first place, to choose a time for the experiment when the air is very nearly at rest, and the disturbance slight, but if at the same moment signal sounds be made at each station and observed at the other, two sounds will be passing in opposite directions through the same body of air and the wind will accelerate one sound almost exactly as it retards the other. Again, in trigonometrical surveys the apparent height of a point will be affected by atmospheric refraction and the curvature of the earth. But if in the case of two points the apparent elevation of each as seen from the other be observed, the corrections will be the same in amount, but reversed in direction, and the mean between the two apparent differences of altitude will give the true difference of level.

In the next two chapters we really pursue the Method of Reversal into more complicated applications.

[1] Quetelet, *Sur la Physique du Globe*, p. 174. Jamin, *Cours de Physique*, vol. i. p. 504.

CHAPTER XVI.

THE METHOD OF MEANS.

ALL results of the measurement of continuous quantity can be only approximately true. Were this assertion doubted, it could readily be proved by direct experience. If any person, using an instrument of the greatest precision, makes and registers successive observations in an unbiassed manner, it will almost invariably be found that the results differ from each other. When we operate with sufficient care we cannot perform so simple an experiment as weighing an object in a good balance without getting discrepant numbers. Only the rough and careless experimenter will think that his observations agree, but in reality he will be found to overlook the differences. The most elaborate researches, such as those undertaken in connection with standard weights and measures, always render it apparent that complete coincidence is out of the question, and that the more accurate our modes of observation are rendered, the more numerous are the sources of minute error which become apparent. We may look upon the existence of error in all measurements as the normal state of things. It is absolutely impossible to eliminate separately the multitude of small disturbing influences, except by balancing them off against each other. Even in drawing a mean it is to be expected that we shall come near the truth rather than exactly to it. In the measurement of continuous quantity, absolute coincidence, if it seems to occur, must be only apparent, and is no indication of precision. It is one of the most embarrassing things we can meet when experimental results agree too closely. Such coincidences should raise our suspicion that the apparatus in use is in some way restricted in its operation, so as not really to give the true result at all, or that the actual results have not been faithfully recorded by the assistant in charge of the apparatus.

If then we cannot get twice over exactly the same result, the question arises, How can we ever attain the truth or select the result which may be supposed to approach most nearly to it ? The quantity of a certain phenomenon is expressed in several numbers which differ from each other; no more than one of them at the most can be true, and it is more probable that they are all false. It may be suggested, perhaps, that the observer should select the one observation which he judged to be the best made, and there will often doubtless be a feeling that one or more results were satisfactory, and the others less trustworthy. This seems to have been the course adopted by the early astronomers. Flamsteed, when he had made several observations of a star, probably chose in an arbitrary manner that which seemed to him nearest to the truth.[1]

When Horrocks selected for his estimate of the sun's semi-diameter a mean between the results of Kepler and Tycho, he professed not to do it from any regard to the idle adage, "Medio tutissimus ibis," but because he thought it from his own observations to be correct.[2] But this method will not apply at all when the observer has made a number of measurements which are equally good in his opinion, and it is quite apparent that in using an instrument or apparatus of considerable complication the observer will not necessarily be able to judge whether slight causes have affected its operation or not.

In this question, as indeed throughout inductive logic, we deal only with probabilities. There is no infallible mode of arriving at the absolute truth, which lies beyond the reach of human intellect, and can only be the distant object of our long-continued and painful approximations. Nevertheless there is a mode pointed out alike by common sense and the highest mathematical reasoning, which is

[1] Baily's *Account of Flamsteed*, p. 376.
[2] *The Transit of Venus across the Sun*, by Horrocks, London, 1859, p. 146.

more likely than any other, as a general rule, to bring us near the truth. The $\overset{\prime}{\alpha}\rho\iota\sigma\tau o\nu$ $\mu\acute{\epsilon}\tau\rho o\nu$, or the *aurea mediocritas*, was highly esteemed in the ancient philosophy of Greece and Rome ; but it is not probable that any of the ancients should have been able clearly to analyse and express the reasons why they advocated the *mean* as the safest course. But in the last two centuries this apparently simple question of the mean has been found to afford a field for the exercise of the utmost mathematical skill. Rcger Cotes, the editor of the *Principia*, appears to have had some insight into the value of the mean; but profound mathematicians such as De Moivre, Daniel Bernoulli, Laplace, Lagrange, Gauss, Quetelet, De Morgan, Airy, Leslie Ellis, Boole, Glaisher, and others, have hardly exhausted the subject.

Several uses of the Mean Result.

The elimination of errors of unknown sources, is almost always accomplished by the simple arithmetical process of taking the *mean*, or, as it is often called, the *average* of several discrepant numbers. To take an average is to add the several quantities together, and divide by the number of quantities thus added, which gives a quotient lying among, or in the *middle* of, the several quantities. Before however inquiring fully into the grounds of this procedure, it is essential to observe that this one arithmetical process is really applied in at least three different cases, for different purposes, and upon different principles, and we must take great care not to confuse one application of the process with another. A *mean result*, then, may have any one of the following significations.

(1) It may give a merely representative number, expressing the general magnitude of a series of quantities, and serving as a convenient mode of comparing them with other series of quantities. Such a number is properly called *The fictitious mean* or *The average result*.

(2) It may give a result approximately free from disturbing quantities, which are known to affect some results in one direction, and other results equally in the opposite direction. We may say that in this case we get a *Precise mean result*.

(3) It may give a result more or less free from unknown and uncertain errors; this we may call the *Probable mean result*.

Of these three uses of the mean the first is entirely different in nature from the two last, since it does not yield an approximation to any natural quantity, but furnishes us with an arithmetic result comparing the aggregate of certain quantities with their number. The third use of the mean rests entirely upon the theory of probability, and will be more fully considered in a later part of this chapter. The second use is closely connected, or even identical with, the Method of Reversal already described, but it will be desirable to enter somewhat fully into all the three employments of the same arithmetical process.

The Mean and the Average.

Much confusion exists in the popular, or even the scientific employment of the terms *mean* and *average*, and they are commonly taken as synonymous. It is necessary to ascertain carefully what significations we ought to attach to them. The English word *mean* is equivalent to *medium*, being derived, perhaps through the French *moyen*, from the Latin *medius*, which again is undoubtedly kindred with the Greek $\mu\epsilon\sigma\sigma$. Etymologists believe, too, that this Greek word is connected with the preposition $\mu\epsilon\tau\alpha$, the German *mitte*, and the true English *mid* or *middle ;* so that after all the *mean* is a technical term identical in its root with the more popular equivalent *middle*.

If we inquire what is the mean in a mathematical point of view, the true answer is that there are several or many kinds of means. The old arithmeticians recognised ten kinds, which are stated by Boethius, and an eleventh was added by Jordanus.[1]

The *arithmetic mean* is the one by far the most commonly denoted by the term, and that which we may understand it to signify in the absence of any qualification. It is the sum of a series of quantities divided by their number, and may be represented by the formula $\frac{1}{2}(a + b)$.

---

[1] De Morgan, Supplement to the *Penny Cyclopædia*, art. *Old Appellations of Numbers.*

But there is also the *geometric mean,* which is the square root of the product, $\sqrt{a \times b}$, or that quantity the logarithm of which is the arithmetic mean of the logarithms of the quantities. There is also the *harmonic mean,* which is the reciprocal of the arithmetic mean of the reciprocals of the quantities. Thus if a and b be the quantities, as before, their reciprocals are $\frac{1}{a}$ and $\frac{1}{b}$, the mean of which is $\frac{1}{2}\left(\frac{1}{a} + \frac{1}{b}\right)$, and the reciprocal again is $\frac{2ab}{a+b}$, which is the harmonic mean. Other kinds of means might no doubt be invented for particular purposes, and we might apply the term, as De Morgan pointed out,[1] to any quantity a function of which is equal to a function of two or more other quantities, and is such that the interchange of these latter quantities among themselves will make no alteration in the value of the function. Symbolically, if $\phi(y, y, y \ldots) = \phi(x_1, x_2, x_3 \ldots)$, then y is a kind of mean of the quantities, x_1, x_2, &c.

The geometric mean is necessarily adopted in certain cases. When we estimate the work done against a force which varies inversely as the square of the distance from a fixed point, the mean force is the geometric mean between the forces at the beginning and end of the path. When in an imperfect balance, we reverse the weights to eliminate error, the true weight will be the geometric mean of the two apparent weights. In almost all the calculations of statistics and commerce the geometric mean ought, strictly speaking, to be used. If a commodity rises in price 100 per cent. and another remains unaltered, the mean rise of a price is not 50 per cent. because the ratio 150 : 200 is not the same as 100 : 150. The mean ratio is as unity to $\sqrt{1\cdot00 \times 2\cdot00}$ or 1 to 1·41. The difference between the three kinds of means in such a case[2] is very considerable; while the rise of price estimated by the Arithmetic mean would be 50 per cent. it would be only 41 and 33 per cent. respectively according to the Geometric and Harmonic means.

[1] *Penny Cyclopædia,* art. *Mean.*
[2] Jevons, *Journal of the Statistical Society,* June 1865, vol. xxviii. p. 296.

In all calculations concerning the average rate of progress of a community, or any of its operations, the geometric mean should be employed. For if a quantity increases 100 per cent. in 100 years, it would not on the average increase 10 per cent. in each ten years, as the 10 per cent. would at the end of each decade be calculated upon larger and larger quantities, and give at the end of 100 years much more than 100 per cent., in fact as much as 159 per cent. The true mean rate in each decade would be $\sqrt[10]{2}$ or about 1·07, that is, the increase would be about 7 per cent. in each ten years. But when the quantities differ very little, the arithmetic and geometric means are approximately the same. Thus the arithmetic mean of 1·000 and 1·001 is 1·0005, and the geometric mean is about 1·0004998, the difference being of an order inappreciable in almost all scientific and practical matters. Even in the comparison of standard weights by Gauss' method of reversal, the arithmetic mean may usually be substituted for the geometric mean which is the true result.

Regarding the mean in the absence of express qualification to the contrary as the common arithmetic mean, we must still distinguish between its two uses where it gives with more or less accuracy and probability a really existing quantity, and where it acts as a mere representative of other quantities. If I make many experiments to determine the atomic weight of an element, there is a certain number which I wish to approximate to, and the mean of my separate results will, in the absence of any reasons to the contrary, be the most probable approximate result. When we determine the mean density of the earth, it is not because any part of the earth is of that exact density ; there may be no part exactly corresponding to the mean density, and as the crust of the earth has only about half the mean density, the internal matter of the globe must of course be above the mean. Even the density of a homogeneous substance like carbon or gold must be regarded as a mean between the real density of its atoms, and the zero density of the intervening vacuous space.

The very different signification of the word "mean" in these two uses was fully explained by Quetelet,[1] and the

[1] *Letters on the Theory of Probabilities*, transl. by Downes, Part ii.

importance of the distinction was pointed out by Sir John Herschel in reviewing his work.[1] It is much to be desired that scientific men would mark the difference by using the word *mean* only in the former sense when it denotes approximation to a definite existing quantity ; and *average*, when the mean is only a fictitious quantity, used for convenience of thought and expression. The etymology of this word " average " is somewhat obscure ; but according to De Morgan [2] it comes from *averia*, " havings or possessions," especially applied to farm stock. By the accidents of language *averagium* came to mean the labour of farm horses to which the lord was entitled, and it probably acquired in this manner the notion of distributing a whole into parts, a sense in which it was early applied to maritime averages or contributions of the other owners of cargo to those whose goods have been thrown overboard or used for the safety of the vessel.

On the Average or Fictitious Mean.

Although the average when employed in its proper sense of a fictitious mean, represents no really existing quantity, it is yet of the highest scientific importance, as enabling us to conceive in a single result a multitude of details. It enables us to make a hypothetical simplification of a problem, and avoid complexity without committing error. The weight of a body is the sum of the weights of infinitely small particles, each acting at a different place, so that a mechanical problem resolves itself, strictly speaking, into an infinite number of distinct problems. We owe to Archimedes the first introduction of the beautiful idea that one point may be discovered in a gravitating body such that the weight of all the particles may be regarded as concentrated in that point, and yet the behaviour of the whole body will be exactly represented by the behaviour of this heavy point. This Centre of Gravity may be within the body, as in the case of a sphere, or it may be in empty space, as in the case of a ring. Any two bodies, whether connected or separate, may be conceived

---

[1] Herschel's *Essays*, &c. pp. 404, 405.
[2] *On the Theory of Errors of Observations, Cambridge Philosophical Transactions*, vol. x. Part ii. 416.

as having a centre of gravity, that of the sun and earth lying within the sun and only 267 miles from its centre.

Although we most commonly use the notion of a centre or average point with regard to gravity, the same notion is applicable to other cases. Terrestrial gravity is a case of approximately parallel forces, and the centre of gravity is but a special case of the more general Centre of Parallel Forces. Wherever a number of forces of whatever amount act in parallel lines, it is possible to discover a point at which the algebraic sum of the forces may be imagined to act with exactly the same effect. Water in a cistern presses against the side with a pressure varying according to the depth, but always in a direction perpendicular to the side. We may then conceive the whole pressure as exerted on one point, which will be one-third from the bottom of the cistern, and may be called the Centre of Pressure. The Centre of Oscillation of a pendulum, discovered by Huyghens, is that point at which the whole weight of the pendulum may be considered as concentrated, without altering the time of oscillation (p. 315). When one body strikes another the Centre of Percussion is that point in the striking body at which all its mass might be concentrated without altering the effect of the stroke. In position the Centre of Percussion does not differ from the Centre of Oscillation. Mathematicians have also described the Centre of Gyration, the Centre of Conversion, the Centre of Friction, &c.

We ought carefully to distinguish between those cases in which an *invariable* centre can be assigned, and those in which it cannot. In perfect strictness, there is no such thing as a true invariable centre of gravity. As a general rule a body is capable of possessing an invariable centre only for perfectly parallel forces, and gravity never does act in absolutely parallel lines. Thus, as usual, we find that our conceptions are only hypothetically correct, and only approximately applicable to real circumstances. There are indeed certain geometrical forms called *Centrobaric*,[1] such that a body of that shape would attract another exactly as if the mass were concentrated at the centre of gravity, whether the forces act in a parallel manner or not.

[1] Thomson and Tait, *Treatise on Natural Philosophy*, vol. i. p. 394.

Newton showed that uniform spheres of matter have this property, and this truth proved of the greatest importance in simplifying his calculations.   But it is after all a purely hypothetical truth, because we can nowhere meet with, nor can we construct, a perfectly spherical and homogeneous body.   The slightest irregularity or protrusion from the surface will destroy the rigorous correctness of the assumption.   The spheroid, on the other hand, has no invariable centre at which its mass may always be regarded as concentrated.   The point from which its resultant attraction acts will move about according to the distance and position of the other attracting body, and it will only coincide with the centre as regards an infinitely distant body whose attractive forces may be considered as acting in parallel lines.

Physicists speak familiarly of the poles of a magnet, and the term may be used with convenience.   But, if we attach any definite meaning to the word, the poles are not the ends of the magnet, nor any fixed points within, but the variable points from which the resultants of all the forces exerted by the particles in the bar upon exterior magnetic particles may be considered as acting.   The poles are, in short, Centres of Magnetic Forces; but as those forces are never really parallel, these centres will vary in position according to the relative place of the object attracted. Only when we regard the magnet as attracting a very distant, or, strictly speaking, infinitely distant particle, do its centres become fixed points, situated in short magnets approximately at one-sixth of the whole length from each end of the bar.   We have in the above instances of centres or poles of force sufficient examples of the mode in which the Fictitious Mean or Average is employed in physical science.

The Precise Mean Result.

We now turn to that mode of employing the mean result which is analogous to the method of reversal, but which is brought into practice in a most extensive manner throughout many branches of physical science.   We find the simplest possible case in the determination of the latitude of a place by observations of the Pole-star.   Tycho

Brahe suggested that if the elevation of any circumpolar
star were observed at its higher and lower passages across
the meridian, half the sum of the elevations would be the
latitude of the place, which is equal to the height of the
pole. Such a star is as much above the pole at its highest
passage, as it is below at its lowest, so that the mean must
necessarily give the height of the pole itself free from
doubt, except as regards incidental errors. The Pole-star
is usually selected for the purpose of such observations
because it describes the smallest circle, and is thus on the
whole least affected by atmospheric refraction.

Whenever several causes are in action, each of which at
one time increases and at another time decreases the joint
effect by equal quantities, we may apply this method and
disentangle the effects. Thus the solar and lunar tides
roll on in almost complete independence of each other.
When the moon is new or full the solar tide coincides, or
nearly so, with that caused by the moon, and the joint
effect is the sum of the separate effects. When the moon
is in quadrature, or half full, the two tides are acting in
opposition, one raising and the other depressing the water,
so that we observe only the difference of the effects. We
have in fact—

Spring tide = lunar tide + solar tide ;
Neap tide = lunar tide − solar tide.

We have only then to add together the heights of the
maximum spring tide and the minimum neap tide, and
half the sum is the true height of the lunar tide. Half
the difference of the spring and neap tides on the other
hand gives the solar tide.

Effects of very small amount may be detected with
great approach to certainty among much greater fluctuations, provided that we have a series of observations suf-
ciently numerous and long continued to enable us to
balance all the larger effects against each other. For this
purpose the observations should be continued over at least
one complete cycle, in which the effects run through all
their variations, and return exactly to the same relative
positions as at the commencement. If casual or irregular
disturbing causes exist, we should probably require many
such cycles of results to render their effect inappreciable.
We obtain the desired result by taking the mean of all the

observations in which a cause acts positively, and the mean of all in which it acts negatively. Half the difference of these means will give the effect of the cause in question, provided that no other effect happens to vary in the same period or nearly so.

Since the moon causes a movement of the ocean, it is evident that its attraction must have some effect upon the atmosphere. The laws of atmospheric tides were investigated by Laplace, but as it would be impracticable by theory to calculate their amounts we can only determine them by observation, as Laplace predicted that they would one day be determined.[1] But the oscillations of the barometer thus caused are far smaller than the oscillations due to several other causes. Storms, hurricanes, or changes of weather produce movements of the barometer sometimes as much as a thousand times as great as the tides in question. There are also regular daily, yearly, or other fluctuations, all greater than the desired quantity. To detect and measure the atmospheric tide it was desirable that observations should be made in a place as free as possible from irregular disturbances. On this account several long series of observations were made at St. Helena, where the barometer is far more regular in its movements than in a continental climate. The effect of the moon's attraction was then detected by taking the mean of all the readings when the moon was on the meridian and the similar mean when she was on the horizon. The difference of these means was found to be only ·00365, yet it was possible to discover even the variation of this tide according as the moon was nearer to or further from the earth, though this difference was only ·00056 inch.[2] It is quite evident that such minute effects could never be discovered in a purely empirical manner. Having no information but the series of observations before us, we could have no clue as to the mode of grouping them which would give so small a difference. In applying this method of means in an extensive manner we must generally then have à priori knowledge as to the periods at which a cause will act in one direction or the other.

---

[1] *Essai Philosophique sur les Probabilités*, pp. 49, 50.
[2] Grant, *History of Physical Astronomy*, p. 163.

We are sometimes able to eliminate fluctuations and take a mean result by purely mechanical arrangements. The daily variations of temperature, for instance, become imperceptible one or two feet below the surface of the earth, so that a thermometer placed with its bulb at that depth gives very nearly the true daily mean temperature. At a depth of twenty feet even the yearly fluctuations are nearly effaced, and the thermometer stands a little above the true mean temperature of the locality. In registering the rise and fall of the tide by a tide-gauge, it is desirable to avoid the oscillations arising from surface waves, which is very readily accomplished by placing the float in a cistern communicating by a small hole with the sea. Only a general rise or fall of the level is then perceptible, just as in the marine barometer the narrow tube prevents any casual fluctuations and allows only a continued change of pressure to manifest itself.

Determination of the Zero point.

In many important observations the chief difficulty consists in defining exactly the zero point from which we are to measure. We can point a telescope with great precision to a star and can measure to a second of arc the angle through which the telescope is raised or lowered; but all this precision will be useless unless we know exactly the centre point of the heavens from which we measure, or, what comes to the same thing, the horizontal line 90° distant from it. Since the true horizon has reference to the figure of the earth at the place of observation, we can only determine it by the direction of gravity, as marked either by the plumb-line or the surface of a liquid. The question resolves itself then into the most accurate mode of observing the direction of gravity, and as the plumb-line has long been found hopelessly inaccurate, astronomers generally employ the surface of mercury in repose as the criterion of horizontality. They ingeniously observe the direction of the surface by making a star the index. From the laws of reflection it follows that the angle between the direct ray from a star and that reflected from a surface of mercury will be exactly double the angle between the surface and the direct ray from the star. Hence the horizontal or zero point is the mean between the apparent place of any star or other very distant object and its reflection in mercury.

A plumb-line is perpendicular, or a liquid surface is horizontal only in an approximate sense; for any irregularity of the surface of the earth, a mountain, or even a house must cause some deviation by its attracting power. To detect such deviation might seem very difficult, because every other plumb-line or liquid surface would be equally affected by gravity. Nevertheless it can be detected; for if we place one plumb-line to the north of a mountain, and another to the south, they will be about equally deflected in opposite directions, and if by observations of the same star we can measure the angle between the plumb-lines, half the inclination will be the deviation of either, after allowance has been made for the inclination due to the difference of latitude of the two places of observation. By this mode of observation applied to the mountain Schiehallion the deviation of the plumb-line was accurately measured by Maskelyne, and thus a comparison instituted between the attractive forces of the mountain and the whole globe, which led to a probable estimate of the earth's density.

In some cases it is actually better to determine the zero point by the average of equally diverging quantities than by direct observation. In delicate weighings by a chemical balance it is requisite to ascertain exactly the point at which the beam comes to rest, and when standard weights are being compared the position of the beam is ascertained by a carefully divided scale viewed through a microscope. But when the beam is just coming to rest, friction, small impediments or other accidental causes may readily obstruct it, because it is near the point at which the force of stability becomes infinitely small. Hence it is found better to let the beam vibrate and observe the terminal points of the vibrations. The mean between two extreme points will nearly indicate the position of rest. Friction and the resistance of air tend to reduce the vibrations, so that this mean will be erroneous by half the amount of this effect during a half vibration. But by taking several observations we may determine this retardation and allow for it. Thus if a, b, c be the readings of the terminal

points of three excursions of the beam from the zero of the
scale, then $\frac{1}{2}(a + b)$ will be about as much erroneous in
one direction as $\frac{1}{2}(b + c)$ in the other, so that the mean
of these two means, or $\frac{1}{4}(a + 2b + c)$, will be exceedingly
near to the point of rest.[1]   A still closer approximation
may be made by taking four readings and reducing them
by the formula $\frac{1}{6}(a + 2b + 2c + d)$.

The accuracy of Baily's experiments, directed to determine the density of the earth, entirely depended upon this
mode of observing oscillations.   The balls whose gravitation was measured were so delicately suspended by a
torsion balance that they never came to rest.   The extreme
points of the oscillations were observed both when the
heavy leaden attracting ball was on one side and on the
other.   The difference of the mean points when the leaden
ball was on the right hand and that when it was on the
left hand gave double the amount of the deflection.

A beautiful instance of avoiding the use of a zero point
is found in Mr. E. J. Stone's observations on the radiant
heat of the fixed stars.   The difficulty of these observations
arose from the comparatively great amounts of heat which
were sent into the telescope from the atmosphere, and which
were sufficient to disguise almost entirely the feeble heat
rays of a star.   But Mr. Stone fixed at the focus of his
telescope a double thermo-electric pile of which the two
parts were reversed in order.   Now any disturbance of
temperature which acted uniformly upon both piles produced no effect upon the galvanometer needle, and when
the rays of the star were made to fall alternately upon
one pile and the other, the total amount of the deflection
represented double the heating power of the star.   Thus
Mr. Stone was able to detect with much certainty a heating
effect of the star Arcturus, which even when concentrated
by the telescope amounted only to $0°.02$ Fahr., and which
represents a heating effect of the direct ray of only about
$0°.0000137$ Fahr., equivalent to the heat which would be
received from a three-inch cubic vessel full of boiling
water at the distance of 400 yards.[2]   It is probable that

[1] Gauss, Taylor's *Scientific Memoirs*, vol. ii. p. 43, &c.
[2] *Proceedings of the Royal Society*, vol. xviii. p. 159 (Jan. 13, 1870).
Philosophical Magazine (4th Series), vol. xxxix. p. 376.

Mr. Stone's arrangement of the pile might be usefully employed in other delicate thermometric experiments subject to considerable disturbing influences.

Determination of Maximum Points.

We employ the method of means in a certain number of observations directed to determine the moment at which a phenomenon reaches its highest point in quantity. In noting the place of a fixed star at a given time there is no difficulty in ascertaining the point to be observed, for a star in a good telescope presents an exceedingly small disc. In observing a nebulous body which from a bright centre fades gradually away on all sides, it will not be possible to select with certainty the middle point. In many such cases the best method is not to select arbitrarily the supposed middle point, but points of equal brightness on either side, and then take the mean of the observations of these two points for the centre. As a general rule, a variable quantity in reaching its maximum increases at a less and less rate, and after passing the highest point begins to decrease by insensible degrees. The maximum may indeed be defined as that point at which the increase or decrease is null. Hence it will usually be the most indefinite point, and if we can accurately measure the phenomenon we shall best determine the place of the maximum by determining points on either side at which the ordinates are equal. There is moreover this advantage in the method that several points may be determined with the corresponding ones on the other side, and the mean of the whole taken as the true place of the maximum. But this method entirely depends upon the existence of symmetry in the curve, so that of two equal ordinates one shall be as far on one side of the maximum as the other is on the other side. The method fails when other laws of variation prevail.

In tidal observations great difficulty is encountered in fixing the moment of high water, because the rate at which the water is then rising or falling, is almost imperceptible. Whewell proposed, therefore, to note the time at which the water passes a fixed point somewhat below the maximum both in rising and falling, and take the mean time as that of high water. But this mode of proceeding unfortunately does not give a correct result, because the tide follows different laws in rising and in falling. There is a difficulty again in selecting the highest spring tide, another object of much importance in tidology. Laplace discovered that the tide of the second day preceding the conjunction of the sun and moon is nearly equal to that of the fifth day following; and, believing that the increase and decrease of the tides proceeded in a nearly symmetrical manner, he decided that the highest tide would occur about thirty-six hours after the conjunction, that is half-way between the second day before and the fifth day after.[1]

This method is also employed in determining the time of passage of the middle or densest point of a stream of meteors. The earth takes two or three days in passing completely through the November stream; but astronomers need for their calculations to have some definite point fixed within a few minutes if possible. When near to the middle they observe the numbers of meteors which come within the sphere of vision in each half hour, or quarter hour, and then, assuming that the law of variation is symmetrical, they select a moment for the passage of the centre equidistant between times of equal frequency.

The eclipses of Jupiter's satellites are not only of great interest as regards the motions of the satellites themselves, but were, and perhaps still are, of use in determining longitudes, because they are events occurring at fixed moments of absolute time, and visible in all parts of the planetary system at the same time, allowance being made for the interval occupied by the light in travelling. But, as is explained by Herschel,[2] the moment of the event is wanting in definiteness, partly because the long cone of Jupiter's shadow is surrounded by a penumbra, and partly because the satellite has itself a sensible disc, and takes time in entering the shadow. Different observers using different telescopes would usually select different moments for that of the eclipse. But the increase of light in the emersion will proceed according to a law the reverse of that observed in the immersion, so that if an observer notes

[1] Airy On Tides and Waves, Encycl. Metrop. pp. 364*—366*.
[2] Outlines of Astronomy, 4th edition, § 538.

the time of both events with the same telescope, he will be
as much too soon in one observation as he is too late in the
other, and the mean moment of the two observations will
represent with considerable accuracy the time when the
satellite is in the middle of the shadow.   Error of judgment of the observer is thus eliminated, provided that
he takes care to act at the emersion as he did at the
immersion.

CHAPTER XVII.

THE LAW OF ERROR.

To bring error itself under law might seem beyond human power. He who errs surely diverges from law, and it might be deemed hopeless out of error to draw truth. One of the most remarkable achievements of the human intellect is the establishment of a general theory which not only enables us among discrepant results to approximate to the truth, but to assign the degree of probability which fairly attaches to this conclusion. It would be a mistake indeed to suppose that this law is necessarily the best guide under all circumstances. Every measuring instrument and every form of experiment may have its own special law of error ; there may in one instrument be a tendency in one direction and in another in the opposite direction. Every process has its peculiar liabilities to disturbance, and we are never relieved from the necessity of providing against special difficulties. The general Law of Error is the best guide only when we have exhausted all other means of approximation, and still find discrepancies, which are due to unknown causes. We must treat such residual differences in some way or other, since they will occur in all accurate experiments, and as their origin is assumed to be unknown, there is no reason why we should treat them differently in different cases. Accordingly the ultimate Law of Error must be a uniform and general one.

It is perfectly recognised by mathematicians that in each case a special Law of Error may exist, and should be discovered if possible. "Nothing can be more unlikely than that the errors committed in all classes of observa-

tions should follow the same law," [1] and the special Laws
of Error which will apply to certain instruments, as for instance the repeating circle, have been investigated by
Bravais.[2] He concludes that every distinct cause of error
gives rise to a curve of possibility of errors, which may
have any form,—a curve which we may either be able or
unable to discover, and which in the first case may be
determined by *à priori* considerations on the peculiar
nature of this cause, or which may be determined *à
posteriori* by observation. Whenever it is practicable and
worth the labour, we ought to investigate these special
conditions of error ; nevertheless, when there are a great
number of different sources of minute error, the general
resultant will always tend to obey that general law which
we are about to consider.

Establishment of the Law of Error.

Mathematicians agree far better as to the form of the
Law of Error than they do as to the manner in which it
can be deduced and proved. They agree that among a
number of discrepant results of observation, that mean
quantity is probably the best approximation to the truth
which makes the sum of the squares of the errors as small
as possible. But there are three principal ways in which
this law has been arrived at respectively by Gauss, by
Laplace and Quetelet, and by Sir John Herschel. Gauss
proceeds much upon assumption ; Herschel rests upon
geometrical considerations ; while Laplace and Quetelet
regard the Law of Error as a development of the doctrine
of combinations. A number of other mathematicians, such
as Adrain of New Brunswick, Bessel, Ivory, Donkin, Leslie
Ellis, Tait, and Crofton have either attempted independent
proofs or have modified or commented on those here to be
described. For full accounts of the literature of the
subject the reader should refer either to Mr. Todhunter's
History of the Theory of Probability or to the able memoir
of Mr. J. W. L. Glaisher.[3]

[1] *Philosophical Magazine*, 3rd Series, vol. xxxvii. p. 324.
[2] *Letters on the Theory of Probabilities*, by Quetelet, translated by
O. G. Downes, Notes to Letter XXVI. pp. 286—295.
[3] *On the Law of Facility of Errors of Observations, and on the
Method of Least Squares*, Memoirs of the Royal Astronomical Society,
vol. xxxix. p. 75.

According to Gauss the Law of Error expresses the comparative probability of errors of various magnitude, and partly from experience, partly from à *priori* considerations, we may readily lay down certain conditions to which the law will certainly conform. It may fairly be assumed as a first principle to guide us in the selection of the law, that large errors will be far less frequent and probable than small ones. We know that very large errors are almost impossible, so that the probability must rapidly decrease as the amount of the error increases. A second principle is that positive and negative errors shall be equally probable, which may certainly be assumed, because we are supposed to be devoid of any knowledge as to the causes of the residual errors. It follows that the probability of the error must be a function of an even power of the magnitude, that is of the square, or the fourth power, or the sixth power, otherwise the probability of the same amount of error would vary according as the error was positive or negative. The even powers x^2, x^4, x^6, &c., are always intrinsically positive, whether x be positive or negative. There is no à *priori* reason why one rather than another of these even powers should be selected. Gauss himself allows that the fourth or sixth power would fulfil the conditions as well as the second;[1] but in the absence of any theoretical reasons we should prefer the second power, because it leads to formulæ of great comparative simplicity. Did the Law of Error necessitate the use of the higher powers of the error, the complexity of the necessary calculations would much reduce the utility of the theory.

By mathematical reasoning which it would be undesirable to attempt to follow in this book, it is shown that under these conditions, the facility of occurrence, or in other words, the probability of error is expressed by a function of the general form $\epsilon^{-h^2 x^2}$, in which x represents the variable amount of errors. From this law, to be more fully described in the following sections, it at once follows that the most probable result of any observa-

---

[1] *Méthode des Moindres Carrés. Mémoires sur la Combinaison des Observations, par Ch. Fr. Gauss. Traduit en Français par J. Bertrand*, Paris, 1855, pp. 6, 133, &c.

tions is that which makes the sum of the squares of
the consequent errors the least possible. Let a, b, c,
&c., be the results of observation, and x the quantity
selected as the most probable, that is the most free
from unknown errors : then we must determine x so that
$(a - x)^2 + (b - x)^2 + (c - x)^2 + \ldots$ shall be the least
possible quantity. Thus we arrive at the celebrated
Method of Least Squares, as it is usually called, which
appears to have been first distinctly put in practice by
Gauss in 1795, while Legendre first published in 1806 an
account of the process in his work, entitled, *Nouvelles
Méthodes pour la Détermination des Orbites des Comètes*. It
is worthy of notice, however, that Roger Cotes had long
previously recommended a method of equivalent nature in
his tract, " Estimatio Erroris in Mixta Mathesi." [1]

Herschel's Geometrical Proof.

A second way of arriving at the Law of Error was
proposed by Herschel, and although only applicable to
geometrical cases, it is remarkable as showing that from
whatever point of view we regard the subject, the same
principle will be detected. After assuming that some
general law must exist, and that it is subject to the
principles of probability, he supposes that a ball is
dropped from a high point with the intention that it
shall strike a given mark on a horizontal plane. In the
absence of any known causes of deviation it will either
strike that mark, or, as is infinitely more probable, diverge
from it by an amount which we must regard as error of
unknown origin. Now, to quote the words of Herschel,[2]
" the probability of that error is the unknown function of
its square, *i.e.* of the sum of the squares of its deviations in
any two rectangular directions. Now, the probability of
any deviation depending solely on its magnitude, and not
on its direction, it follows that the probability of each of
these rectangular deviations must be the same function of
its square. And since the observed oblique deviation is

---

[1] De Morgan, *Penny Cyclopædia*, art. *Least Squares*.
[2] *Edinburgh Review*, July 1850, vol. xcii. p. 17. Reprinted *Essays*,
p. 399. This method of demonstration is discussed by Boole, *Transactions of Royal Society of Edinburgh*, vol. xxi. pp. 627—630.

equivalent to the two rectangular ones, supposed concurrent, and which are essentially independent of one another, and is, therefore, a compound event of which they are the simple independent constituents, therefore its probability will be the product of their separate probabilities. Thus the form of our unknown function comes to be determined from this condition, viz., that the product of such functions of two independent elements is equal to the same function of their sum. But it is shown in every work on algebra that this property is the peculiar characteristic of, and belongs only to, the exponential or antilogarithmic function. This, then, is the function of the square of the error, which expresses the probability of committing that error. That probability decreases, therefore, in geometrical progression, as the square of the error increases in arithmetical."

Laplace's and Quetelet's Proof of the Law.

However much presumption the modes of determining the Law of Error, already described, may give in favour of the law usually adopted, it is difficult to feel that the arguments are satisfactory. The law adopted is chosen rather on the grounds of convenience and plausibility, than because it can be seen to be the necessary law. We can however approach the subject from an entirely different point of view, and yet get to the same result.

Let us assume that a particular observation is subject to four chances of error, each of which will increase the result one inch if it occurs. Each of these errors is to be regarded as an event independent of the rest and we can therefore assign, by the theory of probability, the comparative probability and frequency of each conjunction of errors. From the Arithmetical Triangle (pp. 182-188) we learn that no error at all can happen only in one way ; an error of one inch can happen in 4 ways ; and the ways of happening of errors of 2, 3 and 4 inches respectively, will be 6, 4 and 1 in number.

We may infer that the error of two inches is the most likely to occur, and will occur in the long run in six cases out of sixteen. Errors of one and three inches will be equally likely, but will occur less frequently ; while no error at all or one of four inches will be a comparatively

rare occurrence. If we now suppose the errors to act as
often in one direction as the other, the effect will be to
alter the average error by the amount of two inches, and
we shall have the following results :—

     Negative error of 2 inches. . . . . 1 way
     Negative error of 1 inch . . . . . 4 ways.
     No error at all . . . . 6 ways.
     Positive error of 1 inch . . . . . . 4 ways.
     Positive error of 2 inches . . . . . 1 way.

We may now imagine the number of causes of error
increased and the amount of each error decreased, and the
arithmetical triangle will give us the frequency of the resulting errors. Thus if there be five positive causes of
error and five negative causes, the following table shows
the numbers of errors of various amount which will be the
result :—

Direction of Error.	Positive Error.		Negative Error.
Amount of Error.	5, 4, 3, 2, 1	0	1, 2, 3, 4, 5
Number of such Errors.	1, 10, 45, 120, 210	252	210, 120, 45, 10, 1

It is plain that from such numbers I can ascertain
the probability of any particular amount of error under
the conditions supposed. The probability of a positive
error of exactly one inch is $\frac{210}{1024}$, in which fraction the
numerator is the number of combinations giving one
inch positive error, and the denominator the whole
number of possible errors of all magnitudes. I can also,
by adding together the appropriate numbers get the probability of an error not exceeding a certain amount. Thus
the probability of an error of three inches or less, positive
or negative, is a fraction whose numerator is the sum of
45 + 120 + 210 + 252 + 210 + 120 + 45, and the deno-
minator, as before, giving the result $\frac{1002}{1024}$. We may see at
once that, according to these principles, the probability of
small errors is far greater than of large ones : the odds are
1002 to 22, or more than 45 to 1 that the error will not

exceed three inches ; and the odds are 1022 to 2 against
the occurrence of the greatest possible error of five inches.

If any case should arise in which the observer knows
the number and magnitude of the chief errors which
may occur, he ought certainly to calculate from the Arithmetical Triangle the special Law of Error which would
apply. But the general law, of which we are in search,
is to be used in the dark, when we have no knowledge
whatever of the sources of error. To assume any special
number of causes of error is then an arbitrary proceeding,
and mathematicians have chosen the least arbitrary course
of imagining the existence of an infinite number of infinitely small errors, just as, in the inverse method of
probabilities, an infinite number of infinitely improbable
hypotheses were submitted to calculation (p. 255).
The reasons in favour of this choice are of several
different kinds.

1. It cannot be denied that there may exist infinitely
numerous causes of error in any act of observation.

2. The law resulting from the hypothesis of a moderate
number of causes of error, does not appreciably differ from
that given by the hypothesis of an infinite number of
causes of error.

3. We gain by the hypothesis of infinity a general law
capable of ready calculation, and applicable by uniform
rules to all problems.

4. This law, when tested by comparison with extensive
series of observations, is strikingly verified, as will be
shown in a later section.

When we imagine the existence of any large number of
causes of error, for instance one hundred, the numbers of
combinations become impracticably large, as may be seen
to be the case from a glance at the Arithmetical Triangle,
which proceeds only up to the seventeenth line. Quetelet,
by suitable abbreviating processes, calculated out a table
of probability of errors on the hypothesis of one thousand
distinct causes ;[1] but mathematicians have generally
proceeded on the hypothesis of infinity, and then, by the
devices of analysis, have substituted a general law of easy

[1] *Letters on the Theory of Probabilities*, Letter XV. and Appendix,
note pp. 256 -266.

treatment. In mathematical works upon the subject, it is shown that the standard Law of Error is expressed in the formula

$$y = Y \epsilon^{-cx^2},$$

in which x is the amount of the error, Y the maximum ordinate of the curve of error, and c a number constant for each series of observations, and expressing the amount of the tendency to error, varying between one series of observations and another. The letter ϵ is the mathematical constant, the sum of ratios between the numbers of permutations and combinations, previously referred to (p. 330).

To show the close correspondence of this general law with the special law which might be derived from the supposition of a moderate number of causes of error, I have in the accompanying figure drawn a

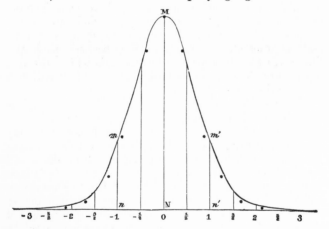

curved line representing accurately the variation of y when x in the above formula is taken equal 0, $\frac{1}{2}$, 1, $\frac{3}{2}$, 2, &c., positive or negative, the arbitrary quantites Y and c being each assumed equal to unity, in order to simplify the calculations. In the same figure are inserted eleven dots, whose heights above the base line are proportional to the numbers in the eleventh line of the Arithmetical Triangle, thus representing the comparative probabilities of errors of various amounts arising from ten equal causes

of error.   The correspondence of the general and the
special Law of Error is almost as close as can be exhibited
in the figure, and the assumption of a greater number of
equal causes of error would render the correspondence far
more close.

It may be explained that the ordinates NM, nm, $n'm'$,
represent values of y in the equation expressing the Law
of Error.   The occurrence of any one definite amount of
error is infinitely improbable, because an infinite number
of such ordinates might be drawn.   But the probability of
an error occurring between certain limits is finite, and is
represented by a portion of the *area* of the curve.   Thus the
probability that an error, positive or negative, not exceeding unity will occur, is represented by the area M$mnn'm'$,
in short, by the area standing upon the line nn'.
Since every observation must either have some definite
error or none at all, it follows that the whole area of the
curve should be considered as the unit expressing certainty,
and the probability of an error falling between particular
limits will then be expressed by the ratio which the area
of the curve between those limits bears to the whole area
of the curve.

The mere fact that the Law of Error allows of the possible existence of errors of every assignable amount shows
that it is only approximately true.   We may fairly say
that in measuring a mile it would be impossible to commit
an error of a hundred miles, and the length of life would
never allow of our committing an error of one million
miles.   Nevertheless the general Law of Error would assign
a probability for an error of that amount or more, but so
small a probability as to be utterly inconsiderable and
almost inconceivable.   All that can, or in fact need, be
said in defence of the law is, that it may be made to represent the errors in any special case to a very close
approximation, and that the probability of large and practically impossible errors, as given by the law, will be so
small as to be entirely inconsiderable.   And as we are
dealing with error itself, and our results pretend to nothing
more than approximation and probability, an indefinitely
small error in our process of approximation is of no importance whatever.

Logical Origin of the Law of Error.

It is worthy of notice that this Law of Error, abstruse though the subject may seem, is really founded upon the simplest principles. It arises entirely out of the difference between permutations and combinations, a subject upon which I may seem to have dwelt with unnecessary prolixity in previous pages (pp. 170, 189). The order in which we add quantities together does not affect the amount of the sum, so that if there be three positive and five negative causes of error in operation, it does not matter in which order they are considered as acting. They may be intermixed in any arrangement, and yet the result will be the same. The reader should not fail to notice how laws or principles which appeared to be absurdly simple and evident when first noticed, reappear in the most complicated and mysterious processes of scientific method. The fundamental Laws of Identity and Difference gave rise to the Logical Alphabet which, after abstracting the character of the differences, led to the Arithmetical Triangle. The Law of Error is defined by an infinitely high line of that triangle, and the law proves that the mean is the most probable result, and that divergencies from the mean become much less probable as they increase in amount. Now the comparative greatness of the numbers towards the middle of each line of the Arithmetical Triangle is entirely due to the indifference of order in space or time, which was first prominently pointed out as a condition of logical relations, and the symbols indicating them (pp. 32-35), and which was afterwards shown to attach equally to numerical symbols, the derivatives of logical terms (p. 160).

Verification of the Law of Error.

The theory of error which we have been considering rests entirely upon an assumption, namely that when known sources of disturbances are allowed for, there yet remain an indefinite, possibly an infinite number of other minute sources of error, which will as often produce excess as deficiency. Granting this assumption, the Law of Error must be as it is usually taken to be, and there is no more need to verify it empirically than to test the truth of one of Euclid's propositions mechanically. Nevertheless, it is an interesting occupation to verify even the propositions of geometry, and it is still more instructive to try whether a large number of observations will justify our assumption of the Law of Error.

Encke has given an excellent instance of the correspondence of theory with experience, in the case of observations of the differences of Right Ascension of the sun and two stars, namely *a* Aquilæ and *a* Canis minoris. The observations were 470 in number, and were made by Bradley and reduced by Bessel, who found the probable error of the final result to be only about one-fourth part of a second (0·2637). He then compared the numbers of errors of each magnitude from 0·1 second upwards, as actually given by the observations, with what should occur according to the Law of Error.

The results were as follow :—[1]

Magnitude of the errors in parts of a second.	Number of errors of each magnitude according to	
	Observation.	Theory.
0·0 to 0·1	94	95
·1 ,, ·2	88	89
·2 ,, ·3	78	78
·3 ,, ·4	58	64
·4 ,, ·5	51	50
·5 ,, ·6	36	36
·6 ,, ·7	26	24
·7 ,, ·8	14	15
·8 ,, ·9	10	9
·9 ,, 1·0	7	5
above 1·0	8	5

The reader will remark that the correspondence is very close, except as regards larger errors, which are excessive in practice. It is one objection, indeed, to the theory of error, that, being expressed in a continuous mathematical function, it contemplates the existence of errors of every magnitude, such as could not practically occur; yet in this case the theory seems to under-estimate the number of large errors.

[1] Encke, *On the Method of Least Squares,* Taylor's *Scientific Memoirs,* vol. ii. pp. 338, 339.

Another comparison of the law with observation was made by Quetelet, who investigated the errors of 487 determinations in time of the Right Ascension of the Pole-Star made at Greenwich during the four years 1836–39. These observations, although carefully corrected for all known causes of error, as well as for nutation, precession, &c., are yet of course found to differ, and being classified as regards intervals of one-half second of time, and then proportionately increased in number, so that their sum may be one thousand, give the following results as compared with what Quetelet's theory would lead us to expect :— [1]

Magnitude of error in tenths of a second.	Number of Errors		Magnitude of error in tenths of a second.	Number of errors	
	by Observation.	by Theory.		by Observation.	by Theory.
0·0	168	163	—	—	—
+ 0·5	148	147	—0·5	150	152
+ 1·0	129	112	—1·0	126	121
+ 1·5	78	72	—1·5	74	82
+ 2·0	33	40	—2·0	43	46
+ 2·5	10	19	—2·5	25	22
+ 3·0	2	10	—3·0	12	10
—	—	—	—3·5	2	4

In this instance also the correspondence is satisfactory, but the divergence between theory and fact is in the opposite direction to that discovered in the former comparison, the larger errors being less frequent than theory would indicate. It will be noticed that Quetelet's theoretical results are not symmetrical.

The Probable Mean Result.

One immediate result of the Law of Error, as thus stated, is that the mean result is the most probable one ; and when there is only a single variable this mean is found by the familiar arithmetical process. An unfortunate error has crept into several works which allude to this subject. Mill, in treating of the " Elimination of Chance," remarks in a note [2] that " the mean is spoken of

---

[1] Quetelet, *Letters on the Theory of Probabilities,* translated by Downes, Letter XIX. p. 88. See also Galton's *Hereditary Genius,* p. 379.

[2] *System of Logic,* bk. iii. chap. 17, § 3. 5th ed. vol. ii. p. 56.

as if it were exactly the same thing as the average. But the mean, for purposes of inductive inquiry, is not the average, or arithmetical mean, though in a familiar illustration of the theory the difference may be disregarded." He goes on to say that, according to mathematical principles, the most probable result is that for which the sums of the squares of the deviations is the least possible. It seems probable that Mill and other writers were misled by Whewell, who says [1] that "The method of least squares is in fact a method of means, but with some peculiar characters. . . . The method proceeds upon this supposition : that all errors are not equally probable, but that small errors are more probable than large ones." He adds that this method "removes much that is arbitrary in the method of means." It is strange to find a mathematician like Whewell making such remarks, when there is no doubt whatever that the Method of Means is only an application of the Method of Least Squares. They are, in fact, the same method, except that the latter method may be applied to cases where two or more quantities have to be determined at the same time. Lubbock and Drinkwater say,[2] "If only one quantity has to be determined, this method evidently resolves itself into taking the mean of all the values given by observation." Encke says,[3] that the expression for the probability of an error "not only contains in itself the principle of the arithmetical mean, but depends so immediately upon it, that for all those magnitudes for which the arithmetical mean holds good in the simple cases in which it is principally applied, no other law of probability can be assumed than that which is expressed by this formula."

The Probable Error of Results.

When we draw a conclusion from the numerical results of observations we ought not to consider it sufficient, in cases of importance, to content ourselves with finding the simple mean and treating it as true. We ought also to ascertain what is the degree of confidence

[1] *Philosophy of the Inductive Sciences*, 2nd ed. vol. ii. pp. 408, 409.
[2] *Essay on Probability*, Useful Knowledge Society, 1833, p. 41.
[3] Taylor's *Scientific Memoirs*, vol. ii. p. 333.

we may place in this mean, and our confidence should be measured by the degree of concurrence of the observations from which it is derived. In some cases the mean may be approximately certain and accurate. In other cases it may really be worth little or nothing. The Law of Error enables us to give exact expression to the degree of confidence proper in any case; for it shows how to calculate the probability of a divergence of any amount from the mean, and we can thence ascertain the probability that the mean in question is within a certain distance from the true number. The *probable error* is taken by mathematicians to mean the limits within which it is as likely as not that the truth will fall. Thus if 5·45 be the mean of all the determinations of the density of the earth, and ·20 be approximately the probable error, the meaning is that the probability of the real density of the earth falling between 5·25 and 5·65 is $\frac{1}{2}$. Any other limits might have been selected at will. We might calculate the limits within which it was one hundred or one thousand to one that the truth would fall; but there is a convention to take the even odds one to one, as the quantity of probability of which the limits are to be estimated.

Many books on probability give rules for making the calculations, but as, in the progress of science, persons ought to become more familiar with these processes, I propose to repeat the rules here and illustrate their use. The calculations, when made in accordance with the directions, involve none but arithmetic or logarithmic operations.

The following are the rules for treating a mean result, so as thoroughly to ascertain its trustworthiness.

1. Draw the mean of all the observed results.

2. Find the excess or defect, that is, the error of each result from the mean.

3. Square each of these reputed errors.

4. Add together all these squares of the errors, which are of course all positive.

5. Divide by one less than the number of observations. This gives the *square of the mean error*.

6. Take the square root of the last result; it is the *mean error of a single observation*.

7. Divide now by the square root of the number of

observations, and we get the *mean error of the mean result*.

8. Lastly, multiply by the natural constant 0·6745 (or approximately by 0·674, or even by $\frac{2}{3}$), and we arrive at the *probable error of the mean result.*

Suppose, for instance, that five measurements of the height of a hill, by the barometer or otherwise, have given the numbers of feet as 293, 301, 306, 307, 313 ; we want to know the probable error of the mean, namely 304. Now the differences between this mean and the above numbers, *paying no regard to direction*, are 11, 3, 2, 3, 9 ; their squares are 121, 9, 4, 9, 81, and the sum of the squares of the errors consequently 224. The number of observations being 5, we divide by 1 less, or 4, getting 56. This is the square of the mean error, and taking its square root we have 7·48 (say 7½), the mean error of a single observation. Dividing by 2·236, the square root of 5, the number of observations, we find the mean error of the *mean result* to be 3·35, or say 3⅓, and lastly, multiplying by ·6745, we arrive at the *probable error of the mean result*, which is found to be 2·259, or say 2¼. The meaning of this is that the probability is one half, or the odds are even that the true height of the mountain lies between 301¾ and 306¼ feet. We have thus an exact measure of the degree of credibility of our mean result, which mean indicates the most likely point for the truth to fall upon.

The reader should observe that as the object in these calculations is only to gain a notion of the degree of confidence with which we view the mean, there is no real use in carrying the calculations to any great degree of precision ; and whenever the neglect of decimal fractions, or even the slight alteration of a number, will much abbreviate the computations, it may be fearlessly done, except in cases of high importance and precision. Brodie has shown how the law of error may be usefully applied in chemical investigations, and some illustrations of its employment may be found in his paper.[1]

The experiments of Benzenberg to detect the revolution of the earth, by the deviation of a ball from the perpen-

dicular line in falling down a deep pit, have been cited by
Encke [1] as an interesting illustration of the Law of Error.
The mean deviation was 5·086 lines, and its probable error
was calculated by Encke to be not more than ·950 line,
that is, the odds were even that the true result lay between
4·136 and 6·036. As the deviation, according to astronomical theory, should be 4·6 lines, which lies well within
the limits, we may consider that the experiments are
consistent with the Copernican system of the universe.

It will of course be understood that the probable error
has regard only to those causes of errors which in the long
run act as much in one direction as another; it takes no
account of constant errors. The true result accordingly
will often fall far beyond the limits of probable error, owing
to some considerable constant error or errors, of the existence of which we are unaware.

Rejection of the Mean Result.

We ought always to bear in mind that the mean of any
series of observations is the best, that is, the most probable
approximation to the truth, only in the absence of knowledge to the contrary. The selection of the mean rests
entirely upon the probability that unknown causes of error
will in the long run fall as often in one direction as the
opposite, so that in drawing the mean they will balance
each other. If we have any reason to suppose that there
exists a tendency to error in one direction rather than the
other, then to choose the mean would be to ignore that
tendency. We may certainly approximate to the length
of the circumference of a circle, by taking the mean of the
perimeters of inscribed and circumscribed polygons of an
equal and large number of sides. The length of the circular line undoubtedly lies between the lengths of the two
perimeters, but it does not follow that the mean is the
best approximation. It may in fact be shown that the
circumference of the circle is *very nearly* equal to the
perimeter of the inscribed polygon, together with one-third
part of the difference between the inscribed and circumscribed polygons of the same number of sides. Having

---

[1] Taylor's *Scientific Memoirs*, vol. ii. pp. 330, 347, &c.

this knowledge, we ought of course to act upon it, instead of trusting to probability.

We may often perceive that a series of measurements tends towards an extreme limit rather than towards a mean. In endeavouring to obtain a correct estimate of the apparent diameter of the brightest fixed stars, we find a continuous diminution in estimates as the powers of observation increased. Kepler assigned to Sirius an apparent diameter of 240 seconds; Tycho Brahe made it 126; Gassendi 10 seconds; Galileo, Hevelius, and J. Cassini, 5 or 6 seconds. Halley, Michell, and subsequently Sir W. Herschel came to the conclusion that the brightest stars in the heavens could not have real discs of a second, and were probably much less in diameter. It would of course be absurd to take the mean of quantities which differ more than 240 times; and as the tendency has always been to smaller estimates, there is a considerable presumption in favour of the smallest.[1]

In many experiments and measurements we know that there is a preponderating tendency to error in one direction. The readings of a thermometer tend to rise as the age of the instrument increases, and no drawing of means will correct this result. Barometers, on the other hand, are likely to read too low instead of too high, owing to the imperfection of the vacuum and the action of capillary attraction. If the mercury be perfectly pure and no appreciable error be due to the measuring apparatus, the best barometer will be that which gives the highest result. In determining the specific gravity of a solid body the chief danger of error arises from bubbles of air adhering to the body, which would tend to make the specific gravity too small. Much attention must always be given to one-sided errors of this kind, since the multiplication of experiments does not remove the error. In such cases one very careful experiment is better than any number of careless ones.

When we have reasonable grounds for supposing that certain experimental results are liable to grave errors, we should exclude them in drawing a mean. If we want to find the most probable approximation to the velocity of

[1] Quetelet, *Letters*, &c. p. 116.

sound in air, it would be absurd to go back to the old
experiments which made the velocity from 1200 to 1474
feet per second; for we know that the old observers did
not guard against errors arising from wind and other
causes. Old chemical experiments are valueless as regards quantitative results. The old chemists found the
atmosphere in different places to differ in composition
nearly ten per cent., whereas modern accurate experimenters find very slight variations. Any method of
measurement which we know to avoid a source of error
is far to be preferred to others which trust to probabilities
for the elimination of the error. As Flamsteed says,[1] " One
good instrument is of as much worth as a hundred indifferent ones." But an instrument is good or bad only in
a comparative sense, and no instrument gives invariable
and truthful results. Hence we must always ultimately
fall back upon probabilities for the selection of the final
mean, when other precautions are exhausted.

Legendre, the discoverer of the method of Least Squares,
recommended that observations differing very much from
the results of his method should be rejected. The subject
has been carefully investigated by Professor Pierce, who has
proposed a criterion for the rejection of doubtful observations based on the following principle: [2]—observations
should be rejected when the probability of the system of
errors obtained by retaining them is less than that of the
system of errors obtained by their rejection multiplied by
the probability of making so many and no more abnormal
observations." Professor Pierce's investigation is given
nearly in his own words in Professor W. Chauvenet's
"Manual of Spherical and Practical Astronomy," which
contains a full and excellent discussion of the methods of
treating numerical observations.[3]

Very difficult questions sometimes arise when one or
more results of a method of experiment diverge widely
from the mean of the rest. Are we or are we not to exclude them in adopting the supposed true mean result of
the method? The drawing of a mean result rests, as I

---

[1] Baily, *Account of Flamsteed,* p. 56.
[2] Gould's *Astronomical Journal,* Cambridge, Mass., vol. ii. p. 161.
[3] Philadelphia (London, Trübner) 1863. Appendix, vol. ii. p. 558.

have frequently explained, upon the assumption that every error acting in one direction will probably be balanced by other errors acting in an opposite direction. If then we know or can possibly discover any causes of error not agreeing with this assumption, we shall be justified in excluding results which seem to be affected by this cause.

In reducing large series of astronomical observations, it is not uncommon to meet with numbers differing from others by a whole degree or half a degree, or some considerable integral quantity. These are errors which could hardly arise in the act of observation or in instrumental irregularity; but they might readily be accounted for by misreading of figures or mistaking of division marks. It would be absurd to trust to chance that such mistakes would balance each other in the long run, and it is therefore better to correct arbitrarily the supposed mistake, or better still, if new observations can be made, to strike out the divergent numbers altogether. When results come sometimes too great or too small in a regular manner, we should suspect that some part of the instrument slips through a definite space, or that a definite cause of error enters at times, and not at others. We should then make it a point of prime importance to discover the exact nature and amount of such an error, and either prevent its occurrence for the future or else introduce a corresponding correction. In many researches the whole difficulty will consist in this detection and avoidance of sources of error. Professor Roscoe found that the presence of phosphorus caused serious and almost unavoidable errors in the determination of the atomic weight of vanadium.[1] Herschel, in reducing his observations of double stars at the Cape of Good Hope, was perplexed by an unaccountable difference of the angles of position as measured by the seven-feet equatorial and the twenty-feet reflector telescopes, and after a careful investigation was obliged to be contented with introducing a correction experimentally determined.[2]

When observations are sufficiently numerous it seems desirable to project the apparent errors into a curve, and then to observe whether this curve exhibits the symmet-

[1] Bakerian Lecture, *Philosophical Transactions* (1868), vol. clviii. p. 6.
[2] *Results of Observations at the Cape of Good Hope*, p. 283.

rical and characteristic form of the curve of error. If so,
it may be inferred that the errors arise from many minute
independent sources, and probably compensate each other
in the mean result. Any considerable irregularity will
indicate the existence of one-sided or large causes of error,
which should be made the subject of investigation.

Even the most patient and exhaustive investigations
will sometimes fail to disclose any reason why some
results diverge from others. The question again recurs—
Are we arbitrarily to exclude them ? The answer should
be in the negative as a general rule. The mere fact of
divergence ought not to be taken as conclusive against a
result, and the exertion of arbitrary choice would open
the way to the fatal influence of bias, and what is commonly known as the "cooking" of figures. It would
amount to judging fact by theory instead of theory by fact.
The apparently divergent number may prove in time to be
the true one. It may be an exception of that valuable
kind which upsets our false theories, a real exception,
exploding apparent coincidences, and opening a way to a
new view of the subject. To establish this position for
the divergent fact will require additional research ; but
in the meantime we should give it some weight in our
mean conclusions, and should bear in mind the discrepancy
as one demanding attention. To neglect a divergent result
is to neglect the possible clue to a great discovery.

Method of Least Squares.

When two or more unknown quantities are so involved
that they cannot be separately determined by the Simple
Method of Means, we can yet obtain their most probable
values by the Method of Least Squares, without more
difficulty than arises from the length of the arithmetical
computations. If the result of each observation gives an
equation between two unknown quantities of the form

$$ax + by = c'$$

then, if the observations were free from error, we should
need only two observations giving two equations; but for
the attainment of greater accuracy, we may take many observations, and reduce the equations so as to give only a
pair with mean coefficients. This reduction is effected by

(I.), multiplying the coefficients of each equation by the first coefficient, and adding together all the similar co-efficients thus resulting for the coefficients of a new equation ; and (2.), by repeating this process, and multi-plying the coefficients of each equation by the coefficient of the second term. Meaning by (sum of a^2) the sum of all quantities of the same kind, and having the same place in the equations as a^2, we may briefly describe the two resulting mean equations as follows :—

$$(\text{sum of } a^2) \cdot x + (\text{sum of } ab) \cdot y = (\text{sum of } ac),$$
$$(\text{sum of } ab) \cdot x + (\text{sum of } b^2) \cdot y = (\text{sum of } bc).$$

When there are three or more unknown quantities the process is exactly the same in nature, and we get additional mean equations by multiplying by the third, fourth, &c., coefficients. As the numbers are in any case approximate, it is usually unnecessary to make the com-putations with accuracy, and places of decimals may be freely cut off to save arithmetical work. The mean equations having been computed, their solution by the ordinary methods of algebra gives the most probable values of the unknown quantities.

Works upon the Theory of Probability.

Regarding the Theory of Probability and the Law of Error as most important subjects of study for any one who desires to obtain a complete comprehension of scientific method as actually applied in physical investigations, I will briefly indicate the works in one or other of which the reader will best pursue the study.

The best popular, and at the same time profound English work on the subject is De Morgan's " Essay on Proba-bilities and on their Application to Life Contingencies and Insurance Offices," published in the *Cabinet Cyclopædia*, and to be obtained (in print) from Messrs. Longman. Mr. Venn's work on *The Logic of Chance* can now be procured in a greatly enlarged second edition ; [1] it contains a most interesting and able discussion of the metaphysical

[1] *The Logic of Chance*, an Essay on the Foundations and Province of the Theory of Probability, with especial reference to its Logical Bearings and its Application to Moral and Social Science. (Mac-millan), 1876.

basis of probability and of related questions concerning
causation, belief, design, testimony, &c.; but I cannot
always agree with Mr. Venn's opinions. No mathematical
knowledge beyond that of common arithmetic is required
in reading these works. Quetelet's *Letters* form a good
introduction to the subject, and the mathematical notes
are of value. Sir George Airy's brief treatise *On the
Algebraical and Numerical Theory of Errors of Observations and the Combination of Observations*, contains a
complete explanation of the Law of Error and its practical applications. De Morgan's treatise "On the Theory
of Probabilities" in the *Encyclopædia Metropolitana*,
presents an abstract of the more abstruse investigations
of Laplace, together with a multitude of profound and
original remarks concerning the theory generally. In
Lubbock and Drinkwater's work on *Probability*, in the
Library of Useful Knowledge, we have a concise but
good statement of a number of important problems. The
Rev. W. A. Whitworth has given, in a work entitled
Choice and Chance, a number of good illustrations of
calculations both in combinations and probabilities. In
Mr. Todhunter's admirable History we have an exhaustive
critical account of almost all writings upon the subject of
probability down to the culmination of the theory in
Laplace's works. The Memoir of Mr. J. W. L. Glaisher
has already been mentioned (p. 375). In spite of the
existence of these and some other good English works,
there seems to be a want of an easy and yet pretty complete mathematical introduction to the study of the theory.

Among French works the *Traité Élémentaire du Calcul
des Probabilités*, by S. F. Lacroix, of which several editions
have been published, and which is not difficult to obtain,
forms probably the best elementary treatise. Poisson's
Recherches sur la Probabilité des Jugements (Paris 1837),
commence with an admirable investigation of the grounds
and methods of the theory. While Laplace's great *Théorie
Analytique des Probabilités* is of course the "Principia"
of the subject; his *Essai Philosophique sur les Probabilités*
is a popular discourse, and is one of the most profound
and interesting essays ever published. It should be
familiar to every student of logical method, and has lost
little or none of its importance by lapse of time.

Detection of Constant Errors.

The Method of Means is absolutely incapable of eliminating any error which is always the same, or which always lies in one direction. We sometimes require to be roused from a false feeling of security, and to be urged to take suitable precautions against such occult errors. " It is to the observer," says Gauss,[1] " that belongs the task of carefully removing the causes of constant errors," and this is quite true when the error is absolutely constant. When we have made a number of determinations with a certain apparatus or method of measurement, there is a great advantage in altering the arrangement, or even devising some entirely different method of getting estimates of the same quantity. The reason obviously consists in the improbability that the same error will affect two or more different methods of experiment. If a discrepancy is found to exist, we shall at least be aware of the existence of error, and can take measures for finding in which way it lies. If we can try a considerable number of methods, the probability becomes great that errors constant in one method will be balanced or nearly so by errors of an opposite effect in the others. Suppose that there be three different methods each affected by an error of equal amount. The probability that this error will in all fall in the same direction is only $\frac{1}{4}$; and with four methods similarly $\frac{1}{8}$. If each method be affected, as is always the case, by several independent sources of error, the probability becomes much greater that in the mean result of all the methods some of the errors will partially compensate the others. In this case as in all others, when human vigilance has exhausted itself, we must trust the theory of probability.

In the determination of a zero point, of the magnitude of the fundamental standards of time and space, in the personal equation of an astronomical observer, we have instances of fixed errors ; but as a general rule a change of procedure is likely to reverse the character of the error, and many instances may be given of the value of this precaution. If we measure over and over again the same

---

[1] Gauss, translated by Bertrand, p. 25.

angular magnitude by the same divided circle, maintained
in exactly the same position, it is evident that the same
mark in the circle will be the criterion in each case, and
any error in the position of that mark will equally affect
all our results. But if in each measurement we use a
different part of the circle, a new mark will come into use,
and as the error of each mark cannot be in the same
direction, the average result will be nearly free from
errors of division. It will be better still to use more
than one divided circle.

Even when we have no perception of the points at
which error is likely to enter, we may with advantage
vary the construction of our apparatus in the hope that we
shall accidentally detect some latent cause of error. Baily's
purpose in repeating the experiments of Michell and Cavendish on the density of the earth was not merely to follow
the same course and verify the previous numbers, but to
try whether variations in the size and substance of the
attracting balls, the mode of suspension, the temperature
of the surrounding air, &c., would yield different results.
He performed no less than 62 distinct series, comprising
2153 experiments, and he carefully classified and discussed
the results so as to disclose the utmost differences. Again,
in experimenting upon the resistance of the air to the
motion of a pendulum, Baily employed no less than 80
pendulums of various forms and materials, in order to
ascertain exactly upon what conditions the resistance
depends. Regnault, in his exact researches upon the
dilatation of gases, made arbitrary changes in the magnitude of parts of his apparatus. He thinks that if, in spite
of such modification, the results are unchanged, the errors
are probably of inconsiderable amount;[1] but in reality it
is always possible, and usually likely, that we overlook
sources of error which a future generation will detect.
Thus the pendulum experiments of Baily and Sabine were
directed to ascertain the nature and amount of a correction
for air resistance, which had been entirely misunderstood
in the experiments by means of the seconds pendulum,
upon which was founded the definition of the standard
yard, in the Act of 5th George IV. c. 74. It has already

[1] Jamin, *Cours de Physique*, vol. ii. p. 60.

been mentioned that a considerable error was discovered in the determination of the standard metre as the ten-millionth part of the distance from the pole to the equator (p. 314).

We shall return in Chapter XXV. to the further consideration of the methods by which we may as far as possible secure ourselves against permanent and undetected sources of error. In the meantime, having completed the consideration of the special methods requisite for treating quantitative phenomena, we must pursue our principal subject, and endeavour to trace out the course by which the physicist, from observation and experiment, collects the materials of knowledge, and then proceeds by hypothesis and inverse calculation to induce from them the laws of nature.

BOOK III.

INDUCTIVE INVESTIGATION.

CHAPTER XVIII.

OBSERVATION.

ALL knowledge proceeds originally from experience. Using the name in a wide sense, we may say that experience comprehends all that we *feel*, externally or internally— the aggregate of the impressions which we receive through the various apertures of perception—the aggregate consequently of what is in the mind, except so far as some portions of knowledge may be the reasoned equivalents of other portions. As the word experience expresses, we *go through* much in life, and the impressions gathered intentionally or unintentionally afford the materials from which the active powers of the mind evolve science.

No small part of the experience actually employed in science is acquired without any distinct purpose. We cannot use the eyes without gathering some facts which may prove useful. A great science has in many cases risen from an accidental observation. Erasmus Bartholinus thus first discovered double refraction in Iceland spar; Galvani noticed the twitching of a frog's leg; Oken was struck by the form of a vertebra; Malus accidentally examined light reflected from distant windows with a double refracting substance; and Sir John Herschel's attention was drawn to the peculiar appearance of a solution of quinine sulphate. In earlier times there must have been some one who first noticed the strange behaviour of a loadstone, or the unaccountable motions produced by amber. As a general rule we shall not know in what direction to look for a great body of phenomena widely different from those familiar to us. Chance then must give us the starting point; but one accidental observation well used may lead us to make thousands of observations in an intentional and organised manner, and thus a science may be gradually worked out from the smallest opening.

Distinction of Observation and Experiment.

It is usual to say that the two sources of experience are Observation and Experiment. When we merely note and record the phenomena which occur around us in the ordinary course of nature we are said *to observe.* When we change the course of nature by the intervention of our muscular powers, and thus produce unusual combinations and conditions of phenomena, we are said *to experiment.* Herschel justly remarked[1] that we might properly call these two modes of experience *passive and active observation.* In both cases we must certainly employ our senses to observe, and an experiment differs from a mere observation in the fact that we more or less influence the character of the events which we observe. Experiment is thus observation *plus* alteration of conditions.

It may readily be seen that we pass upwards by insensible gradations from pure observation to determinate experiment. When the earliest astronomers simply noticed the ordinary motions of the sun, moon, and planets upon the face of the starry heavens, they were pure observers. But astronomers now select precise times and places for important observations of stellar parallax, or the transits of planets. They make the earth's orbit the basis of a well arranged *natural experiment,* as it were, and take well considered advantage of motions which they cannot control. Meteorology might seem to be a science of pure

---

[1] *Preliminary Discourse on the Study of Natural Philosophy,* p. 77.

observation, because we cannot possibly govern the changes
of weather which we record. Nevertheless we may ascend
mountains or rise in balloons, like Gay-Lussac and Glaisher,
and may thus so vary the points of observation as to render
our procedure experimental. We are wholly unable either
to produce or prevent earth-currents of electricity, but
when we construct long lines of telegraph, we gather such
strong currents during periods of disturbance as to render
them capable of easy observation.

The best arranged systems of observation, however, would
fail to give us a large part of the facts which we now
possess. Many processes continually going on in nature
are so slow and gentle as to escape our powers of observation. Lavoisier remarked that the decomposition of water
must have been constantly proceeding in nature, although
its possibility was unknown till his time.[1] No substance
is wholly destitute of magnetic or diamagnetic powers ;
but it required all the experimental skill of Faraday to
prove that iron and a few other metals had no monopoly
of these powers. Accidental observation long ago impressed upon men's minds the phenomena of lightning,
and the attractive properties of amber. Experiment only
could have shown that phenomena so diverse in magnitude
and character were manifestations of the same agent. To
observe with accuracy and convenience we must have
agents under our control, so as to raise or lower their
intensity, to stop or set them in action at will. Just as
Smeaton found it requisite to create an artificial and
governable supply of wind for his investigation of windmills, so we must have governable supplies of light, heat,
electricity, muscular force, or whatever other agents we are
examining.

It is hardly needful to point out too that on the earth's
surface we live under nearly constant conditions of gravity,
temperature, and atmospheric pressure, so that if we are to
extend our inferences to other parts of the universe where
conditions are widely different, we must be prepared to
imitate those conditions on a small scale here. We must
have intensely high and low temperatures ; we must vary

---

[1] Lavoisier's *Elements of Chemistry*, translated by Kerr, 3rd ed.
p. 148.

the density of gases from approximate vacuum upwards; we must subject liquids and solids to pressures or strains of almost unlimited amount.

Mental Conditions of Correct Observation.

Every observation must in a certain sense be true, for the observing and recording of an event is in itself an event. But before we proceed to deal with the supposed meaning of the record, and draw inferences concerning the course of nature, we must take care to ascertain that the character and feelings of the observer are not to a great extent the phenomena recorded. The mind of man, as Francis Bacon said, is like an uneven mirror, and does not reflect the events of nature without distortion. We need hardly take notice of intentionally false observations, nor of mistakes arising from defective memory, deficient light, and so forth. Even where the utmost fidelity and care are used in observing and recording, tendencies to error exist, and fallacious opinions arise in consequence.

It is difficult to find persons who can with perfect fairness register facts for and against their own peculiar views. Among uncultivated observers the tendency to remark favourable and forget unfavourable events is so great, that no reliance can be placed upon their supposed observations. Thus arises the enduring fallacy that the changes of the weather coincide in some way with the changes of the moon, although exact and impartial registers give no countenance to the fact. The whole race of prophets and quacks live on the overwhelming effect of one success, compared with hundreds of failures which are unmentioned and forgotten. As Bacon says, " Men mark when they hit, and never mark when they miss." And we should do well to bear in mind the ancient story, quoted by Bacon, of one who in Pagan times was shown a temple with a picture of all the persons who had been saved from shipwreck, after paying their vows. When asked whether he did not now acknowledge the power of the gods, " Ay," he answered; " but where are they painted that were drowned after their vows ? "

If indeed we could estimate the amount of *bias* existing in any particular observations, it might be treated like one of the forces of the problem, and the true course of external nature might still be rendered apparent. But the feelings of an observer are usually too indeterminate, so that when there is reason to suspect considerable bias, rejection is the only safe course. As regards facts casually registered in past times, the capacity and impartiality of the observer are so little known that we should spare no pains to replace these statements by a new appeal to nature. An indiscriminate medley of truth and absurdity, such as Francis Bacon collected in his *Natural History*, is wholly unsuited to the purposes of science. But of course when records relate to past events like eclipses, conjunctions, meteoric phenomena, earthquakes, volcanic eruptions, changes of sea margins, the existence of now extinct animals, the migrations of tribes, remarkable customs, &c., we must make use of statements however unsatisfactory, and must endeavour to verifiy them by the comparison of independent records or traditions.

When extensive series of observations have to be made, as in astronomical, meteorological, or magnetical observatories, trigonometrical surveys, and extensive chemical or physical researches, it is an advantage that the numerical work should be executed by assistants who are not interested in, and are perhaps unaware of, the expected results. The record is thus rendered perfectly impartial. It may even be desirable that those who perform the purely routine work of measurement and computation should be unacquainted with the principles of the subject. The great table of logarithms of the French Revolutionary Government was worked out by a staff of sixty or eighty computers, most of whom were acquainted only with the rules of arithmetic, and worked under the direction of skilled mathematicians ; yet their calculations were usually found more correct than those of persons more deeply versed in mathematics.[1] In the Indian Ordnance Survey the actual measurers were selected so that they should not have sufficient skill to falsify their results without detection.

Both passive observation and experimentation must, however, be generally conducted by persons who know for

[1] Babbage, *Economy of Manufactures*, p. 194.

what they are to look.   It is only when excited and guided by the hope of verifying a theory that the observer will notice many of the most important points ; and, where the work is not of a routine character, no assistant can supersede the mind-directed observations of the philosopher. Thus the successful investigator must combine diverse qualities ; he must have clear notions of the result he expects and· confidence in the truth of his theories, and yet he must have that candour and flexibility of mind which enable him to accept unfavourable results and abandon mistaken views.

Instrumental and Sensual Conditions of Observation.

In every observation one or more of the senses must be employed, and we should ever bear in mind that the extent of our knowledge may be limited by the power of the sense concerned.   What we learn of the world only forms the lower limit of what is to be learned, and, for all that we can tell, the processes of nature may infinitely surpass in variety and complexity those which are capable of coming within our means of observation.   In some cases inference from observed phenomena may make us indirectly aware of what cannot be directly felt, but we can never be sure that we thus acquire any appreciable fraction of the knowledge that might be acquired.

It is a strange reflection that space may be filled with. dark wandering stars, whose existence could not have yet become in any way known to us.   The planets have already cooled so far as to be no longer luminous, and it may well be that other stellar bodies of various size have fallen into the same condition.   From the consideration, indeed, of variable and extinguished stars, Laplace inferred that there probably exist opaque bodies as great and perhaps as numerous as those we see.[1]   Some of these dark stars might ultimately become known to us, either by reflecting light, or more probably by their gravitating effects upon luminous stars.   Thus if one member of a double star were dark, we could readily detect its existence, and even estimate its size, position, and motions,

---

[1] *System of the World*, translated by Harte, vol. ii. p. 335.

by observing those of its visible companion. It was a
favourite notion of Huyghens that there may exist stars
and vast universes so distant that their light has never
yet had time to reach our eyes ; and we must also bear
in mind that light may possibly suffer slow extinction
in space, so that there is more than one way in which
an absolute limit to the powers of telescopic discovery
may exist.

There are natural limits again to the power of our
senses in detecting undulations of various kinds. It is
commonly said that vibrations of more than 38,000 strokes
per second are not audible as sound; and as some ears
actually do hear sounds of much higher pitch, even two
octaves higher than what other ears can detect, it is
exceedingly probable that there are incessant vibrations
which we cannot call sound because they are never heard.
Insects may communicate by such acute sounds, constituting a language inaudible to us; and the remarkable
agreement apparent among bodies of ants or bees might
thus perhaps be explained. Nay, as Fontenelle long ago
suggested in his scientific romance, there may exist unlimited numbers of senses or modes of perception which
we can never feel, though Darwin's theory would render it
probable that any useful means of knowledge in an an-
cestor would be developed and improved in the descendants.
We might doubtless have been endowed with a sense
capable of feeling electric phenomena with acuteness, so
that the positive or negative state of charge of a body
could be at once estimated. The absence of such a
sense is probably due to its comparative uselessness.

Heat undulations are subject to the same considerations.
It is now apparent that what we call light is the affection
of the eye by certain vibrations, the less rapid of which
are invisible and constitute the dark rays of radiant heat,
in detecting which we must substitute the thermometer
or the thermopile for the eye. At the other end of the
spectrum, again, the ultra-violet rays are invisible, and
only indirectly brought to our knowledge in the phenomena of fluorescence or photo-chemical action. There is
no reason to believe that at either end of the spectrum an
absolute limit has yet been reached.

Just as our knowledge of the stellar universe is limited

by the power of the telescope and other conditions, so our knowledge of the minute world has its limit in the powers and optical conditions of the microscope. There was a time when it would have been a reasonable induction that vegetables are motionless, and animals alone endowed with power of locomotion. We are astonished to discover by the microscope that minute plants are if anything more active than minute animals. We even find that mineral substances seem to lose their inactive character and dance about with incessant motion when reduced to sufficiently minute particles, at least when suspended in a non-conducting medium.[1] Microscopists will meet a natural limit to observation when the minuteness of the objects examined becomes comparable to the length of light undulations, and the extreme difficulty already encountered in determining the forms of minute marks on Diatoms appears to be due to this cause. According to Helmholtz the smallest distance which can be accurately defined depends upon the interference of light passing through the centres of the bright spaces. With a theoretically perfect microscope and a dry lense the smallest visible object would not be less than one 80,000th part of an inch in red light.

Of the errors likely to arise in estimating quantities by the senses I have already spoken, but there are some cases in which we actually see things differently from what they are. A jet of water appears to be a continuous thread, when it is really a wonderfully organised succession of small and large drops, oscillating in form. The drops fall so rapidly that their impressions upon the eye run into each other, and in order to see the separate drops we require some device for giving an instantaneous view.

One insuperable limit to our powers of observation arises from the impossibility of following and identifying the ultimate atoms of matter. One atom of oxygen is probably undistinguishable from another atom; only by

---

[1] This curious phenomenon, which I propose to call *pedesis*, or the *pedetic movement*, from πηδάω, to jump, is carefully described in my paper published in the *Quarterly Journal of Science* for April, 1878, vol. viii. (N.S.) p. 167. See also *Proceedings of the Literary and Philosophical Society of Manchester*, 25th January, 1870, vol. ix. p. 78, *Nature*, 22nd August, 1878, vol. xviii. p. 440, or the *Quarterly Journal of Science*, vol. viii. (N.S.) p. 514.

keeping a certain volume of oxygen safely inclosed in
a bottle can we assure ourselves of its identity ; allow it
to mix with other oxygen, and we lose all power of identification. Accordingly we seem to have no means of
directly proving that every gas is in a constant state of
diffusion of every part into every part. We can only
infer this to be the case from observing the behaviour
of distinct gases which we can distinguish in their course,
and by reasoning on the grounds of molecular theory.[1]

External Conditions of Correct Observation.

Before we proceed to draw inferences from any series of
recorded facts, we must take care to ascertain perfectly,
if possible, the external conditions under which the facts
are brought to our notice. Not only may the observing
mind be prejudiced and the senses defective, but there
may be circumstances which cause one kind of event to
come more frequently to our notice than another. The
comparative numbers of objects of different kinds existing
may in any degree differ from the numbers which come to
our notice. This difference must if possible be taken into
account before we make any inferences.

There long appeared to be a strong presumption that
all comets moved in elliptic orbits, because no comet had
been proved to move in any other kind of path. The
theory of gravitation admitted of the existence of comets
moving in hyperbolic orbits, and the question arose
whether they were really non-existent or were only
beyond the bounds of easy observation. From reasonable suppositions Laplace calculated that the probability
was at least 6000 to 1 against a comet which comes
within the planetary system sufficiently to be visible at
the earth's surface, presenting an orbit which could be
discriminated from a very elongated ellipse or parabola in
the part of its orbit within the reach of our telescopes.[2]
In short, the chances are very much in favour of our
seeing elliptic rather than hyperbolic comets. Laplace's
views have been confirmed by the discovery of six

[1] Maxwell, *Theory of Heat*, p. 301.
[2] Laplace, *Essai Philosophique*, p. 59. Todhunter's *History*,
pp. 491—494.

hyperbolic comets, which appeared in the years 1729, 1771, 1774, 1818, 1840, and 1843,[1] and as only about 800 comets altogether have been recorded, the proportion of hyperbolic ones is quite as large as should be expected.

When we attempt to estimate the numbers of objects which may have existed, we must make large allowances for the limited sphere of our observations. Probably not more than 4000 or 5000 comets have been seen in historical times, but making allowance for the absence of observers in the southern hemisphere, and for the small probability that we see any considerable fraction of those which are in the neighbourhood of our system, we must accept Kepler's opinion, that there are more comets in the regions of space than fishes in the depths of the ocean. When like calculations are made concerning the numbers of meteors visible to us, it is astonishing to find that the number of meteors entering the earth's atmosphere in every twenty-four hours is probably not less than 400,000,000, of which 13,000 exist in every portion of space equal to that filled by the earth.

Serious fallacies may arise from overlooking the inevitable conditions under which the records of past events are brought to our notice. Thus it is only the durable objects manufactured by former races of men, such as flint implements, which can have come to our notice as a general rule. The comparative abundance of iron and bronze articles used by an ancient nation must not be supposed to be coincident with their comparative abundance in our museums, because bronze is far the more durable. There is a prevailing fallacy that our ancestors built more strongly than we do, arising from the fact that the more fragile structures have long since crumbled away. We have few or no relics of the habitations of the poorer classes among the Greeks or Romans, or in fact of any past race ; for the temples, tombs, public buildings, and mansions of the wealthier classes alone endure. There is an immense expanse of past events necessarily lost to us for ever, and we must generally look upon records or relics as exceptional in their character.

The same considerations apply to geological relics. We could not generally expect that animals would be

[1] Chambers' *Astronomy*, 1st ed. p. 203.

preserved unless as regards the bones, shells, strong integu-
ments, or other hard and durable parts. All the infusoria
and animals devoid of mineral framework have probably
perished entirely, distilled perhaps into oils. It has been
pointed out that the peculiar character of some extinct
floras may be due to the unequal preservation of different
families of plants. By various accidents, however, we gain
glimpses of a world that is usually lost to us—as by
insects embedded in amber, the great mammoth preserved
in ice, mummies, casts in solid material like that of the
Roman soldier at Pompeii, and so forth.

We should also remember, that just as there may be
conjunctions of the heavenly bodies that can have happened only once or twice in the period of history, so remarkable terrestrial conjunctions may take place. Great
storms, earthquakes, volcanic eruptions, landslips, floods,
irruptions of the sea, may, or rather must, have occurred,
events of such unusual magnitude and such extreme rarity
that we can neither expect to witness them nor readily
to comprehend their effects. It is a great advantage of
the study of probabilities, as Laplace himself remarked, to
make us mistrust the extent of our knowledge, and pay
proper regard to the probability that events would come
within the sphere of our observations.

Apparent Sequence of Events.

De Morgan has excellently pointed out[1] that there
are no less than four modes in which one event may
seem to follow or be connected with another, without
being really so. These involve mental, sensual, and external causes of error, and I will briefly state and illustrate
them.

Instead of A causing B, it may be *our perception of A
that causes B.* Thus it is that prophecies, presentiments,
and the devices of sorcery and witchcraft often work their
own ends. A man dies on the day which he has always
regarded as his last, from his own fears of the day. An
incantation effects its purpose, because care is taken to
frighten the intended victim, by letting him know his
fate. In all such cases the mental condition is the cause
of apparent coincidence.

[1] *Essay on Probabilities,* Cabinet Cyclopædia, p. 121.

In a second class of cases, *the event A may make our perception of B follow, which would otherwise happen without being perceived.* Thus it was believed to be the result of investigation that more comets appeared in hot than cold summers. No account was taken of the fact that hot summers would be comparatively cloudless, and afford better opportunities for the discovery of comets. Here the disturbing condition is of a purely external character. Certain ancient philosophers held that the moon's rays were cold-producing, mistaking the cold caused by radiation into space for an effect of the moon, which is more likely to be visible at a time when the absence of clouds permits radiation to proceed.

In a third class of cases, *our perception of A may make our perception of B follow.* The event B may be constantly happening, but our attention may not be drawn to it except by our observing **A.** This case seems to be illustrated by the fallacy of the moon's influence on clouds. The origin of this fallacy is somewhat complicated. In the first place, when the sky is densely clouded the moon would not be visible at all; it would be necessary for us to see the full moon in order that our attention should be strongly drawn to the fact, and this would happen most often on those nights when the sky is cloudless. Mr. W. Ellis,[1] moreover, has ingeniously pointed out that there is a general tendency for clouds to disperse at the commencement of night, which is the time when the full moon rises. Thus the change of the sky and the rise of the full moon are likely to attract attention mutually, and the coincidence in time suggests the relation of cause and effect. Mr. Ellis proves from the results of observations at the Greenwich Observatory that the moon possesses no appreciable power of the kind supposed, and yet it is remarkable that so sound an observer as Sir John Herschel was convinced of the connection. In his "Results of Observations at the Cape of Good Hope,"[2] he mentions many evenings when a full moon occurred with a peculiarly clear sky.

[1] *Philosophical Magazine,* 4th Series (1867), vol. xxxiv. p. 64.
[2] See *Notes to Measures of Double Stars,* 1204, 1336, 1477, 1686, 1786, 1816, 1835, 1929, 2081, 2186, pp. 265, &c. See also Herschel's *Familiar Lectures on Scientific Subjects,* p 147, and *Outlines of Astronomy,* 7th ed. p. 285.

There is yet a fourth class of cases, in which *B is really
the antecedent event, but our perception of A, which is a
consequence of B, may be necessary to bring about our
perception of B.* There can be no doubt, for instance,
that upward and downward currents are continually circulating in the lowest stratum of the atmosphere during
the day-time ; but owing to the transparency of the atmosphere we have no evidence of their existence until we
perceive cumulous clouds, which are the consequence of
such currents. In like manner an interfiltration of bodies
of air in the higher parts of the atmosphere is probably in
nearly constant progress, but unless threads of cirrous
cloud indicate these motions we remain ignorant of their
occurrence.[1] The highest strata of the atmosphere are
wholly imperceptible to us, except when rendered luminous
by auroral currents of electricity, or by the passage of
meteoric stones. Most of the visible phenomena of comets
probably arise from some substance which, existing previously invisible, becomes condensed or electrified suddenly
into a visible form. Sir John Herschel attempted to
explain the production of comet tails in this manner by
evaporation and condensation.[2]

Negative Arguments from Non-observation.

From what has been suggested in preceding sections, it
will plainly appear that the non-observation of a phenomenon is not generally to be taken as proving its non-
occurrence. As there are sounds which we cannot hear,
rays of heat which we cannot feel, multitudes of worlds
which we cannot see, and myriads of minute organisms
of which not the most powerful microscope can give us
a view, we must as a general rule interpret our experience
in an affirmative sense only. Accordingly when inferences
have been drawn from the non-occurrence of particular
facts or objects, more extended and careful examination
has often proved their falsity. Not many years since it
was quite a well credited conclusion in geology that no
remains of man were found in connection with those of

[1] Jevons, *On the Cirrous Form of Cloud,* Philosophical Magazine,
July, 1857, 4th Series, vol. xiv. p. 22.

[2] *Astronomy,* 4th ed. p. 358

extinct animals, or in any deposit not actually at present in course of formation. Even Babbage accepted this conclusion as strongly confirmatory of the Mosaic accounts.[1] While the opinion was yet universally held, flint implements had been found disproving such a conclusion, and overwhelming evidence of man's long-continued existence has since been forthcoming. At the end of the last century, when Herschel had searched the heavens with his powerful telescopes, there seemed little probability that planets yet remained unseen within the orbit of Jupiter. But on the first day of this century such an opinion was overturned by the discovery of Ceres, and more than a hundred other small planets have since been added to the lists of the planetary system.

The discovery of the Eozoön Canadense in strata of much greater age than any previously known to contain organic remains, has given a shock to groundless opinions concerning the origin of organic forms; and the oceanic dredging expeditions under Dr. Carpenter and Sir Wyville Thomson have modified some opinions of geologists by disclosing the continued existence of forms long supposed to be extinct. These and many other cases which might be quoted show the extremely unsafe character of negative inductions.

But it must not be supposed that negative arguments are of no force and value. The earth's surface has been sufficiently searched to render it highly improbable that any terrestrial animals of the size of a camel remain to be discovered. It is believed that no new large animal has been encountered in the last eighteen or twenty centuries,[2] and the probability that if existent they would have been seen, increases the probability that they do not exist. We may with somewhat less confidence discredit the existence of any large unrecognised fish, or sea animals, such as the alleged sea-serpent. But, as we descend to forms of smaller size negative evidence loses weight from the less probability of our seeing smaller objects. Even the strong induction in favour of the four-fold division of the animal kingdom into Vertebrata, Annulosa, Mollusca,

[1] Babbage, *Ninth Bridgewater Treatise*, p. 67.
[2] Cuvier, *Essay on the Theory of the Earth*, translation, p. 61, &c.

and Cœlenterata, may break down by the discovery of intermediate or anomalous forms. As civilisation spreads
over the surface of the earth, and unexplored tracts are
gradually diminished, negative conclusions will increase
in force; but we have much to learn yet concerning the
depths of the ocean, almost wholly unexamined as they
are, and covering three-fourths of the earth's surface.

In geology there are many statements to which considerable probability attaches on account of the large
extent of the investigations already made, as, for instance,
that true coal is found only in rocks of a particular geological epoch; that gold occurs in secondary and tertiary
strata only in exceedingly small quantities,[1] probably
derived from the disintegration of earlier rocks. In
natural history negative conclusions are exceedingly
treacherous and unsatisfactory. The utmost patience
will not enable a microscopist or the observer of any
living thing to watch the behaviour of the organism under
all circumstances continuously for a great length of time.
There is always a chance therefore that the critical act or
change may take place when the observer's eyes are withdrawn. This certainly happens in some cases; for though
the fertilisation of orchids by agency of insects is proved
as well as any fact in natural history, Mr. Darwin has
never been able by the closest watching to detect an insect
in the performance of the operation. Mr. Darwin has
himself adopted one conclusion on negative evidence,
namely, that the *Orchis pyramidalis* and certain other
orchidaceous flowers secrete no nectar. But his caution
and unwearying patience in verifying the conclusion give
an impressive lesson to the observer. For twenty-three
consecutive days, as he tells us, he examined flowers in all
states of the weather, at all hours, in various localities.
As the secretion in other flowers sometimes takes place
rapidly and might happen at early dawn, that inconvenient
hour of observation was specially adopted. Flowers of
different ages were subjected to irritating vapours, to moisture, and to every condition likely to bring on the secretion;
and only after invariable failure of this exhaustive inquiry
was the barrenness of the nectaries assumed to be proved.[2]

[1] Murchison's *Siluria*, 1st ed. p. 432.
[2] Darwin's *Fertilisation of Orchids*, p. 48.

In order that a negative argument founded on the non-observation of an object shall have any considerable force, it must be shown to be probable that the object if existent would have been observed, and it is this probability which defines the value of the negative conclusion. The failure of astronomers to see the planet Vulcan, supposed by some to exist within Mercury's orbit, is no sufficient disproof of its existence. Similarly it would be very difficult, or even impossible, to disprove the existence of a second satellite of small size revolving round the earth. But if any person make a particular assertion, assigning place and time, then observation will either prove or disprove the alleged fact. If it is true that when a French observer professed to have seen a planet on the sun's face, an observer in Brazil was carefully scrutinising the sun and failed to see it, we have a negative proof.   False facts in science, it has been well said, are more mischievous than false theories.   A false theory is open to every person's criticism, and is ever liable to be judged by its accordance with facts. But a false or grossly erroneous assertion of a fact often stands in the way of science for a long time, because it may be extremely difficult or even impossible to prove the falsity of what has been once recorded.

In other sciences the force of a negative argument will often depend upon the number of possible alternatives which may exist. It was long believed that the quality of a musical sound as distinguished from its pitch, must depend upon the form of the undulation, because no other cause of it had ever been suggested or was apparently possible. The truth of the conclusion was proved by Helmholtz, who applied a microscope to luminous points attached to the strings of various instruments, and thus actually observed the different modes of undulation. In mathematics negative inductive arguments have seldom much force, because the possible forms of expression, or the possible combinations of lines and circles in geometry, are quite unlimited in number. An enormous number of attempts were made to trisect the angle by the ordinary methods of Euclid's geometry, but their invariable failure did not establish the impossibility of the task. This was shown in a totally different manner, by proving that the problem involves an irreducible cubic equation to which there could be no corresponding plane geometrical solution.[1] This is a case of *reductio ad absurdum*, a form of argument of a totally different character. Similarly no number of failures to obtain a general solution of equations of the fifth degree would establish the impossibility of the task, but in an indirect mode, equivalent to a *reductio ad absurdum*, the impossibility is considered to be proved.

[1] Peacock, *Algebre*, vol. ii. p. 344.
[2] Ibid, p. 359. Serret, *Algèbre Supérieure*, 2nd ed. p. 304.

CHAPTER XIX.

WE may now consider the great advantages which we enjoy in examining the combinations of phenomena when things are within our reach and capable of being experimented on. We are said *to experiment* when we bring substances together under various conditions of temperature, pressure, electric disturbance, chemical action, &c., and then record the changes observed. Our object in inductive investigation is to ascertain exactly the group of circumstances or conditions which being present, a certain other group of phenomena will follow. If we denote by A the antecedent group, and by X subsequent phenomena, our object will usually be to discover a law of the form $A = AX$, the meaning of which is that where A is X will happen.

The circumstances which might be enumerated as present in the simplest experiment are very numerous, in fact almost infinite. Rub two sticks together and consider what would be an exhaustive statement of the conditions. There are the form, hardness, organic structure, and all the chemical qualities of the wood; the pressure and velocity of the rubbing; the temperature, pressure, and all the chemical qualities of the surrounding air; the proximity of the earth with its attractive and electric powers; the temperature and other properties of the persons producing motion; the radiation from the sun, and to and from the sky; the electric excitement possibly existing in any overhanging cloud; even the positions of the heavenly bodies must be mentioned. On *à priori* grounds it is unsafe to assume that any one of these circumstances is without effect, and it is only by experience that we can single out those precise conditions from which the observed heat of friction proceeds.

The great method of experiment consists in removing, one at a time, each of those conditions which may be imagined to have an influence on the result. Our object in the experiment of rubbing sticks is to discover the exact circumstances under which heat appears. Now the presence of air may be requisite ; therefore prepare a vacuum, and rub the sticks in every respect as before, except that it is done *in vacuo.* If heat still appears we may say that air is not, in the presence of the other circumstances, a requisite condition. The conduction of heat from neighbouring bodies may be a condition. Prevent this by making all the surrounding bodies ice cold, which is what Davy aimed at in rubbing two pieces of ice together. If heat still appears we have eliminated another condition, and so we may go on until it becomes apparent that the expenditure of energy in the friction of two bodies is the sole condition of the production of heat.

The great difficulty of experiment arises from the fact that we must not assume the conditions to be independent. Previous to experiment we have no right to say that the rubbing of two sticks will produce heat in the same way when air is absent as before. We may have heat produced in one way when air is present, and in another when air is absent. The inquiry branches out into two lines, and we ought to try in both cases whether cutting off a supply of heat by conduction prevents its evolution in friction. The same branching out of the inquiry occurs with regard to every circumstance which enters into the experiment.

Regarding only four circumstances, say A, B, C, D, we ought to test not only the combinations ABCD, ABCd, ABcD, AbCD, aBCD, but we ought really to go through the whole of the combinations given in the fifth column of the Logical Alphabet. The effect of the absence of each condition should be tried both in the presence and absence of every other condition, and every selection of those conditions. Perfect and exhaustive experimentation would, in short, consist in examining natural phenomena in all their possible combinations and registering all relations between conditions and results which are found capable of existence.   It would thus resemble the exclusion of contradictory combinations carried out in the Indirect Method of Inference, except that the exclusion of combinations is grounded not on prior logical premises, but on *à posteriori* results of actual trial.

The reader will perceive, however, that such exhaustive investigation is practically impossible, because the number of requisite experiments would be immensely great.   Four antecedents only would require sixteen experiments; twelve antecedents would require 4096, and the number increases as the powers of two.   The result is that the experimenter has to fall back upon his own tact and experience in selecting those experiments which are most likely to yield him significant facts.   It is at this point that logical rules and forms begin to fail in giving aid.   The logical rule is—Try all possible combinations; but this being impracticable, the experimentalist necessarily abandons strict logical method, and trusts to his own insight.   Analogy, as we shall see, gives some assistance, and attention should be concentrated on those kinds of conditions which have been found important in like cases.   But we are now entirely in the region of probability, and the experimenter, while he is confidently pursuing what he thinks the right clue, may be overlooking the one condition of importance.   It is an impressive lesson, for instance, that Newton pursued all his exquisite researches on the spectrum unsuspicious of the fact that if he reduced the hole in the shutter to a narrow slit, all the mysteries of the bright and dark lines were within his grasp, provided of course that his prisms were sufficiently good to define the rays.   In like manner we know not what slight alteration in the most familiar experiments may not open the way to realms of new discovery.

Practical difficulties, also, encumber the progress of the physicist.   It is often impossible to alter one condition without altering others at the same time ; and thus we may not get the pure effect of the condition in question. Some conditions may be absolutely incapable of alteration ; others may be with great difficulty, or only in a certain degree, removable.   A very treacherous source of error is the existence of unknown conditions, which of course we cannot remove except by accident. These difficulties we will shortly consider in succession.

It is beautiful to observe how the alteration of a single circumstance sometimes conclusively explains a phenomenon. An instance is found in Faraday's investigation of the behaviour of Lycopodium spores scattered on a vibrating plate. It was observed that these minute spores collected together at the points of greatest motion, whereas sand and all heavy particles collected at the nodes, where the motion was least. It happily occurred to Faraday to try the experiment in the exhausted receiver of an air-pump, and it was then found that the light powder behaved exactly like heavy powder. A conclusive proof was thus obtained that the presence of air was the condition of importance, doubtless because it was thrown into eddies by the motion of the plate, and carried the Lycopodium to the points of greatest agitation. Sand was too heavy to be carried by the air.

Exclusion of Indifferent Circumstances.

From what has been already said it will be apparent that the detection and exclusion of indifferent circumstances is a work of importance, because it allows the concentration of attention upon circumstances which contain the principal condition. Many beautiful instances may be given where all the most obvious antecedents have been shown to have no part in the production of a phenomenon. A person might suppose that the peculiar colours of mother-of-pearl were due to the chemical qualities of the substance. Much trouble might have been spent in following out that notion by comparing the chemical qualities of various iridescent substances. But Brewster accidentally took an impression from a piece of mother-of-pearl in a cement of resin and bees'-wax, and finding the colours repeated upon the surface of the wax, he proceeded to take other impressions in balsam, fusible metal, lead, gum arabic, isinglass, &c., and always found the iridescent colours the same. He thus proved that the chemical nature of the substance is a matter of indifference, and that the form of the surface is the real condition of such colours.[1] Nearly the same may

[1] *Treatise on Optics*, by Brewster, Cab. Cyclo. p. 117.

be said of the colours exhibited by thin plates and films. The rings and lines of colour will be nearly the same in character whatever may be the nature of the substance; nay, a void space, such as a crack in glass, would produce them even though the air were withdrawn by an air-pump. The conditions are simply the existence of two reflecting surfaces separated by a very small space, though it should be added that the refractive index of the intervening substance has some influence on the exact nature of the colour produced.

When a ray of light passes close to the edge of an opaque body, a portion of the light appears to be bent towards it, and produces coloured fringes within the shadow of the body. Newton attributed this inflexion of light to the attraction of the opaque body for the supposed particles of light, although he was aware that the nature of the surrounding medium, whether air or other pellucid substance, exercised no apparent influence on the phenomena. Gravesande proved, however, that the character of the fringes is exactly the same, whether the body be dense or rare, compound or elementary. A wire produces exactly the same fringes as a hair of the same thickness. Even the form of the obstructing edge was subsequently shown to be a matter of indifference by Fresnel, and the interference spectrum, or the spectrum seen when light passes through a fine grating, is absolutely the same whatever be the form or chemical nature of the bars making the grating. Thus it appears that the stoppage of a portion of a beam of light is the sole necessary condition for the diffraction or inflexion of light, and the phenomenon is shown to bear no analogy to the refraction of light, in which the form and nature of the substance are all important.

It is interesting to observe how carefully Newton, in his researches on the spectrum, ascertained the indifference of many circumstances by actual trial. He says:[1] "Now the different magnitude of the hole in the window-shut, and different thickness of the prism where the rays passed through it, and different inclinations of the prism to the horizon, made no sensible changes in the length of the

[1] *Opticks*, 3rd. ed. p. 25.

image. Neither did the different matter of the prisms make any : for in a vessel made of polished plates of glass cemented together in the shape of a prism, and filled with water, there is the like success of the experiment according to the quantity of the refraction." But in the latter statement, as I shall afterwards remark (p. 432), Newton assumed an indifference which does not exist, and fell into an unfortunate mistake.

In the science of sound it is shown that the pitch of a sound depends solely upon the number of impulses in a second, and the material exciting those impulses is a matter of indifference. Whatever fluid, air or water, gas or liquid, be forced into the Siren, the sound produced is the same ; and the material of which an organ-pipe is constructed does not at all affect the pitch of its sound. In the sciencↄ of statical electricity it is an important principle that the nature of the interior of a conducting body is a matter of no importance. The electrical charge is confined to the conducting surface, and the interior remains in a neutral state. A hollow copper sphere takes exactly the same charge as a solid sphere of the same metal.

Some of Faraday's most elegant and successful researches were devoted to the exclusion of conditions which previous experimenters had thought essential for the production of electrical phenomena. Davy asserted that no known fluids, except such as contain water, could be made the medium of connexion between the poles of a battery ; and some chemists believed that water was an essential agent in electro-chemical decomposition. Faraday gave abundant experiments to show that other fluids allowed of electrolysis, and he attributed the erroneous opinion to the very general use of water as a solvent, and its presence in most natural bodies.[1] It was, in fact, upon the weakest kind of negative evidence that the opinion had been founded.

Many experimenters attributed peculiar powers to the poles of a battery, likening them to magnets, which, by their attractive powers, tear apart the elements of a substance. By a beautiful series of experiments,[2] Faraday proved conclusively that, on the contrary, the substance of

---

[1] *Experimental Researches in Electricity,* vol. i. pp. 133, 134.
[2] Ibid. vol. i. pp. 127, 162, &c.

the poles is of no importance, being merely the path
through which the electric force reaches the liquid acted
upon. Poles of water, charcoal, and many diverse substances, even air itself, produced similar results; if the
chemical nature of the pole entered at all into the question,
it was as a disturbing agent.

It is an essential part of the theory of gravitation that
the proximity of other attracting particles is without effect
upon the attraction existing between any two molecules.
Two pound weights weigh as much together as they do
separately. Every pair of molecules in the world have, as
it were, a private communication, apart from their relations to all other molecules. Another undoubted result of
experience pointed out by Newton[1] is that the weight of
a body does not in the least depend upon its form or
texture. It may be added that the temperature, electric
condition, pressure, state of motion, chemical qualities, and
all other circumstances concerning matter, except its mass,
are indifferent as regards its gravitating power.

As natural science progresses, physicists gain a kind of
insight and tact in judging what qualities of a substance
are likely to be concerned in any class of phenomena. The
physical astronomer treats matter in one point of view,
the chemist in another, and the students of physical optics,
sound, mechanics, electricity, &c., make a fair division of
the qualities among them. But errors will arise if too
much confidence be placed in this independence of various
kinds of phenomena, so that it is desirable from time to
time, especially when any unexplained discrepancies come
into notice, to question the indifference which is assumed
to exist, and to test its real existence by appropriate
experiments.

Simplification of Experiments.

One of the most requisite precautions in experimentation
is to vary only one circumstance at a time, and to maintain all other circumstances rigidly unchanged. There are
two distinct reasons for this rule, the first and most obvious being that if we vary two conditions at a time, and

---

[1] *Principia*, bk. iii. Prop. vi. Corollary i.

find some effect, we cannot tell whether the effect is due
to one or the other condition, or to both jointly. A second
reason is that if no effect ensues we cannot safely conclude
that either of them is indifferent; for the one may have
neutralised the effect of the other. In our symbolic logic
AB ·|· Ab was shown to be identical with A (p. 97), so
that B denotes a circumstance which is indifferently
present or absent. But if B always go together with
another antecedent C, we cannot show the same inde-
pendence, for ABC ·|· Abc is not identical with A and
none of our logical processes enables us to reduce it to A.

If we want to prove that oxygen is necessary to life, we
must not put a rabbit into a vessel from which the oxygen
has been exhausted by a burning candle. We should then
have not only an absence of oxygen, but an addition of
carbonic acid, which may have been the destructive agent.
For a similar reason Lavoisier avoided the use of atmospheric air in experiments on combustion, because air was
not a simple substance, and the presence of nitrogen might
impede or even alter the effect of oxygen. As Lavoisier
remarks,[1] "In performing experiments, it is a necessary
principle, which ought never to be deviated from, that
they be simplified as much as possible, and that every
circumstance capable of rendering their results complicated
be carefully removed." It has also been well said by
Cuvier [2] that the method of physical inquiry consists in
isolating bodies, reducing them to their utmost simplicity,
and bringing each of their properties separately into action,
either mentally or by experiment.

The electro-magnet has been of the utmost service in
the investigation of the magnetic properties of matter, by
allowing of the production or removal of a most powerful
magnetic force without disturbing any of the other arrangements of the experiment. Many of Faraday's most
valuable experiments would have been impossible had it
been necessary to introduce a heavy permanent magnet,
which could not be suddenly moved without shaking the
whole apparatus, disturbing the air, producing currents
by changes of temperature, &c. The electro-magnet is

---

[1] Lavoisier's *Chemistry*, translated by Kerr, p. 103.
[2] Cuvier's *Animal Kingdom*, introduction, pp 1, 2.

perfectly under control, and its influence can be brought
into action, reversed, or stopped by merely touching a
button. Thus Faraday was enabled to prove the rotation
of the plane of circularly polarised light by the fact that
certain light ceased to be visible when the electric current
of the magnet was cut off, and re-appeared when the
current was made. "These phenomena," he says, "could
be reversed at pleasure, and at any instant of time, and
upon any occasion, showing a perfect dependence of cause
and effect." [1]

It was Newton's omission to obtain the solar spectrum
under the simplest conditions which prevented him from
discovering the dark lines. Using a broad beam of light
which had passed through a round hole or a triangular
slit, he obtained a brilliant spectrum, but one in which
many different coloured rays overlapped each other. In
the recent history of the science of the spectrum, one
main difficulty has consisted in the mixture of the lines of
several different substances, which are usually to be found
in the light of any flame or spark. It is seldom possible
to obtain the light of any element in a perfectly simple
manner. Angström greatly advanced this branch of science
by examining the light of the electric spark when formed
between poles of various metals, and in the presence of
various gases. By varying the pole alone, or the gaseous
medium alone, he was able to discriminate correctly between the lines due to the metal and those due to the
surrounding gas. [2]

Failure in the Simplification of Experiments.

In some cases it seems to be impossible to carry out the
rule of varying one circumstance at a time. When we
attempt to obtain two instances or two forms of experiment in which a single circumstance shall be present in
one case and absent in another, it may be found that this
single circumstance entails others. Benjamin Franklin's
experiment concerning the comparative absorbing powers
of different colours is well known. "I took," he says, " a

---

[1] *Experimental Researches in Electricity,* vol. iii. p. 4.
[2] *Philosophical Magazine,* 4th Series, vol. ix. p. 327.

number of little square pieces of broadcloth from a tailor's
pattern card, of various colours. They were black, deep
blue, lighter blue, green, purple, red, yellow, white, and
other colours and shades of colour. I laid them all out
upon the snow on a bright sunshiny morning. In a few
hours the black, being most warmed by the sun, was sunk
so low as to be below the stroke of the sun's rays; the
dark blue was almost as low ; the lighter blue not quite
so much as the dark ; the other colours less as they were
lighter. The white remained on the surface of the snow,
not having entered it at all." This is a very elegant and
apparently simple experiment ; but when Leslie had completed his series of researches upon the nature of heat, he
came to the conclusion that the colour of a surface has
very little effect upon the radiating power, the mechanical
nature of the surface appearing to be more influential.
He remarks [1] that "the question is incapable of being positively resolved, since no substance can be made to assume
different colours without at the same time changing its
internal structure." Recent investigation has shown that
the subject is one of considerable complication, because
the absorptive power of a surface may be different according to the character of the rays which fall upon it ;
but there can be no doubt as to the acuteness with which
Leslie points out the difficulty. In Well's investigations
concerning the nature of dew, we have, again, very
complicated conditions. If we expose plates of various
material, such as rough iron, glass, polished metal, to the
midnight sky, they will be dewed in various degrees ;
but since these plates differ both in the nature of the
surface and the conducting power of the material, it would
not be plain whether one or both circumstances were of
importance. We avoid this difficulty by exposing the
same material polished or varnished, so as to present different conditions of surface ; [2] and again by exposing
different substances with the same kind of surface.

When we are quite unable to isolate circumstances we
must resort to the procedure described by Mill under the
name of the Joint Method of Agreement and Difference.

[1] *Inquiry into the Nature of Heat*, p. 95.
[2] Herschel, *Preliminary Discourse*, p. 161.

We must collect as many instances as possible in which a given circumstance produces a given result, and as many as possible in which the absence of the circumstance is followed by the absence of the result. To adduce his example, we cannot experiment upon the cause of double refraction in Iceland spar, because we cannot alter its crystalline condition without altering it altogether, nor can we find substances exactly like calc spar in every circumstance except one. We resort therefore to the method of comparing together all known substances which have the property of doubly-refracting light, and we find that they agree in being crystalline.[1] This indeed is nothing but an ordinary process of perfect or probable induction, already partially described, and to be further discussed under Classification. It may be added that the subject does admit of perfect experimental treatment, since glass, when compressed in one direction, becomes capable of doubly-refracting light, and as there is probably no alteration in the glass but change of elasticity, we learn that the power of double refraction is probably due to a difference of elasticity in different directions.

Removal of Usual Conditions.

One of the great objects of experiment is to enable us to judge of the behaviour of substances under conditions widely different from those which prevail upon the surface of the earth. We live in an atmosphere which does not vary beyond certain narrow limits in temperature or pressure. Many of the powers of nature, such as gravity, which constantly act upon us, are of almost fixed amount. Now it will afterwards be shown that we cannot apply a quantitative law to circumstances much differing from those in which it was observed. In the other planets, the sun, the stars, or remote parts of the Universe, the conditions of existence must often be widely different from what we commonly experience here. Hence our knowledge of nature must remain restricted and hypothetical, unless we can subject substances to unusual conditions by suitable experiments.

[1] *System of Logic*, bk. iii. chap. viii. § 4, 5th ed. vol. i. p. 433.

The electric arc is an invaluable means of exposing metals or other conducting substances to the highest known temperature. By its aid we learn not only that all the metals can be vaporised, but that they all give off distinctive rays of light. At the other extremity of the scale, the intensely powerful freezing mixture devised by Faraday, consisting of solid carbonic acid and ether mixed *in vacuo*, enables us to observe the nature of substances at temperatures immensely below any we meet with naturally on the earth's surface.

We can hardly realise now the importance of the invention of the air-pump, previous to which invention it was exceedingly difficult to experiment except under the ordinary pressure of the atmosphere. The Torricellian vacuum had been employed by the philosophers of the Accademia del Cimento to show the behaviour of water, smoke, sound, magnets, electric substances, &c., *in vacuo*, but their experiments were often unsuccessful from the difficulty of excluding air.[1]

Among the most constant circumstances under which we live is the force of gravity, which does not vary, except by a slight fraction of its amount, in any part of the earth's crust or atmosphere to which we can attain. This force is sufficient to overbear and disguise various actions, for instance, the mutual gravitation of small bodies. It was an interesting experiment of Plateau to neutralise the action of gravity by placing substances in liquids of exactly the same specific gravity. Thus a quantity of oil poured into the middle of a suitable mixture of alcohol and water assumes a spherical shape ; on being made to rotate it becomes spheroidal, and then successively separates into a ring and a group of spherules. Thus we have an illustration of the mode in which the planetary system may have been produced,[2] though the extreme difference of scale prevents our arguing with confidence from the experiment to the conditions of the nebular theory.

It is possible that the so-called elements are elementary only to us, because we are restricted to temperatures at which they are fixed. Lavoisier carefully defined an

[1] *Essayes of Natural Experiments made in the Accademia del Cimento.* Englished by Richard Waller, 1684, p. 40, &c.
[2] Plateau, Taylor's *Scientific Memoirs*, vol. iv. pp. 16—43.

element as a substance which cannot be decomposed *by
any known means;* but it seems almost certain that some
series of elements, for instance Iodine, Bromine, and Chlorine, are really compounds of a simpler substance. We
must look to the production of intensely high temperatures,
yet quite beyond our means, for the decomposition of these
so-called elements. Possibly in this age and part of the
universe the dissipation of energy has so far proceeded
that there are no sources of heat sufficiently intense to
effect the decomposition.

Interference of Unsuspected Conditions.

It may happen that we are not aware of all the conditions
under which our researches are made. Some substance
may be present or some power may be in action, which
escapes the most vigilant examination. Not being aware
of its existence, we are unable to take proper measures to
exclude it, and thus determine the share which it has in
the results of our experiments. There can be no doubt
that the alchemists were misled and encouraged in their
vain attempts by the unsuspected presence of traces of
gold and silver in the substances they proposed to trans-
mute. Lead, as drawn from the smelting furnace, almost
always contains some silver, and gold is associated with
many other metals. Thus small quantities of noble metal
would often appear as the result of experiment and raise
delusive hopes.

In more than one case the unsuspected presence of
common salt in the air has caused great trouble. In
the early experiments on electrolysis it was found that
when water was decomposed, an acid and an alkali were
produced at the poles, together with oxygen and hydrogen.
In the absence of any other explanation, some chemists
rushed to the conclusion that electricity must have the
power of *generating* acids and alkalies, and one chemist
thought he had discovered a new substance called *electric
acid.* But Davy proceeded to a systematic investigation
of the circumstances, by varying the conditions. Changing
the glass vessel for one of agate or gold, he found that far
less alkali was produced; excluding impurities by the use
of carefully distilled water, he found that the quantities of

acid and alkali were still further diminished ; and having
thus obtained a clue to the cause, he completed the exclusion of impurities by avoiding contact with his fingers,
and by placing the apparatus under an exhausted receiver,
no acid or alkali being then detected. It would be difficult
to meet with a more elegant case of the detection of a
condition previously unsuspected.[1]

It is remarkable that the presence of common salt in
the air, proved to exist by Davy, nevertheless continued a
stumbling-block in the science of spectrum analysis, and
probably prevented men, such as Brewster, Herschel, and
Talbot, from anticipating by thirty years the discoveries
of Bunsen and Kirchhoff. As I pointed out,[2] the utility
of the spectrum was known in the middle of the last
century to Thomas Melvill, a talented Scotch physicist,
who died at the early age of 27 years.[3] But Melvill
was struck in his examination of coloured flames by the
extraordinary predominance of homogeneous yellow light,
which was due to some circumstance escaping his attention. Wollaston and Fraunhofer were equally struck by
the prominence of the yellow line in the spectrum of
nearly every kind of light. Talbot expressly recommended
the use of the prism for detecting the presence of substances
by what we now call spectrum analysis, but he found that
all substances, however different the light they yielded in
other respects, were identical as regards the production of
yellow light. Talbot knew that the salts of soda gave this
coloured light, but in spite of Davy's previous difficulties
with salt in electrolysis, it did not occur to him to assert
that where the light is, there sodium must be. He suggested water as the most likely source of the yellow light,
because of its frequent presence ; but even substances
which were apparently devoid of water gave the same
yellow light.[4] Brewster and Herschel both experimented

---

[1] *Philosophical Transactions* [1826], vol. cxvi. pp. 388, 389. Works
of Sir Humphry Davy, vol. v. pp. 1—12.

[2] *National Review,* July, 1861, p. 13.

[3] His published works are contained in *The Edinburgh Physical
and Literary Essays,* vol. ii. p. 34 ; *Philosophical Transactions* [1753],
vol. xlviii. p. 261 ; see also Morgan's Papers in *Philosophical Transactions* [1785], vol. lxxv. p. 190.

[4] *Edinburgh Journal of Science,* vol. v. p. 79.

upon flames almost at the same time as Talbot, and Herschel unequivocally enounced the principle of spectrum analysis.[1]   Nevertheless Brewster, after numerous experiments attended with great trouble and disappointment, found that yellow light might be obtained from the combustion of almost any substance.   It was not until 1856 that Swan discovered that an almost infinitesimal quantity of sodium chloride, say a millionth part of a grain, was sufficient to tinge a flame of a bright yellow colour. The universal diffusion of the salts of sodium, joined to this unique light-producing power, was thus shown to be the unsuspected condition which had destroyed the confidence of all previous experimenters in the use of the prism.   Some references concerning the history of this curious point are given below.[2]

In the science of radiant heat, early inquirers were led to the conclusion that radiation proceeded only from the surface of a solid, or from a very small depth below it. But they happened to experiment upon surfaces covered by coats of varnish, which is highly athermanous or opaque to heat.   Had they properly varied the character of the surface, using a highly diathermanous substance like rock salt, they would have obtained very different results.[3]

One of the most extraordinary instances of an erroneous opinion due to overlooking interfering agents is that concerning the increase of rainfall near to the earth's surface. More than a century ago it was observed that rain-gauges placed upon church steeples, house tops, and other elevated places, gave considerably less rain than if they were on the ground, and it has been recently shown that the variation is most rapid in the close neighbourhood of the ground.[4] All kinds of theories have been started to explain this phenomenon ; but I have shown [5] that it is simply due to

[1] *Encyclopædia Metropolitana*, art. *Light*, § `524; Herschel's *Familiar Lectures*, p. 266.

[2] Talbot, *Philosophical Magazine*, 3rd Series, vol. ix. p. 1 (1836); Brewster, *Transactions of the Royal Society of Edinburgh* [1823], vol. ix. pp. 433, 455 ; Swan, ibid. [1856] vol. xxi. p. 411 ; *Philosophical Magazine*, 4th Series, vol. xx. p. 173 [Sept. 1860] ; Roscoe, *Spectrum Analysis*, Lecture III.

[3] Balfour Stewart, *Elementary Treatise on Heat*, p. 192.

[4] British Association, Liverpool, 1870. *Report on Rainfall*, p. 176.

[5] *Philosophical Magazine.* Dec. 1861. 4th Series, vol. xxii. p. 421.

the interference of wind, which deflects more or less rain from all the gauges which are exposed to it.

The great magnetic power of iron renders it a source of disturbance in magnetic experiments. In building a magnetic observatory great care must therefore be taken that no iron is employed in the construction, and that no masses of iron are near at hand. In some cases magnetic observations have been seriously disturbed by the existence of masses of iron ore in the neighbourhood. In Faraday's experiments upon feebly magnetic or diamagnetic substances he took the greatest precautions against the presence of disturbing substances in the copper wire, wax, paper, and other articles used in suspending the test objects. It was his custom to try the effect of the magnet upon the apparatus in the absence of the object of experiment, and without this preliminary trial no confidence could be placed in the results.[1] Tyndall has also employed the same mode for testing the freedom of electro-magnetic coils from iron, and was thus enabled to obtain them devoid of any cause of disturbance.[2] It is worthy of notice that in the very infancy of the science of magnetism, the acute experimentalist Gilbert correctly accounted for the opinion existing in his day that magnets would attract silver, by pointing out that the silver contained iron.

Even when we are not aware by previous experience of the probable presence of a special disturbing agent, we ought not to assume the absence of unsuspected interference. If an experiment is of really high importance, so that any considerable branch of science rests upon it, we ought to try it again and again, in as varied conditions as possible. We should intentionally disturb the apparatus in various ways, so as if possible to hit by accident upon any weak point. Especially when our results are more regular than we have fair grounds for anticipating, ought we to suspect some peculiarity in the apparatus which causes it to measure some other phenomenon than that in question, just as Foucault's pendulum almost always indicates the movement of the axes of its own elliptic path instead of the rotation of the globe.

[1] *Experimental Researches in Electricity,* vol. iii. p. 84. &c.
[2] *Lectures on Heat,* p. 21.

It was in this cautious spirit that Baily acted in his experiments on the density of the earth. The accuracy of his results depended upon the elimination of all disturbing influences, so that the oscillation of his torsion balance should measure gravity alone. Hence he varied the apparatus in many ways, changing the small balls subject to attraction, changing the connecting rod, and the means of suspension. He observed the effect of disturbances, such as the presence of visitors, the occurrence of violent storms, &c., and as no real alteration was produced in the results, he confidently attributed them to gravity.[1]

Newton would probably have discovered the mode of constructing achromatic lenses, but for the unsuspected effect of some sugar of lead which he is supposed to have dissolved in the water of a prism. He tried, by means of a glass prism combined with a water prism, to produce dispersion of light without refraction, and if he had succeeded there would have been an obvious mode of producing refraction without dispersion. His failure is attributed to his adding lead acetate to the water for the purpose of increasing its refractive power, the lead having a high dispersive power which frustrated his purpose.[2] Judging from Newton's remarks, in the *Philosophical Transactions*, it would appear as if he had not, without many unsuccessful trials, despaired of the construction of achromatic glasses.[3]

The Academicians of Cimento, in their early and ingenious experiments upon the vacuum, were often misled by the mechanical imperfections of their apparatus. They concluded that the air had nothing to do with the production of sounds, evidently because their vacuum was not sufficiently perfect. Otto von Guericke fell into a like mistake in the use of his newly-constructed air-pump, doubtless from the unsuspected presence of air sufficiently dense to convey the sound of the bell.

It is hardly requisite to point out that the doctrine of spontaneous generation is due to the unsuspected presence

---

[1] Baily, *Memoirs of the Royal Astronomical Society*, vol. xiv. pp. 29, 30.

[2] Grant, *History of Physical Astronomy*, p. 531.

[3] *Philosophical Transactions*, abridged by Lowthorp, 4th edition, vol. i. p. 202.

of germs, even after the most careful efforts to exclude
them, and in the case of many diseases, both of animals
and plants, germs which we have no means as yet of detecting are doubtless the active cause.   It has long been
a subject of dispute, again, whether the plants which spring
from newly turned land grow from seeds long buried in
that land, or from seeds brought by the wind.   Argument
is unphilosophical when direct trial can readily be applied ;
for by turning up some old ground, and covering a portion
of it with a glass case, the conveyance of seeds by the
wind can be entirely prevented, and if the same plants
appear within and without the case, it will become clear
that the seeds are in the earth.   By gross oversight some
experimenters have thought before now that crops of rye
had sprung up where oats had been sown.

Blind or Test Experiments.

Every conclusive experiment necessarily consists in the
comparison of results between two different combinations
of circumstances.   To give a fair probability that A is the
cause of X, we must maintain invariable all surrounding
objects and conditions, and we must then show that where
A is X is, and where A is not X is not.   This cannot really
be accomplished in a single trial.   If, for instance, a
chemist places a certain suspected substance in Marsh's
test apparatus, and finds that it gives a small deposit of
metallic arsenic, he cannot be sure that the arsenic really
proceeds from the suspected substance ; the impurity of the
zinc or sulphuric acid may have been the cause of its
appearance.   It is therefore the practice of chemists to
make what they call a *blind experiment,* that is to try
whether arsenic appears in the absence of the suspected
substance.   The same precaution ought to be taken in all
important analytical operations.   Indeed, it is not merely
a precaution, it is an essential part of any experiment.   If
the blind trial be not made, the chemist merely assumes
that he knows what would happen.   Whenever we assert
that because A and X are found together A is the cause of
X, we assume that if A were absent X would be absent.
But wherever it is possible, we ought not to take this
as a mere assumption, or even as a matter of inference.

Experience is ultimately the basis of all our inferences, but if we can bring immediate experience to bear upon the point in question we should not trust to anything more remote and liable to error.   When Faraday examined the magnetic properties of the bearing apparatus, in the absence of the substance to be experimented on, he really made a blind experiment (p. 431).

We ought, also, to test the accuracy of a method of experiment whenever we can, by introducing known amounts of the substance or force to be detected.   A new analytical process for the quantitative estimation of an element should be tested by performing it upon a mixture compounded so as to contain a known quantity of that element. The accuracy of the gold assay process greatly depends upon the precaution of assaying alloys of gold of exactly known composition.[1]   Gabriel Plattes' works give evidence of much scientific spirit, and when discussing the supposed merits of the divining rod for the discovery of subterranean treasure, he sensibly suggests that the rod should be tried in places where veins of metal are known to exist.[2]

Negative Results of Experiment.

When we pay proper regard to the imperfection of all measuring instruments and the possible minuteness of effects, we shall see much reason for interpreting with caution the negative results of experiments.   We may fail to discover the existence of an expected effect, not because that effect is really non-existent, but because it is of a magnitude inappreciable to our senses, or confounded with other effects of much greater amount.   As there is no limit on à priori grounds to the smallness of a phenomenon, we can never, by a single experiment, prove the non-existence of a supposed effect.   We are always at liberty to assume that a certain amount of effect might have been detected by greater delicacy of measurement. We cannot safely affirm that the moon has no atmosphere at all.   We may doubtless show that the atmosphere, if present, is less dense than the air in the so-called vacuum

---

[1] Jevons in Watts' *Dictionary of Chemistry*, vol. ii. pp. 936, 937.
[2] *Discovery of Subterraneal Treasure.* London, 1639, p. 48.

of an air-pump, as did Du Sejour.   It is equally impossible to prove that gravity occupies *no time* in transmission.
Laplace indeed ascertained that the velocity of propagation
of the influence was at least fifty million times greater than
that of light;[1] but it does not really follow that it is instantaneous; and were there any means of detecting the
action of one star upon another exceedingly distant star,
we might possibly find an appreciable interval occupied in
the transmission of the gravitating impulse.   Newton
could not demonstrate the absence of all resistance to
matter moving through empty space; but he ascertained by
an experiment with the pendulum (p. 443), that if such
resistance existed, it was in amount less than one five-
thousandth part of the external resistance of the air.[2]

A curious instance of false negative inference is furnished by experiments on light.   Euler rejected the corpuscular theory on the ground that particles of matter
moving with the immense velocity of light would possess
momentum, of which there was no evidence.   Bennet had
attempted to detect the momentum of light by concentrat-
ing the rays of the sun upon a delicately balanced body.
Observing no result, it was considered to be proved that
light had no momentum.   Mr. Crookes, however, having
suspended thin vanes, blacked on one side, in a nearly
vacuous globe, found that they move under the influence
of light.   It is now allowed that this effect can be explained in accordance with the undulatory theory of light,
and the molecular theory of gases.   It comes to this—that
Bennet failed to detect an effect which he might have
detected with a better method of experimenting; but if he
had found it, the phenomenon would have confirmed, not
the corpuscular theory of light, as was expected, but the
rival undulatory theory.   The conclusion drawn from
Bennet's experiment was falsely drawn, but it was nevertheless true in matter.

Many incidents in the history of science tend to show
that phenomena, which one generation has failed to discover, may become accurately known to a succeeding
generation.   The compressibility of water which the

[1] Laplace, *System of the World*, translated by Harte, vol. ii. p. 322.
[2] *Principia*, bk. ii. sect. 6, Prop. xxxi. Motte's translation, vol. ii.
p. 108.

Academicians of Florence could not detect, because at a
low pressure the effect was too small to perceive, and at a
high pressure the water oozed through their silver vessel,[1]
has now become the subject of exact measurement and
precise calculation. Independently of Newton, Hooke
entertained very remarkable notions concerning the nature
of gravitation. In this and other subjects he showed,
indeed, a genius for experimental investigation which
would have placed him in the first rank in any other age
than that of Newton. He correctly conceived that the
force of gravity would decrease as we recede from the
centre of the earth, and he boldly attempted to prove it by
experiment. Having exactly counterpoised two weights
in the scales of a balance, or rather one weight against
another weight and a long piece of fine cord, he removed
his balance to the top of the dome of St. Paul's, and tried
whether the balance remained in equilibrium after one
weight was allowed to hang down to a depth of 240 feet.
No difference could be perceived when the weights were at
the same and at different levels, but Hooke rightly held
that the failure arose from the insufficient elevation. He
says, " Yet I am apt to think some difference might be discovered in greater heights." [2] The radius of the earth
being about 20,922,000 feet, we can now readily calculate
from the law of gravity that a height of 240 would not
make a greater difference than one part in 40,000 of the
weight. Such a difference would doubtless be inappreciable
in the balances of that day, though it could readily be detected by balances now frequently constructed. Again, the
mutual gravitation of bodies at the earth's surface is so
small that Newton appears to have made no attempt to
demonstrate its existence experimentally, merely remarking that it was too small to fall under the observation of
our senses.[3] It has since been successfully detected and
measured by Cavendish, Baily, and others.

The smallness of the quantities which we can sometimes
observe is astonishing. A balance will weigh to one
millionth part of the load. Whitworth can measure to
the millionth part of an inch. A rise of temperature of

[1] *Essayes of Natural Experiments*, &c. p. 117.
[2] Hooke's *Posthumous Works*, p. 182.
[3] *Principia*, bk. iii. Prop. vii. Corollary ᴢ.

the 8800th part of a degree centigrade has been detected
by Dr. Joule.   The spectroscope has revealed the presence
of the 10,000,000th part of a gram.   It is said that the
eye can observe the colour produced in a drop of water by
the 50,000,000th part of a gram of fuschine, and about the
same quantity of cyanine.   By the sense of smell we can
probably feel still smaller quantities of odorous matter.[1]
We must nevertheless remember that quantitative effects
of far less amount than these must exist, and we should
state our negative results with corresponding caution.   We
can only disprove the existence of a quantitative phenomenon by showing deductively from the laws of nature, that
if present it would amount to a perceptible quantity.   As
in the case of other negative arguments (p. 414), we must
demonstrate that the effect wor'd appear, where it is by
experiment found not to appear.

Limits of Experiment.

It will be obvious that there are many operations of
nature which we are quite incapable of imitating in our
experiments.   Our object is to study the conditions under
which a certain effect is produced ; but one of those conditions may involve a great length of time.   There are
instances on record of experiments extending over five or
ten years, and even over a large part of a lifetime ; but
such intervals of time are almost nothing to the time
during which nature may have been at work.   The contents of a mineral vein in Cornwall may have been undergoing gradual change for a hundred million years.   All
metamorphic rocks have doubtless endured high temperature and enormous pressure for inconceivable periods of
time, so that chemical geology is generally beyond the
scope of experiment.
Arguments have been brought against Darwin's theory,
founded upon the absence of any clear instance of the
production of a new species.   During an historical interval
of perhaps four thousand years, no animal, it is said, has
been so much domesticated as to become different in

[1] Keill's *Introduction to Natural Philosophy*, 3rd ed., London,
1733, pp. 48—54.

species. It might as well be argued that no geological changes are taking place, because no new mountain has risen in Great Britain within the memory of man. Our actual experience of geological changes is like a point in the infinite progression of time. When we know that rain water falling on limestone will carry away a minute portion of the rock in solution, we do not hesitate to multiply that quantity by millions, and infer that in course of time a mountain may be dissolved away. We have actual experience concerning the rise of land in some parts of the globe and its fall in others to the extent of some feet. Do we hesitate to infer what may thus be done in course of geological ages? As Gabriel Plattes long ago remarked, "The sea never resting, but perpetually winning land in one place and losing in another, doth show what may be done in length of time by a continual operation, not subject unto ceasing or intermission." [1] The action of physical circumstances upon the forms and characters of animals by natural selection is subject to exactly the same remarks. As regards animals living in a state of nature, the change of circumstances which can be ascertained to have occurred is so slight, that we could not expect to observe any change in those animals whatever. Nature has made no experiment at all for us within historical times. Man, however, by taming and domesticating dogs, horses, oxen, pigeons, &c., has made considerable change in their circumstances, and we find considerable change also in their forms and characters. Supposing the state of domestication to continue unchanged, these new forms would continue permanent so far as we know, and in this sense they are permanent. Thus the arguments against Darwin's theory, founded on the non-observation of natural changes within the historical period, are óf the weakest character, being purely negative.

[1] *Discovery of Subterraneal Treasure*, 1639, p. 52.

CHAPTER XX.

EXPERIMENTS may be of two kinds, experiments of simple fact, and experiments of quantity. In the first class of experiments we combine certain conditions, and wish to ascertain whether or not a certain effect of any quantity exists. Hooke wished to ascertain whether or not there was any difference in the force of gravity at the top and bottom of St. Paul's Cathedral. The chemist continually performs analyses for the purpose of ascertaining whether or not a given element exists in a particular mineral or mixture; all such experiments and analyses are qualitative rather than quantitative, because though the result may be more or less, the particular amount of the result is not the object of the inquiry.

So soon, however, as a result is known to be discoverable, the scientific man ought to proceed to the quantitative inquiry, how great a result follows from a certain amount of the conditions which are supposed to constitute the cause? The possible numbers of experiments are now infinitely great, for every variation in a quantitative condition will usually produce a variation in the amount of the effect. The method of variation which thus arises is no narrow or special method, but it is the general application of experiment to phenomena capable of continuous variation. As Mr. Fowler has well remarked,[1] the observation of variations is really an integration of a supposed infinite number of applications of the so-called method of difference, that is of experiment in its perfect form.

[1] *Elements of Inductive Logic*, 1st edit. p. 175.

In induction we aim at establishing a general law, and if we deal with quantities that law must really be expressed more or less obviously in the form of an equation, or equations. We treat as before of conditions, and of what happens under those conditions. But the conditions will now vary, not in quality, but quantity, and the effect will also vary in quantity, so that the result of quantitative induction is always to arrive at some mathematical expression involving the quantity of each condition, and expressing the quantity of the result. In other words, we wish to know what function the effect is of its conditions. We shall find that it is one thing to obtain the numerical results, and quite another thing to detect the law obeyed by those results, the latter being an operation of an inverse and tentative character.

The Variable and the Variant.

Almost every series of quantitative experiments is directed to obtain the relation between the different values of one quantity which is varied at will, and another quantity which is caused thereby to vary. We may conveniently distinguish these as respectively the *variable* and the *variant*. When we are examining the effect of heat in expanding bodies, heat, or one of its dimensions, temperature, is the variable, length the variant. If we compress a body to observe how much it is thereby heated, pressure, or it may be the dimensions of the body, forms the variable, heat the variant. In the thermo-electric pile we make heat the variable and measure electricity as the variant. That one of the two measured quantities which is an antecedent condition of the other will be the variable.

It is always convenient to have the variable entirely under our command. Experiments may indeed be made with accuracy, provided we can exactly measure the variable at the moment when the quantity of the effect is determined. But if we have to trust to the action of some capricious force, there may be great difficulty in making exact measurements, and those results may not be disposed over the whole range of quantity in a convenient manner. It is one prime object of the experimenter, therefore, to obtain a regular and governable supply of the force which he is investigating. To determine correctly the efficiency of windmills, when the natural winds were constantly varying in force, would be exceedingly difficult. Smeaton, therefore, in his experiments on the subject, created a uniform wind of the required force by moving his models against the air on the extremity of a revolving arm.[1] The velocity of the wind could thus be rendered greater or less, it could be maintained uniform for any length of time, and its amount could be exactly ascertained. In determining the laws of the chemical action of light it would be out of the question to employ the rays of the sun, which vary in intensity with the clearness of the atmosphere, and with every passing cloud. One great difficulty in photometry and the investigation of the chemical action of light consists in obtaining a uniform and governable source of light rays.[2]

Fizeau's method of measuring the velocity of light enabled him to appreciate the time occupied by light in travelling through a distance of eight or nine thousand metres. But the revolving mirror of Wheatstone subsequently enabled Foucault and Fizeau to measure the velocity in a space of four metres. In this latter method there was the advantage that various media could be substituted for air, and the temperature, density, and other conditions of the experiment could be accurately governed and measured.

Measurement of the Variable.

There is little use in obtaining exact measurements of an effect unless we can also exactly measure its conditions.

It is absurd to measure the electrical resistance of a piece of metal, its elasticity, tenacity, density, or other physical qualities, if these vary, not only with the minute impurities of the metal, but also with its physical condition. If the same bar changes its properties by being

---

[1] *Philosophical Transactions,* vol. li. p. 138 ; abridgment, vol. xi. p. 355.

[2] See Bunsen and Roscoe's researches, in *Philosophical Transactions* (1859), vol. cxlix. p. 880, &c., where they describe a constant flame of carbon monoxide gas.

heated and cooled, and we cannot exactly define the state in which it is at any moment, our care in measuring will be wasted, because it can lead to no law. It is of little use to determine very exactly the electric conductibility of carbon, which as graphite or gas carbon conducts like a metal, as diamond is almost a non-conductor, and in several other forms possesses variable and intermediate powers of conduction. It will be of use only for immediate practical applications. Before measuring these we ought to have something to measure of which the conditions are capable of exact definition, and to which at a future time we can recur. Similarly the accuracy of our measurement need not much surpass the accuracy with which we can define the conditions of the object treated.

The speed of electricity in passing through a conductor mainly depends upon the inductive capacity of the surrounding substances, and, except for technical or special purposes, there is little use in measuring velocities which in some cases are one hundred times as great as in other cases. But the maximum speed of electric conduction is probably a constant quantity of great scientific importance, and according to Prof. Clerk Maxwell's determination in 1868 is 174,800 miles per second, or little less than that of light. The true boiling point of water is a point on which practical thermometry depends, and it is highly important to determine that point in relation to the absolute thermometric scale. But when water free from air and impurity is heated there seems to be no definite limit to the temperature it may reach, a temperature of 180° Cent. having been actually observed. Such temperatures, therefore, do not require accurate measurement. All meteorological measurements depending on the accidental condition of the sky are of far less importance than physical measurements in which such accidental conditions do not intervene. Many profound investigations depend upon our knowledge of the radiant energy continually poured upon the earth by the sun; but this must be measured when the sky is perfectly clear, and the absorption of the atmosphere at its minimum. The slightest interference of cloud destroys the value of such a measurement, except for meteorological purposes, which are of vastly less generality and importance. It is seldom useful, again, to measure the height of a snow-covered mountain within a foot, when the thickness of the snow alone may cause it to vary 25 feet or more, when in short the height itself is indefinite to that extent.[1]

Maintenance of Similar Conditions.

Our ultimate object in induction must be to obtain the complete relation between the conditions and the effect, but this relation will generally be so complex that we can only attack it in detail. We must, as far as possible, confine the variation to one condition at a time, and establish a separate relation between each condition and the effect. This is at any rate the first step in approximating to the complete law, and it will be a subsequent question how far the simultaneous variation of several conditions modifies their separate actions. In many experiments, indeed, it is only one condition which we wish to study, and the others are interfering forces which we would avoid if possible. One of the conditions of the motion of a pendulum is the resistance of the air, or other medium in which it swings; but when Newton was desirous of proving the equal gravitation of all substances, he had no interest in the air. His object was to observe a single force only, and so it is in a great many other experiments. Accordingly, one of the most important precautions in investigation consists in maintaining all conditions constant except that which is to be studied. As that admirable experimental philosopher, Gilbert, expressed it,[2] " There is always need of similar preparation, of similar figure, and of equal magnitude, for in dissimilar and unequal circumstances the experiment is doubtful."

In Newton's decisive experiment similar conditions were provided for, with the simplicity which characterises the highest art. The pendulums of which the oscillations were compared consisted of equal boxes of wood, hanging by equal threads, and filled with different substances, so that the total weights should be equal and the centres of oscillation at the same distance from the points of suspension.

---

[1] Humboldt's *Cosmos* (Bohn), vol. i. p. 7.
[2] Gilbert, *De Magnete*, p. 109.

Hence the resistance of the air became approximately a matter of indifference ; for the outward size and shape of the pendulums being the same, the absolute force of resistance would be the same, so long as the pendulums vibrated with equal velocity ; and the weights being equal the resistance would diminish the velocity equally. Hence if any inequality were observed in the vibrations of the two pendulums, it must arise from the only circumstance which was different, namely the chemical nature of the matter within the boxes. No inequality being observed, the chemical nature of substances can have no appreciable influence upon the force of gravitation.[1]

A beautiful experiment was devised by Dr. Joule for the purpose of showing that the gain or loss of heat by a gas is connected, not with the mere change of its volume and density, but with the energy received or given out by the gas. Two strong vessels, connected by a tube and stopcock were placed in water after the air had been exhausted from one vessel and condensed in the other to the extent of twenty atmospheres. The whole apparatus having been brought to a uniform temperature by agitating the water, and the temperature having been exactly observed, the stopcock was opened, so that the air at once expanded and filled the two vessels uniformly. The temperature of the water being again noted was found to be almost unchanged. The experiment was then repeated in an exactly similar manner, except that the strong vessels were placed in separate portions of the water. Now cold was produced in the vessel from which the air rushed, and an almost exactly equal quantity of heat appeared in that to which it was conducted. Thus Dr. Joule clearly proved that rarefaction produces as much heat as cold, and that only when there is disappearance of mechanical energy will there be production of heat.[2] What we have to notice, however, is not so much the result of the experiment, as the simple manner in which a single change in the apparatus, the separation of the portions of water surrounding the air vessels, is made to give indications of the utmost significance.

[1] *Principia*, bk. iii. Prop. vi.
[2] *Philosophical Magazine*, 3rd Series, vol. xxvi. p. 375.

Collective Experiments.

There is an interesting class of experiments which enable us to observe a number of quantitative results in one act. Generally speaking, each experiment yields us but one number, and before we can approach the real processes of reasoning we must laboriously repeat measurement after measurement, until we can lay out a curve of the variation of one quantity as depending on another. We can sometimes abbreviate this labour, by making a quantity vary in different parts of the same apparatus through every required amount. In observing the height to which water rises by the capillary attraction of a glass vessel, we may take a series of glass tubes of different bore, and measure the height through which it rises in each. But if we take two glass plates, and place them vertically in water, so as to be in contact at one vertical side, and slightly separated at the other side, the interval between the plates varies through every intermediate width, and the water rises to a corresponding height, producing at its upper surface a hyperbolic curve.

The absorption of light in passing through a coloured liquid may be beautifully shown by enclosing the liquid in a wedge-shaped glass, so that we have at a single glance an infinite variety of thicknesses in view. As Newton himself remarked, a red liquid viewed in this manner is found to have a pale yellow colour at the thinnest part, and it passes through orange into red, which gradually becomes of a deeper and darker tint.[1] The effect may be noticed in a conical wine-glass. The prismatic analysis of light from such a wedge-shaped vessel discloses the reason, by exhibiting the progressive absorption of different rays of the spectrum as investigated by Dr. J. H. Gladstone.[2]

A moving body may sometimes be made to mark out its own course, like a shooting star which leaves a tail behind it. Thus an inclined jet of water exhibits in the clearest manner the parabolic path of a projectile. In Wheatstone's Kaleidophone the curves produced by the combination of vibrations of different ratios are shown by

[1] *Opticks*, 3rd edit. p. 159.
[2] Watts, *Dictionary of Chemistry*, vol. iii. p. 637.

placing bright reflective buttons on the tops of wires of various forms. The motions are performed so quickly that the eye receives the impression of the path as a complete whole, just as a burning stick whirled round produces a continuous circle. The laws of electric induction are beautifully shown when iron filings are brought under the influence of a magnet, and fall into curves corresponding to what Faraday called the Lines of Magnetic Force. When Faraday tried to define what he meant by his lines of force, he was obliged to refer to the filings. " By mag- netic curves," he says,[1] " I mean lines of magnetic forces which would be depicted by iron filings." Robison had previously produced similar curves by the action of fric- tional electricity, and from a mathematical investigation of the forms of such curves we may infer that magnetic and electric attractions obey the general law of emanation, that of the inverse square of the distance. In the electric brush we have a similar exhibition of the laws of electric attraction.

There are several branches of science in which collective experiments have been used with great advantage. Lich- tenberg's electric figures, produced by scattering electrified powder on an electrified resin cake, so as to show the con- dition of the latter, suggested to Chladni the notion of discovering the state of vibration of plates by strewing sand upon them. The sand collects at the points where the motion is least, and we gain at a glance a comprehension of the undulations of the plate. To this method of experi- ment we owe the beautiful observations of Savart. The exquisite coloured figures exhibited by plates of crystal, when examined by polarised light, afford a more compli- cated example of the same kind of investigation. They led Brewster and Fresnel to an explanation of the properties of the optic axes of crystals. The unequal conduction of heat in crystalline substances has also been shown in a similar manner, by spreading a thin layer of wax over the plate of crystal, and applying heat to a single point. The wax then melts in a circular or elliptic area according as the rate of conduction is uniform or not. Nor should we forget that Newton's rings were an early and most impor-

[1] *Faraday's Life,* by Bence Jones, vol. ii. p. 5.

tant instance of investigations of the same kind, showing the effects of interference of light undulations of all magnitudes at a single view. Herschel gave to all such opportunities of observing directly the results of a general law, the name of *Collective Instances*,[1] and I propose to adopt the name *Collective Experiments*.

Such experiments will in many subjects only give the first hint of the nature of the law in question, but will not admit of any exact measurements. The parabolic form of a jet of water may well have suggested to Galileo his views concerning the path of a projectile; but it would not serve now for the exact investigation of the laws of gravity. It is unlikely that capillary attraction could be exactly measured by the use of inclined plates of glass, and tubes would probably be better for precise investigation. As a general rule, these collective experiments would be most useful for popular illustration. But when the curves are of a precise and permanent character, as in the coloured figures produced by crystalline plates, they may admit of exact measurement. Newton's rings and diffraction fringes allow of very accurate measurements.

Under collective experiments we may perhaps place those in which we render visible the motions of gas or liquid by diffusing some opaque substance in it. The behaviour of a body of air may often be studied in a beautiful way by the use of smoke, as in the production of smoke rings and jets. In the case of liquids lycopodium powder is sometimes employed. To detect the mixture of currents or strata of liquid, I employed very dilute solutions of common salt and silver nitrate, which produce a visible cloud wherever they come into contact.[2] Atmospheric clouds often reveal to us the movements of great volumes of air which would otherwise be quite unapparent.

Periodic Variations.

A large class of investigations is concerned with Periodic Variations. We may define a periodic phenomenon as one which, with the uniform change of the variable, returns

---

[1] *Preliminary Discourse*, &c., p. 185.
[2] *Philosophical Magazine*, July, 1857, 4th Series, vol. xiv. p. 24.

time after time to the same value. If we strike a pendulum it presently returns to the point from which we disturbed it, and while time, the variable, progresses uniformly, it goes on making excursions and returning, until stopped by the dissipation of its energy. If one body in space approaches by gravity towards another, they will revolve round each other in elliptic orbits, and return for an indefinite number of times to the same relative positions. On the other hand a single body projected into empty space, free from the action of any extraneous force, would go on moving for ever in a straight line, according to the first law of motion. In the latter case the variation is called *secular*, because it proceeds during ages in a similar manner, and suffers no περίοδος or going round. It may be doubted whether there really is any motion in the universe which is not periodic. Mr. Herbert Spencer long since adopted the doctrine that all motion is ultimately rhythmical,[1] and abundance of evidence may be adduced in favour of his view.

The so-called secular acceleration of the moon's motion is certainly periodic, and as, so far as we can tell, no body is beyond the attractive power of other bodies, rectilinear motion becomes purely hypothetical, or at least infinitely improbable. All the motions of all the stars must tend to become periodic. Though certain disturbances in the planetary system seem to be uniformly progressive, Laplace is considered to have proved that they really have their limits, so that after an immense time, all the planetary bodies might return to the same places, and the stability of the system be established. Such a theory of periodic stability is really hypothetical, and does not take into account phenomena resulting in the dissipation of energy, which may be a really secular process. For our present purposes we need not attempt to form an opinion on such questions. Any change which does not present the appearance of a periodic character will be empirically regarded as a secular change, so that there will be plenty of non-periodic variations.

The variations which we produce experimentally will often be non-periodic. When we communicate heat to a

---

[1] *First Principles*, 3rd edit. chap. x. p. 253.

gas it increases in bulk or pressure, and as far as we can go
the higher the temperature the higher the pressure. Our
experiments are of course restricted in temperature both
above and below, but there is every reason to believe that
the bulk being the same, the pressure would never return
to the same point at any two different temperatures. We
may of course repeatedly raise and lower the temperature
at regular or irregular intervals entirely at our will, and
the pressure of the gas will vary in like manner and
exactly at the same intervals, but such an arbitrary series
of changes would not constitute Periodic Variation. It
would constitute a succession of distinct experiments,
which would place beyond reasonable doubt the connexion
of cause and effect.

Whenever a phenomenon recurs at equal or nearly
equal intervals, there is, according to the theory of probability, considerable evidence of connexion, because if the
recurrences were entirely casual it is unlikely that they
would happen at equal intervals. The fact that a brilliant
comet had appeared in the years 1301, 1378, 1456, 1531,
1607, and 1682 gave considerable presumption in favour
of the identity of the body, apart from similarity of the
orbit. There is nothing which so fascinates the attention
of men as the recurrence time after time of some unusual
event. Things and appearances which remain ever the
same, like mountains and valleys, fail to excite the curiosity
of a primitive people. It has been remarked by Laplace
that even in his day the rising of Venus in its brightest
phase never failed to excite surprise and interest. So
there is little doubt that the first germ of science arose
in the attention given by Eastern people to the changes
of the moon and the motions of the planets. Perhaps the
earliest astronomical discovery consisted in proving the
identity of the morning and evening stars, on the grounds
of their similarity of aspect and invariable alternation.[1]
Periodical changes of a somewhat complicated kind must
have been understood by the Chaldeans, because they were
aware of the cycle of 6585 days or 19 years which brings
round the new and full moon upon the same days, hours,
and even minutes of the year. The earliest efforts of

[1] Laplace, *System of the World*, vol. i. pp. 50, 54, &c.

scientific prophecy were founded upon this knowledge,
and if at present we cannot help wondering at the precise
anticipations of the nautical almanack, we may imagine
the wonder excited by such predictions in early times.

Combined Periodic Changes.

We shall seldom find a body subject to a single periodic
variation, and free from other disturbances. We may expect the periodic variation itself to undergo variation,
which may possibly be secular, but is more likely to
prove periodic ; nor is there any limit to the complication
of periods beyond periods, or periods within periods, which
may ultimately be disclosed. In studying a phenomenon
of rhythmical character we have a succession of questions
to ask. Is the periodic variation uniform ? If not, is the
change uniform ? If not, is the change itself periodic ?
Is that new period uniform, or subject to any other change,
or not ? and so on *ad infinitum.*

In some cases there may be many distinct causes of
periodic variations, and according to the principle of the
superposition of small effects, to be afterwards considered,
these periodic effects will be simply added together, or at
least approximately so, and the joint result may present a
very complicated subject of investigation. The tides of
the ocean consist of a series of superimposed undulations.
Not only are there the ordinary semi-diurnal tides caused
by sun and moon, but a series of minor tides, such as the
lunar diurnal, the solar diurnal, the lunar monthly, the
lunar fortnightly, the solar annual and solar semi-annual
are gradually being disentangled by the labours of Sir W.
Thomson, Professor Haughton and others.

Variable stars present interesting periodic phenomena ;
while some stars, δ Cephei for instance, are subject to very
regular variations, others, like Mira Ceti, are less constant
in the degrees of brilliancy which they attain or the
rapidity of the changes, possibly on account of some longer
periodic variation.[1] The star β Lyræ presents a double
maximum and minimum in each of its periods of nearly 13
days, and since the discovery of this variation the period

[1] Herschel's *Outlines of Astronomy,* 4th edit. pp. 555—557.

iu a period has probably been on the increase. " At first
the variability was more rapid, then it became gradually
slower ; and this decrease in the length of time reached
its limit between the years 1840 and 1844. During that
time its period was nearly invariable ; at present it is again
decidedly on the decrease.[1] The tracing out of such
complicated variations presents an unlimited field for interesting investigation. The number of such variable stars
already known is considerable, and there is no reason
to suppose that any appreciable fraction of the whole
number has yet been detected.

Principle of Forced Vibrations.

Investigations of the connection of periodic causes and
effects rest upon a principle, which has been demonstrated
by Sir John Herschel for some special cases, and clearly
explained by him in several of his works.[2] The principle
may be formally stated in the following manner : " If one
part of any system connected together either by material
ties, or by the mutual attractions of its members, be continually maintained by any cause, whether inherent in
the constitution of the system or external to it, in a state
of regular periodic motion, that motion will be propagated
throughout the whole system, and will give rise, in every
member of it, and in every part of each member, to
periodic movements executed in equal periods, with that
to which they owe their origin, though not necessarily
synchronous with them in their maxima and minima."
The meaning of the proposition is that the effect of a
periodic cause will be periodic, and will recur at intervals
equal to those of the cause. Accordingly when we find
two phenomena which do proceed, time after time, through
changes of the same period, there is much probability
that they are connected. In this manner, doubtless, Pliny
correctly inferred that the cause of the tides lies in the
sun and the moon, the intervals between successive high
tides being equal to the intervals between the moon's

---

[1] Humboldt's *Cosmos* (Bohn), vol. iii. p. 229.
[2] *Encyclopædia Metropolitana*, art. *Sound*, § 323 ; *Outlines of
Astronomy*, 4th edit., § 650. pp. 410, 487—88 ; *Meteorology, Encyclopædia Britannica*, Reprint, p. 197.

passage across the meridian. Kepler and Descartes too
admitted the connection previous to Newton's demonstration of its precise nature. When Bradley discovered the
apparent motion of the stars arising from the aberration
of light, he was soon able to attribute it to the earth's
annual motion, because it went through its phases in a
year.

The most beautiful instance of induction concerning
periodic changes which can be cited, is the discovery of
an eleven-year period in various meteorological phenomena. It would be difficult to mention any two things
apparently more disconnected than the spots upon the
sun and auroras. As long ago as 1826, Schwabe commenced a regular series of observations of the spots upon
the sun, which has been continued to the present time,
and he was able to show that at intervals of about
eleven years the spots increased much in size and number.
Hardly was this discovery made known, when Lamont
pointed out a nearly equal period of variation in the
declination of the magnetic needle. Magnetic storms or
sudden disturbances of the needle were next shown to
take place most frequently at the times when sun-spots
were prevalent, and as auroras are generally coincident
with magnetic storms, these phenomena were brought
into the cycle. It has since been shown by Professor
Piazzi Smyth and Mr. E. J. Stone, that the temperature
of the earth's surface as indicated by sunken thermome-
ters gives some evidence of a like period. The existence
of a periodic cause having once been established, it is
quite to be expected, according to the principle of forced
vibrations, that its influence will be detected in all
meteorological phenomena.

Integrated Variations.

In considering the various modes in which one effect
may depend upon another, we must set in a distinct
class those which arise from the accumulated effects of
a constantly acting cause. When water runs out of a
cistern, the velocity of motion depends, according to
Torricelli's theorem, on the height of the surface of the
water above the vent; but the amount of water which

leaves the cistern in a given time depends upon the aggregate result of that velocity, and is only to be ascertained by the mathematical process of integration. When one gravitating body falls towards another, the force of gravity varies according to the inverse square of the distance; to obtain the velocity produced we must integrate or sum the effects of that law ; and to obtain the space passed over by the body in a given time, we must integrate again.

In periodic variations the same distinction must be drawn. The heating power of the sun's rays at any place on the earth varies every day with the height attained, and is greatest about noon; but the temperature of the air will not be greatest at the same time. This temperature is an integrated effect of the sun's heating power, and as long as the sun is able to give more heat to the air than the air loses in other ways, the temperature continues to rise, so that the maximum is deferred until about 3 P.M. Similarly the hottest day of the year falls, on an average, about one month later than the summer solstice, and all the seasons lag about a month behind the motions of the sun. In the case of the tides, too, the effect of the moon's attractive power is never greatest when the power is greatest; the effect always lags more or less behind the cause. Yet the intervals between successive tides are equal, in the absence of disturbance, to the intervals between the passages of the moon across the meridian. Thus the principle of forced vibrations holds true.

In periodic phenomena, however, curious results sometimes follow from the integration of effects. If we strike a pendulum, and then repeat the stroke time after time at the same part of the vibration, all the strokes concur in adding to the momentum, and we can thus increase the extent and violence of the vibrations to any degree. We can stop the pendulum again by strokes applied when it is moving in the opposite direction, and the effects being added together will soon bring it to rest. Now if we alter the intervals of the strokes so that each two successive strokes act in opposite manners they will neutralise each other, and the energy expended will be turned into heat or sound at the point of percussion. Similar effects occur in all cases of rhythmical motion. If a musical note is sounded in a room containing a piano, the string corresponding to it will be thrown into vibration, because every successive stroke of the air-waves upon the string finds it in like position as regards the vibration, and thus adds to its energy of motion. But the other strings being incapable of vibrating with the same rapidity are struck at various points of their vibrations, and one stroke will soon be opposed by one contrary in effect. All phenomena of *resonance* arise from this coincidence in time of undulation. The air in a pipe closed at one end, and about 12 inches in length, is capable of vibrating 512 times in a second. If, then, the note C is sounded in front of the open end of the pipe, every successive vibration of the air is treasured up as it were in the motion of the air. In a pipe of different length the pulses of air would strike each other, and the mechanical energy being transmuted into heat would become no longer perceptible as sound.

Accumulated vibrations sometimes become so intense as to lead to unexpected results. A glass vessel if touched with a violin bow at a suitable point may be fractured with the violence of vibration. A suspension bridge may be broken down if a company of soldiers walk across it in steps the intervals of which agree with the vibrations of the bridge itself. But if they break the step or march in either quicker or slower pace, they may have no perceptible effect upon the bridge. In fact if the impulses communicated to any vibrating body are synchronous with its vibrations, the energy of those vibrations will be unlimited, and may fracture any body.

Let us now consider what will happen if the strokes be not exactly at the same intervals as the vibrations of the body, but, say, a little slower. Then a succession of strokes will meet the body in nearly but not quite the same position, and their efforts will be accumulated. Afterwards the strokes will begin to fall when the body is in the opposite phase. Imagine that one pendulum moving from one extreme point to another in a second, should be struck by another pendulum which makes 61 beats in a minute; then, if the pendulums commence together, they will at the end of 30½ beats be moving in opposite directions. Hence whatever energy was communicated in the first half minute will be neutralised by the opposite effect of that given in the second half. The effect of the strokes of the second pendulum will therefore be alternately to increase and decrease the vibrations of the first, so that a new kind of vibration will be produced running through its phases in 61 seconds. An effect of this kind was actually observed by Ellicott, a member of the Royal Society, in the case of two clocks.[1] He found that through the wood-work by which the clocks were connected a slight impulse was transmitted, and each pendulum alternately lost and gained momentum. Each clock, in fact, tended to stop the other at regular intervals, and in the intermediate times to be stopped by the other.

Many disturbances in the planetary system depend upon the same principle; for if one planet happens always to pull another in the same direction in similar parts of their orbits, the effects, however slight, will be accumulated, and a disturbance of large ultimate amount and of long period will be produced. The long inequality in the motions of Jupiter and Saturn is thus due to the fact that five times the mean motion of Saturn is very nearly equal to twice the mean motion of Jupiter, causing a coincidence in their relative positions and disturbing powers. The rolling of ships depends mainly upon the question whether the period of vibration of the ship corresponds or not with the intervals at which the waves strike her. Much which seems at first sight unaccountable in the behaviour of vessels is thus explained, and the loss of the *Captain* is a sad case in point.

[1] *Philosophical Transactions*, (1739), vol. xli. p. 126.

CHAPTER XXI.

THEORY OF APPROXIMATION.

In order that we may gain a true understanding of the kind, degree, and value of the knowledge which we acquire by experimental investigation, it is requisite that we should be fully conscious of its approximate character. We must learn to distinguish between what we can know and cannot know—between the questions which admit of solution, and those which only seem to be solved. Many persons may be misled by the expression *exact science*, and may think that the knowledge acquired by scientific methods admits of our reaching absolutely true laws, exact to the last degree. There is even a prevailing impression that when once mathematical formulæ have been successfully applied to a branch of science, this portion of knowledge assumes a new nature, and admits of reasoning of a higher character than those sciences which are still unmathematical.

The very satisfactory degree of accuracy attained in the science of astronomy gives a certain plausibility to erroneous notions of this kind. Some persons no doubt consider it to be *proved* that planets move in ellipses, in such a manner that all Kepler's laws hold exactly true; but there is a double error in any such notions. In the first place, Kepler's laws are *not proved*, if by proof we mean certain demonstration of their exact truth. In the next place, even assuming Kepler's laws to be exactly true in a theoretical point of view, the planets never move according to those laws. Even if we could observe the motions of a planet, of a perfect globular form, free from all perturbing or retarding forces, we could never prove that it moved in a perfect ellipse. To prove the elliptical form we should have to measure infinitely small angles, and infinitely small fractions of a second; we should have to perform impossibilities. All we can do is to show that the motion of an unperturbed planet approaches *very nearly* to the form of an ellipse, and more nearly the more accurately our observations are made. But if we go on to assert that the path *is* an ellipse we pass beyond our data, and make an assumption which cannot be verified by observation.

But, secondly, as a matter of fact no planet does move in a perfect ellipse, or manifest the truth of Kepler's laws exactly. The law of gravity prevents its own results from being clearly exhibited, because the mutual perturbations of the planets distort the elliptical paths. Those laws, again, hold exactly true only of infinitely small bodies, and when two great globes, like the sun and Jupiter, attract each other, the law must be modified. The periodic time is then shortened in the ratio of the square root of the number expressing the sun's mass, to that of the sum of the numbers expressing the masses of the sun and planet, as was shown by Newton.[1] Even at the present day discrepancies exist between the observed dimensions of the planetary orbits and their theoretical magnitudes, after making allowance for all disturbing causes.[2] Nothing is more certain in scientific method than that approximate coincidence alone can be expected. In the measurement of continuous quantity perfect correspondence must be accidental, and should give rise to suspicion rather than to satisfaction.

One remarkable result of the approximate character of our observations is that we could never prove the existence of perfectly circular or parabolic movement, even if it existed. The circle is a singular case of the ellipse, for which the eccentricity is zero; it is infinitely improbable that any planet, even if undisturbed by other bodies, would have a circle for its orbit; but if the orbit were a circle we could never prove the entire absence of eccen-

---

[1] *Principia*, bk. iii. Prop. 15.
[2] Lockyer's *Lessons in Elementary Astronomy*, p. 301.

tricity. All that we could do would be to declare the divergence from the circular form to be inappreciable. Delambre was unable to detect the slightest ellipticity in the orbit of Jupiter's first satellite, but he could only infer that the orbit was *nearly* circular. The parabola is the singular limit between the ellipse and the hyperbola. As there are elliptic and hyperbolic comets, so we might conceive the existence of a parabolic comet. Indeed if an undisturbed comet fell towards the sun from an infinite distance it would move in a parabola ; but we could never prove that it so moved.

Substitution of Simple Hypotheses.

In truth men never can solve problems fulfilling the complex circumstances of nature. All laws and explanations are in a certain sense hypothetical, and apply exactly to nothing which we can know to exist. In place of the actual objects which we see and feel, the mathematician substitutes imaginary objects, only partially resembling those represented, but so devised that the discrepancies are not of an amount to alter seriously the character of the solution. When we probe the matter to the bottom physical astronomy is as hypothetical as Euclid's elements. There may exist in nature perfect straight lines, triangles, circles, and other regular geometrical figures ; to our science it is a matter of indifference whether they do or do not exist, because in any case they must be beyond our powers of perception. If we submitted a perfect circle to the most rigorous scrutiny, it is impossible that we should discover whether it were perfect or not. Nevertheless in geometry we argue concerning perfect curves, and rectilinear figures, and the conclusions apply to existing objects so far as we can assure ourselves that they agree with the hypothetical conditions of our reasoning. This is in reality all that we can do in the most perfect of the sciences.

Doubtless in astronomy we meet with the nearest approximation to actual conditions. The law of gravity is not a complex one in itself, and we believe it with much probability to be exactly true ; but we cannot calculate out in any real case its accurate results. The law asserts

that every particle of matter in the universe attracts every
other particle, with a force depending on the masses of
the particles and their distances. We cannot know the
force acting on any particle unless we know the masses
and distances and positions of all other particles in the
universe. The physical astronomer has made a sweeping
assumption, namely, that all the millions of existing
systems exert no perturbing effects on our planetary
system, that is to say, no effects in the least appreciable.
The problem at once becomes hypothetical, because there
is little doubt that gravitation between our sun and planets
and other systems does exist. Even when they consider
the relations of our planetary bodies *inter se*, all their
processes are only approximate. In the first place they
assume that each of the planets is a perfect ellipsoid,
with a smooth surface and a homogeneous interior. That
this assumption is untrue every mountain and valley, every
sea, every mine affords conclusive evidence. If astronomers
are to make their calculations perfect, they must not only
take account of the Himalayas and the Andes, but must
calculate separately the attraction of every hill, nay, of
every ant-hill. So far are they from having considered
any local inequality of the surface, that they have not yet
decided upon the general form of the earth ; it is still a
matter of speculation whether or not the earth is an ellipsoid with three unequal axes. If, as is probable, the globe
is irregularly compressed in some directions, the calculations of astronomers will have to be repeated and refined,
in order that they may approximate to the attractive
power of such a body. If we cannot accurately learn the
form of our own earth, how can we expect to ascertain
that of the moon, the sun, and other planets, in some of
which probably are irregularities of greater proportional
amount ?

In a further way the science of physical astronomy is
merely approximate and hypothetical. Given homogeneous
ellipsoids acting upon each other according to the law of
gravity, the best mathematicians have never and perhaps
never will determine exactly the resulting movements.
Even when three bodies simultaneously attract each other
the complication of effects is so great that only approximate calculations can be made. Astronomers have not

even attempted the general problem of the simultaneous attractions of four, five, six, or more bodies; they resolve the general problem into so many different problems of three bodies. The principle upon which the calculations of physical astronomy proceed, is to neglect every quantity which does not seem likely to lead to an effect appreciable in observation, and the quantities rejected are far more numerous and complex than the few larger terms which are retained. All then is merely approximate.

Concerning other branches of physical science the same statements are even more evidently true. We speak and calculate about inflexible bars, inextensible lines, heavy points, homogeneous substances, uniform spheres, perfect fluids and gases, and we deduce a great number of beautiful theorems; but all is hypothetical. There is no such thing as an inflexible bar, an inextensible line, nor any one of the other perfect objects of mechanical science; they are to be classed with those mythical existences, the straight line, triangle, circle, &c., about which Euclid so freely reasoned. Take the simplest operation considered in statics—the use of a crowbar in raising a heavy stone, and we shall find, as Thomson and Tait have pointed out, that we neglect far more than we observe.[1] If we suppose the bar to be quite rigid, the fulcrum and stone perfectly hard, and the points of contact real points, we may give the true relation of the forces. But in reality the bar must bend, and the extension and compression of different parts involve us in difficulties. Even if the bar be homogeneous in all its parts, there is no mathematical theory capable of determining with accuracy all that goes on; if, as is infinitely more probable, the bar is not homogeneous, the complete solution will be immensely more complicated, but hardly more hopeless. No sooner had we determined the change of form according to simple mechanical principles, than we should discover the interference of thermodynamic principles. Compression produces heat and extension cold, and thus the conditions of the problem are modified throughout. In attempting a fourth approximation we should have to allow for the conduction of heat from one part of the bar to another. All these effects are

[1] *Treatise on Natural Philosophy*, vol. i. pp. 337, &c.

utterly inappreciable in a practical point of view, if the
bar be a good stout one ; but in a theoretical point of
view they entirely prevent our saying that we have solved
a natural problem.   The faculties of the human mind,
even when aided by the wonderful powers of abbreviation
conferred by analytical methods, are utterly unable to cope
with the complications of any real problem.   And had
we exhausted all the known phenomena of a mechanical
problem, how can we tell that hidden phenomena, as yet
undetected, do not intervene in the commonest actions ?
It is plain that no phenomenon comes within the sphere of
our senses unless it possesses a momentum capable of
irritating the appropriate nerves.   There may then be
worlds of phenomena too slight to rise within the scope of
our consciousness.

All the instruments with which we perform our measurements are faulty.   We assume that a plumb-line gives a
vertical line; but this is never true in an absolute sense,
owing to the attraction of mountains and other inequalities
in the surface of the earth.   In an accurate trigonometrical
survey, the divergencies of the plumb-line must be approximately determined and allowed for.   We assume a
surface of mercury to be a perfect plane, but even in the
breadth of 5 inches there is a calculable divergence from a
true plane of about one ten-millionth part of an inch ; and
this surface further diverges from true horizontality as the
plumb-line does from true verticality.   That most perfect
instrument, the pendulum, is not theoretically perfect,
except for infinitely small arcs of vibration, and the
delicate experiments performed with the torsion balance
proceed on the assumption that the force of torsion of a
wire is proportional to the angle of torsion, which again is
only true for infinitely small angles.

Such is the purely approximate character of all our
operations that it is not uncommon to find the theoretically
worse method giving truer results than the theoretically
perfect method.   The common pendulum which is not
isochronous is better for practical purposes than the
cycloidal pendulum, which is isochronous in theory but
subject to mechanical difficulties.   The spherical form is
not the correct form for a speculum or lense, but it differs
so slightly from the true form, and is so much more easily

produced mechanically, that it is generally best to rest content with the spherical surface. Even in a six-feet mirror the difference between the parabola and the sphere is only about one ten-thousandth part of an inch, a thickness which would be taken off in a few rubs of the polisher. Watts' ingenious parallel motion was intended to produce rectilinear movement of the piston-rod. In reality the motion was always curvilinear, but for his purposes a certain part of the curve approximated sufficiently to a straight line.

Approximation to Exact Laws.

Though we can not prove numerical laws with perfect accuracy, it would be a great mistake to suppose that there is any inexactness in the laws of nature. We may even discover a law which we believe to represent the action of forces with perfect exactness. The mind may seem to pass in advance of its data, and choose out certain numerical results as absolutely true. We can never really pass beyond our data, and so far as assumption enters in, so far want of certainty will attach to our conclusions ; nevertheless we may sometimes rightly prefer a probable assumption of a precise law to numerical results, which are at the best only approximate. We must accordingly draw a strong distinction between the laws of nature which we believe to be accurately stated in our formulas, and those to which our statements only make an approximation, so that at a future time the law will be differently stated.

The law of gravitation is expressed in the form $F = \dfrac{Mm}{D^2}$, meaning that gravity is proportional directly to the product of the gravitating masses, and indirectly to the square of their distance. The latent heat of steam is expressed by the equation $\log F = a + ba^t + c\beta^t$, in which are five quantities a, b, c, a, β, to be determined by experiment. There is every reason to believe that in the progress of science the law of gravity will remain entirely unaltered, and the only effect of further inquiry will be to render it a more and more probable expression of the absolute truth. The law of the latent heat of steam on the other hand, will be modified by every new series of experiments, and it may not improbably be shown that the assumed law can never be made to agree exactly with the results of experiment.

Philosophers have not always supposed that the law of gravity was exactly true. Newton, though he had the highest confidence in its truth, admitted that there were motions in the planetary system which he could not reconcile with the law. Euler and Clairaut who were, with D'Alembert, the first to apply the full powers of mathematical analysis to the theory of gravitation as explaining the perturbations of the planets, did not think the law sufficiently established to attribute all discrepancies to the errors of calculation and observation. They did not feel certain that the force of gravity exactly obeyed the well-known rule. The law might involve other powers of the distance. It might be expressed in the form

$$F = \cdots + \frac{a}{D} + \frac{b}{D^2} + \frac{c}{D^3} + \cdots$$

and the coefficients a and c might be so small that those terms would become apparent only in very accurate comparisons with fact. Attempts have been made to account for difficulties, by attributing value to such neglected terms. Gauss at one time thought the even more fundamental principle of gravity, that the force is dependent only on mass and distance, might not be exactly true, and he undertook accurate pendulum experiments to test this opinion. Only as repeated doubts have time after time been resolved in favour of the law of Newton, has it been assumed as precisely correct. But this belief does not rest on experiment or observation only. The calculations of physical astronomy, however accurate, could never show that the other terms of the above expression were absolutely devoid of value. It could only be shown that they had such slight value as never to become apparent.

There are, however, other reasons why the law is probably complete and true as commonly stated. Whatever influence spreads from a point, and expands uniformly through space, will doubtless vary inversely in intensity as the square of the distance, because the area over which it is spread increases as the square of the radius. This part of the law of gravity may be considered as due to the properties of space, and there is a perfect analogy in this respect between gravity and all other *emanating* forces, as was pointed out by Keill.[1] Thus the undulations of light, heat, and sound, and the attractions of electricity and magnetism obey the very same law so far as we can ascertain. If the molecules of a gas or the particles of matter constituting odour were to start from a point and spread uniformly, their distances would increase and their density decrease according to the same principle.

Other laws of nature stand in a similar position. Dalton's laws of definite combining proportions never have been, and never can be, exactly proved; but chemists having shown, to a considerable degree of approximation, that the elements combine together as if each element had atoms of an invariable mass, assume that this is exactly true. They go even further. Prout pointed out in 1815 that the equivalent weights of the elements appeared to be simple numbers ; and the researches of Dumas, Pelouze, Marignac, Erdmann, Stas, and others have gradually rendered it likely that the atomic weights of hydrogen, carbon, oxygen, nitrogen, chlorine, and silver, are in the ratios of the numbers 1, 12, 16, 14, 35·5, and 108. Chemists then step beyond their data; they throw aside their actual experimental numbers, and assume that the true ratios are not those exactly indicated by any weighings, but the simple ratios of these numbers. They boldly assume that the discrepancies are due to experimental errors, and they are justified by the fact that the more elaborate and skilful the researches on the subject, the more nearly their assumption is verified. Potassium is the only element whose atomic weight has been determined with great care, but which has not shown an approach to a simple ratio with the other elements. This exception may be due to some unsuspected cause of error.[2] A similar assumption is made in the law of definite combining volumes of gases, and Brodie has clearly pointed out the line of argument by which the chemist, observing that the discrepancies between the law and fact are within the limits of experimental error, assumes that they are due to error.[3]

---

[1] *An Introduction to Natural Philosophy*, 3rd edit. 1733, p, 5.
[2] Watts, *Dictionary of Chemistry*, vol. i. p. 455.
[3] *Philosophical Transactions*, (1866) vol. clvi. p. 809.

Faraday, in one of his researches, expressly makes an assumption of the same kind. Having shown, with some degree of experimental precision, that there exists a simple proportion between quantities of electrical energy and the quantities of chemical substances which it can decompose, so that for every atom dissolved in the battery cell an atom ought theoretically, that is without regard to dissipation of some of the energy, to be decomposed in the electrolytic cell, he does not stop at his numerical results. " I have not hesitated," he says,[1] " to apply the more strict results of chemical analysis to correct the numbers obtained as electrolytic results. This, it is evident, may be done in a great number of cases, without using too much liberty towards the due severity of scientific research."

The law of the conservation of energy, one of the widest of all physical generalisations, rests upon the same footing. The most that we can do by experiment is to show that the energy entering into any experimental combination is almost equal to what comes out of it, and more nearly so the more accurately we perform the measurements. Absolute equality is always a matter of assumption. We cannot even prove the indestructibility of matter; for were an exceedingly minute fraction of existing matter to vanish in any experiment, say one part in ten millions, we could never detect the loss.

Successive Approximations to Natural Conditions.

When we examine the history of scientific problems, we find that one man or one generation is usually able to make but a single step at a time. A problem is solved for the first time by making some bold hypothetical simplification, upon which the next investigator makes hypothetical modifications approaching more nearly to the truth. Errors are successively pointed out in previous solutions, until at last there might seem little more to be desired. Careful examination, however, will show that a series of minor inaccuracies remain to be corrected and explained, were our powers of reasoning sufficiently great, and the purpose adequate in importance.

---

[1] *Experimental Researches in Electricity*, vol. i. p. 246.

Newton's successful solution of the problem of the planetary movements entirely depended at first upon a great simplification. The law of gravity only applies directly to two infinitely small particles, so that when we deal with vast globes like the earth, Jupiter, and the sun, we have an immense aggregate of separate attractions to deal with, and the law of the aggregate need not coincide with the law of the elementary particles. But Newton, by a great effort of mathematical reasoning, was able to show that two homogeneous spheres of matter act as if the whole of their masses were concentrated at the centres ; in short, that such spheres are centrobaric bodies (p. 364). He was then able with comparative ease to calculate the motions of the planets on the hypothesis of their being spheres, and to show that the results roughly agreed with observation.   Newton, indeed, was one of the few men who could make two great steps at once.   He did not rest contented with the spherical hypothesis ; having reason to believe that the earth was really a spheroid with a protuberance around the equator, he proceeded to a second approximation, and proved that the attraction of the protuberant matter upon the moon accounted for the precession of the equinoxes, and led to various complicated effects.   But, (p. 459), even the spheroidal hypothesis is far from the truth.   It takes no account of the irregularities of surface, the great protuberance of land in Central Asia and South America, and the deficiency in the bed of the Atlantic.

To determine the law according to which a projectile, such as a cannon ball, moves through the atmosphere is a problem very imperfectly solved at the present day, but in which many successive advances have been made.   So little was known concerning the subject three or four centuries ago that a cannon ball was supposed to move at first in a straight line, and after a time to be deflected into a curve.   Tartaglia ventured to maintain that the path was curved throughout, as by the principle of continuity it should be ; but the ingenuity of Galileo was required to prove this opinion, and to show that the curve was approximately a parabola.   It is only, however, under forced hypotheses that we can assert the path of a projectile to be truly a parabola : the path must be through a perfect vacuum, where there is no resisting medium of any kind; the force of gravity must be uniform and act in parallel lines; or else the moving body must be either a mere point, or a perfect centrobaric body, that is a body possessing a definite centre of gravity. These conditions cannot be really fulfilled in practice. The next great step in the problem was made by Newton and Huyghens, the latter of whom asserted that the atmosphere would offer a resistance proportional to the velocity of the moving body, and concluded that the path would have in consequence a logarithmic character. Newton investigated in a general manner the subject of resisting media, and came to the conclusion that the resistance is more nearly proportional to the square of the velocity. The subject then fell into the hands of Daniel Bernoulli, who pointed out the enormous resistance of the air in cases of rapid movement, and calculated that a cannon ball, if fired vertically in a vacuum, would rise eight times as high as in the atmosphere. In recent times an immense amount both of theoretical and experimental investigation has been spent upon the subject, since it is one of importance in the art of war. Successive approximations to the true law have been made, but nothing like a complete and final solution has been achieved or even hoped for.[1]

It is quite to be expected that the earliest experimenters in any branch of science will overlook errors which afterwards become most apparent. The Arabian astronomers determined the meridian by taking the middle point between the places of the sun when at equal altitudes on the same day. They overlooked the fact that the sun has its own motion in the time between the observations. Newton thought that the mutual disturbances of the planets might be disregarded, excepting perhaps the effect of the mutual attraction of the greater planets, Jupiter and Saturn, near their conjunction.[2] The expansion of quicksilver was long used as the measure of temperature, no clear idea being possessed of temperature apart from some of its more obvious effects. Rumford, in the first experiment leading to a determination of the mechanical

---

[1] Hutton's *Mathematical Dictionary*, vol. ii. pp. 287—292.
[2] *Principia*, bk. iii. Prop. 13.

equivalent of heat, disregarded the heat absorbed by the apparatus, otherwise he would, in Dr. Joule's opinion, have come nearly to the correct result.   •

It is surprising to learn the number of causes of error which enter into the simplest experiment, when we strive to attain rigid accuracy. We cannot accurately perform the simple experiment of compressing gas in a bent tube by a column of mercury, in order to test the truth of Boyle's Law, without paying regard to—(1) the variations of atmospheric pressure, which are communicated to the gas through the mercury; (2) the compressibility of mercury, which causes the column of mercury to vary in density; (3) the temperature of the mercury throughout the column; (4) the temperature of the gas, which is with difficulty maintained invariable; (5) the expansion of the glass tube containing the gas. Although Regnault took all these circumstances into account in his examination of the law,[1] there is no reason to suppose that he exhausted the sources of inaccuracy.

The early investigations concerning the nature of waves in elastic media proceeded upon the assumption that waves of different lengths would travel with equal speed. Newton's theory of sound led him to this conclusion, and observation (p. 295) had verified the inference. When the undulatory theory came to be applied at the commencement of this century to explain the phenomena of light, a great difficulty was encountered. The angle at which a ray of light is refracted in entering a denser medium depends, according to that theory, on the velocity with which the wave travels, so that if all waves of light were to travel with equal velocity in the same medium, the dispersion of mixed light by the prism and the production of the spectrum could not take place. Some most striking phenomena were thus in direct conflict with the theory. Cauchy first pointed out the explanation, namely, that all previous investigators had made an arbitrary assumption for the sake of simplifying the calculations. They had assumed that the particles of the vibrating medium are so close together that the intervals are inconsiderable compared with the length of the wave.

---

[1] Jamin, *Cours de Physique*, vol. i. pp. 282, 283.

This hypothesis happened to be approximately true in the case of air, so that no error was discovered in experiments on sound. Had it not been so, the earlier analysts would probably have failed to give any solution, and the progress of the subject might have been retarded. Cauchy was able to make a new approximation under the more difficult supposition, that the particles of the vibrating medium are situated at considerable distances, and act and react upon the neighbouring particles by attractive and repulsive forces. To calculate the rate of propagation of disturbance in such a medium is a work of excessive difficulty. The complete solution of the problem appears indeed to be beyond human power, so that we must be content, as in the case of the planetary motions, to look forward to successive approximations. All that Cauchy could do was to show that certain quantities, neglected in previous theories, became of considerable amount under the new conditions of the problem, so that there will exist a relation between the length of the wave, and the velocity at which it travels. To remove, then, the difficulties in the way of the undulatory theory of light, a new approach to probable conditions was needed.[1]

In a similar manner Fourier's theory of the conduction and radiation of heat was based upon the hypothesis that the quantity of heat passing along any line is simply proportional to the rate of change of temperature. But it has since been shown by Forbes that the conductivity of a body diminishes as its temperature increases. All the details of Fourier's solution therefore require modification, and the results are in the meantime to be regarded as only approximately true.[2]

We ought to distinguish between those problems which are physically and those which are merely mathematically incomplete. In the latter case the physical law is correctly seized, but the mathematician neglects, or is more often unable to follow out the law in all its results. The law of gravitation and the principles of harmonic or undulatory-movement, even supposing the data to be correct,

---

[1] Lloyd's *Lectures on the Wave Theory*, pp. 22, 23.
[2] Tait's *Thermodynamics*, p. 10.

can never be followed into all their ultimate results. Young explained the production of Newton's rings by supposing that the rays reflected from the upper and lower surfaces of a thin film of a certain thickness were in opposite phases, and thus neutralised each other. It was pointed out, however, that as the light reflected from the nearer surface must be undoubtedly a little brighter than that from the further surface, the two rays ought not to neutralise each other so completely as they are observed to do. It was finally shown by Poisson that the discrepancy arose only from incomplete solution of the problem ; for the light which has once got into the film must be to a certain extent reflected backwards and forwards *ad infinitum ;* and if we follow out this course of the light by perfect mathematical analysis, absolute darkness may be shown to result from the interference of the rays.[1] In this case the natural laws concerned, those of reflection and refraction, are accurately known, and the only difficulty consists in developing their full consequences.

Discovery of Hypothetically Simple Laws.

In some branches of science we meet with natural laws of a simple character which are in a certain point of view exactly true and yet can never be manifested as exactly true in natural phenomena. Such, for instance, are the laws concerning what is called a *perfect gas.* The gaseous state of matter is that in which the properties of matter are exhibited in the simplest manner. There is much advantage accordingly in approaching the question of molecular mechanics from this side. But when we ask the question—What is a gas ? the answer must be a hypothetical one. Finding that gases *nearly* obey the law of Boyle and Mariotte ; that they *nearly* expand by heat at the uniform rate of one part in 272·9 of their volume at 0° for each degree centigrade ; and that they *more nearly* fulfil these conditions the more distant the point of temperature at which we examine them from the liquefying point, we pass by the principle of con-

---

[1] Lloyd's *Lectures on the Wave Theory*, pp. 82, 83.

tinuity to the conception of a perfect gas. Such a gas would probably consist of atoms of matter at so great a distance from each other as to exert no attractive forces upon each other ; but for this condition to be fulfilled the distances must be infinite, so that an absolutely perfect gas cannot exist. But the perfect gas is not merely a limit to which we may approach, it is a limit passed by at least one real gas. It has been shown by Despretz, Pouillet, Dulong, Arago, and finally Regnault, that all gases diverge from the Boylean law, and in nearly all cases the density of the gas increases in a somewhat greater ratio than the pressure, indicating a tendency on the part of the molecules to approximate of their own accord. In the more condensable gases such as sulphurous acid, ammonia, and cyanogen, this tendency is strongly apparent near the liquefying point. Hydrogen, on the contrary, diverges from the law of a perfect gas in the opposite direction, that is, the density increases less than in the ratio of the pressure.[1] This is a singular exception, the bearing of which I am unable to comprehend.

All gases diverge again from the law of uniform expansion by heat, but the divergence is less as the gas in question is less condensable, or examined at a temperature more removed from its liquefying point. Thus the perfect gas must have an infinitely high temperature. According to Dalton's law each gas in a mixture retains its own properties unaffected by the presence of any other gas.[2] This law is probably true only by approximation, but it is obvious that it would be true of the perfect gas with infinitely distant particles.[3]

Mathematical Principles of Approximation.

The approximate character of physical science will be rendered more plain if we consider it from a mathematical point of view. Throughout quantitative investigations we deal with the relation of one quantity to other quantities,

[1] Jamin, *Cours de Physique*, vol. i. pp. 283—288.
[2] Joule and Thomson, *Philosophical Transactions*, 1854, vol. cxliv. p. 337.
[3] The properties of a perfect gas have been described by Rankine, *Transactions of the Royal Society of Edinburgh*, vol. xxv. p. 561.

of which it is a function ; but the subject is sufficiently complicated if we view one quantity as a function of one other. Now, as a general rule, a function can be developed or expressed as the sum of quantities, the values of which depend upon the successive powers of the variable quantity. If y be a function of x then we may say that

$$y = A + Bx + Cx^2 + Dx^3 + Ex^4 \ldots$$

In this equation, A, B, C, D, &c., are fixed quantities, of different values in different cases. The terms may be infinite in number or after a time may cease to have any value. Any of the coefficients A, B, C, &c., may be zero or negative ; but whatever they be they are fixed. The quantity x on the other hand may be made what we like, being variable. Suppose, in the first place, that x and y are both lengths. Let us assume that $\frac{1}{10,000}$ part of an inch is the least that we can take note of. Then when x is one hundredth of an inch, we have $x^2 = \frac{1}{10,000}$, and if C be less than unity, the term Cx^2 will be inappreciable, being less than we can measure. Unless any of the quantities D, E, &c., should happen to be very great, it is evident that all the succeeding terms will also be inappreciable, because the powers of x become rapidly smaller in geometrical ratio. Thus when x is made small enough the quantity y seems to obey the equation

$$y = A + Bx.$$

If x should be still less, if it should become as small, for instance, as $\frac{1}{1,000,000}$ of an inch, and B should not be very great, then y would appear to be the fixed quantity A, and would not seem to vary with x at all. On the other hand, were x to grow greater, say equal to $\frac{1}{10}$ inch, and C not be very small, the term Cx^2 would become appreciable, and the law would now be more complicated.

We can invert the mode of viewing this question, and suppose that while the quantity y undergoes variations depending on many powers of x, our power of detecting the changes of value is more or less acute. While our powers of observation remain very rude we may be unable to detect any change in the quantity at all, that is to say, Bx may always be too small to come within

our notice, just as in former days the fixed stars were so
called because they remained at apparently fixed distances
from each other. With the use of telescopes and micrometers we become able to detect the existence of some
motion, so that the distance of one star from another may
be expressed by $A + Bx$, the term including x^2 being
still inappreciable. Under these circumstances the star
will seem to move uniformly, or in simple proportion to
the time x. With much improved means of measurement
it will probably be found that this uniformity of motion
is only apparent, and that there exists some acceleration
or retardation. More careful investigation will show the
law to be more and more complicated than was previously
supposed.

There is yet another way of explaining the apparent
results of a complicated law. If we take any curve and
regard a portion of it free from any kind of discontinuity,
we may represent the character of such portion by an
equation of the form

$$y = A + Bx + Cx^2 + Dx^3 + \ldots \ldots$$

Restrict the attention to a very small portion of the curve,
and the eye will be unable to distinguish its difference
from a straight line, which amounts to saying that in the
portion examined the term Cx^2 has no value appreciable
by the eye. Take a larger portion of the curve and it will
be apparent that it possesses curvature, but it will be
possible to draw a parabola or ellipse so that the curve
shall apparently coincide with a portion of that parabola
or ellipse. In the same way if we take larger and larger
arcs of the curve it will assume the character successively
of a curve of the third, fourth, and perhaps higher degrees ;
that is to say, it corresponds to equations involving the
third, fourth, and higher powers of the variable quantity.

We have arrived then at the conclusion that every phenomenon, when its amount can only be rudely measured,
will either be of fixed amount, or will seem to vary uniformly like the distance between two inclined straight
lines. More exact measurement may show the error of
this first assumption, and the variation will then appear
to be like that of the distance between a straight line
and a parabola or ellipse. We may afterwards find that
a curve of the third or higher degrees is really required

to represent the variation. I propose to call the variation of a quantity *linear, elliptic, cubic, quartic, quintic,* &c., according as it is discovered to involve the first, second, third, fourth, fifth, or higher powers of the variable. It is a general rule in quantitative investigation that we commence by discovering linear, and afterwards proceed to elliptic or more complicated laws of variation. The approximate curves which we employ are all, according to De Morgan's use of the name, parabolas of some order or other; and since the common parabola of the second order is approximately the same as a very elongated ellipse, and is in fact an infinitely elongated ellipse, it is convenient and proper to call variation of the second order *elliptic.* It might also be called *quadric* variation.

As regards many important phenomena we are yet only in the first stage of approximation. We know that the sun and many so-called fixed stars, especially 61 Cygni, have a proper motion through space, and the direction of this motion at the present time is known with some degree of accuracy. But it is hardly consistent with the theory of gravity that the path of any body should really be a straight line. Hence, we must regard a rectilinear path as only a provisional description of the motion, and look forward to the time when its curvature will be detected, though centuries perhaps must first elapse.

We are accustomed to assume that on the surface of the earth the force of gravity is uniform, because the variation is of so slight an amount that we are scarcely able to detect it. But supposing we could measure the variation, we should find it simply proportional to the height. Taking the earth's radius to be unity, let h be the height at which we measure the force of gravity. Then by the well-known law of the inverse square, that force will be proportional to

$$\frac{g}{(1 + h)^2}, \text{ or to } g(1 - 2h + 3h^2 - 4h^3 + \ldots \ldots).$$

But at all heights to which we can attain h will be so small a fraction of the earth's radius that $3 h^2$ will be inappreciable, and the force of gravity will seem to follow the law of linear variation, being proportional to $1 - 2h$.

When the circumstances of an experiment are much altered, different powers of the variable may become prominent. The resistance of a liquid to a body moving through it may be approximately expressed as the sum of two terms respectively involving the first and second powers of the velocity. At very low velocities the first power is of most importance, and the resistance, as Professor Stokes has shown, is nearly in simple proportion to the velocity. When the motion is rapid the resistance increases in a still greater degree, and is more nearly proportional to the square of the velocity.

Approximate Independence of Small Effects.

One result of the theory of approximation possesses such importance in physical science, and is so often applied, that we may consider it separately. The investigation of causes and effects is immensely simplified when we may consider each cause as producing its own effect invariably, whether other causes are acting or not. Thus, if the body P produces x, and Q produces y, the question is whether P and Q acting together will produce the sum of the separate effects, $x + y$. It is under this supposition that we treated the methods of eliminating error (Chap. XV.), and errors of a less amount would still remain if the supposition was a forced one. There are probably some parts of science in which the supposition of independence of effects holds rigidly true. The mutual gravity of two bodies is entirely unaffected by the presence of other gravitating bodies. People do not usually consider that this important principle is involved in such a simple thing as putting two pound weights in the scale of a balance. How do we know that two pounds together will weigh twice as much as one ? Do we know it to be exactly so ? Like other results founded on induction we cannot prove it absolutely, but all the calculations of physical astronomy proceed upon the assumption, so that we may consider it proved to a very high degree of approximation. Had not this been true, the calculations of physical astronomy would have been infinitely more complex than they actually are, and the progress of knowledge would have been much slower.

It is a general principle of scientific method that if effects be of small amount, comparatively to our means of observation, all joint effects will be of a higher order of smallness, and may therefore be rejected in a first approximation. This principle was employed by Daniel Bernoulli in the theory of sound, under the title of *The Principle of the Coexistence of Small Vibrations.* He showed that if a string is affected by two kinds of vibrations, we may consider each to be going on as if the other did not exist. We cannot perceive that the sounding of one musical instrument prevents or even modifies the sound of another, so that all sounds would seem to travel through the air, and act upon the ear in independence of each other. A similar assumption is made in the theory of tides, which are great waves. One wave is produced by the attraction of the moon, and another by the attraction of the sun, and the question arises, whether when these waves coincide, as at the time of spring tides, the joint wave will be simply the sum of the separate waves. On the principle of Bernoulli this will be so, because the tides on the ocean are very small compared with the depth of the ocean.

The principle of Bernoulli, however, is only approximately true. A wave never is exactly the same when another wave is interfering with it, but the less the displacement of particles due to each wave, the less in a still higher degree is the effect of one wave upon the other. In recent years Helmholtz was led to suspect that some of the phenomena of sound might after all be due to resultant effects overlooked by the assumption of previous physicists. He investigated the secondary waves which would arise from the interference of considerable disturbances, and was able to show that certain summation or resultant tones ought to be heard, and experiments subsequently devised for the purpose showed that they might be heard.

Throughout the mechanical sciences the *Principle of the Superposition of Small Motions* is of fundamental importance,[1] and it may be thus explained. Suppose

---

[1] Thomson and Tait's *Natural Philosophy*, vol. i. p. 60.

that two forces, acting from the points B and C, are
simultaneously moving a body A. Let the force acting
from B be such that in one second it would move A
to *p*, and similarly let the second force, acting alone,
move A to *r*. The question
arises, then, whether their joint
action will urge A to *q* along
the diagonal of the parallelogram. May we say that A will
move the distance A*p* in the
direction AB, and A*r* in the
direction AC, or, what is the
same thing, along the parallel
line *pq*? In strictness we cannot say so; for when A has
moved towards *p*, the force from C will no longer act along
the line AC, and similarly the motion of A towards *r* will
modify the action of the force from B. This interference
of one force with the line of action of the other will
evidently be greater the larger is the extent of motion
considered; on the other hand, as we reduce the parallelogram A*pqr*, compared with the distances AB and AC,
the less will be the interference of the forces. Accordingly mathematicians avoid all error by considering the
motions as infinitely small, so that the interference becomes of a still higher order of infinite smallness, and
may be entirely neglected. By the resources of the differential calculus it is possible to calculate the motion of the
particle A, as if it went through an infinite number of
infinitely small diagonals of parallelograms. The great
discoveries of Newton really arose from applying this
method of calculation to the movements of the moon
round the earth, which, while constantly tending to move
onward in a straight line, is also deflected towards the
earth by gravity, and moves through an elliptic curve,
composed as it were of the infinitely small diagonals of
infinitely numerous parallelograms. The mathematician,
in his investigation of a curve, always treats it as made
up of a great number of straight lines, and it may be
doubted whether he could treat it in any other manner.
There is no error in the final results, because having obtained the formulæ flowing from this supposition, each
straight line is then regarded as becoming infinitely small,

and the polygonal line becomes undistinguishable from a perfect curve.[1]

In abstract mathematical theorems the approximation to absolute truth is perfect, because we can treat of infinitesimals. In physical science, on the contrary, we treat of the least quantities which are perceptible. Nevertheless, while carefully distinguishing between these two different cases, we may fearlessly apply to both the principle of the superposition of small effects. In physical science we have only to take care that the effects really are so small that any joint effect will be unquestionably imperceptible. Suppose, for instance, that there is some cause which alters the dimensions of a body in the ratio of 1 to $1 + a$, and another cause which produces an alteration in the ratio of 1 to $1 + \beta$. If they both act at once the change will be in the ratio of 1 to $(1 + a)(1 + \beta)$, or as 1 to $1 + a + \beta + a\beta$. But if a and β be both very small fractions of the total dimensions, $a\beta$ will be yet far smaller and may be disregarded; the ratio of change is then approximately that of 1 to $1 + a + \beta$, or the joint effect is the sum of the separate effects. Thus if a body were subjected to three strains, at right angles to each other, the total change in the volume of the body would be approximately equal to the sum of the changes produced by the separate strains, provided that these are very small. In like manner not only is the expansion of every solid and liquid substance by heat approximately proportional to the change of temperature, when this change is very small in amount, but the cubic expansion may also be considered as being three times as great as the linear expansion. For if the increase of temperature expands a bar of metal in the ratio of 1 to $1 + a$, and the expansion be equal in all directions, then a cube of the same metal would expand as 1 to $(1 + a)^3$, or as 1 to $1 + 3a + 3a^2 + a^3$. When a is a very small quantity the third term $3a^2$ will be imperceptible, and still more so the fourth term a^3. The coefficients of expansion of solids are in fact so small, and so imperfectly determined, that physicists seldom take into account their second and higher powers.

[1] Challis, *Notes on the Principles of Pure and Applied Calculation*, 1869, p. 83.

It is a result of these principles that all small errors may
be assumed to vary in simple proportion to their causes—a
new reason why, in eliminating errors, we should first of
all make them as small as possible. Let us suppose that
there is a right-angled triangle of which the two sides
containing the right angle are really of the lengths 3 and
4, so that the hypothenuse is $\sqrt{3^2 + 4^2}$ or 5. Now, if in
two measurements of the first side we commit slight
errors, making it successively 4·001 and 4·002, then calculation will give the lengths of the hypothenuse as almost
exactly 5·0008 and 5·0016, so that the error in the
hypothenuse will seem to vary in simple proportion to
that of the side, although it does not really do so with
perfect exactness. The logarithm of a number does not
vary in proportion to that number—nevertheless we find
the difference between the logarithms of the numbers
100000 and 100001 to be almost exactly equal to that
between the numbers 100001 and 100002. It is thus a
general rule that very small differences between successive
values of a function are approximately proportional to
the small differences of the variable quantity.

On these principles it is easy to draw up a series of
rules such as those given by Kohlrausch[1] for performing
calculations in an abbreviated form when the variable
quantity is very small compared with unity. Thus for
$1 \div (1 + a)$ we may substitute $1 - a$; for $1 \div (1 - a)$
we may put $1 + a$; $1 \div \sqrt{1 + a}$ becomes $1 - \frac{1}{2}a$, and so
forth.

Four Meanings of Equality.

Although it might seem that there are few terms more
free from ambiguity than the term *equal*, yet scientific
men do employ it with at least four meanings, which it
is desirable to distinguish. These meanings I may describe
as

(1) Absolute Equality.
(2) Sub-equality.
(3) Apparent Equality.
(4) Probable Equality.

[1] *An Introduction to Physical Measurements,* translated by Waller
and Procter, 1873, p. 10.

By *absolute equality* we signify that which is complete and perfect to the last degree ; but it is obvious that we can only know such equality in a theoretical or hypothetical manner. The areas of two triangles standing upon the same base and between the same parallels are absolutely equal. Hippocrates beautifully proved that the area of a lunula or figure contained between two segments of circles was absolutely equal to that of a certain right-angled triangle. As a general rule all geometrical and other elementary mathematical theorems involve absolute equality.

De Morgan proposed to describe as *sub-equal* those quantities which are equal within an infinitely small quantity, so that x is sub-equal to $x + dx$. The differential calculus may be said to arise out of the neglect of infinitely small quantities, and in mathematical science other subtle distinctions may have to be drawn between kinds of equality, as De Morgan has shown in a remarkable memoir " On Infinity ; and on the sign of Equality." [1]

Apparent equality is that with which physical science deals. Those magnitudes are apparently equal which differ only by an imperceptible quantity. To the carpenter anything less than the hundredth part of an inch is non-existent ; there are few arts or artists to which the hundred-thousandth of an inch is of any account. Since all coincidence between physical magnitudes is judged by one or other sense, we must be restricted to a knowledge of apparent equality.

In reality even apparent equality is rarely to be expected. More commonly experiments will give only *probable equality*, that is results will come so near to each other that the difference may be ascribed to unimportant disturbing causes. Physicists often assume quantities to be equal provided that they fall within the limits of probable error of the processes employed. We cannot expect observations to agree with theory more closely than they agree with each other, as Newton remarked of his investigations concerning Halley's Comet.

[1] *Cambridge Philosophical Transactions* (1865), vol. xi. Part I.

Arithmetic of Approximate Quantities.

Considering that almost all the quantities which we treat in physical and social science are approximate only, it seems desirable that attention should be paid in the teaching of arithmetic to the correct interpretation and treatment of approximate numerical statements. We seem to need notation for expressing the approximateness or exactness of decimal numbers. The fraction ·025 may mean either precisely one 40th part, or it may mean anything between ·0245 and 0255. I propose that when a decimal fraction is completely and exactly given, a *small cipher* or circle should be added to indicate that there is nothing more to come, as in ·025₀. When the first figure of the decimals rejected is 5 or more, the first figure retained should be raised by a unit, according to a rule approved by De Morgan, and now generally recognised. To indicate that the fraction thus retained is more than the truth, a point has been placed over the last figure in some tables of logarithms; but a similar point is used to denote the period of a repeating decimal, and I should therefore propose to employ a colon *after* the figure; thus ·025: would mean that the true quantity lies between ·0245° and ·025° inclusive of the lower but not the higher limit. When the fraction is less than the truth, two dots might be placed horizontally as in ·025.. which would mean anything between ·025° and ·0255° not inclusive.

When approximate numbers are added, subtracted, multiplied, or divided, it becomes a matter of some complexity to determine the degree of accuracy of the result. There are few persons who could assert off-hand that the sum of the approximate numbers 34·70, 52·693, 80·1, is 167·5 *within less than* ·07. Mr. Sandeman has traced out the rules of approximate arithmetic in a very thorough manner, and his directions are worthy of careful attention.[1] The third part of Sonnenschein and Nesbitt's excellent book on arithmetic [2] describes fully all kinds of approximate calculations, and shows both how to avoid needless labour

---

[1] Sandeman, *Pelicotetics*, p. 214.
[2] *The Science and Art of Arithmetic for the Use of Schools.* (Whitaker and Co.)

and how to take proper account of inaccuracy in operating
with approximate decimal fractions. A simple investigation of the subject is to be found in Sonnet's *Algèbre
Elémentaire* (Paris, 1848) chap. xiv., "Des Approximations
Absolues et Relatives." There is also an American work
on the subject.[1]

Although the accuracy of measurement has so much
advanced since the time of Leslie, it is not superfluous to
repeat his protest against the unfairness of affecting by a
display of decimal fractions a greater degree of accuracy
than the nature of the case requires and admits.[2] I have
known a scientific man to register the barometer to a
second of time when the nearest quarter of an hour would
have been amply sufficient. Chemists often publish results
of analysis to the ten-thousandth or even the millionth
part of the whole, when in all probability the processes
employed cannot be depended on beyond the hundredth
part. It is seldom desirable to give more than one place
of figures of uncertain amount; but it must be allowed
that a nice perception of the degree of accuracy possible
and desirable is requisite to save misapprehension and
needless computation on the one hand, and to secure all
attainable exactness on the other hand.

[1] *Principles of Approximate Calculations,* by J. J. Skinner, C.E.
(New York, Henry Holt), 1876.
[2] Leslie, *Inquiry into the Nature of Heat,* p. 505.

CHAPTER XXII

WE have not yet formally considered any processes of reasoning which have for their object to disclose laws of nature expressed in quantitative equations. We have been inquiring into the modes by which a phenomenon may be measured, and, if it be a composite phenomenon, may be resolved, by the aid of several measurements, into its component parts. We have also considered the precautions to be taken in the performance of observations and experiments in order that we may know what phenomena we really do measure, but we must remember that no number of facts and observations can by themselves constitute science. Numerical facts, like other facts, are but the raw materials of knowledge, upon which our reasoning faculties must be exerted in order to draw forth the principles of nature. It is by an inverse process of reasoning that we can alone discover the mathematical laws to which varying quantities conform. By well-conducted experiments we gain a series of values of a variable, and a corresponding series of values of a variant, and we now want to know what mathematical function the variant is as regards the variable. In the usual progress of a science three questions will have to be answered as regards every important quantitative phenomenon :—

(1) Is there any constant relation between a variable and a variant?

(2) What is the empirical formula expressing this relation?

(3) What is the rational formula expressing the law of nature involved?

Probable Connection of Varying Quantities.

We find it stated by Mill,[1] that "Whatever phenomenon varies in any manner whenever another phenomenon varies in some particular manner, is either a cause
or an effect of that phenomenon, or is connected with it
through some fact of causation." This assertion may be
considered true when it is interpreted with sufficient
caution ; but it might otherwise lead us into error. There
is nothing whatever in the nature of things to prevent the
existence of two variations which should apparently follow
the same law, and yet have no connection with each other.
One binary star might be going through a revolution
which, so far as we could tell, was of equal period with
that of another binary star, and according to the above
rule the motion of one would be the cause of the motion
of the other, which would not be really the case. Two
astronomical clocks might conceivably be made so nearly
perfect that, for several years, no difference could be detected, and we might then infer that the motion of one
clock was the cause or effect of the motion of the other.
This matter requires careful discrimination. We must
bear in mind that the continuous quantities of space,
time, force, &c., which we measure, are made up of an
infinite number of infinitely small units. We may then
meet with two variable phenomena which follow laws
so nearly the same, that in no part of the variations open
to our observation can any discrepancy be discovered.
I grant that if two clocks could be shown to have kept
exactly the same time during any finite interval, the probability would become infinitely high that there was a
connection between their motions. But we can never
absolutely prove such coincidences to exist. Allow that
we may observe a difference of one-tenth of a second in
their time, yet it is possible that they were independently
regulated so as to go together within less than that
quantity of time. In short, it would require either an infinitely long time of observation, or infinitely acute powers
of measuring discrepancy, to decide positively whether
two clocks were or were not in relation with each other.

[1] *System of Logic,* bk. iii. chap. viii. § 6.

A similar question actually occurs in the case of the moon's motion. We have no record that any other portion of the moon was ever visible to men than such as we now see. This fact sufficiently proves that within the historical period the rotation of the moon on its own axis has coincided with its revolutions round the earth. Does this coincidence prove a relation of cause and effect to exist ? The answer must be in the negative, because there might have been so slight a discrepancy between the motions that there has not yet been time to produce any appreciable effect. There may nevertheless be a high probability of connection.

The whole question of the relation of quantities thus resolves itself into one of probability. When we can only rudely measure a quantitative result, we can assign but slight importance to any correspondence. Because the brightness of two stars seems to vary in the same manner, there is no considerable probability that they have any relation with each other. Could it be shown that their periods of variation were the same to infinitely small quantities it would be certain, that is infinitely probable, that they were connected, however unlikely this might be on other grounds. The general mode of estimating such probabilities is identical with that applied to other inductive problems. That any two periods of variation should by chance become *absolutely equal* is infinitely improbable; hence if, in the case of the moon or other moving bodies, we could prove absolute coincidence we should have certainty of connection.[1] With approximate measurements, which alone are within our power, we must hope for approximate certainty at the most.

The principles of inference and probability, according to which we treat causes and effects varying in amount, are exactly the same as those by which we treated simple experiments. Continuous quantity, however, affords us an infinitely more extensive sphere of observation, because every different amount of cause, however little different, ought to be followed by a different amount of effect. If we can measure temperature to the one-hundredth part of a degree centigrade, then between 0° and 100° we have

---

[1] Laplace, *System of the World*, translated by Harte, vol. ii. p. 366.

10,000 possible trials. If the precision of our measurements is increased, so that the one-thousandth part of a degree can be appreciated, our trials may be increased tenfold. The probability of connection will be proportional to the accuracy of our measurements.

When we can vary the quantity of a cause at will it is easy to discover whether a certain effect is due to that cause or not. We can then make as many irregular changes as we like, and it is quite incredible that the supposed effect should by chance go through exactly the corresponding series of changes except by dependence. If we have a bell ringing *in vacuo*, the sound increases as we let in the air, and it decreases again as we exhaust the air. Tyndall's singing flames evidently obeyed the directions of his own voice; and Faraday when he discovered the relation of magnetism and light found that, by making or breaking or reversing the current of the electro-magnet, he had complete command over a ray of light, proving beyond all reasonable doubt the dependence of cause and effect. In such cases it is the perfect coincidence in time between the change in the effect and that in the cause which raises a high improbability of casual coincidence.

It is by a simple case of variation that we infer the existence of a material connection between two bodies moving with exactly equal velocity, such as the locomotive engine and the train which follows it. Elaborate observations were requisite before astronomers could all be convinced that the red hydrogen flames seen during solar eclipses belonged to the sun, and not to the moon's atmosphere as Flamsteed assumed. As early as 1706, Stannyan noticed a blood-red streak in an eclipse which he witnessed at Berne, and he asserted that it belonged to the sun; but his opinion was not finally established until photographs of the eclipse in 1860, taken by Mr. De la Rue, shewed that the moon's dark body gradually covered the red prominences on one side, and uncovered those on the other; in short, that these prominences moved precisely as the sun moved, and not as the moon moved.

Even when we have no means of accurately measuring the variable quantities we may yet be convinced of their connection, if one always varies perceptibly at the same time as the other. Fatigue increases with exertion;

hunger with abstinence from food; desire and degree of
utility decrease with the quantity of commodity consumed.   We know that the sun's heating power depends
upon his height of the sky; that the temperature of the
air falls in ascending a mountain; that the earth's crust
is found to be perceptibly warmer as we sink mines into
it; we infer the direction in which a sound comes from
the change of loudness as we approach or recede.   The
facility with which we can time after time observe the
increase or decrease of one quantity with another sufficiently shows the connection, although we may be unable to assign any precise law of relation.   The probability
in such cases depends upon frequent coincidence in time.

Empirical Mathematical Laws.

It is important to acquire a clear comprehension of the
part which is played in scientific investigation by empirical formulæ and laws.   If we have a table containing
certain values of a variable and the corresponding values
of the variant, there are mathematical processes by which
we can infallibly discover a mathematical formula yielding numbers in more or less exact agreement with the
table.   We may generally assume that the quantities will
approximately conform to a law of the form

$$y = A + B x + C x^2,$$

in which x is the variable and y the variant.   We can
then select from the table three values of y, and the corresponding values of x; inserting them in the equation,
we obtain three equations by the solution of which we
gain the values of A, B, and C.   It will be found as a
general rule that the formula thus obtained yields the
other numbers of the table to a considerable degree of
approximation.

In many cases even the second power of the variable
will be unnecessary; Regnault found that the results
of his elaborate inquiry into the latent heat of steam at
different pressures were represented with sufficient accuracy by the empirical formula

$$\lambda = 606 \cdot 5 + 0 \cdot 305 \, t,$$

in which λ is the total heat of the steam, and t the tem-

perature.[1] In other cases it may be requisite to include
the third power of the variable. Thus physicists assume
the law of the dilatation of liquids to be of the form

$$\delta_t = a\,t + b\,t^2 + c\,t^3,$$

and they calculate from results of observation the values
of the three constants a, b, c, which are usually small
quantities not exceeding one-hundredth part of a unit,
but requiring to be determined with great accuracy.[2]
Theoretically speaking, this process of empirical representation might be applied with any degree of accuracy ;
we might include still higher powers in the formula, and
with sufficient labour obtain the values of the constants,
by using an equal number of experimental results. The
method of least squares may also be employed to obtain
the most probable values of the constants.

In a similar manner all periodic variations may be represented with any required degree of accuracy by formulæ
involving the sines and cosines of angles and their multiples. The form of any tidal or other wave may thus be
expressed, as Sir G. B. Airy has explained.[3] Almost all
the phenomena registered by meteorologists are periodic
in character, and when freed from disturbing causes may
be embodied in empirical formulæ. Bessel has given a
rule by which from any regular series of observations we
may, on the principle of the method of least squares,
calculate out with a moderate amount of labour a formula
expressing the variation of the quantity observed, in the
most probable manner. In meteorology three or four
terms are usually sufficient for representing any periodic
phenomenon, but the calculation might be carried to any
higher degree of accuracy. As the details of the process
have been described by Herschel in his treatise on
Meteorology,[4] I need not further enter into them.

The reader might be tempted to think that in these
processes of calculation we have an infallible method of
discovering inductive laws, and that my previous statements (Chap. VII.) as to the purely tentative and inverse
character of the inductive process are negatived. Were

[1] *Chemical Reports and Memoirs*, Cavendish Society, p. 294.
[2] Jamin, *Cours de Physique*, vol. ii. p. 38.
[3] *On Tides and Waves*, Encyclopædia Metropolitana, p. 366*.
[4] *Encyclopædia Britannica*, art. *Meteorology*. Reprint, §§ 152—156.

there indeed any general method of inferring laws from
facts it would overturn my statement, but it must be
carefully observed that these empirical formulæ do not
coincide with natural laws. They are only approximations
to the results of natural laws founded upon the general
principles of approximation. It has already been pointed
out that however complicated be the nature of a curve,
we may examine so small a portion of it, or we may examine it with such rude means of measurement, that its
divergence from an elliptic curve will not be apparent.
As a still ruder approximation a portion of a straight line
will always serve our purpose ; but if we need higher precision a curve of the third or fourth degree will almost
certainly be sufficient. Now empirical formulæ really represent these approximate curves, but they give us no
information as to the precise nature of the curve itself to
which we are approximating. We do not learn what function the variant is of the variable, but we obtain another
function which, within the bounds of observation, gives
nearly the same values.

Discovery of Rational Formulæ.

Let us now proceed to consider the modes in which
from numerical results we can establish the actual relation
between the quantity of the cause and that of the effect.
What we want is a *rational* formula or function, which
will exhibit the *reason* or exact nature and origin of the
law in question. There is no word more frequently used
by mathematicians than the word *function*, and yet it
is difficult to define its meaning with perfect accuracy.
Originally it meant performance or execution, being equivalent to the Greek λειτουργία or τέλεσμα. Mathematicians
at first used it to mean *any power of a quantity*, but
afterwards generalised it so as to include " any quantity
formed in any manner whatsoever from another quantity." [1]
Any quantity, then, which depends upon and varies with
another quantity may be called a function of it, and
either may be considered a function of the other.
Given the quantities, we want the function of which

---

[1] Lagrange, *Leçons sur le Calcul des Fonctions*, 1806, p. 4.

they are the values. Simple inspection of the numbers cannot as a general rule disclose the function. In an earlier chapter (p. 124) I put before the reader certain numbers, and requested him to point out the law which they obey, and the same question will have to be asked in every case of quantitative induction. There are perhaps three methods, more or less distinct, by which we may hope to obtain an answer:

(1) By purely haphazard trial.

(2) By noting the general character of the variation of the quantities, and trying by preference functions which give a similar form of variation.

(3) By deducing from previous knowledge the form of the function which is most likely to suit.

Having numerical results we are always at liberty to invent any kind of mathematical formula we like, and then try whether, by the suitable selection of values for the unknown constant quantities, we can make it give the required results. If ever we fall upon a formula which does so, to a fair degree of approximation, there is a presumption in favour of its being the true function, although there is no certainty whatever in the matter. In this way I discovered a simple mathematical law which closely agreed with the results of my experiments on muscular exertion. This law was afterwards shown by Professor Haughton to be the true rational law according to his theory of muscular action.[1]

But the chance of succeeding in this manner is small. The number of possible functions is infinite, and even the number of comparatively simple functions is so large that the probability of falling upon the correct one by mere chance is very slight. Even when we obtain the law it is by a deductive process, not by showing that the numbers give the law, but that the law gives the numbers.

In the second way, we may, by a survey of the numbers, gain a general notion of the kind of law they are likely to obey, and we may be much assisted in this

[1] Haughton, *Principles of Animal Mechanics*, 1873, pp. 444—450. Jevons, *Nature*, 30th of June, 1870, vol. ii. p. 158. See also the experiments of Professor Nipher, of Washington University, St. Louis, in *American Journal of Science*, vol. ix. p. 130, vol. x. p. 1; *Nature*, vol. xi. pp. 256, 276

process by drawing them out in the form of a curve. We can in this way ascertain with some probability whether the curve is likely to return into itself, or whether it has infinite branches; whether such branches are asymptotic, that is, approach infinitely towards straight lines; whether it is logarithmic in character, or trigonometric. This indeed we can only do if we remember the results of previous investigations. The process is still inversely deductive, and consists in noting what laws give particular curves, and then inferring inversely that such curves belong to such laws. If we can in this way discover the class of functions to which the required law belongs, our chances of success are much increased, because our haphazard trials are now reduced within a narrower sphere. But, unless we have almost the whole curve before us, the identification of its character must be a matter of great uncertainty; and if, as in most physical investigations, we have a mere fragment of the curve, the assistance given would be quite illusory. Curves of almost any character can be made to approximate to each other for a limited extent, so that it is only by a kind of *divination* that we fall upon the actual function, unless we have theoretical knowledge of the kind of function applicable to the case.

When we have once obtained what we believe to be the correct form of function, the remainder of the work is mere mathematical computation to be performed infallibly according to fixed rules,[1] which include those employed in the determination of empirical formulæ (p. 487). The function will involve two or three or more unknown constants, the values of which we need to determine by our experimental results. Selecting some of our results widely apart and nearly equidistant, we form by means of them as many equations as there are constant quantities to be determined. The solution of these equations will then give us the constants required, and having now the actual function we can try whether it gives with sufficient accuracy the remainder of our experimental results. If not, we must either make a new selection of results to give a new set of equations, and thus obtain a new set of values for the constants, or we must acknowledge that our

---

[1] Jamin, *Cours de Physique*, vol. ii. p. 50.

form of function has been wrongly chosen. If it appears that the form of function has been correctly ascertained, we may regard the constants as only approximately accurate and may proceed by the Method of Least Squares (p. 393) to determine the most probable values as given by the whole of the experimental results.

In most cases we shall find ourselves obliged to fall back upon the third mode, that is, anticipation of the form of the law to be expected on the ground of previous knowledge. Theory and analogical reasoning must be our guides. The general nature of the phenomenon will often indicate the kind of law to be looked for. If one form of energy or one kind of substance is being converted into another, we may expect the law of direct simple proportion. In one distinct class of cases the effect already produced influences the amount of the ensuing effect, as for instance in the cooling of a heated body, when the law will be of an exponential form. When the direction of a force influences its action, trigonometrical functions enter. Any influence which spreads freely through tridimensional space will be subject to the law of the inverse square of the distance. From such considerations we may sometimes arrive deductively and analogically at the general nature of the mathematical law required.

The Graphical Method.

In endeavouring to discover the mathematical law obeyed by experimental results it is often desirable to call in the aid of space-representations. Every equation involving two variable quantities corresponds to some kind of plane curve, and every plane curve may be represented symbolically in an equation containing two unknown quantities. Now in an experimental research we obtain a number of values of the variant corresponding to an equal number of values of the variable; but all the numbers are affected by more or less error, and the values of the variable will often be irregularly disposed. Even if the numbers were absolutely correct and disposed at regular intervals, there is, as we have seen, no direct mode of discovering the law, but the difficulty of discovery is much increased by the uncertainty and irregularity of the results.

Under such circumstances, the best mode of proceeding is to prepare a paper divided into equal rectangular spaces, a convenient size for the spaces being one-tenth of an inch square. The values of the variable being marked off on the lowest horizontal line, a point is marked for each corresponding value of the variant perpendicularly above that of the variable, and at such a height as corresponds to the value of the variant.

The exact scale of the drawing is not of much importance, but it may require to be adjusted according to circumstances, and different values must often be attributed to the upright and horizontal divisions, so as to make the variations conspicuous but not excessive. If a curved line be drawn through all the points or ends of the ordinates, it will probably exhibit irregular inflections, owing to the errors which affect the numbers. But, when the results are numerous, it becomes apparent which results are more divergent than others, and guided by a so-called *sense of continuity*, it is possible to trace a line among the points which will approximate to the true law more nearly than the points themselves. The accompanying figure sufficiently explains itself.

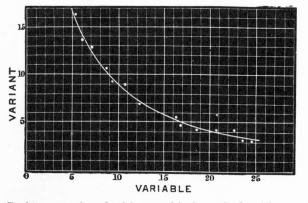

Perkins employed this graphical method with much care in exhibiting the results of his experiments on the compression of water.[1] The numerical results were marked

---

[1] *Philosophical Transactions*, 1826, p. 544.

upon a sheet of paper very exactly ruled at intervals of one-tenth of an inch, and the original marks were left in order that the reader might judge of the correctness of the curve drawn, or choose another for himself. Regnault carried the method to perfection by laying off the points with a screw dividing engine; [1] and he then formed a table of results by drawing a continuous curve, and measuring its height for equidistant values of the variable. Not only does a curve drawn in this manner enable us to infer numerical results more free from accidental errors than any of the numbers obtained directly from experiment, but the form of the curve sometimes indicates the class of functions to which our results belong.

Engraved sheets of paper prepared for the drawing of curves may be obtained from Mr. Stanford at Charing Cross, Messrs. W. and A. K. Johnston, of London and Edinburgh, Waterlow and Sons, Letts and Co., and probably other publishers. When we do not require great accuracy, paper ruled by the common machine-ruler into equal squares of about one-fifth or one-sixth of an inch square will serve well enough. I have met with engineers' and surveyors' memorandum books ruled with one-twelfth inch squares. When a number of curves have to be drawn, I have found it best to rule a good sheet of drawing paper with lines carefully adjusted at the most convenient distances, and then to prick the points of the curve through it upon another sheet fixed underneath. In this way we obtain an accurate curve upon a blank sheet, and need only introduce such division lines as are requisite to the understanding of the curve.

In some cases our numerical results will correspond, not to the height of single ordinates, but to the area of the curve between two ordinates, or the average height of ordinates between certain limits. If we measure, for instance, the quantities of heat absorbed by water when raised in temperature from 0° to 5°, from 5° to 10°, and so on, these quantities will really be represented by *areas* of the curve denoting the specific heat of water; and since the specific heat varies continuously between every two points of temperature, we shall not get the correct curve

[1] Jamin, *Cours de Physique*, vol. ii. p. 24, &c.

by simply laying off the quantities of heat at the mean temperatures, namely $2\frac{1}{2}°$, and $7\frac{1}{2}°$, and so on.   Lord Rayleigh
has shown that if we have drawn such an incorrect curve,
we can with little trouble correct it by a simple geometrical process, and obtain to a close approximation the
true ordinates instead of those denoting areas.[1]

Interpolation and Extrapolation.

When we have by experiment obtained two or more
numerical results, and endeavour, without further experiment, to calculate intermediate results, we are said to
interpolate.   If we wish to assign by reasoning results
lying beyond the limits of experiment, we may be said,
using an expression of Sir George Airy, to *extrapolate*.
These two operations are the same in principle, but differ
in practicability.   It is a matter of great scientific importance to apprehend precisely how far we can practise
interpolation or extrapolation, and on what grounds we
proceed.

In the first place, if the interpolation is to be more than
empirical, we must have not only the experimental results,
but the laws which they obey—we must in fact go through
the complete process of scientific investigation.   Having
discovered the laws of nature applying to the case, and
verified them by showing that they agree with the experiments in question, we are then in a position to anticipate
the results of similar experiments.   Our knowledge even
now is not certain, because we cannot completely prove
the truth of any assumed law, and we cannot possibly
exhaust all the circumstances which may affect the result.
At the best then our interpolations will partake of the
want of certainty and precision attaching to all our knowledge of nature.   Yet, having the supposed laws, our results
will be as sure and accurate as any we can attain to.   But
such a complete procedure is more than we commonly
mean by interpolation, which usually denotes some method
of estimating in a merely approximate manner the results

---

[1] J. W. Strutt, *On a correction sometimes required in curves professing to represent the connexion between two physical magnitudes.*
Philosophical Magazine, 4th Series, vol. xlii. p. 441.

which might have been expected independently of a theoretical investigation.

Regarded in this light, interpolation is in reality an indeterminate problem. From given values of a function it is impossible to determine that function; for we can invent an infinite number of functions which will give those values if we are not restricted by any conditions, just as through a given series of points we can draw an infinite number of curves, if we may diverge between or beyond the points into bends and cusps as we think fit.[1] In interpolation we must in fact be guided more or less by *à priori* considerations; we must know, for instance, whether or not periodical fluctuations are to be expected. Supposing that the phenomenon is non-periodic, we proceed to assume that the function can be expressed in a limited series of the powers of the variable. The number of powers which can be included depends upon the number of experimental results available, and must be at least one less than this number. By processes of calculation, which have been already alluded to in the section on empirical formulæ, we then calculate the coefficients of the powers, and obtain an empirical formula which will give the required intermediate results. In reality, then, we return to the methods treated under the head of approximation and empirical formulæ; and interpolation, as commonly understood, consists in assuming that a curve of simple character is to pass through certain determined points. If we have, for instance, two experimental results, and only two, we assume that the curve is a straight line; for the parabolas which can be passed through two points are infinitely various in magnitude, and quite indeterminate. One straight line alone can pass through two points, and it will have an equation of the form, $y = mx + n$, the constant quantities of which can be determined from two results. Thus, if the two values for x, 7 and 11, give the values for y, 35 and 53, the solution of two equations gives $y = 4.5 \times x + 35$ as the equation, and for any other value of x, for instance 10, we get a value of y, that is 48.5. When we take a mean value of x, namely 9, this process yields a simple mean result, namely 44. Three experimental results

---

[1] Herschel : Lacroix' *Differential Calculus*, p. 551.

being given, we assume that they fall upon a portion of a parabola and algebraic calculation gives the position of any intermediate point upon the parabola. Concerning the process of interpolation as practised in the science of meteorology the reader will find some directions in the French edition of Kaëmtz's Meteorology.[1]

When we have, either by direct experiment or by the use of a curve, a series of values of the variant for equidistant values of the variable, it is instructive to take the differences between each value of the variant and the next, and then the differences between those differences, and so on. If any series of differences approaches closely to zero it is an indication that the numbers may be correctly represented by a finite empirical formula; if the nth differences are zero, then the formula will contain only the first $n - 1$ powers of the variable. Indeed we may sometimes obtain by the calculus of differences a correct empirical formula; for if p be the first term of the series of values, and $\triangle p$, $\triangle^2 p$, $\triangle^3 p$, be the first number in each column of differences, then the mth term of the series of values will be

$$p + m \triangle p + m \frac{m - 1}{2} \triangle^2 p + m \frac{m - 1}{2} \frac{m - 2}{3} \triangle^3 p + \&c.$$

A closely equivalent but more practicable formula for interpolation by differences, as devised by Lagrange, will be found in Thomson and Tait's *Elements of Natural Philosophy*, p. 115.

If no column of differences shows any tendency to become zero throughout, it is an indication that the law is of a more complicated, for instance of an exponential character, so that it requires different treatment. Dr. J. Hopkinson has suggested a method of arithmetical interpolation,[2] which is intended to avoid much that is arbitrary in the graphical method. His process will yield the same results in all hands.

So far as we can infer the results likely to be obtained by variations beyond the limits of experiment, we must

[1] *Cours complet de Météorologie,* Note A, p. 449.
[2] *On the Calculation of Empirical Formulæ. The Messenger of Mathematics,* New Series, No. 17, 1872.

proceed upon the same principles. If possible we must detect the exact laws in action, and then trust to them as a guide when we have no experience. If not, an empirical formula of the same character as those employed in interpolation is our only resource. But to extend our inference far beyond the limits of experience is exceedingly unsafe. Our knowledge is at the best only approximate, and takes no account of small tendencies. Now it usually happens that tendencies small within our limits of observation become perceptible or great under extreme circumstances. When the variable in our empirical formula is small, we are justified in overlooking the higher powers, and taking only two or three lower powers. But as the variable increases, the higher powers gain in importance, and in time yield the principal part of the value of the function.

This is no mere theoretical inference. Excepting the few primary laws of nature, such as the law of gravity, of the conservation of energy, &c., there is hardly any natural law which we can trust in circumstances widely different from those with which we are practically acquainted. From the expansion or contraction, fusion or vaporisation of substances by heat at the surface of the earth, we can form a most imperfect notion of what would happen near the centre of the earth, where the pressure almost infinitely exceeds anything possible in our experiments. The physics of the earth give us a feeble, and probably a misleading, notion of a body like the sun, in which an inconceivably high temperature is united with an inconceivably high pressure. If there are in the realms of space nebulæ consisting of incandescent and unoxidised vapours of metals and other elements, so highly heated perhaps that chemical composition is out of the question, we are hardly able to treat them as subjects of scientific inference. Hence arises the great importance of experiments in which we investigate the properties of substances under extreme circumstances of cold or heat, density or rarity, intense electric excitation, &c. This insecurity in extending our inferences arises from the approximate character of our measurements. Had we the power of appreciating infinitely small quantities, we should by the principle of continuity discover some trace of every change which a substance could undergo under unattainable circumstances. By observing, for instance, the tension of aqueous vapour between 0° and 100° C., we ought theoretically to be able to infer its tension at every other temperature; but this is out of the question practically because we cannot really ascertain the law precisely between those temperatures.

Many instances might be given to show that laws which appear to represent correctly the results of experiments within certain limits altogether fail beyond those limits. The experiments of Roscoe and Dittmar, on the absorption of gases in water[1] afford interesting illustrations, especially in the case of hydrochloric acid, the quantity of which dissolved in water under different pressures follows very closely a linear law of variation, from which however it diverges widely at low pressures.[2] Herschel, having deduced from observations of the double star γ Virginis an elliptic orbit for the motion of one component round the centre of gravity of both, found that for a time the motion of the star agreed very well with this orbit. Nevertheless divergence began to appear and after a time became so great that an entirely new orbit, of more than double the dimensions of the old one, had ultimately to be adopted.[3]

Illustrations of Empirical Quantitative Laws.

Although our object in quantitative inquiry is to discover the exact or rational formulæ, expressing the laws which apply to the subject, it is instructive to observe in how many important branches of science, no precise laws have yet been detected. The tension of aqueous vapour at different temperatures has been determined by a succession of eminent experimentalists—Dalton, Kaëmtz, Dulong, Arago, Magnus, and Regnault—and by the last mentioned the measurements were conducted with extraordinary care.

---

[1] Watts' Dictionary of Chemistry, vol. ii. p. 790.
[2] Quarterly Journal of the Chemical Society, vol. viii. p. 15.
[3] Results of Observations at the Cape of Good Hope, p. 293.

Yet no incontestable general law has been established. Several functions have been proposed to express the elastic force of the vapour as depending on the temperature. The first form is that of Young, namely $F = (a + b\ t)^m$, in which a, b, and m are unknown quantities to be determined by observation. Roche proposed, on theoretical grounds, a complicated formula of an exponential form, and a third form of function is that of Biot,[1] as follows—$\log F = a + ba^t + c\ \beta^t$. I mention these formulæ, because they well illustrate the feeble powers of empirical inquiry. None of the formulæ can be made to correspond closely with experimental results, and the two last forms correspond almost equally well. There is very little probability that the real law has been reached, and it is unlikely that it will be discovered except by deduction from mechanical theory.

Much ingenious labour has been spent upon the discovery of some general law of atmospheric refraction. Tycho Brahe and Kepler commenced the inquiry: Cassini first formed a table of refractions, calculated on theoretical grounds : Newton entered into some profound investigations upon the subject: Brooke Taylor, Bouguer, Simpson, Bradley, Mayer, and Kramp successively attacked the question, which is of the highest practical importance as regards the correction of astronomical observations. Laplace next laboured on the subject without exhausting it, and Brinkley and Ivory have also treated it. The true law is yet undiscovered. A closely connected problem, that regarding the relation between the pressure and elevation in different strata of the atmosphere, has received the attention of a long succession of physicists and was most carefully investigated by Laplace. Yet no invariable and general law has been detected. The same may be said concerning the law of human mortality; abundant statistics on this subject are available, and many hypotheses more or less satisfactory have been put forward as to the form of the curve of mortality, but it seems to be impossible to discover more than an approximate law.

It may perhaps be urged that in such subjects no single invariable law can be expected. The atmosphere may be

---

[1] Jamin, *Cours de Physique*, vol. ii. p. 138.

divided into several variable strata which by their unconnected changes frustrate the exact calculations of astronomers.   Human life may be subject at different ages to
a succession of different influences incapable of reduction
under any one law.   The results observed may in fact be
aggregates of an immense number of separate results each
governed by its own separate laws, so that the subjects
may be complicated beyond the possibility of complete
resolution by empirical methods.   This is certainly true
of the mathematical functions which must some time or
other be introduced into the science of political economy.

Simple Proportional Variation.

When we first treat numerical results in any novel kind
of investigation, our impression will probably be that one
quantity varies in *simple proportion* to another, so as to
obey the law $y = mx + n$.   We must learn to distinguish
carefully between the cases where this proportionality is
really, and where it is only apparently true.   In considering the principles of approximation we found that a
small portion of any curve will appear to be a straight line.
When our modes of measurement are comparatively rude,
we must expect to be unable to detect the curvature.
Kepler made meritorious attempts to discover the law of
refraction, and he approximated to it when he observed
that the angles of incidence and refraction *if small* bear
a constant ratio to each other.   Angles when small are
nearly as their sines, so that he reached an approximate
result of the true law.   Cardan assumed, probably as a
mere guess, that the force required to sustain a body on
an inclined plane was simply proportional to the angle of
elevation of the plane.   This is approximately the case
when the angle is small, but in reality the law is much
more complicated, the power required being proportional
to the sine of the angle.   The early thermometer-makers
were unaware whether the expansion of mercury was
proportional or not to the heat communicated to it, and
it is only in the present century that we have learnt it
to be not so.   We now know that even gases obey the
law of uniform expansion by heat only in an approximate

manner. Until reason to the contrary is shown, we should
do well to look upon every law of simple proportion as
only provisionally true.

Nevertheless many important laws of nature are in the
form of simple proportions. Wherever a cause acts in
independence of its previous effects, we may expect this
relation. An accelerating force acts equally upon a
moving and a motionless body. Hence the velocity
produced is in simple proportion to the force, and to the
duration of its uniform action. As gravitating bodies
never interfere with each other's gravity, this force is in
direct simple proportion to the mass of each of the attracting bodies, the mass being measured by, or proportional
to inertia. Similarly, in all cases of " direct unimpeded
action," as Herschel has remarked,[1] we may expect simple
proportion to manifest itself. In such cases the equation
expressing the relation may have the simple form $y = mx$.

A similar relation holds true when there is conversion
of one substance or form of energy into another. The
quantity of a compound is equal to the quantity of the
elements which combine. The heat produced in friction
is exactly proportional to the mechanical energy absorbed.
It was experimentally proved by Faraday that " the chemical power of the current of electricity is in direct proportion to the quantity of electricity which passes." When
an electric current is produced, the quantity of electric
energy is simply proportional to the weight of metal
dissolved. If electricity is turned into heat, there is
again simple proportion. Wherever, in fact, one thing
is but another thing with a new aspect, we may expect
to find the law of simple proportion. But it is only in
the most elementary cases that this simple relation will
hold true. Simple conditions do not, generally speaking,
produce simple results. The planets move in approximate
circles round the sun, but the apparent motions, as seen
from the earth, are very various. All those motions, again,
are summed up in the law of gravity, of no great complexity; yet men never have been, and never will be, able
to exhaust the complications of action and reaction arising
from that law, even among a small number of planets

---

[1] *Preliminary Discourse*, &c., p. 152.

We should be on our guard against a tendency to assume that the connection of cause and effect is one of direct proportion. Bacon reminds us of the woman in Æsop's fable, who expected that her hen, with a double measure of barley, would lay two eggs a day instead of one, whereas it grew fat, and ceased to lay any eggs at all. It is a wise maxim that the half is often better than the whole.

CHAPTER XXIII.

THE USE OF HYPOTHESIS.

IF the views upheld in this work be correct, all inductive investigation consists in the marriage of hypothesis and experiment. When facts are in our possession, we frame an hypothesis to explain their relations, and by the success of this explanation is the value of the hypothesis to be judged. In the invention and treatment of such hypotheses, we must avail ourselves of the whole body of science already accumulated, and when once we have obtained a probable hypothesis, we must not rest until we have verified it by comparison with new facts. We must endeavour by deductive reasoning to anticipate such phenomena, especially those of a singular and exceptional nature, as would happen if the hypothesis be true. Out of the infinite number of experiments which are possible, theory must lead us to select those critical ones which are suitable for confirming or negativing our anticipations.

This work of inductive investigation cannot be guided by any system of precise and infallible rules, like those of deductive reasoning. There is, in fact, nothing to which we can apply rules of method, because the laws of nature must be in our possession before we can treat them. If there were any rule of inductive method, it would direct us to make an exhaustive arrangement of facts in all possible orders. Given the specimens in a museum, we might arrive at the best classification by going systematically through all possible classifications, and, were we endowed with infinite time and patience, this would be an effective method. It is the method by which the first simple steps

are taken in an incipient branch of science. Before the dig-
nified name of science is applicable, some coincidences will
force themselves upon the attention. Before there was a
science of meteorology observant persons learned to associate clearness of the atmosphere with coming rain, and a
colourless sunset with fine weather. Knowledge of this
kind is called *empirical*, as seeming to come directly from
experience ; and there is a considerable portion of knowledge which bears this character.

We may be obliged to trust to the casual detection
of coincidences in those branches of knowledge where
we are deprived of the aid of any guiding notions; but
a little reflection will show the utter insufficiency of
haphazard experiment, when applied to investigations of
a complicated nature. At the best, it will be the simple
identity, or partial identity, of classes, as illustrated
in pages 127 or 134, which can be thus detected. It was
pointed out that, even when a law of nature involves only
two circumstances, and there are one hundred distinct circumstances which may possibly be connected, there will
be no less than 4,950 pairs of circumstances between
which coincidence may exist. When a law involves three
or more circumstances, the possible number of relations
becomes vastly greater. When considering the subject
of combinations and permutations, it became apparent
that we could never cope with the possible variety of
nature. An exhaustive examination of the possible metallic alloys, or chemical compounds, was found to be out
of the question (p. 191).

It is on such considerations that we can explain the
very small additions made to our knowledge by the alchemists. Many of them were men of the greatest acuteness, and their indefatigable labours were pursued through
many centuries. A few things were discovered by them,
but a true insight into nature, now enables chemists to
discover more useful facts in a year than were yielded by
the alchemists during many centuries. There can be no
doubt that Newton was an alchemist, and that he often
laboured night and day at alchemical experiments. But
in trying to discover the secret by which gross metals
might be rendered noble, his lofty powers of deductive investigation were wholly useless. Deprived of all

guiding clues, his experiments were like those of all the alchemists, purely tentative and haphazard. While his hypothetical and deductive investigations have given us the true system of the Universe, and opened the way in almost all the great branches of natural philosophy, the whole results of his tentative experiments are comprehended in a few happy guesses, given in his celebrated " Queries."

Even when we are engaged in apparently passive observation of a phenomenon, which we cannot modify experimentally, it is advantageous that our attention should be guided by theoretical anticipations. A phenomenon which seems simple is, in all probability, really complex, and unless the mind is actively engaged in looking for particular details, it is likely that the critical circumstances will be passed over. Bessel regretted that no distinct theory of the constitution of comets had guided his observations of Halley's comet;[1] in attempting to verify or refute a hypothesis, not only would there be a chance of establishing a true theory, but if confuted, the confutation would involve a store of useful observations.

It would be an interesting work, but one which I cannot undertake, to trace out the gradual reaction which has taken place in recent times against the purely empirical or Baconian theory of induction. Francis Bacon, seeing the futility of the scholastic logic, which had long been predominant, asserted that the accumulation of facts and the orderly abstraction of axioms, or general laws from them, constituted the true method of induction. Even Bacon was not wholly unaware of the value of hypothetical anticipation. In one or two places he incidentally acknowledges it, as when he remarks that the subtlety of nature surpasses that of reason, adding that " axioms abstracted from particular facts in a careful and orderly manner, readily suggest and mark out new particulars."

Nevertheless Bacon's method, as far as we can gather the meaning of the main portions of his writings, would correspond to the process of empirically collecting facts

<hr/>

[1] Tyndall, *On Cometary Theory*, Philosophical Magazine, April 1869. 4th Series, vol. xxxvii. p. 243.

and exhaustively classifying them, to which I alluded.
The value of this method may be estimated historically
by the fact that it has not been followed by any of
the great masters of science. Whether we look to Galileo
who preceded Bacon, to Gilbert, his contemporary, or
to Newton and Descartes, Leibnitz and Huyghens, his
successors, we find that discovery was achieved by the
opposite method to that advocated by Bacon. Throughout Newton's works, as I shall show, we find deductive
reasoning wholly predominant, and experiments are employed, as they should be, to confirm or refute hypothetical anticipations of nature. In my "Elementary Lessons
in Logic" (p. 258), I stated my belief that there was no
kind of reference to Bacon in Newton's works. I have
since found that Newton does once or twice employ the
expression *experimentum crucis* in his "Opticks," but this
is the only expression, so far as I am aware, which could
indicate on the part of Newton direct or indirect acquaintance with Bacon's writings.[1]

Other great physicists of the same age were equally
prone to the use of hypotheses rather than the blind
accumulation of facts in the Baconian manner. Hooke
emphatically asserts in his posthumous work on Philosophical Method, that the first requisite of the Natural
Philosopher is readiness at guessing the solution of phenomena and making queries. "He ought to be very well
skilled in those several kinds of philosophy already
known, to understand their several hypotheses, suppositions, collections, observations, &c., their various ways
of ratiocinations and proceedings, the several failings and
defects, both in their way of raising and in their way of
managing their several theories : for by this means the
mind will be somewhat more ready at guessing at the
solution of many phenomena almost at first sight, and
thereby be much more prompt at making queries, and at
tracing the subtlety of Nature, and in discovering and
searching into the true reason of things."

We find Horrocks, again, than whom no one was more

---

[1] See *Philosophical Transactions*, abridged by Lowthorp. 4th edit.
vol. i. p. 130. I find that opinions similar to those in the text have
been briefly expressed by De Morgan in his remarkable preface to
From Matter to Spirit. by C.D., pp. xxi. xxii.

filled with the scientific spirit, telling us how he tried theory after theory in order to discover one which was in accordance with the motions of Mars.[1] Huyghens, who possessed one of the most perfect philosophical intellects, followed the deductive process combined with continual appeal to experiment, with a skill closely analogous to that of Newton. As to Descartes and Leibnitz, they fell into excess in the use of hypothesis, since they sometimes adopted hypothetical reasoning to the exclusion of experimental verification. Throughout the eighteenth century science was supposed to be advancing by the pursuance of the Baconian method, but in reality hypothetical investigation was the main instrument of progress. It is only in the present century that physicists began to recognise this truth. So much opprobrium had been attached by Bacon to the use of hypotheses, that we find Young speaking of them in an apologetic tone. " The practice of advancing general principles and applying them to particular instances is so far from being fatal to truth in all sciences, that when those principles are advanced on sufficient grounds, it constitutes the essence of true philosophy ; "[2] and he quotes cases in which Davy trusted to his theories rather than his experiments.

Herschel, who was both a practical physicist and an abstract logician, entertained the deepest respect for Bacon, and made the " Novum Organum " as far as possible the basis of his own admirable *Discourse on the Study of Natural Philosophy.* Yet we find him in Chapter VII. recognising the part which the formation and verification of theories takes in the higher and more general investigations of physical science. J. S. Mill carried on the reaction by describing the Deductive Method in which ratiocination, that is deductive reasoning, is employed for the discovery of new opportunities of testing and verifying an hypothesis. Nevertheless throughout the other parts of his system he inveighed against the value of the deductive process, and even asserted that empirical inference from particulars to particulars is the true type of reasoning.

[1] Horrocks, *Opera Posthuma* (1673), p. 276.
[2] Young's *Works*, vol. i. p. 593.

The irony of fate will probably decide that the most original and valuable part of Mill's System of Logic is irreconcilable with those views of the syllogism and of the nature of inference which occupy the main part of the treatise, and are said to have effected a revolution in logical science. Mill would have been saved from much confusion of thought had he not failed to observe that the inverse use of deduction constitutes induction. In later years Professor Huxley has strongly insisted upon the value of hypothesis. When he advocates the use of "working hypotheses" he means no doubt that any hypothesis is better that none, and that we cannot avoid being guided in our observations by some hypothesis or other. Professor Tyndall's views as to the use of the Imagination in the pursuit of Science put the same truth in another light.

It ought to be pointed out that Neil in his *Art of Reasoning*, a popular but able exposition of the principles of Logic, published in 1853, fully recognises in Chapter XI. the value and position of hypothesis in the discovery of truth. He endeavours to show, too (p. 109), that Francis Bacon did not object to the use of hypothesis.

The true course of inductive procedure is that which has yielded all the more lofty results of science. It consists in *Anticipating Nature*, in the sense of forming hypotheses as to the laws which are probably in operation; and then observing whether the combinations of phenomena are such as would follow from the laws supposed. The investigator begins with facts and ends with them. He uses facts to suggest probable hypotheses; deducing other facts which would happen if a particular hypothesis is true, he proceeds to test the truth of his notion by fresh observations. If any result prove different from what he expects, it leads him to modify or to abandon his hypothesis; but every new fact may give some new suggestion as to the laws in action. Even if the result in any case agrees with his anticipations, he does not regard it as finally confirmatory of his theory, but proceeds to test the truth of the theory by new deductions and new trials.

In such a process the investigator is assisted by the whole body of science previously accumulated. He may employ analogy, as I shall point out, to guide him in the choice of hypotheses. The manifold connections between one science and another give him clues to the kind of laws to be expected, and out of the infinite number of possible hypotheses he selects those which are, as far as can be foreseen at the moment, most probable. Each experiment, therefore, which he performs is that most likely to throw light upon his subject, and even if it frustrate his first views, it tends to put him in possession of the correct clue.

Requisites of a good Hypothesis.

There is little difficulty in pointing out to what condition an hypothesis must conform in order to be accepted as probable and valid. That condition, as I conceive, is the single one of enabling us to infer the existence of phenomena which occur in our experience. *Agreement with fact is the sole and sufficient test of a true hypothesis.*

Hobbes has named two conditions which he considers requisite in an hypothesis, namely (1) That it should be conceivable and not absurd; (2) That it should allow of phenomena being necessarily inferred. Boyle, in noticing Hobbes' views, proposed to add a third condition, to the effect that the hypothesis should not be inconsistent with any other truth on phenomenon of nature.[1] I think that of these three conditions, the first cannot be accepted, unless by *inconceivable* and *absurd* we mean self-contradictory or inconsistent with the laws of thought and nature. I shall have to point out that some satisfactory theories involve suppositions which are wholly *inconceivable* in a certain sense of the word, because the mind cannot sufficiently extend its ideas to frame a notion of the actions supposed to take place. That the force of gravity should act instantaneously between the most distant parts of the planetary system, or that a ray of violet light should consist of about 700 billions of vibrations in a second, are statements of an inconceivable and absurd character in one sense; but they are so far from being opposed to fact that we cannot on any other suppositions account for phenomena observed. But if an hypothesis involve self-contradiction, or is inconsistent with known

---

[1] Boyle's *Physical Examen*, p. 84

laws of nature, it is self-condemned. We cannot even
apply deductive reasoning to a self-contradictory notion;
and being opposed to the most general and certain laws
known to us, the primary laws of thought, it thereby conspicuously fails to agree with facts. Since nature, again,
is never self-contradictory, we cannot at the same time
accept two theories which lead to contradictory results.
If the one agrees with nature, the other cannot. Hence if
there be a law which we believe with high probability to
be verified by observation, we must not frame an hypothesis
in conflict with it, otherwise the hypothesis will necessarily
be in disagreement with observation. Since no law or
hypothesis is proved, indeed, with absolute certainty, there
is always a chance, however slight, that the new hypothesis may displace the old one; but the greater the probability which we assign to that old hypothesis, the greater
must be the evidence required in favour of the new and
conflicting one.

I assert, then, that there is but one test of a good
hypothesis, namely, *its conformity with observed facts;* but
this condition may be said to involve three constituent
conditions, nearly equivalent to those suggested by Hobbes
and Boyle, namely :—

(1) That it allow of the application of deductive reasoning and the inference of consequences capable of comparison with the results of observation.

(2) That it do not conflict with any laws of nature, or
of mind, which we hold to be true.

(3) That the consequences inferred do agree with facts
of observation.

Possibility of Deductive Reasoning.

As the truth of an hypothesis is to be proved by its
conformity with fact, the first condition is that we be able
to apply methods of deductive reasoning, and learn what
should happen according to such an hypothesis. Even
if we could imagine an object acting according to laws
hitherto wholly unknown it would be useless to do so,
because we could never decide whether it existed or not.
We can only infer what would happen under supposed
conditions by applying the knowledge of nature we possess

to those conditions. Hence, as Boscovich truly said, we are to understand by hypotheses "not fictions altogether arbitrary, but suppositions conformable to experience or analogy." It follows that every hypothesis worthy of consideration must suggest some likeness, analogy, or common law, acting in two or more things. If, in order to explain certain facts, a, a', a'', &c., we invent a cause A, then we must in some degree appeal to experience as to the mode in which A will act. As the laws of nature are not known to the mind intuitively, we must point out some other cause, B, which supplies the requisite notions, and all we do is to invent a fourth term to an analogy. As B is to its effects b, b', b'', &c., so is A to its effects a, a', a'', &c. When we attempt to explain the passage of light and heat radiations through space unoccupied by matter, we imagine the existence of the so-called *ether*. But if this ether were wholly different from anything else known to us, we should in vain try to reason about it. We must apply to it at least the laws of motion, that is we must so far liken it to matter. And as, when applying those laws to the elastic medium air, we are able to infer the phenomena of sound, so by arguing in a similar manner concerning ether we are able to infer the existence of light phenomena corresponding to what do occur. All that we do is to take an elastic substance, increase its elasticity immensely, and denude it of gravity and some other properties of matter, but we must retain sufficient likeness to matter to allow of deductive calculations.

The force of gravity is in some respects an incomprehensible existence, but in other respects entirely conformable to experience. We observe that the force is proportional to mass, and that it acts in entire independence of other matter which may be present or intervening. The law of the decrease of intensity, as the square of the distance increases, is observed to hold true of light, sound, and other influences emanating from a point, and spreading uniformly through space. The law is doubtless connected with the properties of space, and is so far in agreement with our necessary ideas.

It may be said, however, that no hypothesis can be so much as framed in the mind unless it be more or less conformable to experience. As the material of our ideas is derived from sensation we cannot figure to ourselves any agent, but as endowed with some of the properties of matter. All that the mind can do in the creation of new existences is to alter combinations, or the intensity of sensuous properties. The phenomenon of motion is familiar to sight and touch, and different degrees of rapidity are also familiar; we can pass beyond the limits of sense, and imagine the existence of rapid motion, such as our senses could not observe. We know what is elasticity, and we can therefore in a way figure to ourselves elasticity a thousand or a million times greater than any which is sensuously known to us. The waves of the ocean are many times higher than our own bodies ; other waves, are many times less ; continue the proportion, and we ultimately arrive at waves as small as those of light. Thus it is that the powers of mind enable us from a sensuous basis to reason concerning agents and phenomena different in an unlimited degree. If no hypothesis then can be absolutely opposed to sense, accordance with experience must always be a question of degree.

In order that an hypothesis may allow of satisfactory comparison with experience, it must possess definiteness and in many cases mathematical exactness allowing of the precise calculation of results. We must be able to ascertain whether it does or does not agree with facts. The theory of vortices is an instance to the contrary, for it did not present any mode of calculating the exact relations between the distances and periods of the planets and satellites ; it could not, therefore, undergo that rigorous testing to which Newton scrupulously submitted his theory of gravity before its promulgation. Vagueness and incapability of precise proof or disproof often enable a false theory to live ; but with those who love truth, vagueness should excite suspicion. The upholders of the ancient doctrine of Nature's abhorrence of a vacuum, had been unable to anticipate the important fact that water would not rise more than 33 feet in a common suction pump. Nor when the fact was pointed out could they explain it, except by introducing a special alteration of the theory to the effect that Nature's abhorrence of a vacuum was limited to 33 feet.

Consistency with the Laws of Nature.

In the second place an hypothesis must not be contradictory to what we believe to be true concerning Nature. It must not involve self-inconsistency which is opposed to the highest and simplest laws, namely, those of Logic. Neither ought it to be irreconcilable with the simple laws of motion, of gravity, of the conservation of energy, nor any parts of physical science which we consider to be established beyond reasonable doubt. Not that we are absolutely forbidden to entertain such an hypothesis, but if we do so we must be prepared to disprove some of the best demonstrated truths in the possession of mankind. The fact that conflict exists means that the consequences of the theory are not verified if previous discoveries are correct, and we must therefore show that previous discoveries are incorrect before we can verify our theory.

An hypothesis will be exceedingly improbable, not to say absurd, if it supposes a substance to act in a manner unknown in other cases; for it then fails to be verified in our knowledge of that substance. Several physicists, especially Euler and Grove, have supposed that we might dispense with an ethereal basis of light, and infer from the interstellar passage of rays that there was a kind of rare gas occupying space. But if so, that gas must be excessively rare, as we may infer from the apparent absence of an atmosphere around the moon, and from other facts known to us concerning gases and the atmosphere; yet it must possess an elastic force at least a billion times as great as atmospheric air at the earth's surface, in order to account for the extreme rapidity of light rays. Such an hypothesis then is inconsistent with our knowledge concerning gases.

Provided that there be no clear and absolute conflict with known laws of nature, there is no hypothesis so improbable or apparently inconceivable that it may not be rendered probable, or even approximately certain, by a sufficient number of concordances. In fact the two best founded and most successful theories in physical science involve the most absurd suppositions. Gravity is a force which appears to act between bodies through vacuous space; it is in positive contradiction to the old dictum that nothing can act but through some medium. It is even more puzzling that the force acts in perfect indifference to intervening obstacles. Light in spite of its extreme velocity shows much respect to matter, for it is almost instantaneously stopped by opaque substances, and to a considerable extent absorbed and deflected by transparent ones. But to gravity all media are, as it were, absolutely transparent, nay non-existent; and two particles at opposite points of the earth affect each other exactly as if the globe were not between. The action is, so far as we can observe, instantaneous, so that every particle of the universe is at every moment in separate cognisance, as it were, of the relative position of every other particle throughout the universe at that same moment of time. Compared with such incomprehensible conditions, the theory of vortices deals with commonplace realities. Newton's celebrated saying *hypotheses non fingo*, bears the appearance of irony; and it was not without apparent grounds that Leibnitz and the continental philosophers charged Newton with re-introducing occult powers and qualities.

The undulatory theory of light presents almost equal difficulties of conception. We are asked by physical philosophers to give up our prepossessions, and to believe that interstellar space which seems empty is not empty at all, but filled with *something* immensely more solid and elastic than steel. As Young himself remarked,[1] " the luminiferous ether, pervading all space, and penetrating almost all substances, is not only highly elastic, but absolutely solid!!! " Herschel calculated the force which may be supposed, according to the undulatory theory of light, to be constantly exerted at each point in space, and finds it to be 1,148,000,000,000 times the elastic force ot ordinary air at the earth's surface, so that the pressure of ether per square inch must be about seventeen billions of pounds.[2] Yet we live and move without appreciable resistance through this medium, immensely harder and more elastic than adamant. All our ordinary notions must be laid aside in contemplating such an hypothesis;

---

[1] Young's *Works*, vol. i. p. 415.
[2] *Familiar Lectures on Scientific Subjects*, p. 282.

yet it is no more than the observed phenomena of light
and heat force us to accept. We cannot deny even the
strange suggestion of Young, that there may be independent
worlds, some possibly existing in different parts of space,
but others perhaps pervading each other unseen and
unknown in the same space.[1] For if we are bound to
admit the conception of this adamantine firmament, it is
equally easy to admit a plurality of such. We see, then,
that mere difficulties of conception must not discredit a
theory which otherwise agrees with facts, and we must
only reject hypotheses which are inconceivable in the
sense of breaking distinctly the primary laws of thought
and nature.

Conformity with Facts.

Before we accept a new hypothesis it must be shown
to agree not only with the previously known laws of nature, but also with the particular facts which it is framed
to explain. Assuming that these facts are properly
established, it must agree with all of them. A single
absolute conflict between fact and hypothesis, is fatal to
the hypothesis; *falsa in uno, falsa in omnibus.*

Seldom, indeed snall we have a theory free from
difficulties and apparent inconsistency with facts. Though
one real inconsistency would overturn the most plausible
theory, yet there is usually some probability that the fact
may be misinterpreted, or that some supposed law of
nature, on which we are relying, may not be true. It may
be expected, moreover, that a good hypothesis, besides
agreeing with facts already noticed, will furnish us with
distinct credentials by enabling us to anticipate deductively
series of facts which are not already connected and
accounted for by any equally probable hypothesis. We
cannot lay down any precise rule as to the number of
accordances which can establish the truth of an hypothesis,
because the accordances will vary much in value. While,
on the one hand, no finite number of accordances will
give entire certainty, the probability of the hypothesis
will increase very rapidly with the number of accordances.

[1] Young's *Works*, vol. i. p. 417.

Almost every problem in science thus takes the form of a balance of probabilities. It is only when difficulty after difficulty has been successfully explained away, and decisive *experimenta crucis* have, time after time, resulted in favour of our theory, that we can venture to assert the falsity of all objections.

The sole real test of an hypothesis is its accordance with fact. Descartes' celebrated system of vortices is exploded, not because it was intrinsically absurd and inconceivable, but because it could not give results in accordance with the actual motions of the heavenly bodies. The difficulties of conception involved in the apparatus of vortices, are child's play compared with those of gravitation and the undulatory theory already described. Vortices are on the whole plausible suppositions; for planets and satellites bear at first sight much resemblance to objects carried round in whirlpools, an analogy which doubtless suggested the theory. The failure was in the first and third requisites; for, as already remarked, the theory did not allow of precise calculation of planetary motions, and was thus incapable of rigorous verification. But so far as we can institute a comparison, facts are entirely against the vortices. Newton did not ridicule the theory as absurd, but showed[1] that it was "pressed with many difficulties." He carefully pointed out that the Cartesian theory was inconsistent with the laws of Kepler, and would represent the planets as moving more rapidly at their aphelia than at their perihelia.[2] The rotatory motion of the sun and planets on their own axes is in striking conflict with the revolutions of the satellites carried round them; and comets, the most flimsy of bodies, calmly pursue their courses in elliptic paths, irrespective of the vortices which they pass through. We may now also point to the interlacing orbits of the minor planets as a new and insuperable difficulty in the way of the Cartesian ideas.

Newton, though he established the best of theories, was also capable of proposing one of the worst; and if we want an instance of a theory decisively contradicted by

[1] *Principia*, bk. iii. Prop. 43. General Scholium.
[2] Ibid. bk. ii. Sect. ix. Prop. 53.

facts, we have only to turn to his views concerning the origin of natural colours. Having analysed, with incomparable skill, the origin of the colours of thin plates, he suggests that the colours of all bodies are determined in like manner by the size of their ultimate particles. A thin plate of a definite thickness will reflect a definite colour; hence, if broken up into fragments it will form a powder of the same colour. But, if this be a sufficient explanation of coloured substances, then every coloured fluid ought to reflect the complementary colour of that which it transmits. Colourless transparency arises, according to Newton, from particles being too minute to reflect light ; but if so, every black substance should be transparent. Newton himself so acutely felt this last difficulty as to suggest that true blackness is due to some internal refraction of the rays to and fro, and an ultimate stifling of them, which he did not attempt to explain further. Unless some other process comes into operation, neither refraction nor reflection, however often repeated, will destroy the energy of light. The theory therefore gives no account, as Brewster shows, of 24 parts out of 25 of the light which falls upon a black coal, and the remaining part which is reflected from the lustrous surface is equally inconsistent with the theory, because fine coal-dust is almost entirely devoid of reflective power.[1] It is now generally believed that the colours of natural bodies are due to the unequal absorption of rays of light of different refrangibility.

Experimentum Crucis.

As we deduce more and more conclusions from a theory, and find them verified by trial, the probability of the theory increases in a rapid manner ; but we never escape the risk of error altogether. Absolute certainty is beyond the powers of inductive investigation, and the most plausible supposition may ultimately be proved false. Such is the groundwork of similarity in nature, that two very different conditions may often give closely similar results. We sometimes find ourselves therefore

[1] Brewster's *Life of Newton*, 1st edit. chap. vii.

in possession of two or more hypotheses which both agree with so many experimental facts as to have great appearance of truth. Under such circumstances we have need of some new experiment, which shall give results agreeing with one hypothesis but not with the other.

Any such experiment which decides between two rival theories may be called an *Experimentum Crucis*, an Experiment of the Finger Post. Whenever the mind stands, as it were, at cross-roads and knows not which way to select, it needs some decisive guide, and Bacon therefore assigned great importance and authority to instances which serve in this capacity. The name given by Bacon has become familiar; it is almost the only one of Bacon's figurative expressions which has passed into common use. Even Newton, as I have mentioned (p. 507), used the name.

I do not think, indeed, that the common use of the word at all agrees with that intended by Bacon. Herschel says that " we make an experiment of the crucial kind when we form combinations, and put in action causes from which some particular one shall be deliberately excluded, and some other purposely admitted." [1] This, however, seems to be the description of any special experiment not made at haphazard. Pascal's experiment of causing a barometer to be carried to the top of the Puy-de-Dôme has often been considered as a perfect *experimentum crucis*, if not the first distinct one on record; [2] but if so, we must dignify the doctrine of Nature's abhorrence of a vacuum with the position of a rival theory. A crucial experiment must not simply confirm one theory, but must negative another; it must decide a mind which is in equilibrium, as Bacon says, [3] between two equally plausible views. " When in search of any nature, the understanding comes to an equilibrium, as it were, or stands suspended as to which of two or more natures the cause of nature inquired after should be attributed or assigned, by reason of the frequent and common occurrence of several natures, then these Crucial Instances show the true and inviolable association of one

---

[1] *Discourse on the Study of Natural Philosophy*, p. 151.
[2] Ibid. p. 229.
[3] *Novum Organum*, bk. ii. Aphorism 36

of these natures to the nature sought, and the uncertain and separable alliance of the other, whereby the question is decided, the former nature admitted for the cause, and the other rejected. These instances, therefore, afford great light, and have a kind of overruling authority, so that the course of interpretation will sometimes terminate in them, or be finished by them."

The long-continued strife between the Corpuscular and Undulatory theories of light forms the best possible illustration of an Experimentum Crucis. It is remarkable in how plausible a manner both these theories agreed with the ordinary laws of geometrical optics, relating to reflection and refraction. According to the first law of motion a moving particle proceeds in a perfectly straight line, when undisturbed by extraneous forces. If the particle being perfectly elastic, strike a perfectly elastic plane, it will bound off in such a path that the angles of incidence and reflection will be equal. Now a ray of light proceeds in a straight line, or appears to do so, until it meets a reflecting body, when its path is altered in a manner exactly similar to that of the elastic particle. Here is a remarkable correspondence which probably suggested to Newton's mind the hypothesis that light consists of minute elastic particles moving with excessive rapidity in straight lines. The correspondence was found to extend also to the law of simple refraction; for if particles of light be supposed capable of attracting matter, and being attracted by it at insensibly small distances, then a ray of light, falling on the surface of a transparent medium, will suffer an increase in its velocity perpendicular to the surface, and the law of sines is the consequence. This remarkable explanation of the law of refraction had doubtless a very strong effect in leading Newton to entertain the corpuscular theory, and he appears to have thought that the analogy between the propagation of rays of light and the motion of bodies was perfectly exact, whatever might be the actual nature of light.[1] It is highly remarkable, again, that Newton was able to give by his corpuscular theory, a plausible explanation of the inflection of light as dis-

[1] *Principia*, bk. i. Sect. xiv. Prop. 96. Scholium. *Opticks*, Prop. vi. 3rd edit. p. 70.

covered by Grimaldi. The theory would indeed have been a very probable one could Newton's own law of gravity have applied ; but this was out of the question, because the particles of light, in order that they may move in straight lines, must be devoid of any influence upon each other.

The Huyghenian or Undulatory theory of light was also able to explain the same phenomena, but with one remarkable difference. If the undulatory theory be true, light must move more slowly in a dense refracting medium than in a rarer one; but the Newtonian theory assumed that the attraction of the dense medium caused the particles of light to move more rapidly than in the rare medium. On this point, then, there was complete discrepancy between the theories, and observation was required to show which theory was to be preferred. Now by simply cutting a uniform plate of glass into two pieces, and slightly inclining one piece so as to increase the length of the path of a ray passing through it, experimenters were able to show that light does move more slowly in glass than in air.[1] More recently Fizeau and Foucault independently measured the velocity of light in air and in water, and found that the velocity is greater in air.[2]

There are a number of other points at which experience decides against Newton, and in favour of Huyghens and Young. Laplace pointed out that the attraction supposed to exist between matter and the corpuscular particles of light would cause the velocity of light to vary with the size of the emitting body, so that if a star were 250 times as great in diameter as our sun, its attraction would prevent the emanation of light altogether.[3] But experience shows that the velocity of light is uniform, and independent of the magnitude of the emitting body, as it should be according to the undulatory theory. Lastly, Newton's explanation of diffraction or inflection fringes of colours was only *plausible*, and not true; for Fresnel ascertained that the dimensions of the fringes are not what they would be according to Newton's theory.

Although the Science of Light presents us with the

---

[1] Airy's *Mathematical Tracts*, 3rd edit. pp. 286—288.
[2] Jamin, *Cours de Physique*, vol. iii. p. 372.
[3] Young's *Lectures on Natural Philosophy* (1845), vol. i. p. 361.

most beautiful examples of crucial experiments and observations, instances are not wanting in other branches of
science. Copernicus asserted, in opposition to the ancient
Ptolemaic theory, that the earth moved round the sun, and
he predicted that if ever the sense of sight could be
rendered sufficiently acute and powerful, we should see
phases in Mercury and Venus. Galileo with his telescope
was able, in 1610 to verify the prediction as regards Venus,
and subsequent observations of Mercury led to a like conclusion. The discovery of the aberration of light added a
new proof, still further strengthened by the more recent
determination of the parallax of fixed stars. Hooke proposed to prove the existence of the earth's diurnal motion
by observing the deviation of a falling body, an experiment successfully accomplished by Benzenberg; and
Foucault's pendulum has since furnished an additional
indication of the same motion, which is indeed also
apparent in the trade winds. All these are crucial facts in
favour of the Copernican theory.

Descriptive Hypotheses.

There are hypotheses which we may call *descriptive
hypotheses*, and which serve for little else than to furnish
convenient names. When a phenomenon is of an unusual
kind, we cannot even speak of it without using some
analogy. Every word implies some resemblance between
the thing to which it is applied, and some other thing,
which fixes the meaning of the word. If we are to speak
of what constitutes electricity, we must search for the
nearest analogy, and as electricity is characterised by the
rapidity and facility of its movements, the notion of a fluid
of a very subtle character presents itself as appropriate.
There is the single-fluid and the double-fluid theory of
electricity, and a great deal of discussion has been uselessly
spent upon them. The fact is, that if these theories be
understood as more than convenient modes of describing
the phenomena, they are altogether invalid. The analogy
extends only to the rapidity of motion, or rather the fact
that a phenomenon occurs successively at different points
of the body. The so-called electric fluid adds nothing to
the weight of the conductor, and to suppose that it really

consists of particles of matter is even more absurd than to
reinstate the corpuscular theory of light. A far closer
analogy exists between electricity and light undulations,
which are about equally rapid in propagation. We shall
probably continue for a long time to talk of the *electric
fluid*, but there can be no doubt that this expression
represents merely a phase of molecular motion, a wave of
disturbance. The invalidity of these fluid theories is
shown moreover in the fact that they have not led to the
invention of a single new experiment.

Among these merely descriptive hypotheses I should
place Newton's theory of Fits of Easy Reflection and
Refraction. That theory did not do more than describe
what took place. It involved no analogy to other phenomena of nature, for Newton could not point to any other
substance which went through these extraordinary fits.
We now know that the true analogy would have been
waves of sound, of which Newton had acquired in other
respects so complete a comprehension. But though the
notion of interference of waves had distinctly occurred to
Hooke, Newton failed to see how the periodic phenomena
of light could be connected with the periodic character of
waves. His hypothesis fell because it was out of analogy
with everything else in nature, and it therefore did not
allow him, as in other cases, to descend by mathematical
deduction to consequences which could be verified or
refuted.

We are at freedom to imagine the existence of a new
agent, and to give it an appropriate name, provided there
are phenomena incapable of explanation from known
causes. We may speak of *vital force* as occasioning life,
provided that we do not take it to be more than a name
for an undefined something giving rise to inexplicable
facts, just as the French chemists called Iodine the Substance X, so long as they were unaware of its real character and place in chemistry.[1] Encke was quite justifed
in speaking of the *resisting medium* in space so long as the
retardation of his comet could not be otherwise accounted
for. But such hypotheses will do much harm whenever
they divert us from attempts to reconcile the facts with

---

[1] Paris, *Life of Davy*, p. 274.

known laws, or when they lead us to mix up discrete things. Because we speak of vital force we must not assume that it is a really existing physical force like electricity ; we do not know what it is. We have no right to confuse Encke's supposed resisting medium with the basis of light without distinct evidence of identity. The name protoplasm, now so familiarly used by physiologists, is doubtless legitimate so long as we do not mix up different substances under it, or imagine that the name gives us any knowledge of the obscure origin of life. To name a substance protoplasm no more explains the infinite variety of forms of life which spring out of the substance, than does the *vital force* which may be supposed to reside in the protoplasm. Both expressions are mere names for an inexplicable series of causes which out of apparently similar conditions produce the most diverse results.

Hardly to be distinguished from descriptive hypotheses are certain imaginary objects which we frame for the ready comprehension of a subject. The mathematician, in treating abstract questions of probability, finds it convenient to represent the conditions by a concrete hypothesis in the shape of a ballot-box. Poisson proved the principle of the inverse method of probabilities by imagining a number of ballot-boxes to have their contents mixed in one great ballot-box (p. 244). Many such devices are used by mathematicians. The Ptolemaic theory of *cycles* and *epi-cycles* was no grotesque and useless work of the imagination, but a perfectly valid mode of analysing the motions of the heavenly bodies ; in reality it is used by mathematicians at the present day. Newton employed the pendulum as a means of representing the nature of an undulation. Centres of gravity, oscillation, &c., poles of the magnet, lines of force, are other imaginary existences employed to assist our thoughts (p. 364). Such devices may be called *Representative Hypotheses*, and they are only permissible so far as they embody analogies. Their further consideration belongs either to the subject of Analogy, or to that of language and representation, founded upon analogy.

CHAPTER XXIV.

EMPIRICAL KNOWLEDGE, EXPLANATION, AND PREDICTION.

INDUCTIVE investigation, as we have seen, consists in the union of hypothesis and experiment, deductive reasoning being the link by which experimental results are made to confirm or confute the hypothesis. Now when we consider this relation between hypothesis and experiment it is obvious that we may classify our knowledge under four heads.

(1) We may be acquainted with facts which have not yet been brought into accordance with any hypothesis. Such facts constitute what is called *Empirical Knowledge*.

(2) Another extensive portion of our knowledge consists of facts which having been first observed empirically, have afterwards been brought into accordance with other facts by an hypothesis concerning the general laws applying to them. This portion of our knowledge may be said to be *explained, reasoned,* or *generalised*.

(3) In the third place comes the collection of facts, minor in number, but most important as regards their scientific interest, which have been anticipated by theory and afterwards verified by experiment.

(4) Lastly, there exists knowledge which is accepted solely on the ground of theory, and is incapable of experimental confirmation, at least with the instrumental means in our possession.

It is a work of much interest to compare and illustrate the relative extent and value of these four groups of knowledge. We shall observe that as a general rule a great branch of science originates in facts observed accidentally.

or without distinct consciousness of what is to be expected.
As a science progresses, its power of foresight rapidly
increases, until the mathematician in his library acquires
the power of anticipating nature, and predicting what will
happen in circumstances which the eye of man has never
examined.

Empirical Knowledge.

By empirical knowledge we mean such as is derived
directly from the examination of detached facts, and rests
entirely on those facts, without corroboration from other
branches of knowledge.   It is contrasted with generalised
and theoretical knowledge, which embraces many series of
facts under a few comprehensive principles, so that each
series serves to throw light upon each other series of facts.
Just as, in the map of a half-explored country, we see
detached bits of rivers, isolated mountains, and undefined
plains, not connected into any complete plan, so a new
branch of knowledge consists of groups of facts, each group
standing apart, so as not to allow us to reason from one to
another.

Before the time of Descartes, and Newton, and Huyghens,
there was much empirical knowledge of the phenomena of
light.   The rainbow had always struck the attention of
the most careless observers, and there was no difficulty
in perceiving that its conditions of occurrence consisted in
rays of the sun shining upon falling drops of rain.   It was
impossible to overlook the resemblance of the ordinary
rainbow to the comparatively rare lunar rainbow, to the
bow which appears upon the spray of a waterfall, or even
upon beads of dew suspended on grass and spiders' webs.
In all these cases the uniform conditions are rays of light
and round drops of water.   Roger Bacon had noticed these
conditions, as well as the analogy of the rainbow colours
to those produced by crystals.[1]   But the knowledge was
empirical until Descartes and Newton showed how the
phenomena were connected with facts concerning the
refraction of light.

There can be no better instance of an empirical truth

[1] *Opus Majus.*   Edit. 1733.   Cap. x. p. 460.

than that detected by Newton concerning the high refractive powers of combustible substances. Newton's
chemical notions were almost as vague as those prevalent
in his day, but he observed that certain "fat, sulphureous,
unctuous bodies," as he calls them, such as camphor, oils
spirit of turpentine, amber, &c., have refractive powers
two or three times greater than might be anticipated from
their densities.[1] The enormous refractive index of diamond,
led him with great sagacity to regard this substance as
of the same unctuous or inflammable nature, so that he
may be regarded as predicting the combustibility of the
diamond, afterwards demonstrated by the Florentine
Academicians in 1694. Brewster having entered into a
long investigation of the refractive powers of different
substances, confirmed Newton's assertions, and found that
the three elementary combustible substances, diamond,
phosphorus, and sulphur, have, in comparison with their
densities, by far the highest known refractive indices,[2] and
there are only a few substances, such as chromate of lead
or glass of antimony, which exceed them in absolute power
of refraction. The oils and hydrocarbons generally possess
excessive indices. But all this knowledge remains to the
present day purely empirical, no connection having been
pointed out between this coincidence of inflammability and
high refractive power, with other laws of chemistry or optics.
It is worth notice, as pointed out by Brewster, that if
Newton had argued concerning two minerals, Greenockite
and Octahedrite, as he did concerning diamond, his predictions would have proved false, showing sufficiently that
he did not make any sure induction on the subject. In
the present day, the relation of the refractive index to the
density and atomic weight of a substance is becoming a
matter of theory; yet there remain specific differences of
refracting power known only on empirical grounds, and it
is curious that in hydrogen an abnormally high refractive
power has been found to be joined to inflammability.

The science of chemistry, however much its theory may
have progressed, still presents us with a vast body of empirical knowledge. Not only is it as yet hopeless to attempt

---

[1] Newton's *Opticks*. Third edit. p. 249.
[2] Brewster. *Treatise on New Philosophical Instruments*, p. 266, &c.

to account for the particular group of qualities belonging to each element, but there are multitudes of particular facts of which no further account can be given. Why should the sulphides of many metals be intensely black? Why should a slight amount of phosphoric acid have so great a power of interference with the crystallisation of vanadic acid?[1] Why should the compound silicates of alkalies and alkaline metals be transparent? Why should gold be so highly ductile. and gold and silver the only two sensibly translucent metals? Why should sulphur be capable of so many peculiar changes into allotropic modifications?

There are whole branches of chemical knowledge which are mere collections of disconnected facts. The properties of alloys are often remarkable ; but no laws have yet been detected, and the laws of combining proportions seem to have no clear application.[2]   Not the slightest explanation can be given of the wonderful variations of the qualities of iron, according as it contains more or less carbon and silicon, nay, even the facts of the case are often involved in uncertainty. Why, again, should the properties of steel be remarkably affected by the presence of a little tungsten or manganese? All that was determined by Matthiessen concerning the conducting powers of copper, was of a purely empirical character.[3]   Many animal substances cannot be shown to obey the laws of combining proportions. Thus for the most part chemistry is yet an empirical science occupied with the registration of immense numbers of disconnected facts, which may at some future time become the basis of a greatly extended theory.

We must not indeed suppose that any science will ever entirely cease to be empirical. Multitudes of phenomena have been explained by the undulatory theory of light ; but there yet remain many facts to be treated. The natural colours of bodies and the rays given off by them when heated, are unexplained, and yield few empirical coincidences. The theory of electricity is partially understood, but the conditions of the production of frictional electricity defy explanation, although they have been

[1] Roscoe, Bakerian Lecture, *Philosophical Transactions* (1868), vol. clviii. p. 6.
[2] *Life of Faraday*, vol. ii. p. 104.
[3] Watts, *Dictionary of Chemistry*, vol. ii. p. 39, &c.

studied for two centuries. I shall subsequently point out that even the establishment of a wide and true law of nature is but the starting-point for the discovery of exceptions and divergences giving a new scope to empirical discovery.

There is probably no science, I have said, which is entirely free from empirical and unexplained facts. Logic approaches most nearly to this position, as it is merely a deductive development of the laws of thought and the principle of substitution. Yet some of the facts established in the investigation of the inverse logical problem may be considered empirical. That a proposition of the form A=BC ∙|∙ $b\ c$ possesses the least number of distinct logical variations, and the greatest number of logical equivalents of the same form among propositions involving three classes (p. 141), is a case in point. So also is the fact discovered by Professor Clifford that in regard to statements involving four classes, there is only one example of two dissimilar statements having the same distances (p. 144). Mathematical science often yields empirical truths. Why, for instance, should the value of π, when expressed to a great number of figures, contain the digit 7 much less frequently than any other digit?[1] Even geometry may allow of empirical truths, when the matter does not involve quantities of space, but numerical results and the positive or negative character of quantities, as in De Morgan's theorem concerning negative areas.

Accidental Discovery.

There are not a few cases where almost pure accident has determined the moment when a new branch of knowledge was to be created. The laws of the structure of crystals were not discovered until Haüy happened to drop a beautiful crystal of calc-spar upon a stone pavement. His momentary regret at destroying a choice specimen was quickly removed when, in attempting to join the fragments together, he observed regular geometrical faces, which did not correspond with the external facets of the crystals. A great many more crystals were soon broken intentionally,

---

[1] De Morgan's *Budget of Paradoxes*, p. 291.

to observe the planes of cleavage, and the discovery of the internal structure of crystalline substances was the result. Here we see how much more was due to the reasoning power of the philosopher, than to an accident which must often have happened to other persons.

In a similar manner, a fortuitous occurrence led Malus to discover the polarisation of light by reflection. The phenomena of double refraction had been long known, and when engaged in Paris in 1808, in investigating the character of light thus polarised, Malus chanced to look through a double refracting prism at the light of the setting sun, reflected from the windows of the Luxembourg Palace. In turning the prism round, he was surprised to find that the ordinary image disappeared at two opposite positions of the prism. He remarked that the reflected light behaved like light which had been polarised by passing through another prism. He was induced to test the character of light reflected under other circumstances, and it was eventually proved that polarisation is invariably connected with reflection. Some of the general laws of optics, previously unsuspected, were thus discovered by pure accident. In the history of electricity, accident has had a large part. For centuries some of the more common effects of magnetism and of frictional electricity had presented themselves as unaccountable deviations from the ordinary course of Nature. Accident must have first directed attention to such phenomena, but how few of those who witnessed them had any conception of the all-pervading character of the power manifested. The very existence of galvanism, or electricity of low tension, was unsuspected until Galvani accidentally touched the leg of a frog with pieces of metal. The decomposition of water by voltaic electricity also was accidentally discovered by Nicholson in 1801, and Davy speaks of this discovery as the foundation of all that had since been done in electro-chemical science.

It is otherwise with the discovery of electro-magnetism. Oersted, in common with many others, had suspected the existence of some relation between the magnet and electricity, and he appears to have tried to detect its exact nature. Once, as we are told by Hansteen, he had employed a strong galvanic battery during a lecture, and at

the close it occurred to him to try the effect of placing
the conducting wire parallel to a magnetic needle, instead
of at right angles, as he had previously done. The needle
immediately moved and took up a position nearly at right
angles to the wire ; he inverted the direction of the
current, and the needle deviated in a contrary direction.
The great discovery was made, and if by accident, it was
such an accident as happens, as Lagrange remarked of
Newton, only to those who deserve it.[1] There was,
in fact, nothing accidental, except that, as in all totally
new discoveries, Oersted did not know what to look for.
He could not infer from previous knowledge the nature
of the relation, and it was only repeated trial in different
modes which could lead him to the right combination.
High and happy powers of inference, and not accident,
subsequently led Faraday to reverse the process, and to
show that the motion of the magnet would occasion an
electric current in the wire.

Sufficient investigation would probably show that almost
every branch of art and science had an accidental beginning. In historical times almost every important new
instrument as the telescope, the microscope, or the compass,
was probably suggested by some accidental occurrence.
In pre-historic times the germs of the arts must have
arisen still more exclusively in the same way. Cultivation of plants probably arose, in Mr. Darwin's opinion,
from some such accident as the seeds of a fruit falling upon
a heap of refuse, and producing an unusually fine variety.
Even the use of fire must, some time or other, have been
discovered in an accidental manner.

With the progress of a branch of science, the element
of chance becomes much reduced. Not only are laws
discovered which enable results to be predicted, as we
shall see, but the systematic examination of phenomena
and substances often leads to discoveries which can in no
sense be said to be accidental. It has been asserted that
the anæsthetic properties of chloroform were disclosed by a
little dog smelling at a saucerful of the liquid in a chemist's
shop in Linlithgow, the singular effects upon the dog being
reported to Simpson, who turned the incident to good

[1] *Life of Faraday*, vol. ii. p. 396.

account. This story, however, has been shown to be a fabrication, the fact being that Simpson had for many years been endeavouring to discover a better anæsthetic than those previously employed, and that he tested the properties of chloroform, among other substances, at the suggestion of Waldie, a Liverpool chemist. The valuable powers of chloral hydrate have since been discovered in a like manner, and systematic inquiries are continually being made into the therapeutic or economic values of new chemical compounds.

If we must attempt to draw a conclusion concerning the part which chance plays in scientific discovery, it must be allowed that it more or less affects the success of all inductive investigation, but becomes less important with the progress of science. Accident may bring a new and valuable combination to the notice of some person who had never expressly searched for a discovery of the kind, and the probabilities are certainly in favour of a discovery being occasionally made in this manner. But the greater the tact and industry with which a physicist applies himself to the study of nature, the greater is the probability that he will meet with fortunate accidents, and will turn them to good account. Thus it comes to pass that, in the refined investigations of the present day, genius united to extensive knowledge, cultivated powers, and indomitable industry, constitute the characteristics of the successful discoverer.

Empirical Observations subsequently Explained.

The second great portion of scientific knowledge consists of facts which have been first learnt in a purely empirical manner, but have afterwards been shown to follow from some law of nature, that is, from some highly probable hypothesis. Facts are said to be explained when they are thus brought into harmony with other facts, or bodies of general knowledge. There are few words more familiarly used in scientific phraseology than this word *explanation*, and it is necessary to decide exactly what we mean by it, since the question touches the deepest points concerning the nature of science. Like most terms referring to mental actions, the verbs *to explain*, or *to explicate*, involve material similes. The action is *ex plicis plana reddere*, to take out the folds, and render a thing plain or even. Explanation thus renders a thing clearly comprehensible in all its points, so that there is nothing left outstanding or obscure.

Every act of explanation consists in pointing out a resemblance between facts, or in showing that similarity exists between apparently diverse phenomena. This similarity may be of any extent and depth ; it may be a general law of nature, which harmonises the motions of all the heavenly bodies by showing that there is a similar force which governs all those motions, or the explanation may involve nothing more than a single identity, as when we explain the appearance of shooting stars by showing that they are identical with portions of a comet. Wherever we detect resemblance, there is a more or less explanation. The mind is disquieted when it meets a novel phenomenon, one which is *sui generis ;* it seeks at once for parallels which may be found in the memory of past sensations. The so-called sulphurous smell which attends a stroke of lightning often excited attention, and it was not explained until the exact similarity of the smell to that of ozone was pointed out. The marks upon a flagstone are explained when they are shown to correspond with the feet of an extinct animal, whose bones are elsewhere found. Explanation, in fact, generally commences by the discovery of some simple resemblance ; the theory of the rainbow began as soon as Antonio de Dominis pointed out the resemblance between its colours and those presented by a ray of sunlight passing through a glass globe full of water.

The nature and limits of explanation can only be fully considered, after we have entered upon the subjects of generalisation and analogy. It must suffice to remark, in this place, that the most important process of explanation consists in showing that an observed fact is one case of a general law or tendency. Iron is always found combined with sulphur, when it is in contact with coal, whereas in other parts of the carboniferous strata it always occurs as a carbonate. We explain this empirical fact as being due to the reducing power of carbon and hydrogen, which prevents the iron from combining with oxygen, and leaves it open to the affinity of sulphur. The uniform strength and direction of the trade-winds were long familiar to mariners, before they were explained by Halley on hydrostatical principles. The winds were found to arise from the action of gravity, which causes a heavier body to displace a lighter one, while the direction from east to west was explained as a result of the earth's rotation. Whatever body in the northern hemisphere changes its latitude, whether it be a bird, or a railway train, or a body of air, must tend towards the right hand. Dove's law of the winds is that the winds tend to veer in the northern hemisphere in the direction N.E.S.W., and in the southern hemisphere in the direction N.W.S.E. This tendency was shown by him to be the necessary effect of the same conditions which apply to the trade winds. Whenever, then, any fact is connected by resemblance, law, theory, or hypothesis, with other facts, it is explained.

Although the great mass of recorded facts must be empirical, and awaiting explanation, such knowledge is of minor value, because it does not admit of safe and extensive inference. Each recorded result informs us exactly what will be experienced again in the same circumstances, but has no bearing upon what will happen in other circumstances.

Overlooked Results of Theory.

We must by no means suppose that, when a scientific truth is in our possession, all its consequences will be foreseen. Deduction is certain and infallible, in the sense that each step in deductive reasoning will lead us to some result, as certain as the law itself. But it does not follow that deduction will lead the reasoner to every result of a law or combination of laws. Whatever road a traveller takes, he is sure to arrive somewhere, but unless he proceeds in a systematic manner, it is unlikely that he will reach every place to which a network of roads will conduct him.

In like manner there are many phenomena which were virtually within the reach of philosophers by inference from their previous knowledge, but were never discovered until accident or systematic empirical observation disclosed their existence.

That light travels with a uniform high velocity was proved by Roemer from observations of the eclipses of Jupiter's satellites. Corrections were thenceforward made in all astronomical observations requiring it, for the difference of absolute time at which an event happened, and that at which it would be seen on the earth. But no person happened to remark that the motion of light compounded with that of the earth in its orbit would occasion a small apparent displacement of the greater part of the heavenly bodies. Fifty years elapsed before Bradley empirically discovered this effect, called by him aberration, when reducing his observations of the fixed stars.

When once the relation between an electric current and a magnet had been detected by Oersted and Faraday, it ought to have been possible for them to foresee the diverse results which must ensue in different circumstances. If, for instance, a plate of copper were placed beneath an oscillating magnetic needle, it should have been seen that the needle would induce currents in the copper, but as this could not take place without a certain reaction against the needle, it ought to have been seen that the needle would come to rest more rapidly than in the absence of the copper. This peculiar effect was accidentally discovered by Gambey in 1824. Arago acutely inferred from Gambey's experiment that if the copper were set in rotation while the needle was stationary the motion would gradually be communicated to the needle. The phenomenon nevertheless puzzled the whole scientific world, and it required the deductive genius of Faraday to show that it was a result of the principles of electro-magnetism.[1]

Many other curious facts might be mentioned which when once noticed were explained as the effects of well-known laws. It was accidentally discovered that the navigation of canals of small depth could be facilitated by increasing the speed of the boats, the resistance being actually reduced by this increase of speed, which enables the boat to ride as it were upon its own forced wave. Now mathematical theory might have predicted this

---

[1] *Experimental Researches in Electricity*, 1st Series, pp. 24—44.

result had the right application of the formulæ occurred to any one.[1] Giffard's injector for supplying steam boilers with water by the force of their own steam, was, I believe, accidentally discovered, but no new principles of mechanics are involved in it, so that it might have been theoretically invented. The same may be said of the curious experiment in which a stream of air or steam issuing from a pipe is made to hold a free disc upon the end of the pipe and thus obstruct its own outlet. The possession then of a true theory does not by any means imply the foreseeing of all the results. The effects of even a few simple laws may be manifold, and some of the most curious and useful effects may remain undetected until accidental observation brings them to our notice.

Predicted Discoveries.

The most interesting of the four classes of facts specified in p. 525, is probably the third, containing those the occurrence of which has been first predicted by theory and then verified by observation. There is no more convincing proof of the soundness of knowledge than that it confers the gift of foresight. Auguste Comte said that " Prevision is the test of true theory ; " I should say that it is *one test* of true theory, and that which is most likely to strike the public attention. Coincidence with fact is the test of true theory, but when the result of theory is announced before-hand, there can be no doubt as to the unprejudiced spirit in which the theorist interprets the results of his own theory.

The earliest instance of scientific prophecy is naturally furnished by the science of Astronomy, which was the earliest in development. Herodotus[2] narrates that, in the midst of a battle between the Medes and Lydians, the day was suddenly turned into night, and the event had been foretold by Thales, the Father of Philosophy. A cessation of the combat and peace confirmed by marriages were the consequences of this happy scientific effort. Much controversy has taken place concerning the date of

[1] Airy, *On Tides and Waves,* Encyclopædia Metropolitana, p. 348*.
[2] Lib. i. cap. 74.

this occurrence, Baily assigning the year 610 B.C, but
Airy has calculated that the exact day was the 28th of
May, 584 B.C. There can be no doubt that this and other
predictions of eclipses attributed to ancient philosophers
were due to a knowledge of the Metonic Cycle, a period of
6,585 days, or 223 lunar months, or about 19 years, after
which a nearly perfect recurrence of the phases and
eclipses of the moon takes place; but if so, Thales must
have had access to long series of astronomical records of
the Egyptians or the Chaldeans. There is a well-known
story as to the happy use which Columbus made of the
power of predicting eclipses in overawing the islanders of
Jamaica who refused him necessary supplies of food for his
fleet. He threatened to deprive them of the moon's light.
"His threat was treated at first with indifference, but
when the eclipse actually commenced, the barbarians vied
with each other in the production of the necessary supplies
for the Spanish fleet."

Exactly the same kind of awe which the ancients experienced at the prediction of eclipses, has been felt in
modern times concerning the return of comets. Seneca
asserted in distinct terms that comets would be found to
revolve in periodic orbits and return to sight. The ancient
Chaldeans and the Pythagoreans are also said to have
entertained a like opinion. But it was not until the age
of Newton and Halley that it became possible to calculate
the path of a comet in future years. A great comet
appeared in 1682, a few years before the first publication of
the *Principia*, and Halley showed that its orbit corresponded
with that of remarkable comets recorded to have appeared
in the years 1531 and 1607. The intervals of time were
not quite equal, but Halley conceived the bold idea that
this difference might be due to the disturbing power of
Jupiter, near which the comet had passed in the interval
1607–1682. He predicted that the comet would return
about the end of 1758 or the beginning of 1759, and
though Halley did not live to enjoy the sight, it was
actually detected on the night of Christmas-day, 1758.
A second return of the comet was witnessed in 1835
nearly at the anticipated time.

In recent times the discovery of Neptune has been the
most remarkable instance of prevision in astronomical

science. A full account of this discovery may be found in several works, as for instance Herschel's *Outlines of Astronomy*, and *Grant's History of Physical Astronomy*, Chapters XII and XIII.

Predictions in the Science of Light.

Next after astronomy the science of physical optics has furnished the most beautiful instances of the prophetic power of correct theory. These cases are the more striking because they proceed from the profound application of mathematical analysis and show an insight into the mysterious workings of matter which is surprising to all, but especially to those who are unable to comprehend the methods of research employed. By its power of prevision the truth of the undulatory theory of light has been conspicuously proved, and the contrast in this respect between the undulatory and Corpuscular theories is remarkable. Even Newton could get no aid from his corpuscular theory in the invention of new experiments, and to his followers who embraced that theory we owe little or nothing in the science of light. Laplace did not derive from the theory a single discovery. As Fresnel remarks : [1]

" The assistance to be derived from a good theory is not to be confined to the calculation of the forces when the laws of the phenomena are known. There are certain laws so complicated and so singular, that observation alone, aided by analogy, could never lead to their discovery. To divine these enigmas we must be guided by theoretical ideas founded on a *true* hypothesis. The theory of luminous vibrations presents this character, and these precious advantages ; for to it we owe the discovery of optical laws the most complicated and most difficult to divine."

Physicists who embraced the corpuscular theory had nothing but their own quickness of observation to rely upon. Fresnel having once seized the conditions of the true undulatory theory, as previously stated by Young, was enabled by the mere manipulation of his mathematical symbols to foresee many of the complicated phenomena of light. Who could possibly suppose, that by stopping a

[1] Taylor's *Scientific Memoirs*, vol. v. p. 241.

portion of the rays passing through a circular aperture, the illumination of a point upon a screen behind the aperture might be many times multiplied. Yet this paradoxical effect was predicted by Fresnel, and verified both by himself, and in a careful repetition of the experiment, by Billet. Few persons are aware that in the middle of the shadow of an opaque circular disc is a point of light sensibly as bright as if no disc had been interposed. This startling fact was deduced from Fresnel's theory by Poisson, and was then verified experimentally by Arago. Airy, again, was led by pure theory to predict that Newton's rings would present a modified appearance if produced between a lens of glass and a plate of metal. This effect happened to have been observed fifteen years before by Arago, unknown to Airy. Another prediction of Airy, that there would be a further modification of the rings when made between two substances of very different refractive indices, was verified by subsequent trial with a diamond. A reversal of the rings takes place when the space intervening between the plates is filled with a substance of intermediate refractive power, another phenomenon predicted by theory and verified by experiment. There is hardly a limit to the number of other complicated effects of the interference of rays of light under different circumstances which might be deduced from the mathematical expressions, if it were worth while, or which, being previously observed, can be explained. An interesting case was observed by Herschel and explained by Airy.[1]

By a somewhat different effort of scientific foresight, Fresnel discovered that any solid transparent medium might be endowed with the power of double refraction by mere compression. As he attributed the double refracting power of crystals to unequal elasticity in different directions, he inferred that unequal elasticity, if artificially produced, would give similar phenomena. With a powerful screw and a piece of glass, he then produced not only the colours due to double refraction, but the actual duplication of images. Thus, by a great scientific generalisation, are the remarkable properties of Iceland spar shown to belong to all transparent substances under certain conditions.[2]

[1] Airy's *Mathematical Tracts*, 3rd edit. p. 312.
[2] Young's *Works*, vol. i. p. 412.

All other predictions in optical science are, however, thrown into the shade by the theoretical discovery of conical refraction by the late Sir W. R. Hamilton, of Dublin. In investigating the passage of light through certain crystals, Hamilton found that Fresnel had slightly misinterpreted his own formulæ, and that, when rightly understood, they indicated a phenomenon of a kind never witnessed. A small ray of light sent into a crystal of arragonite in a particular direction, becomes spread out into an infinite number of rays, which form a hollow cone within the crystal, and a hollow cylinder when emerging from the opposite side. In another case, a different, but equally strange, effect is produced, a ray of light being spread out into a hollow cone at the point where it quits the crystal. These phenomena are peculiarly interesting, because cones and cylinders of light are not produced in any other cases. They are opposed to all analogy, and constitute singular exceptions, of a kind which we shall afterwards consider more fully. Their strangeness rendered them peculiarly fitted to test the truth of the theory by which they were discovered ; and when Professor Lloyd, at Hamilton's request, succeeded, after considerable difficulty, in witnessing the new appearances, no further doubt could remain of the validity of the wave theory which we owe to Huyghens, Young, and Fresnel.[1]

Predictions from the Theory of Undulations.

It is curious that the undulations of light, although inconceivably rapid and small, admit of more accurate measurement than waves of any other kind. But so far as we can carry out exact experiments on other kinds of waves, we find the phenomena of interference repeated, and analogy gives considerable power of prediction. Herschel was perhaps the first to suggest that two sounds might be made to destroy each other by interference.[2] For if one-half of a wave travelling through a tube could be sepa-

---

[1] Lloyd's *Wave Theory*, Part ii. pp. 52—58. Babbage, *Ninth Bridgewater Treatise*, p. 104, quoting Lloyd, *Transactions of the Royal Irish Academy*, vol. xvii. Clifton, *Quarterly Journal of Pure and Applied Mathematics*, January 1860.

[2] *Encyclopædia Metropolitana*, art. *Sound*, p. 753.

rated, and conducted by a longer passage, so as, on rejoin-
ing the other half, to be one-quarter of a vibration behind-
hand, the two portions would exactly neutralise each
other. This experiment has been performed with success.
The interference arising between the waves from the two
prongs of a tuning-fork was also predicted by theory, and
proved to exist by Weber; indeed it may be observed by
merely holding a vibrating fork close to the ear and turning it round.[1]

It is a result of the theory of sound that, if we move
rapidly towards a sounding body, or if it move rapidly
towards us, the pitch of the sound will be a little more
acute; and, *vice versâ*, when the relative motion is in the
opposite direction, the pitch will be more grave. This arises
from the less or greater intervals of time elapsing between
the successive strokes of waves upon the auditory nerve,
according as the ear moves towards or from the source
of sound relatively speaking. This effect was predicted
by theory, and afterwards verified by the experiments of
Buys Ballot, on Dutch railways, and of Scott Russell, in
England. Whenever one railway train passes another,
on the locomotive of which the whistle is being sounded,
the drop in the acuteness of the sound may be noticed at
the moment of passing. This change gives the sound a
peculiar howling character, which many persons must have
noticed. I have calculated that with two trains travelling
thirty miles an hour, the effect would amount to rather
more than half a tone, and with some express trains it
would amount to a tone. A corresponding effect is produced in the case of light undulations, when the eye and
the luminous body approach or recede from each other. It
is shown by a slight change in the refrangibility of the
rays of light, and a consequent change in the place of the
lines of the spectrum, which has been made to give important and unexpected information concerning the relative
approach or recession of stars.

Tides are vast waves, and were the earth's surface entirely covered by an ocean of uniform depth, they would
admit of exact theoretical investigation. The irregular
form of the seas introduces unknown quantities and com-

[1] Tyndall's *Sound*, pp. 261, 273.

plexities with which theory cannot cope. Nevertheless, Whewell, observing that the tides of the German Ocean consist of interfering waves, which arrive partly round the North of Scotland and partly through the British Channel, was enabled to predict that at a point about midway between Brill on the coast of Holland, and Lowestoft no tides would be found to exist. At that point the two waves would be of the same amount, but in opposite phases, so as to neutralise each other. This prediction was verified by a surveying vessel of the British navy.[1]

Prediction in other Sciences.

Generations, or even centuries, may elapse before mankind are in possession of a mathematical theory of the constitution of matter as complete as the theory of gravitation. Nevertheless, mathematical physicists have in recent years acquired a hold of some of the relations of the physical forces, and the proof is found in anticipations of curious phenomena which had never been observed. Professor James Thomson deduced from Carnot's theory of heat that the application of pressure would lower the melting-point of ice. He even ventured to assign the amount of this effect, and his statement was afterwards verified by Sir W. Thomson.[2] " In this very remarkable speculation, an entirely novel physical phenomenon was *predicted*, in anticipation of any direct experiments on the subject ; and the actual observation of the phenomenon was pointed out as a highly interesting object for experimental research." Just as liquids which expand in solidifying will have the temperature of solidification lowered by pressure, so liquids which contract in solidifying will exhibit the reverse effect. They will be assisted in solidifying, as it were, by pressure, so as to become solid at a higher temperature, as the pressure is greater. This latter result was verified by Bunsen and Hopkins, in the case of paraffin, spermaceti, wax, and stearin. The effect upon water has more recently been carried to such an extent by Mousson, that under the vast

[1] Whewell's *History of the Inductive Sciences*, vol. ii. p. 471. Herschel's *Physical Geography*, § 77.
[2] Maxwell's *Theory of Heat*, p. 174. *Philosophical Magazine*, August 1850. Third Series, vol. xxxvii. p. 123.

pressure of 1300 atmospheres, water did not freeze until cooled down to −18° C. Another remarkable prediction of Professor Thomson was to the effect that, if a metallic spring be weakened by a rise of temperature, work done against the spring in bending it will cause a cooling effect. Although the effect to be expected in a certain apparatus was only about four-thousandths of a degree Centigrade, Dr. Joule[1] succeeded in measuring it to the extent of three-thousandths of a degree, such is the delicacy of modern heat measurements. I cannot refrain from quoting Dr. Joule's reflections upon this fact. "Thus even in the above delicate case," he says, "is the formula of Professor Thomson completely verified. The mathematical investigation of the thermo-elastic qualities of metals has enabled my illustrious friend to predict with certainty a whole class of highly interesting phenomena. To him especially do we owe the important advance which has been recently made to a new era in the history of science, when the famous philosophical system of Bacon will be to a great extent superseded, and when, instead of arriving at discovery by induction from experiment, we shall obtain our largest accessions of new facts by reasoning deductively from fundamental principles."

The theory of electricity is a necessary part of the general theory of matter, and is rapidly acquiring the power of prevision. As soon as Wheatstone had proved experimentally that the conduction of electricity occupies time, Faraday remarked in 1838, with wonderful sagacity, that if the conducting wires were connected with the coatings of a large Leyden jar, the rapidity of conduction would be lessened. This prediction remained unverified for sixteen years, until the submarine cable was laid beneath the Channel. A considerable retardation of the electric spark was then detected, and Faraday at once pointed out that the wire surrounded by water resembles a Leyden jar on a large scale, so that each message sent through the cable verified his remark of 1838.[2]

The joint relations of heat and electricity to the metals constitute a new science of thermo-electricity by which

---

[1] *Philosophical Transactions.* 1858, vol. cxlviii. p. 127.
[2] Tyndall's *Faraday*, pp. 73, 74 ; *Life of Faraday*, vol. ii. pp. 82, 83.

Sir W. Thomson was enabled to anticipate the following curious effect, namely, that an electric current passing in an iron bar from a hot to a cold part produces a cooling effect, but in a copper bar the effect is exactly opposite in character, that is, the bar becomes heated.[1] The action of crystals with regard to heat and electricity was partly foreseen on the grounds of theory by Poisson.

Chemistry, although to a great extent an empirical science, has not been without prophetic triumphs. The existence of the metals potassium and sodium was foreseen by Lavoisier, and their elimination by Davy was one of the chief *experimenta crucis* which established Lavoisier's system. The existence of many other metals which eye had never seen was a natural inference, and theory has not been at fault. In the above cases the compounds of the metal were well known, and it was the result of decomposition that was foretold. The discovery in 1876 of the metal gallium is peculiarly interesting because the existence of this metal, previously wholly unknown, had been inferred from theoretical considerations by M. Mendelief, and some of its properties had been correctly predicted. No sooner, too, had a theory of organic compounds been conceived by Professor A. W. Williamson than he foretold the formation of a complex substance consisting of water in which both atoms of hydrogen are replaced by atoms of acetyle. This substance, known as the acetic anhydride, was afterwards produced by Gerhardt. In the subsequent progress of organic chemistry occurrences of this kind have become common. The theoretical chemist by the classification of his specimens and the manipulation of his formulæ can plan out whole series of unknown oils, acids, and alcohols, just as a designer might draw out a multitude of patterns. Professor Cayley has even calculated for certain cases the possible numbers of chemical compounds.[2] The formation of many such substances is a matter of course; but there is an interesting prediction given by Hofmann, concerning the possible existence of new compounds of sulphur and

[1] Tait's *Thermodynamics*, p. 77.
[2] *On the Analytical Forms called Trees, with Application to the Theory of Chemical Combinations.* Report of the British Association, 1875, p. 257.

selenium, and even oxides of ammonium, which it remains for chemists to verify.[1]

Prediction by Inversion of Cause and Effect.

There is one process of experiment which has so often led to important discoveries as to deserve separate illustration—I mean the inversion of Cause and Effect. Thus if A and B in one experiment produce C as a consequent, then antecedents of the nature of B and C may usually be made to produce a consequent of the nature of A inverted in direction. When we apply heat to a gas it tends to expand; hence if we allow the gas to expand by its own elastic force, cold is the result; that is, B (air) and C (expansion) produce the negative of A (heat). Again, B (air) and compression, the negative of C, produce A (heat). Similar results may be expected in a multitude of cases. It is a familiar law that heat expands iron. What may be expected, then, if instead of increasing the length of an iron bar by heat we use mechanical force and stretch the bar? Having the bar and the former consequent, expansion, we should expect the negative of the former antecedent, namely cold. The truth of this inference was proved by Dr. Joule, who investigated the amount of the effect with his usual skill.[2]

This inversion of cause and effect in the case of heat may be itself inverted in a highly curious manner. It happens that there are a few substances which are unexplained exceptions to the general law of expansion by heat. India-rubber especially is remarkable for *contracting* when heated. Since, then, iron and india-rubber are oppositely related to heat, we may expect that as distension of the iron produced cold, distension of the india-rubber will produce heat. This is actually found to be the case, and anyone may detect the effect by suddenly stretching an india-rubber band while the middle part is in the mouth. When being stretched it grows slightly warm, and when relaxed cold.

The reader will see that some of the scientific predictions mentioned in preceding sections were due to the principle

---

[1] Hofmann's *Introduction to Chemistry*, pp. 224, 225.
[2] *Philosophical Transactions* (1855), vol. cxlv. pp. 100, &c.

of inversion; for instance, Thomson's speculations on the relation between pressure and the melting-point. But many other illustrations could be adduced. The usual agent by which we melt a substance is heat; but if we can melt a substance without heat, then we may expect the negative of heat as an effect. This is the foundation of all freezing mixtures. The affinity of salt for water causes it to melt ice, and we may thus reduce the temperature to Fahrenheit's zero. Calcium chloride has so much higher an attraction for water that a temperature of $-45°$ C. may be attained by its use. Even the solution of a certain alloy of lead, tin, and bismuth in mercury, may be made to reduce the temperature through $27°$ C. All the other modes of producing cold are inversions of more familiar uses of heat. Carré's freezing machine is an inverted distilling apparatus, the distillation being occasioned by chemical affinity instead of heat. Another kind of freezing machine is the exact inverse of the steam-engine.

A very paradoxical effect is due to another inversion. It is hard to believe that a current of steam at $100°$ C. can raise a body of liquid to a higher temperature than the steam itself possesses. But Mr. Spence has pointed out that if the boiling-point of a saline solution be above $100°$; it will continue, on account of its affinity for water, to condense steam when above $100°$ in temperature. It will condense the steam until heated to the point at which the tension of its vapour is equal to that of the atmosphere, that is, its own boiling-point.[1] Again, since heat melts ice, we might expect to produce heat by the inverse change from water into ice. This is accomplished in the phenomenon of suspended freezing. Water may be cooled in a clean glass vessel many degrees below the freezing-point, and yet retained in the liquid condition. But if disturbed, and especially if brought into contact with a small particle of ice, it instantly solidifies and rises in temperature to $0°$ C. The effect is still better displayed in the lecture-room experiment of the suspended crystallisation of a solution of sodium sulphate, in which a sudden rise of temperature of $15°$ or $20°$ C. is often manifested.

The science of electricity is full of most interesting cases

---

[1] *Proceedings of the Manchester Philosophical Society*, Feb. 1870.

of inversion. As Professor Tyndall has remarked, Faraday had a profound belief in the reciprocal relations of the physical forces. The great starting-point of his researches, the discovery of electro-magnetism, was clearly an inversion. Oersted and Ampère had proved that with an electric current and a magnet in a particular position as antecedents, motion is the consequent. If then a magnet, a wire and *motion* be the antecedents, an *opposite* electric current will be the consequent. It would be an endless task to trace out the results of this fertile relationship. Another part of Faraday's researches was occupied in ascertaining the direct and inverse relations of magnetic and diamagnetic, amorphous and crystalline substances in various circumstances. In all other relations of electricity the principle of inversion holds. The voltameter or the electro-plating cell is the inverse of the galvanic battery. As heat applied to a junction of antimony and bismuth bars produces electricity, it follows that an electric current passed through such a junction will produce cold. But it is now sufficiently apparent that inversion of cause and effect is a most fertile means of discovery and prediction.

Facts known only by Theory.

Of the four classes of facts enumerated in p. 525 the last remains unconsidered. It includes the unverified predictions of science. Scientific prophecy arrests the attention of the world when it refers to such striking events as an eclipse, the appearance of a great comet, or any phenomenon which people can verify with their own eyes. But it is surely a matter for greater wonder that a physicist describes and measures phenomena which eye cannot see, nor sense of any kind detect. In most cases this arises from the effect being too small in amount to affect our organs of sense, or come within the powers of our instruments as at present constructed. But there is a class of yet more remarkable cases, in which a phenomenon cannot possibly be observed, and yet we can say what it would be if it were observed.

In astronomy, systematic aberration is an effect of the sun's proper motion almost certainly known to exist, but which we have no hope of detecting by observation in the

present age of the world. As the earth's motion round the
sun combined with the motion of light causes the stars to
deviate apparently from their true positions to the extent
of about 18″ at the most, so the motion of the whole planetary system through space must occasion a similar displacement of at most 5″. The ordinary aberration can be readily
detected with modern astronomical instruments, because it
goes through a yearly change in direction or amount ; but
systematic aberration is constant so long as the planetary
system moves uniformly in a sensibly straight line. Only
then in the course of ages, when the curvature of the sun's
path becomes apparent, can we hope to verify the existence
of this kind of aberration. A curious effect must also be
produced by the sun's proper motion upon the apparent
periods of revolution of the binary stars.

To my mind, some of the most interesting truths in the
whole range of science are those which have not been, and
in many cases probably never can be, verified by trial.
Thus the chemist assigns, with a very high degree of probability, the vapour densities of such elements as carbon
and silicon, which have never been observed separately in
a state of vapour. The chemist is also familiar with the
vapour densities of elements at temperatures at which the
elements in question never have been, and probably never
can be, submitted to experiment in the form of vapour.

Joule and others have calculated the actual velocity of
the molecules of a gas, and even the number of collisions
which must take place per second during their constant
circulation. Physicists have not yet given us the exact
magnitudes of the particles of matter, but they have ascertained by several methods the limits within which their
magnitudes must lie. Such scientific results must be for
ever beyond the power of verification by the senses. I
have elsewhere had occasion to remark that waves of light,
the intimate processes of electrical changes, the properties
of the ether which is the base of all phenomena, are necessarily determined in a hypothetical, but not therefore a
less certain manner.

Though only two of the metals, gold and silver, have
ever been observed to be transparent, we know on the
grounds of theory that they are all more or less so ; we
can even estimate by theory their refractive indices, and

prove that they are exceedingly high. The phenomena
of elliptic polarisation, and perhaps also those of internal
radiation,[1] depend upon the refractive index, and thus, even
when we cannot observe any refracted rays, we can indirectly learn how they would be refracted.

In many cases large quantities of electricity must be
produced, which we cannot observe because it is instantly
discharged. In the common electric machine the cylinder
and rubber are made of non-conductors, so that we can
separate and accumulate the electricity. But a little damp,
by serving as a conductor, prevents this separation from
enduring any sensible time. Hence there is no doubt that
when we rub two good conductors against each other, for
instance two pieces of metals, much electricity is produced,
but instantaneously converted into some other form of
energy. Joule believes that all the heat of friction is
transmuted electricity.

As regards phenomena of insensible amount, nature is
absolutely full of them. We must regard those changes
which we can observe as the comparatively rare aggregates
of minuter changes. On a little reflection we must allow
that no object known to us remains for two instants of
exactly the same temperature. If so, the dimensions of
objects must be in a perpetual state of variation. The
minor planetary and lunar perturbations are infinitely
numerous, but usually too small to be detected by observation, although their amounts may be assigned by theory.
There is every reason to believe that chemical and electric
actions of small amount are constantly in progress. The
hardest substances, if reduced to extremely small particles,
and diffused in pure water, manifest oscillatory movements
which must be due to chemical and electric changes, so
slight that they go on for years without affecting appreciably
the weight of the particles.[2] The earth's magnetism must
more or less affect every object which we handle. As
Tyndall remarks, " An upright iron stone influenced by the
earth's magnetism becomes a magnet, with its bottom a
north and its top a south pole. Doubtless, though in an
immensely feebler degree, every erect marble statue is a

[1] Balfour Stewart, *Elementary Treatise on Heat*, 1st edit. p. 198.
[2] Jevons, *Proceedings of the Manchester Literary and Philosophical Society*, 25th January, 1870, vol. ix. p. 78.

true diamagnet, with its head a north pole and its feet a south pole. The same is certainly true of man as he stands upon the earth's surface, for all the tissues of the human body are diamagnetic." [1] The sun's light produces a very quick and perceptible effect upon the photographic plate; in all probability it has a less effect upon a great variety of substances. We may regard every phenomenon as an exaggerated and conspicuous case of a process which is, in infinitely numerous cases, beyond the means of observation.

[1] *Philosophical Transactions,* vol. cxlvi. p. 240.

CHAPTER XXV.

ACCORDANCE OF QUANTITATIVE THEORIES.

In the preceding chapter we found that facts may be classed under four heads as regards their connection with theory, and our powers of explanation or prediction. The facts hitherto considered were generally of a qualitative rather than a quantitative nature; but when we look exclusively to the quantity of a phenomenon, and the various modes in which we may determine its amount, nearly the same system of classification will hold good. There will, however, be five possible cases :—

(1) We may directly and empirically measure a phenomenon, without being able to explain why it should have any particular quantity, or to connect it by theory with other quantities.

(2) In a considerable number of cases we can theoretically predict the existence of a phenomenon, but are unable to assign its amount, except by direct measurement, or to explain the amount theoretically when thus ascertained.

(3) We may measure a quantity, and afterwards explain it as related to other quantities, or as governed by known quantitative laws.

(4) We may predict the quantity of an effect on theoretical grounds, and afterwards confirm the prediction by direct measurement.

(5) We may indirectly determine the quantity of an effect without being able to verify it by experiment.

These classes of quantitative facts might be illustrated by an immense number of interesting points in the history

of physical science. Only a few instances of each class
can be given here.

Empirical Measurements.

Under the first head of purely empirical measurements,
which have not been brought under any theoretical system,
may be placed the great bulk of quantitative facts recorded
by scientific observers. The tables of numerical results
which abound in books on chemistry and physics, the huge
quartos containing the observations of public observatories,
the multitudinous tables of meteorological observations,
which are continually being published, the more abstruse
results concerning terrestrial magnetism—such results of
measurement, for the most part, remain empirical, either
because theory is defective, or the labour of calculation
and comparison is too formidable. In the Greenwich
Observatory, indeed, the salutary practice has been maintained by the present Astronomer Royal, of always reducing the observations, and comparing them with the theories
of the several bodies. The divergences from theory thus
afford material for the discovery of errors or of new phenomena ; in short, the observations have been turned to
the use for which they were intended. But it is to be
feared that other establishments are too often engaged in
merely recording numbers of which no real use is made,
because the labour of reduction and comparison with
theory is too great for private inquirers to undertake. In
meteorology, especially, great waste of labour and money
is taking place, only a small fraction of the results recorded
being ever used for the advancement of the science. For
one meteorologist like Quetelet, Dove, or Baxendell, who
devotes himself to the truly useful labour of reducing other
people's observations, there are hundreds who labour under
the delusion that they are advancing science by loading
our book-shelves with numerical tables. It is to be feared,
in like manner, that almost the whole bulk of statistical
numbers, whether commercial, vital, or moral, is of little
scientific value. Purely empirical measurements may
have a direct practical value, as when tables of the specific
gravity, or strength of materials, assist the engineer ; the
specific gravities of mixtures of water with acids, alcohols.

salts, &c., are useful in chemical manufactories, custom-
house gauging, &c. ; observations of rainfall are requisite
for questions of water supply ; the refractive index of
various kinds of glass must be known in making achromatic lenses ; but in all such cases the use made of the
measurements is not scientific but practical. It may be
asserted, that no number which remains isolated, and
uncompared by theory with other numbers, is of scientific
value. Having tried the tensile strength of a piece of iron
in a particular condition, we know what will be the strength
of the same kind of iron in a similar condition, provided
we can ever meet with that exact kind of iron again ; but
we cannot argue from piece to piece, nor lay down any laws
exactly connecting the strength of iron with the quantity
of its impurities.

Quantities indicated by Theory, but Empirically Measured.

In many cases we are able to foresee the existence of
a quantitative effect, on the ground of general principles,
but are unable, either from the want of numerical data,
or from the entire absence of any mathematical theory, to
assign the amount of such effect. We then have recourse
to direct experiment to determine its amount. Whether
we argued from the oceanic tides by analogy, or deductively from the theory of gravitation, there could be no
doubt that atmospheric tides of some amount must occur
in the atmosphere. Theory, however, even in the hands
of Laplace, was not able to overcome the complicated
mechanical conditions of the atmosphere, and predict the
amounts of such tides ; and, on the other hand, these
amounts were so small, and were so masked by far larger
undulations arising from the heating power of the sun,
and from other meteorological disturbances, that they
would probably have never been discovered by purely
empirical observations. Theory having, however, indicated their existence and their periods, it was easy to
make series of barometrical observations in places selected
so as to be as free as possible from casual fluctuations, and
then, by the suitable application of the method of means, to
detect the small effects in question. The principal lunar

atmospheric tide was thus proved to amount to between
·003 and ·004 inch.[1]

Theory yields the greatest possible assistance in applying
the method of means. For if we have a great number of
empirical measurements, each representing the joint effect
of a number of causes, our object will be to take the mean
of all those in which the effect to be measured is present,
and compare it with the mean of the remainder in which
the effect is absent, or acts in the opposite direction. The
difference will then represent the amount of the effect, or
double the amount respectively. Thus, in the case of the
atmospheric tides, we take the mean of all the observations
when the moon was on the meridian, and compare it with
the mean of all observations when she was on the horizon.
In this case we trust to chance that all other effects will
lie about as often in one direction as the other, and will
neutralise themselves in the drawing of each mean. It is
a great advantage, however, to be able to decide by theory
when each principal disturbing effect is present or absent;
for the means may then be drawn so as to separate each
such effect, leaving only minor and casual divergences to
the law of error. Thus, if there be three principal effects,
and we draw means giving respectively the sum of all
three, the sum of the first two, and the sum of the last
two, then we gain three simple equations, by the solution
of which each quantity is determined.

Explained Results of Measurement.

The second class of measured phenomena contains those
which, after being determined in a direct and purely empirical application of measuring instruments, are afterwards
shown to agree with some hypothetical explanation. Such
results are turned to their proper use, and several advantages may arise from the comparison. The correspondence
with theory will seldom or never be precise; and, even if
it be so, the coincidence must be regarded as accidental.
If the divergences between theory and experiment be
comparatively small, and variable in amount and direction,
they may often be safely attributed to inconsiderable

Grant's *History of Physical Astronomy*, p. 162.

sources of error in the experimental processes. The strict. method of procedure is to calculate the probable error of the mean of the observed results (p. 387), and then observe whether the theoretical result falls within the limits of probable error. If it does, and if the experimental results agree as well with theory as they agree with each other, then the probability of the theory is much increased, and we may employ the theory with more confidence in the anticipation of further results. The probable error, it should be remembered, gives a measure only of the effects of incidental and variable sources of error, but in no degree indicates the amount of fixed causes of error. Thus, if the mean results of two modes of determining a quantity are so far apart that the limits of probable error do not overlap, we may infer the existence of some overlooked source of fixed error in one or both modes. We will further consider in a subsequent section the discordance of measurements.

Quantities determined by Theory and verified by Measurement.

One of the most satisfactory tests of a theory consists in its application not only to predict the nature of a phenomenon, and the circumstances in which it may be observed, but also to assign the precise quantity of the phenomenon. If we can subsequently apply accurate instruments and measure the amount of the phenomenon witnessed, we have an excellent opportunity of verifying or negativing the theory. It was in this manner that Newton first attempted to verify his theory of gravitation. He knew approximately the velocity produced in falling bodies at the earth's surface, and if the law of the inverse square of the distance held true, and the reputed distance of the moon was correct, he could infer that the moon ought to fall towards the earth at the rate of fifteen feet in one minute. Now, the actual divergence of the moon from the tangent of its orbit appeared to amount only to thirteen feet in one minute, and there was a discrepancy of two feet in fifteen, which caused Newton to lay " aside at that time any further thoughts of this matter." Many years afterwards, probably fifteen or sixteen years, Newton obtained more precise data from which he could calculate the size of the moon's orbit, and he then found the discrepancy to be inconsiderable.

His theory of gravitation was thus verified as far as the moon was concerned; but this was to him only the beginning of a long course of deductive calculations, each ending in a verification. If the earth and moon attract each other, and also the sun and the earth, there is reason to expect that the sun and moon should attract each other. Newton followed out the consequences of this inference, and showed that the moon would not move as if attracted by the earth only, but sometimes faster and sometimes slower. Comparison with Flamsteed's observations of the moon showed that such was the case. Newton argued again, that as the waters of the ocean are not rigidly attached to the earth, they might attract the moon, and be attracted in return, independently of the rest of the earth. Certain daily motions resembling the tides would then be caused, and there were the tides to verify the reasoning. It was the extraordinary power with which Newton traced out geometrically the consequences of his theory, and submitted them to repeated comparison with experience, which constitutes his pre-eminence over all physicists.

Quantities determined by Theory and not verified.

It will continually happen that we are able, from certain measured phenomena and a correct theory, to determine the amount of some other phenomenon which we may either be unable to measure at all, or to measure with an accuracy corresponding to that required to verify the prediction. Thus Laplace having worked out a theory of the motions of Jupiter's satellites on the hypothesis of gravitation, found that these motions were greatly affected by the spheroidal form of Jupiter. The motions of the satellites can be observed with great accuracy owing to their frequent eclipses and transits, and from these motions he was able to argue inversely, and assign the ellipticity of the planet. The ratio of the polar and equatorial axes thus determined was very nearly that of 13 to 14; and it agrees well with such direct micrometrical measurements of the planet as have been made; but Laplace believed that the theory gave a more accurate result than direct observation could yield, so that the theory could hardly be said to admit of direct verification.

The specific heat of air was believed on the grounds of direct experiment to amount to 0·2669, the specific heat of water being taken as unity ; but the methods of experiment were open to considerable causes of error. Rankine showed in 1850 that it was possible to calculate from the mechanical equivalent of heat and other thermodynamic data, what this number should be, and he found it to be 0·2378. This determination was at the time accepted as the most satisfactory result, although not verified ; subsequently in 1853 Regnault obtained by direct experiment the number 0·2377, proving that the prediction had been well grounded.

It is readily seen that in quantitative questions verification is a matter of degree and probability. A less accurate method of measurement cannot verify the results of a more accurate method, so that if we arrive at a determination of the same physical quantity in several distinct modes it is often a delicate matter to decide which result is most reliable, and should be used for the indirect determination of other quantities. For instance, Joule's and Thomson's ingenious experiments upon the thermal phenomena of fluids in motion [1] involved, as one physical constant, the mechanical equivalent of heat; if requisite, then, they might have been used to determine that important constant. But if more direct methods of experiment give the mechanical equivalent of heat with superior accuracy, then the experiments on fluids will be turned to a better use in determining various quantities relating to the theory of fluids. We will further consider questions of this kind in succeeding sections.

There are of course many quantities assigned on theoretical grounds which we are quite unable to verify with corresponding accuracy. The thickness of a film of gold leaf, the average depths of the oceans, the velocity of a star's approach to or regression from the earth as inferred from spectroscopic data (pp. 296-99), are cases in point ; but many others might be quoted where direct verification seems impossible. Newton and subsequent physicists

[1] *Philosophical Transactions* (1854), vol. cxliv. p. 364.

have measured light undulations, and by several methods we learn the velocity with which light travels. Since an undulation of the middle green is about five ten-millionths of a metre in length, and travels at the rate of nearly 300,000,000 of metres per second, it follows that about 600,000,000,000,000 undulations must strike in one second the retina of an eye which perceives such light. But how are we to verify such an astounding calculation by directly counting pulses which recur six hundred billions of times in a second?

Discordance of Theory and Experiment.

When a distinct want of accordance is found to exist between the results of theory and direct measurement, interesting questions arise as to the mode in which we can account for this discordance. The ultimate explanation of the discrepancy may be accomplished in at least four ways as follows :—

(1) The direct measurement may be erroneous owing to various sources of casual error.

(2) The theory may be correct as far as regards the general form of the supposed laws, but some of the constant numbers or other quantitative data employed in the theoretical calculations may be inaccurate.

(3) The theory may be false, in the sense that the forms of the mathematical equations assumed to express the laws of nature are incorrect.

(4) The theory and the involved quantities may be approximately accurate, but some regular unknown cause may have interfered, so that the divergence may be regarded as a *residual effect* representing possibly a new and interesting phenomenon.

No precise rules can be laid down as to the best mode of proceeding to explain the divergence, and the experimentalist will have to depend upon his own insight and knowledge ; but the following recommendations may be made.

If the experimental measurements are **not** numerous, repeat them and take a more extensive mean result, the probable accuracy of which, as regards casual errors, will increase as the square root of the number of experiments. Supposing that no considerable modification of the result is thus effected, we may suspect the existence of more deep-seated sources of error in our method of measurement. The next resource will be to change the size and form of the apparatus employed, and to introduce various modifications in the materials employed or the course of procedure, in the hope (p. 396) that some cause of constant error may thus be removed. If the inconsistency with theory still remains unreduced we may attempt to invent some widely different mode of arriving at the same physical quantity, so that we may be almost sure that the same cause of error will not affect both the new and old results. In some cases it is possible to find five or six essentially different modes of arriving at the same determination.

Supposing that the discrepancy still exists we may begin to suspect that our direct measurements are correct, and that the data employed in the theoretical calculations are inaccurate. We must now review the grounds on which these data depend, consisting as they must ultimately do of direct measurements. A comparison of the recorded data will show the degree of probability attaching to the mean result employed; and if there is any ground for imagining the existence of error, we should repeat the observations, and vary the forms of experiment just as in the case of the previous direct measurements. The continued existence of the discrepancy must show that we have not attained to a complete acquaintance with the theory of the causes in action, but two different cases still remain. We may have misunderstood the action of those causes which we know to exist, or we may have overlooked the existence of one or more other causes. In the first case our hypothesis appears to be wrongly chosen and inapplicable ; but whether we are to reject it will depend upon whether we can form another hypothesis which yields a more accurate accordance. The probability of an hypothesis, it will be remembered (p. 243), is to be judged, in the absence of à *priori* grounds of judgment, by the probability that if the supposed causes exist the observed result follows ; but as there is now little probability of reconciling the original hypothesis with our direct measurements the field is open for new hypotheses, and any one which gives a closer accordance with measurement will so far have better claims to attention. Of course we must never estimate the probability of an hypothesis merely by its accordance with a few results only. Its general analogy and accordance with other known laws of nature, and the fact that it does not conflict with other probable theories, must be taken into account, as we shall see in the next book. The requisite condition of a good hypothesis, that it must admit of the deduction of facts verified in observation, must be interpreted in the widest manner, as including all ways in which there may be accordance or discordance. All our attempts at reconciliation having failed, the only conclusion we can come to is that some unknown cause of a new character exists. If the measurements be accurate and the theory probable, then there remains a *residual phenomenon*, which, being devoid of theoretical explanation, must be set down as a new empirical fact worthy of further investigation. Outstanding residual discrepancies have often been found to involve new discoveries of the greatest importance.

Accordance of Measurements of Astronomical Distances.

One of the most instructive instances which we can meet, of the manner in which different measurements confirm or check each other, is furnished by the determination of the velocity of light, and the dimensions of the planetary system. Roemer first discovered that light requires time to travel, by observing that the eclipses of Jupiter's satellites, although they occur at fixed moments of absolute time, are visible at different moments in different parts of the earth's orbit, according to the distance between the earth and Jupiter. The time occupied by light in traversing the mean semi-diameter of the earth's orbit is found to be about eight minutes. The mean distance of the sun and earth was long assumed by astronomers as being about 95,274,000 miles, this result being deduced by Bessel from the observations of the transit of Venus, which occurred in 1769, and which were found to give the solar parallax, or which is the same thing, the apparent angular magnitude of the earth seen from the sun, as equal to $8''\cdot578$. Dividing the mean distance of the sun and earth by the

number of seconds in 8^m. $13^s.3$ we find the velocity of light
to be about 192,000 miles per second.

Nearly the same result was obtained in what seems a
different manner. The aberration of light is the apparent
change in the direction of a ray of light owing to the composition of its motion with that of the earth's motion
round the sun. If we know the amount of aberration and
the mean velocity of the earth, we can estimate that of
light, which is thus found to be 191,100 miles per second.
Now this determination depends upon a new physical
quantity, that of aberration, which is ascertained by direct
observation of the stars, so that the close accordance of the
estimates of the velocity of light as thus arrived at by different methods might seem to leave little room for doubt,
the difference being less than one per cent.

Nevertheless, experimentalists were not satisfied until
they had succeeded in measuring the velocity of light by
direct experiments performed upon the earth's surface.
Fizeau, by a rapidly revolving toothed wheel, estimated the
velocity at 195,920 miles per second. As this result differed by about one part in sixty from estimates previously
accepted, there was thought to be room for further investigation. The revolving mirror, used by Wheatstone in
measuring the velocity of electricity, was now applied in a
more refined manner by Fizeau and by Foucault to determine the velocity of light. The latter physicist came to
the startling conclusion that the velocity was not really
more than 185,172 miles per second. No repetition of the
experiment would shake this result, and there was accordingly a discrepancy between the astronomical and the experimental results of about 7,000 miles per second. The
latest experiments, those of M. Cornu, only slightly raise
the estimate, giving 186, 660 miles per second. A little
consideration shows that both the astronomical determinations involve the magnitude of the earth's orbit as one
datum, because our estimate of the earth's velocity in its
orbit depends upon our estimate of the sun's mean distance.
Accordingly as regards this quantity the two astronomical
results count only for one. Though the transit of Venus
had been considered to give the best data for the calculation of the sun's parallax, yet astronomers had not neglected
less favourable opportunities. Hansen, calculating from

certain inequalities in the moon's motion, had estimated it at 8″·916; Winneke, from observations of Mars, at 8″·964 ; Leverrier, from the motions of Mars, Venus, and the moon, at 8″·950. These independent results agree much better with each other than with that of Bessel (8″·578) previously received, or that of Encke (8″·58) deduced from the transits of Venus in 1761 and 1769, and though each separately might be worthy of less credit, yet their close accordance renders their mean result (8″·943) comparable in probability with that of Bessel. It was further found that if Foucault's value for the velocity of light were assumed to be correct, and the sun's distance were inversely calculated from that, the sun's parallax would be 8″·960, which closely agreed with the above mean result. This further correspondence of independent results threw the balance of probability strongly against the results of the transit of Venus, and rendered it desirable to reconsider the observations made on that occasion. Mr. E. J. Stone, having re-discussed those observations,[1] found that grave oversights had been made in the calculations, which being corrected would alter the estimate of parallax to 8″·91, a quantity in such comparatively close accordance with the other results that astronomers did not hesitate at once to reduce their estimate of the sun's mean distance from 95,274,000 to 91,771,000, miles, although this alteration involved a corresponding correction in the assumed magnitudes and distances of most of the heavenly bodies. The solar parallax is now (1875) believed to be about 8″·878, the number deduced from Cornu's experiments on the velocity of light. This result agrees very closely with 8″·879, the estimate obtained from new observations on the transit of Venus, by the French observers, and with 8″·873, the result of Galle's observations of the planet Flora. When all the observations of the late transit of Venus are fully discussed the sun's distance will probably be known to less than one part in a thousand, if not one part in ten thousand.[2]

[1] *Monthly Notices of the Royal Astronomical Society,* vol. xxviii. p. 264.

[2] It would seem to be absurd to repeat the profuse expenditure of 1874 at the approaching transit in 1882. The aggregate sum spent in 1874 by various governments and individuals can hardly be less than

In this question the theoretical relations between the velocity of light, the constant of aberration, the sun's parallax, and the sun's mean distance, are of the simplest character, and can hardly be open to any doubt, so that the only doubt was as to which result of observation was the most reliable. Eventually the chief discrepancy was found to arise from misapprehension in the reduction of observations, but we have a satisfactory example of the value of different methods of estimation in leading to the detection of a serious error. Is it not surprising that Foucault by measuring the velocity of light when passing through the space of a few yards, should lead the way to a change in our estimates of the magnitudes of the whole universe?

Selection of the best Mode of Measurement.

When we once obtain command over a question of physical science by comprehending the theory of the subject, we often have a wide choice opened to us as regards the methods of measurement, which may thenceforth be made to give the most accurate results. If we can measure one fundamental quantity very precisely we may be able by theory to determine accurately many other quantitative results. Thus, if we determine satisfactorily the atomic weights of certain elements, we do not need to determine with equal accuracy the composition and atomic weights of their several compounds. Having learnt the relative atomic weights of oxygen and sulphur, we can calculate the composition by weight of the several oxides of sulphur. Chemists accordingly select with the greatest care that compound of two elements which seems to allow of the most accurate analysis, so as to give the ratio of their atomic weights. It is obvious that we only need the ratio of the atomic weight of each element to that of some common element, in order to calculate that of each to each. Moreover the atomic weight stands in simple relation to other quantitative facts. The weights of equal volumes of elementary gases at equal temperature and pressure have

£200,000, a sum which, wisely expended on scientific investigations, would give a hundred important results.

the same ratios as the atomic weights ; now, as nitrogen under such circumstances weighs 14·06 times as much as hydrogen, we may infer that the atomic weight of nitrogen is about 14·06, or more probably 14·00, that of hydrogen being unity. There is much evidence, again, that the specific heats of elements are inversely as their atomic weights, so that these two classes of quantitative data throw light mutually upon each other. In fact the atomic weight, the atomic volume, and the atomic heat of an element, are quantities so closely connected that the determination of one will lead to that of the others. The chemist has to solve a complicated problem in deciding in the case of each of 60 or 70 elements which mode of determination is most accurate. Modern chemistry presents us with an almost infinitely extensive web of numerical ratios developed out of a few fundamental ratios.

In hygrometry we have a choice among at least four modes of measuring the quantity of aqueous vapour contained in a given bulk of air. We can extract the vapour by absorption in sulphuric acid, and directly weigh its amount ; we can place the air in a barometer tube and observe how much the absorption of the vapour alters the elastic force of the air; we can observe the dew-point of the air, that is the temperature at which the vapour becomes saturated ; or, lastly, we can insert a dry and wet bulb thermometer and observe the temperature of an evaporating surface. The results of each mode can be connected by theory with those of the other modes, and we can select for each experiment that mode which is most accurate or most convenient. The chemical method of direct measurement is capable of the greatest accuracy, but is troublesome; the dry and wet bulb thermometer is sufficiently exact for meteorological purposes and is most easy to use.

Agreement of Distinct Modes of Measurement.

Many illustrations might be given of the accordance which has been found to exist in some cases between the results of entirely different methods of arriving at the measurement of a physical quantity. While such accordance must, in the absence of information to the contrary.

be regarded as the best possible proof of the approximate correctness of the mean result, yet instances have occurred to show that we can never take too much trouble in confirming results of great importance. When three or even more distinct methods have given nearly coincident numbers, a new method has sometimes disclosed a discrepancy which it is yet impossible to explain.

The ellipticity of the earth is known with considerable approach to certainty and accuracy, for it has been estimated in three independent ways. The most direct mode is to measure long arcs extending north and south upon the earth's surface, by means of trigonometrical surveys, and then to compare the lengths of these arcs with their curvature as determined by observations of the altitude of certain stars at the terminal points. The most probable ellipticity of the earth deduced from all measurements of this kind was estimated by Bessel at $\frac{1}{300}$, though subsequent measurements might lead to a slightly different estimate. The divergence from a globular form causes a small variation in the force of gravity at different parts of the earth's surface, so that exact pendulum observations give the data for an independent estimate of the ellipticity, which is thus found to be $\frac{1}{320}$. In the third place the spheroidal protuberance about the earth's equator leads to a certain inequality in the moon's motion, as shown by Laplace; and from the amount of that inequality, as given by observations, Laplace was enabled to calculate back to the amount of its cause. He thus inferred that the ellipticity is $\frac{1}{305}$, which lies between the two numbers previously given, and was considered by him the most satisfactory determination. In this case the accordance is undisturbed by subsequent results, so that we are obliged to accept Laplace's result as a highly probable one.

The mean density of the earth is a constant of high importance, because it is necessary for the determination of the masses of all the other heavenly bodies. Astronomers and physicists accordingly have bestowed a great deal of labour upon the exact estimation of this constant. The method of procedure consists in comparing the gravitation of the globe with that of some body of matter of which the mass is known in terms of the assumed unit of mass. This body of matter, serving as an intermediate term of comparison, may be variously chosen; it may consist of a mountain, or a portion of the earth's crust, or a heavy ball of metal. The method of experiment varies so much according as we select one body or the other, that we may be said to have three independent modes of arriving at the desired result.

The mutual gravitation of two balls is so exceedingly small compared with their gravitation towards the immense mass of the earth, that it is usually quite imperceptible, and although asserted by Newton to exist, on the ground of theory, was never observed until the end of the 18th century. Michell attached two small balls to the extremities of a delicately suspended torsion balance, and then bringing heavy balls of lead alternately to either side of these small balls was able to detect a slight deflection of the torsion balance. He thus furnished a new verification of the theory of gravitation. Cavendish carried out the experiment with more care, and estimated the gravitation of the balls by treating the torsion balance as a pendulum ; then taking into account the respective distances of the balls from each other and from the centre of the earth, he was able to assign 5·48 (or as re-computed by Baily, 5·448) as the probable mean density of the earth. Newton's sagacious guess to the effect that the density of the earth was between five and six times that of water, was thus remarkably confirmed. The same kind of experiment repeated by Reich gave 5·438. Baily having again performed the experiment with every possible refinement obtained a slightly higher number, 5·660.

A different method of procedure consisted in ascertaining the effect of a mountain mass in deflecting the plumb-line ; for, assuming that we can determine the dimensions and mean density of the mountain, the plumb-line enables us to compare its mass with that of the whole earth. The mountain Schehallien was selected for the experiment, and observations and calculations performed by Maskelyne, Hutton, and Playfair, gave as the most probable result 4·713. The difference from the experimental results already mentioned is considerable and is important, because the instrumental operations are of an entirely different character from those of Cavendish and Baily's experiments. Sir Henry James' similar determination from the attraction of Arthur's Seat gave 5·14.

A third distinct method consists in determining the force of gravity at points elevated above the surface of the earth on mountain ranges, or sunk below it in mines. Carlini experimented with a pendulum at the hospice of Mont Cenis, 6,375 feet above the sea, and by comparing the attractive forces of the earth and the Alps, found the density to be still smaller, namely, 4·39, or as corrected by Giulio, 4·950. Lastly, the Astronomer Royal has on two occasions adopted the opposite method of observing a pendulum at the bottom of a deep mine, so as to compare the density of the strata penetrated with the density of the whole earth. On the second occasion he carried his method into effect at the Harton Colliery, 1,260 feet deep; all that could be done by skill in measurement and careful consideration of all the causes of errror, was accomplished in this elaborate series of observations [1] (p. 291). No doubt Sir George Airy was much perplexed when he found that his new result considerably exceeded that obtained by any other method, being no less than 6·566, or 6·623 as finally corrected. In this case we learn an impressive lesson concerning the value of repeated determinations by distinct methods in disabusing our minds of the reliance which we are only too apt to place in results which show a certain degree of coincidence.

In 1844 Herschel remarked in his memoir of Francis Baily,[2] "that the mean specific gravity of this our planet is, in all human probability, quite as well determined as that of an ordinary hand-specimen in a mineralogical cabinet, —a marvellous result, which should teach us to despair of nothing which lies within the compass of number, weight and measure." But at the same time he pointed out that Baily's final result, of which the probable error was only 0·0032, was the highest of all determinations then known, and Airy's investigation has since given a much higher result, quite beyond the limits of probable error of any of

[1] *Philosophical Transactions* (1856), vol. cxlvi. p. 342.
[2] *Monthly Notices of the Royal Astronomical Society*, for 8th Nov. 1844, No. X. vol. vi. p. 89.

the previous experiments. If we treat all determinations yet made as of equal weight, the simple mean is about 5·45, the mean error nearly 0·5, and the probable error almost 0·2, so that it is as likely as not that the truth lies between 5·65 and 5·25 on this view of the matter. But it is remarkable that the two most recent and careful series of observations by Baily and Airy,[1] lie beyond these limits, and as with the increase of care the estimate rises, it seems requisite to reject the earlier results, and look upon the question as still requiring further investigation. Physicists often take 5⅔ or 5·67 as the best guess at the truth, but it is evident that new experiments are much required. I cannot help thinking that a portion of the great sums of money which many governments and private individuals spent upon the transit of Venus expeditions in 1874, and which they will probably spend again in 1882 (p. 562), would be better appropriated to new determinations of the earth's density. It seems desirable to repeat Baily's experiment in a vacuous case, and with the greater mechanical refinements which the progress of the last forty years places at the disposal of the experimentalist. It would be desirable, also, to renew the pendulum experiments of Airy in some other deep mine. It might even be well to repeat upon some suitable mountain the observations performed at Schehallien. All these operations might be carried out for the cost of one of the superfluous transit expeditions.

Since the establishment of the dynamical theory of heat it has become a matter of the greatest importance to determine with accuracy the mechanical equivalent of heat, or the quantity of energy which must be given, or received, in a definite change of temperature effected in a definite quantity of a standard substance, such as water. No less than seven almost entirely distinct modes of determining this constant have been tried. Dr. Joule first ascertained by the friction of water that to raise the temperature of one kilogram of water through one degree centigrade, we must employ energy sufficient to raise 424 kilograms through the height of one metre against the force of gravity at the earth's surface. Joule, Mayer.

[1] *Philosophical Magazine*, 2nd Series, vol. xxvi. p. 61.

Clausius,[1] Favre and other experimentalists have made determinations by less direct methods. Experiments on the mechanical properties of gases give 426 kilogram-metres as the constant; the work done by a steam-engine gives 413; from the heat evolved in electrical experiments several determinations have been obtained; thus from induced electric currents we get 452; from the electro-magnetic engine 443; from the circuit of a battery 420; and, from an electric current, the lowest result of all, namely, 400.[2]

Considering the diverse and in many cases difficult methods of observation, these results exhibit satisfactory accordance, and their mean (423·9) comes very close to the number derived by Dr. Joule from the apparently most accurate method. The constant generally assumed as the most probable result is 423·55 kilogrammetres.

Residual Phenomena.

Even when the experimental data employed in the verification of a theory are sufficiently accurate, and the theory itself is sound, there may exist discrepancies demanding further investigation. Herschel pointed out the importance of such outstanding quantities, and called them *residual phenomena*.[3] Now if the observations and the theory be really correct, such discrepancies must be due to the incompleteness of our knowledge of the causes in action, and the ultimate explanation must consist in showing that there is in action, either

(1) Some agent of known nature whose presence was not suspected;

Or (2) Some new agent of unknown nature.

In the first case we can hardly be said to make a new discovery, for our ultimate success consists merely in reconciling the theory with known facts when our investigation is more comprehensive. But in the second case we meet with a totally new fact, which may lead us

---

[1] Clausius in *Philosophical Magazine*, 4th Series, vol ii. p 119.
[2] Watts' *Dictionary of Chemistry*, vol. iii. p. 129.
[3] *Preliminary Discourse*, §§ 158, 174. *Outlines of Astronomy*, 4th edit. § 856.

to realms of new discovery. Take the instance adduced by
Herschel. The theory of Newton and Halley concerning
comets was that they were gravitating bodies revolving
round the sun in elliptic orbits, and the return of Halley's
Comet, in 1758, verified this theory. But, when accurate
observations of Encke's Comet came to be made, the verification was not found to be exact. Encke's Comet returned
each time a little sooner than it ought to do, the period
regularly decreasing from 1212·79 days, between 1786 and
1789, to 1210·44 between 1855 and 1858; and the hypothesis has been started that there is a resisting medium
filling the space through which the comet passes. This
hypothesis is a *deus ex machinâ* for explaining this solitary
phenomenon, and cannot possess much probability unless
it can be shown that other phenomena are deducible from it.
Many persons have identified this medium with that through
which light undulations pass, but I am not aware that
there is anything in the undulatory theory of light to show
that the medium would offer resistance to a moving body.
If Professor Balfour Stewart can prove that a rotating disc
would experience resistance in a vacuous receiver, here is
an experimental fact which distinctly supports the hypothesis. But in the mean time it is open to question
whether other known agents, for instance electricity, may
not be brought in, and I have tried to show that if, as is
believed, the tail of a comet is an electrical phenomenon,
it is a necessary result of the conservation of energy
that the comet shall exhibit a loss of energy manifested
in a diminution of its mean distance from the sun
and its period of revolution.[1]   It should be added that if

---

[1] *Proceedings of the Manchester Literary and Philosophical Society*,
28th November, 1871, vol. xi. p. 33.   Since the above remarks were
written, Professor Balfour Stewart has pointed out to me his paper
in the *Proceedings of the Manchester Literary and Philosophical
Society* for 15th November, 1870 (vol. x. p. 32), in which he shows
that a body moving in an enclosure of uniform temperature would
probably experience resistance independently of the presence of a
ponderable medium, such as gas, between the moving body and the
enclosure.   The proof is founded on the theory of the dissipation of
energy, and this view is said to be accepted by Professors Thomson and
Tait.   The enclosure is used in this case by Professor Stewart simply
as a means of obtaining a proof, just as it was used by him on a
previous occasion to obtain a proof of certain consequences of the

Professor Tait's theory be correct, as seems very probable, and comets consist of swarms of small meteors, there is no difficulty in accounting for the retardation. It has long been known that a collection of small bodies travelling together in an orbit round a central body will tend to fall towards it. In either case, then, this residual phenomenon seems likely to be reconciled with known laws of nature.

In other cases residual phenomena have involved important inferences not recognised at the time. Newton showed how the velocity of sound in the atmosphere could be calculated by a theory of pulses or undulations from the observed tension and density of the air. He inferred that the velocity in the ordinary state of the atmosphere at the earth's surface would be 968 feet per second, and rude experiments made by him in the cloisters of Trinity College seemed to show that this was not far from the truth. Subsequently it was ascertained by other experimentalists that the velocity of sound was more nearly 1,142 feet, and the discrepancy being one-sixth part of the whole was far too much to attribute to casual errors in the numerical data. Newton attempted to explain away this discrepancy by hypotheses as to the reactions of the molecules of air, but without success.

New investigations having been made from time to time concerning the velocity of sound, both as observed experimentally and as calculated from theory, it was found that each of Newton's results was inaccurate, the theoretical velocity being 916 feet per second, and the real velocity about 1,090 feet. The discrepancy, nevertheless, remained as serious as ever, and it was not until the year 1816 that Laplace showed it to be due to the heat developed by the sudden compression of the air in the passage of the wave, this heat having the effect of increasing the elasticity of the air and accelerating the impulse. It is now perceived

Theory of Exchanges. He is of opinion that in both of these cases when once the proof has been obtained, the enclosure may be dispensed with. We know, for instance, that the relation between the inductive and absorptive powers of bodies—although this relation may have been proved by means of an enclosure, does not depend upon its presence, and Professor Stewart thinks that in like manner two bodies, or at least two bodies possessing heat such as the sun and the earth in motion relative to each other, will have the differential motion retarded until perhaps it is ultimately destroyed.

that this discrepancy really involves the doctrine of the equivalence of heat and energy, and it was applied by Mayer, at least by implication, to give an estimate of the mechanical equivalent of heat. The estimate thus derived agrees satisfactorily with direct determinations by Dr. Joule and other physicists, so that the explanation of the residual phenomenon which exercised Newton's ingenuity is now complete, and forms an important part of the new science of thermodynamics.

As Herschel observed, almost all great astronomical discoveries have been disclosed in the form of residual differences. It is the practice at well-conducted observatories to compare the positions of the heavenly bodies as actually observed with what might have been expected theoretically. This practice was introduced by Halley when Astronomer Royal, and his reduction of the lunar observations gave a series of residual errors from 1722 to 1739, by the examination of which the lunar theory was improved. Most of the greater astronomical variations arising from nutation, aberration, planetary perturbation were discovered in the same manner. The precession of the equinox was perhaps the earliest residual difference observed; the systematic divergence of Uranus from its calculated places was one of the latest, and was the clue to the remarkable discovery of Neptune. We may also class under residual phenomena all the so-called *proper motions* of the stars. A complete star catalogue, such as that of the British Association, gives a greater or less amount of proper motion for almost every star, consisting in the apparent difference of position of the star as derived from the earliest and latest good observations. But these apparent motions are often due, as explained by Baily,[1] the author of the catalogue, to errors of observation and reduction. In many cases the best astronomical authorities have differed as to the very direction of the supposed proper motion of stars, and as regards the amount of the motion, for instance of *a* Polaris, the most different estimates have been formed. Residual quantities will often be so small that their very existence is doubtful. Only the gradual progress of theory and of measurement will show clearly whether a discrepancy is to

---

[1] *British Association Catalogue of Stars*, p. 49.

be referred to casual errors of observation or to some new phenomenon. But nothing is more requisite for the progress of science than the careful recording and investigation of such discrepancies. In no part of physical science can we be free from exceptions and outstanding facts, of which our present knowledge can give no account. It is among such anomalies that we must look for the clues to new realms of facts worthy of discovery. They are like the floating waifs which led Columbus to suspect the existence of the new world.

CHAPTER XXVI.

IN the present age there seems to be a tendency to believe that the importance of individual genius is less than it was—

"The individual withers, and the world is more and more."

Society, it is supposed, has now assumed so highly developed a form, that what was accomplished in past times by the solitary exertions of a great intellect, may now be worked out by the united labours of an army of investigators. Just as the well-organised power of a modern army supersedes the single-handed bravery of the mediæval knights, so we are to believe that the combination of intellectual labour has superseded the genius of an Archimedes, a Newton, or a Laplace. So-called original research is now regarded as a profession, adopted by hundreds of men, and communicated by a system of training. All that we need to secure additions to our knowledge of nature is the erection of great laboratories, museums, and observatories, and the offering of pecuniary rewards to those who can invent new chemical compounds, detect new species, or discover new comets. Doubtless this is not the real meaning of the eminent men who are now urging upon Government the endowment of physical research. They can only mean that the greater the pecuniary and material assistance given to men of science, the greater the result which the available genius of the country may be expected to produce. Money and opportunities of study can no more produce genius than sunshine and moisture can generate living beings; the inexplicable germ is wanting in both cases. But as, when the germ is present, the plant will grow more or less vigorously according to the circumstances in which it is placed, so it may be allowed that pecuniary assistance may favour development of intellect. Public opinion however is not discriminating, and is likely to interpret the agitation for the endowment of science as meaning that science can be had for money.

All such notions are erroneous. In no branch of human affairs, neither in politics, war, literature, industry, nor science, is the influence of genius less considerable than it was. It is possible that the extension and organisation of scientific study, assisted by the printing-press and the accelerated means of communication, has increased the rapidity with which new discoveries are made known, and their details worked out by many heads and hands. A Darwin now no sooner propounds original ideas concerning the evolution of living creatures, than those ideas are discussed and illustrated, and applied by naturalists in every part of the world. In former days his discoveries would have been hidden for decades of years in scarce manuscripts, and generations would have passed away before his theory had enjoyed the same amount of criticism and corroboration as it has already received. The result is that the genius of Darwin is more valuable, not less valuable, than it would formerly have been. The advance of military science and the organisation of enormous armies has not decreased the value of a skilful general; on the contrary, the rank and file are still more in need than they used to be of the guiding power of a far-seeing intellect. The swift destruction of the French military power was not due alone to the perfection of the German army, nor to the genius of Moltke; it was due to the combination of a well-disciplined multitude with a leader of the highest powers., So in every branch of human affairs the influence of the individual is not withering, but is growing with the extent of the material resources which are at his command.

Turning to our own subject, it is a work of undiminished interest to reflect upon those qualities of mind which lead to great advances in natural knowledge. Nothing, indeed, is less amenable than genius to scientific analysis and explanation. Even definition is out of the question. Buffon said that " genius is patience," and certainly patience is one of its most requisite components. But no one can suppose that patient labour alone will invariably lead to those conspicuous results which we attribute to genius. In every branch of science, literature, art, or industry, there are thousands of men and women who work with unceasing patience, and thereby ensure moderate success; but it would be absurd to suppose that equal amounts of intellectual labour yield equal results. A Newton may modestly attribute his discoveries to industry and patient thought, and there is reason to believe that genius is unconscious and unable to account for its own peculiar powers. As genius is essentially creative, and consists in divergence from the ordinary grooves of thought and action, it must necessarily be a phenomenon beyond the domain of the laws of nature. Nevertheless, it is always an interesting and instructive work to trace out, as far as possible, the characteristics of mind by which great discoveries have been achieved, and we shall find in the analysis much to illustrate the principles of scientific method.

Error of the Baconian Method.

Hundreds of investigators may be constantly engaged in experimental inquiry; they may compile numberless note-books full of scientific facts, and endless tables of numerical results; but, if the views of induction here maintained be true, they can never by such work alone rise to new and great discoveries. By a system of research they may work out deductively the details of a previous discovery, but to arrive at a new principle of nature is another matter. Francis Bacon spread abroad the notion that to advance science we must begin by accumulating facts, and then draw from them, by a process of digestion, successive laws of higher and higher generality. In protesting against the false method of the scholastic logicians, he exaggerated a partially true philosophy, until it became as false as that which preceded it. His notion of scientific method was a kind of scientific bookkeeping. Facts were to be indiscriminately gathered from every source, and posted in a ledger, from which would emerge in time a balance of truth. It is difficult to imagine a less likely way of arriving at great discoveries. The greater the array of facts, the less is the probability that they will by any routine system of classification disclose the laws of nature they embody. Exhaustive classification in all possible orders is out of the question, because the possible orders are practically infinite in number.

It is before the glance of the philosophic mind that facts must display their meaning, and fall into logical order. The natural philosopher must therefore have, in the first place, a mind of impressionable character, which is affected by the slightest exceptional phenomenon. His associating and identifying powers must be great, that is, a strange fact must suggest to his mind whatever of like nature has previously come within his experience. His imagination must be active, and bring before his mind multitudes of relations in which the unexplained facts may possibly stand with regard to each other, or to more common facts. Sure and vigorous powers of deductive reasoning must then come into play, and enable him to infer what will happen under each supposed condition. Lastly, and above all, there must be the love of certainty leading him diligently and with perfect candour, to compare his speculations with the test of fact and experiment.

Freedom of Theorising.

It would be an error to suppose that the great discoverer seizes at once upon the truth, or has any unerring method of divining it. In all probability the errors of the great mind exceed in number those of the less vigorous one. Fertility of imagination and abundance of guesses at truth are among the first requisites of discovery; but the erroneous guesses must be many times as numerous as those which prove well founded. The weakest analogies, the most whimsical notions, the most apparently absurd theories, may pass through the teeming brain, and no record remain of more than the hundredth part. There is nothing really absurd except that which proves contrary to logic and experience. The truest theories involve suppositions which are inconceivable, and no limit can really be placed to the freedom of hypothesis.

Kepler is an extraordinary instance to this effect. No minor laws of nature are more firmly established than those which he detected concerning the orbits and motions of planetary masses, and on these empirical laws the theory of gravitation was founded. Did we not learn from his own writings the multitude of errors into which he fell, we might have imagined that he had some special faculty of seizing on the truth. But, as is well known, he was full of chimerical notions ; his favourite and long-studied theory was founded on a fanciful analogy between the planetary orbits and the regular solids. His celebrated laws were the outcome of a lifetime of speculation, for the most part vain and groundless. We know this because he had a curious pleasure in dwelling upon erroneous and futile trains of reasoning, which most persons consign to oblivion. But Kepler's name was destined to be immortal, on account of the patience with which he submitted his hypotheses to comparison with observation, the candour with which he acknowledged failure after failure, and the perseverance and ingenuity with which he renewed his attack upon the riddles of nature.

Next after Kepler perhaps Faraday is the physical philosopher who has given us the best insight into the progress of discovery, by recording erroneous as well as successful speculations. The recorded notions, indeed, are probably but a tithe of the fancies which arose in his active brain. As Faraday himself said—" The world little knows how many of the thoughts and theories which have passed through the mind of a scientific investigator, have been crushed in silence and secresy by his own severe criticism and adverse examination; that in the most successful instances not a tenth of the suggestions, the hopes, the wishes, the preliminary conclusions have been realised."

Nevertheless, in Faraday's researches, published in the *Philosophical Transactions,* in minor papers, in manuscript note-books, or in other materials, made known in his interesting life by Dr. Bence Jones, we find invaluable lessons for the experimentalist. These writings are full of speculations which we must not judge by the light of subsequent discovery It may perhaps be said that Faraday committed to the printing press crude ideas which a friend would have counselled him to keep back. There was occasionally even a wildness and vagueness in his notions, which in a less careful experimentalist would have been fatal to the attainment of truth. This is especially apparent in a curious paper concerning Ray-vibrations; but fortunately Faraday was aware of the shadowy character of his speculations, and expressed the feeling in words which must be quoted. " I think it likely," he says,[1] " that I have made many mistakes in the preceding pages, for even to myself my ideas on this point appear only as the shadow of a speculation, or as one of those impressions upon the mind, which are allowable for a time as guides to thought and research. He who labours in experimental inquiries knows how numerous these are, and how often their apparent fitness and beauty vanish before the progress and development of real natural truth." If, then, the experimentalist has no royal road to the discovery of the truth, it is an interesting matter to consider by what logical procedure he attains the truth.

If I have taken a correct view of logical method, there is really no such thing as a distinct process of induction. The probability is infinitely small that a collection of complicated facts will fall into an arrangement capable of exhibiting directly the laws obeyed by them. The mathematician might as well expect to integrate his functions by a ballot-box, as the experimentalist to draw deep truths from haphazard trials. All induction is but the inverse application of deduction, and it is by the inexplicable action of a gifted mind that a multitude of heterogeneous facts are ranged in luminous order as the results of some uniformly acting law. So different, indeed, are the qualities of mind required in different branches of science, that it would be absurd to attempt to give an exhaustive description of the character of mind which leads to discovery. The labours of Newton could not have been accomplished except by a mind of the utmost mathematical genius; Faraday, on the other hand, has made the most extensive additions to human knowledge without passing beyond common arithmetic. I do not remember meeting in Faraday's writings with a single

---

[1] *Experimental Researches in Chemistry and Physics*, p. 372. *Philosophical Magazine*, 3rd Series, May 1846, vol. xxviii. p. 350.

algebraic formula or mathematical problem of any complexity. Professor Clerk Maxwell, indeed, in the preface to his new *Treatise on Electricity*, has strongly recommended the reading of Faraday's researches by all students of science, and has given his opinion that though Faraday seldom or never employed mathematical formulæ, his methods and conceptions were not the less mathematical in their nature.[1] I have myself protested against the prevailing confusion between a mathematical and an exact science,[2] yet I certainly think that Faraday's experiments were for the most part qualitative, and that his mathematical ideas were of a rudimentary character. It is true that he could not possibly investigate such a subject as magne-crystallic action without involving himself in geometrical relations of some complexity. Nevertheless I think that he was deficient in mathematical deductive power, that power which is so highly developed by the modern system of mathematical training at Cambridge.

Faraday was acquainted with the forms of his celebrated lines of force, but I am not aware that he ever entered into the algebraic nature of those curves, and I feel sure that he could not have explained their forms as depending on the resultant attractions of all the magnetic particles. There are even occasional indications that he did not understand some of the simpler mathematical doctrines of modern physical science. Although he so clearly foresaw the correlation of the physical forces, and laboured so hard with his own hands to connect gravity with other forces, it is doubtful whether he understood the doctrine of the conservation of energy as applied to gravitation. Faraday was probably equal to Newton in experimental skill, and in that peculiar kind of deductive power which leads to the invention of simple qualitative experiments; but it must be allowed that he exhibited little of that mathematical power which enabled Newton to follow out intuitively the quantitative results of a complicated problem with such wonderful facility. Two instances, Newton and Faraday, are sufficient to show that minds of widely

[1] See also *Nature*, September 18, 1873 ; vol. viii. p. 398.
[2] *Theory of Political Economy*, pp. 3—14.

different conformation will meet with suitable regions of research. Nevertheless, there are certain traits which we may discover in all the highest scientific minds.

The Newtonian Method, the True Organum.

Laplace was of opinion that the *Principia* and the *Opticks* of Newton furnished the best models then available of the delicate art of experimental and theoretical investigation. In these, as he says, we meet with the most happy illustrations of the way in which, from a series of inductions, we may rise to the causes of phenomena, and thence descend again to all the resulting details.

The popular notion concerning Newton's discoveries is that in early life, when driven into the country by the Great Plague, a falling apple accidentally suggested to him the existence of gravitation, and that, availing himself of this hint, he was led to the discovery of the law of gravitation, the explanation of which constitutes the *Principia*. It is difficult to imagine a more ludicrous and inadequate picture of Newton's labours. No originality, or at least priority, was claimed by Newton as regards the discovery of the law of the inverse square, so closely associated with his name. In a well-known Scholium [1] he acknowledges that Sir Christopher Wren, Hooke, and Halley, had severally observed the accordance of Kepler's third law of motion with the principle of the inverse square.

Newton's work was really that of developing the methods of deductive reasoning and experimental verification, by which alone great hypotheses can be brought to the touchstone of fact. Archimedes was the greatest of ancient philosophers, for he showed how mathematical theory could be wedded to physical experiments; and his works are the first true Organum. Newton is the modern Archimedes, and the *Principia* forms the true Novum Organum of scientific method. The laws which he established are great, but his example of the manner of establishing them is greater still. Excepting perhaps

---

[1] *Principia,* bk. i. Prop. iv.

chemistry and electricity, there is hardly a progressive branch of physical and mathematical science, which has not been developed from the germs of true scientific procedure which he disclosed in the *Principia* or the *Opticks*. Overcome by the success of his theory of universal gravitation, we are apt to forget that in his theory of sound he originated the mathematical investigation of waves and the mutual action of particles ; that in his corpuscular theory of light, however mistaken, he first ventured to apply mathematical calculation to molecular attractions and repulsions ; that in his prismatic experiments he showed how far experimental verification could be pushed; that in his examination of the coloured rings named after him, he accomplished the most remarkable instance of minute measurement yet known, a mere practical application of which by Fizeau was recently deemed worthy of a medal by the Royal Society.   We only learn by degrees how complete was his scientific insight; a few words in his third law of motion display his acquaintance with the fundamental principles of modern thermodynamics and the conservation of energy, while manuscripts long overlooked prove that in his inquiries concerning atmospheric refraction he had overcome the main difficulties of applying theory to one of the most complex of physical problems.

After all, it is only by examining the way in which he effected discoveries, that we can rightly appreciate his greatness.   The *Principia* treats not of gravity so much as of forces in general, and the methods of reasoning about them.   He investigates not one hypothesis only, but mechanical hypotheses in general.   Nothing so much strikes the reader of the work as the exhaustiveness of his treatment, and the unbounded power of his insight.   If he treats of central forces, it is not one law of force which he discusses, but many, or almost all imaginable laws, the results of each of which he sketches out in a few pregnant words.   If his subject is a resisting medium, it is not air or water alone, but resisting media in general.   We have a good example of his method in the scholium to the twenty-second proposition of the second book, in which he runs rapidly over many suppositions as to the laws of the compressing forces which might conceivably act in an

atmosphere of gas, a consequence being drawn from each
case, and that one hypothesis ultimately selected which
yields results agreeing with experiments upon the pressure
and density of the terrestrial atmosphere.

Newton said that he did not frame hypotheses, but, in
reality, the greater part of the *Principia* is purely hypothetical, endless varieties of causes and laws being
imagined which have no counterpart in nature.   The
most grotesque hypotheses of Kepler or Descartes were
not more imaginary.   But Newton's comprehension of
logical method was perfect ; no hypothesis was entertained
unless it was definite in conditions, and admitted of unquestionable deductive reasoning; and the value of each
hypothesis was entirely decided by the comparison of its
consequences with facts.   I do not entertain a doubt that
the general course of his procedure is identical with that
view of the nature of induction, as the inverse application
of deduction, which I advocate throughout this book.
Francis Bacon held that science should be founded on
experience, but he mistook the true mode of using experience, and, in attempting to apply his method, ludicrously
failed.   Newton did not less found his method on experience, but he seized the true method of treating it, and
applied it with a power and success never since equalled.
It is a great mistake to say that modern science is the
result of the Baconian philosophy ; it is the Newtonian
philosophy and the Newtonian method which have led to
all the great triumphs of physical science, and I repeat
that the *Principia* forms the true "Novum Organum."

In bringing his theories to a decisive experimental verification, Newton showed, as a general rule, exquisite skill
and ingenuity.   In his hands a few simple pieces of apparatus were made to give results involving an unsuspected
depth of meaning.   His most beautiful experimental inquiry was that by which he proved the differing refrangibility of rays of light.   To suppose that he originally discovered the power of a prism to break up a beam of white
light would be a mistake, for he speaks of procuring a
glass prism to try the "celebrated phenomena of colours."
But we certainly owe to him the theory that white light is
a mixture of rays differing in refrangibility, and that lights
which differ in colour, differ also in refrangibility.   Other

persons might have conceived this theory ; in fact, any person regarding refraction as a quantitative effect must see that different parts of the spectrum have suffered different amounts of refraction. But the power of Newton is shown in the tenacity with which he followed his theory into every consequence, and tested each result by a simple but conclusive experiment. He first shows that different coloured spots are displaced by different amounts when viewed through a prism, and that their images come to a focus at different distances from the lense, as they should do, if the refrangibility differed. After excluding by many experiments a variety of indifferent circumstances, he fixes his attention upon the question whether the rays are merely shattered, disturbed, and spread out in a chance manner, as Grimaldi supposed, or whether there is a constant relation between the colour and the refrangibility.

If Grimaldi was right, it might be expected that a part of the spectrum taken separately, and subjected to a second refraction, would suffer a new breaking up, and produce some new spectrum. Newton inferred from his own theory that a particular ray of the spectrum would have a constant refrangibility, so that a second prism would merely bend it more or less, but not further disperse it in any considerable degree. By simply cutting off most of the rays of the spectrum by a screen, and allowing the remaining narrow ray to fall on a second prism, he proved the truth of this conclusion ; and then slowly turning the first prism, so as to vary the colour of the ray falling on the second one, he found that the spot of light formed by the twice-refracted ray travelled up and down, a palpable proof that the amount of refrangibility varies with the colour. For his further satisfaction, he sometimes refracted the light a third or fourth time, and he found that it might be refracted upwards or downwards or sideways, and yet for each colour there was a definite amount of refraction through each prism. He completed the proof by showing that the sepa rated rays may again be gathered together into white light by an inverted prism, so that no number of refractions alters the character of the light. The conclusion thus obtained serves to explain the confusion arising in the use of a common lense ; he shows that with homogeneous light there is one distinct focus, with mixed light an infinite number of foci, which prevent a clear view from being obtained at any point.

What astonishes the reader of the *Opticks* is the persistence with which Newton follows out the consequences of a preconceived theory, and tests the one notion by a wonderful variety of simple comparisons with fact. The ease with which he invents new combinations, and foresees the results, subsequently verified, produces an insuperable conviction in the reader that he has possession of the truth. And it is certainly the theory which leads him to the experiments, most of which could hardly be devised by accident. Newton actually remarks that it was by mathematically determining all kinds of phenomena of colours which could be produced by refraction that he had " invented " almost all the experiments in the book, and he promises that others who shall " argue truly," and try the experiments with care, will not be disappointed in the results.[1]

The philosophic method of Huyghens was the same as that of Newton, and Huyghens' investigation of double refraction furnishes almost equally beautiful instances of theory guiding experiment. So far as we know double refraction was first discovered by accident, and was described by Erasmus Bartholinus in 1669. The phenomenon then appeared to be entirely exceptional, and the laws governing the two paths of the refracted rays were so unapparent and complicated, that Newton altogether misunderstood the phenomenon, and it was only at the latter end of the last century that scientific men began to comprehend its laws.

Nevertheless, Huyghens had, with rare genius, arrived at the true theory as early as 1678. He regarded light as an undulatory motion of some medium, and in his *Traité de la Lumière* he pointed out that, in ordinary refraction, the velocity of propagation of the wave is equal in all directions, so that the front of an advancing wave is spherical, and reaches equal distances in equal times. But in crystals, as he supposed, the medium would be of unequal elasticity in different directions, so that a disturbance would reach unequal distances in equal times, and the wave produced would have a spheroidal form.

[1] *Opticks*, bk. i. part ii. Prop. 3. 3rd ed. p. 115.

Huyghens was not satisfied with an unverified theory. He calculated what might be expected to happen when a crystal of calc-spar was cut in various directions, and he says : " I have examined in detail the properties of the extraordinary refraction of this crystal, to see if each phenomenon which is deduced from theory would agree with what is really observed. And this being so, it is no slight proof of the truth of our suppositions and prin- ciples ; but what I am going to add here confirms them still more wonderfully ; that is, the different modes of cutting this crystal, in which the surfaces produced give rise to refraction exactly such as they ought to be, and as I had foreseen them, according to the preceding theory."

Newton's mistaken corpuscular theory of light caused the theories and experiments of Huyghens to be disregarded for more than a century ; but it is not easy to imagine a more beautiful or successful application of the true method of inductive investigation, theory guiding experiment, and yet wholly relying on experiment for confirmation.

Candour and Courage of the Philosophic Mind.

Perfect readiness to reject a theory inconsistent with fact is a primary requisite of the philosophic mind. But it would be a mistake to suppose that this candour has any- thing akin to fickleness ; on the contrary, readiness to reject a false theory may be combined with a peculiar pertinacity and courage in maintaining an hypothesis as long as its falsity is not actually apparent. There must, indeed, be no prejudice or bias distorting the mind, and causing it to pass over the unwelcome results of experiment. There must be that scrupulous honesty and flexibility of mind, which assigns adequate value to all evidence ; indeed, the more a man loves his theory, the more scrupulous should be his attention to its faults. It is common in life to meet with some theorist, who, by long cogitation over a single theory, has allowed it to mould his mind, and render him incapable of receiving anything but as a contribution to the truth of his one theory. A narrow and intense course of thought may sometimes lead to great results, but the adop- tion of a wrong theory at the outset is in such a mind irre- trievable. The man of one idea has but a single chance of truth. The fertile discoverer, on the contrary, chooses between many theories, and is never wedded to any one, unless impartial and repeated comparison has convinced him of its validity. He does not choose and then compare ; but he compares time after time, and then chooses.

Having once deliberately chosen, the philosopher may rightly entertain his theory with the strongest fidelity. He will neglect no objection ; for he may chance at any time to meet a fatal one ; but he will bear in mind the inconsiderable powers of the human mind compared with the tasks it has to undertake. He will see that no theory can at first be reconciled with all objections, because there may be many interfering causes, and the very consequences of the theory may have a complexity which prolonged investigation by successive generations of men may not exhaust. If, then, a theory exhibit a number of striking coincidences with fact, it must not be thrown aside until at least one *conclusive discordance* is proved, regard being had to possible error in establishing that discordance. In science and philosophy something must be risked. He who quails at the least difficulty will never establish a new truth, and it was not unphilosophic in Leslie to remark concerning his own inquiries into the nature of heat—

" In the course of investigation, I have found myself compelled to relinquish some preconceived notions ; but I have not abandoned them hastily, nor, till after a warm and obstinate defence, I was driven from every post." [1]

Faraday's life, again, furnishes most interesting illustrations of this tenacity of the philosophic mind. Though so candid in rejecting some theories, there were others to which he clung through everything. One of his favourite notions resulted in a brilliant discovery ; another remains in doubt to the present day.

The Philosophic Character of Faraday.

In Faraday's researches concerning the connection of magnetism and light, we find an excellent instance of the pertinacity with which a favourite theory may be pursued,

---

[1] *Experimental Inquiry into the Nature of Heat.* Preface, p. xv.

so long as the results of experiment do not clearly negative
the notions entertained. In purely quantitative questions,
as we have seen, the absence of apparent effect can seldom
be regarded as proving the absence of all effect. Now
Faraday was convinced that some mutual relation must
exist between magnetism and light. As early as 1822, he
attempted to produce an effect upon a ray of polarised light,
by passing it through water placed between the poles of a
voltaic battery; but he was obliged to record that not the
slightest effect was observable. During many years the
subject, we are told,[1] rose again and again to his mind,
and no failure could make him relinquish his search after
this unknown relation. It was in the year 1845 that he
gained the first success; on August 30th he began to
work with common electricity, vainly trying glass, quartz,
Iceland spar, &c. Several days of labour gave no result;
yet he did not desist. Heavy glass, a transparent medium
of great refractive powers, composed of borate of lead, was
now tried, being placed between the poles of a powerful
electro-magnet while a ray of polarised light was transmitted through it. When the poles of the electro-magnet
were arranged in certain positions with regard to the
substance under trial, no effects were apparent; but at
last Faraday happened fortunately to place a piece of
heavy glass so that contrary magnetic poles were on the
same side, and now an effect was witnessed. The glass
was found to have the power of twisting the plane of
polarisation of the ray of light.

All Faraday's recorded thoughts upon this great experiment are replete with curious interest. He attributes his
success to the opinion, almost amounting to a conviction,
that the various forms, under which the forces of matter
are made manifest, have one common origin, and are so
directly related and mutually dependent that they are
convertible. " This strong persuasion," he says,[2] " extended
to the powers of light, and led to many exertions having
for their object the discovery of the direct relation of light
and electricity. These ineffectual exertions could not
remove my strong persuasion, and I have at last suc-

[1] Bence Jones, *Life of Faraday*, vol. i. p. 362.
[2] Ibid. vol. ii. p. 199.

ceeded." He describes the phenomenon in somewhat figurative language as *the magnetisation of a ray of light*,
and also as *the illumination of a magnetic curve or line
of force*. He has no sooner got the effect in one case,
than he proceeds, with his characteristic comprehensive-
ness of research, to test the existence of a like phenomenon
in all the substances available. He finds that not only
heavy glass, but solids and liquids, acids and alkalis,
oils, water, alcohol, ether, all possess this power; but he
was not able to detect its existence in any gaseous substance. His thoughts cannot be restrained from running
into curious speculations as to the possible results of the
power in certain cases. " What effect," he says, " does this
force have in the earth where the magnetic curves of the
earth traverse its substance ? Also what effect in a magnet ? " And then he falls upon the strange notion that
perhaps this force tends to make iron and oxide of iron
transparent, a phenomenon never observed. We can meet
with nothing more instructive as to the course of mind by
which great discoveries are made, than these records of
Faraday's patient labours, and his varied success and
failure. Nor are his unsuccessful experiments upon the
relation of gravity and electricity less interesting, or less
worthy of study.

Throughout a large part of his life, Faraday was possessed by the idea that gravity cannot be unconnected
with the other forces of nature. On March 19th, 1849,
he wrote in his laboratory book,—" Gravity. Surely this
force must be capable of an experimental relation to electricity, magnetism, and the other forces, so as to bind it
up with them in reciprocal action and equivalent effect ? " [1]
He filled twenty paragraphs or more with reflections and
suggestions, as to the mode of treating the subject by experiment. He anticipated that the mutual approach of
two bodies would develop electricity in them, or that a
body falling through a conducting helix would excite a
current changing in direction as the motion was reversed.
" *All this is a dream*," he remarks ; " still examine it by a
few experiments. Nothing is too wonderful to be true, if

[1] See also his more formal statement in the *Experimental Researches
in Electricity*, 24th Series, § 2702, vol. iii. p. 161.

it be consistent with the laws of nature; and in such things as these, experiment is the best test of such consistency."

He executed many difficult and tedious experiments, which are described in the 24th Series of Experimental Researches. The result was *nil*, and yet he concludes: "Here end my trials for the present. The results are negative; they do not shake my strong feeling of the existence of a relation between gravity and electricity, though they give no proof that such a relation exists."

He returned to the work when he was ten years older, and in 1858-9 recorded many remarkable reflections and experiments. He was much struck by the fact that electricity is essentially a *dual force*, and it had always been a conviction of Faraday that no body could be electrified positively without some other body becoming electrified negatively; some of his researches had been simple developments of this relation. But observing that between two mutually gravitating bodies there was no apparent circumstance to determine which should be positive and which negative, he does not hesitate to call in question an old opinion. "The evolution of *one* electricity would be a new and very remarkable thing. The idea throws a doubt on the whole; but still try, for who knows what is possible in dealing with gravity?" We cannot but notice the candour with which he thus acknowledges in his laboratory book the doubtfulness of the whole thing, and is yet prepared as a forlorn hope to frame experiments in opposition to all his previous experience of the course of nature. For a time his thoughts flow on as if the strange detection were already made, and he had only to trace out its consequences throughout the universe. "Let us encourage ourselves by a little more imagination prior to experiment," he says; and then he reflects upon the infinity of actions in nature, in which the mutual relations of electricity and gravity would come into play; he pictures to himself the planets and the comets charging themselves as they approach the sun; cascades, rain, rising vapour, circulating currents of the atmosphere, the fumes of a volcano, the smoke in a chimney become so many electrical machines. A multitude of events and changes in the atmosphere seem to be at once elucidated by such actions; for a moment his reveries have the vividness of fact. " I think we have been dull and blind not to have suspected some such results," and he sums up rapidly the consequences of his great but imaginary theory ; an entirely new mode of exciting heat or electricity, an entirely new relation of the natural forces, an analysis of gravitation, and a justification of the conservation of force.

Such were Faraday's fondest dreams of what might be, and to many a philosopher they would have been sufficient basis for the writing of a great book. But Faraday's imagination was within his full control ; as he himself says, " Let the imagination go, guarding it by judgment and principle, and holding it in and directing it by experiment." His dreams soon took a very practical form, and for many days he laboured with ceaseless energy, on the staircase of the Royal Institution, in the clock tower of the Houses of Parliament, or at the top of the Shot Tower in Southwark, raising and lowering heavy weights, and combining electrical helices and wires in every conceivable way. His skill and long experience in experiment were severely taxed to eliminate the effects of the earth's magnetism, and time after time he saved himself from accepting mistaken indications, which to another man might have seemed conclusive verifications of his theory. When all was done there remained absolutely no results. " The experiments," he says, "were well made, but the results are negative ; " and yet, he adds, " I cannot accept them as conclusive." In this position the question remains to the present day ; it may be that the effect was too slight to be detected, or it may be that the arrangements adopted were not suited to develop the particular relation which exists, just as Oersted could not detect electro-magnetism, so long as his wire was perpendicular to the plane of motion of his needle. But these are not matters which concern us further here. We have only to notice the profound conviction in the unity of natural laws, the active powers of inference and imagination, the unbounded licence of theorising, combined above all with the utmost diligence in experimental verification which this remarkable research exhibits.

Reservation of Judgment.

There is yet another characteristic needed in the philosophic mind; it is that of suspending judgment when the data are insufficient. Many people will express a confident opinion on almost any question which is put before them, but they thereby manifest not strength, but narrowness of mind. To see all sides of a complicated subject, and to weigh all the different facts and probabilities correctly, require no ordinary powers of comprehension. Hence it is most frequently the philosophic mind which is in doubt, and the ignorant mind which is ready with a positive decision. Faraday has himself said, in a very interesting lecture:[1] "Occasionally and frequently the exercise of the judgment ought to end in *absolute reservation*. It may be very distasteful, and great fatigue, to suspend a conclusion; but as we are not infallible, so we ought to be cautious; we shall eventually find our advantage, for the man who rests in his position is not so far from right as he who, proceeding in a wrong direction, is ever increasing his distance."

Arago presented a conspicuous example of this high quality of mind, as Faraday remarks; for when he made known his curious discovery of the relation of a magnetic needle to a revolving copper plate, a number of supposed men of science in different countries gave immediate and confident explanations of it, which were all wrong. But Arago, who had both discovered the phenomenon and personally investigated its conditions, declined to put forward publicly any theory at all.

At the same time we must not suppose that the truly philosophic mind can tolerate a state of doubt, while a chance of decision remains open. In science nothing like compromise is possible, and truth must be one. Hence, doubt is the confession of ignorance, and involves a painful feeling of incapacity. But doubt lies between error and truth, so that if we choose wrongly we are further away than ever from our goal.

Summing up, then, it would seem as if the mind of the great discoverer must combine contradictory attributes.

---

[1] Printed in *Modern Culture*, edited by Youmans, p. 219.

He must be fertile in theories and hypotheses, and yet full of facts and precise results of experience. He must entertain the feeblest analogies, and the merest guesses at truth, and yet he must hold them as worthless till they are verified in experiment. When there are any grounds of probability he must hold tenaciously to an old opinion, and yet he must be prepared at any moment to relinquish it when a clearly contradictory fact is encountered. " The philosopher," says Faraday,[1] " should be a man willing to listen to every suggestion, but determined to judge for himself. He should not be biased by appearances ; have no favourite hypothesis ; be of no school ; and in doctrine have no master. He should not be a respecter of persons, but of things. Truth should be his primary object. If to these qualities be added industry, he may indeed hope to walk within the veil of the temple of nature."

[1] *Life of Faraday,* vol. i. p. 225.

BOOK V.

GENERALISATION, ANALOGY, AND CLASSIFICATION.

CHAPTER XXVII.

GENERALISATION.

I HAVE endeavoured to show in preceding chapters that all inductive reasoning is an inverse application of deductive reasoning, and consists in demonstrating that the consequences of certain assumed laws agree with facts of nature gathered by active or passive observation. The fundamental process of reasoning, as stated in the outset, consists in inferring of a thing what we know of similar objects, and it is on this principle that the whole of deductive reasoning, whether simply logical or mathematico-logical, is founded. All inductive reasoning must be founded on the same principle. It might seem that by a plain use of this principle we could avoid the complicated processes of induction and deduction, and argue directly from one particular case to another, as Mill proposed. If the Earth, Venus, Mars, Jupiter, and other planets move in elliptic orbits, cannot we dispense with elaborate precautions, and assert that Neptune, Ceres, and the last discovered planet must do so likewise ? Do we not know that Mr. Gladstone must die, because he is like other

men? May we not argue that because some men die
therefore he must? Is it requisite to ascend by induction
to the general proposition "all men must die," and then
descend by deduction from that general proposition to the
case of Mr. Gladstone? My answer undoubtedly is that
we must ascend to general propositions. The fundamental
principle of the substitution of similars gives us no warrant
in affirming of Mr. Gladstone what we know of other men,
because we cannot be sure that Mr. Gladstone is exactly
similar to other men. Until his death we cannot be perfectly sure that he possesses all the attributes of other
men ; it is a question of probability, and I have endeavoured
to explain the mode in which the theory of probability is
applied to calculate the probability that from a series of
similar events we may infer the recurrence of like events
under identical circumstances. There is then no such
process as that of inferring from particulars to particulars.
A careful analysis of the conditions under which such an
inference appears to be made, shows that the process is
really a general one, and that what is inferred of a particular case might be inferred of all similar cases. All
reasoning is essentially general, and all science implies
generalisation. In the very birth-time of philosophy this
was held to be so : " Nulla scientia est de individuis, sed
de solis universalibus," was the doctrine of Plato, delivered
by Porphyry. And Aristotle[1] held a like opinion—
Οὐδεμία δὲ τέχνη σκοπεῖ τὸ καθ' ἕκαστον . . . τὸ δὲ καθ'
ἕκαστον ἄπειρον καὶ οὐκ ἐπιστητόν. "No art treats of
particular cases ; for particulars are infinite and cannot be
known." No one who holds the doctrine that reasoning
may be from particulars to particulars, can be supposed
to have the most rudimentary notion of what constitutes
reasoning and science.

At the same time there can be no doubt that practically what we find to be true of many similar objects will
probably be true of the next similar object. This is the
result to which an analysis of the Inverse Method of
Probabilities leads us, and, in the absence of precise data
from which we may calculate probabilities, we are usually
obliged to make a rough assumption that similars in some

---

[1] Aristotle's *Rhetoric*, Liber I. 2. 11.

respects are similars in other respects. Thus it comes to pass that a large part of the reasoning processes in which scientific men are engaged, consists in detecting similarities between objects, and then rudely assuming that the like similarities will be detected in other cases.

Distinction of Generalisation and Analogy.

There is no distinction but that of degree between what is known as reasoning by *generalisation* and reasoning by *analogy*. In both cases from certain observed resemblances we infer, with more or less probability, the existence of other resemblances. In generalisation the resemblances have great extension and usually little intension, whereas in analogy we rely upon the great intension, the extension being of small amount (p. 26). If we find that the qualities A and B are associated together in a great many instances, and have never been found separate, it is highly probable that on the next occasion when we meet with A, B will also be present, and *vice versâ*. Thus wherever we meet with an object possessing gravity, it is found to possess inertia also, nor have we met with any material objects possessing inertia without discovering that they also possess gravity. The probability has therefore become very great, as indicated by the rules founded on the Inverse Method of Probabilities (p. 257), that whenever in the future we meet an object possessing either of the properties of gravity and inertia, it will be found on examination to possess the other of these properties. This is a clear instance of the employment of generalisation.

In analogy, on the other hand, we reason from likeness in many points to likeness in other points. The qualities or points of resemblance are now numerous, not the objects. At the poles of Mars are two white spots which resemble in many respects the white regions of ice and snow at the poles of the earth. There probably exist no other similar objects with which to compare these, yet the exactness of the resemblance enables us to infer, with high probability, that the spots on Mars consist of ice and snow. In short, many points of resemblance imply many more. From the appearance and behaviour of those white spots we infer that they have all the chemical and physical

properties of frozen water. The inference is of course only
probable, and based upon the improbability that aggregates
of many qualities should be formed in a like manner in
two or more cases, without being due to some uniform
condition or cause.

In reasoning by analogy, then, we observe that two
objects A B C D E . . . . . and A'B'C'D'E' . . . . . have
many like qualities, as indicated by the identity of the
letters, and we infer that, since the first has another
quality, X, we shall discover this quality in the second case
by sufficiently close examination. As Laplace says,—
"Analogy is founded on the probability that similar things
have causes of the same kind, and produce the same effects.
The more perfect this similarity, the greater is this probability." [1] The nature of analogical inference is aptly
described in the work on Logic attributed to Kant, where
the rule of ordinary induction is stated in the words, " *Eines
in vielen, also in allen,*" one quality in many things, therefore in all; and the rule of analogy is " *Vieles in einem, also
auch das übrige in demselben* "[2] many (qualities) in one,
therefore also the remainder in the same. It is evident
that there may be intermediate cases in which, from the
identity of a moderate number of objects in several properties, we may infer to other objects. Probability must
rest either upon the number of instances or the depth of
resemblance, or upon the occurrence of both in sufficient
degrees. What there is wanting in extension must be
made up by intension, and *vice versâ.*

Two Meanings of Generalisation.

The term generalisation, as commonly used, includes two
processes which are of different character, but are often
closely associated together. In the first place, we generalise
when we recognise even in two objects a common nature.
We cannot detect the slightest similarity without opening
the way to inference from one case to the other. If we
compare a cubical crystal with a regular octahedron, there
is little apparent similarity; but, as soon as we perceive

---

[1] *Essai Philosophique sur les Probabilités,* p. 86.
[2] Kant's *Logik,* § 84, Königsberg, 1800, p. 207.

that either can be produced by the symmetrical modification of the other, we discover a groundwork of similarity in the crystals, which enables us to infer many things of one, because they are true of the other. Our knowledge of ozone took its rise from the time when the similarity of smell, attending electric sparks, strokes of lightning, and the slow combustion of phosphorus, was noticed by Schönbein. There was a time when the rainbow was an inexplicable phenomenon—a portent, like a comet, and a cause of superstitious hopes and fears. But we find the true spirit of science in Roger Bacon, who desires us to consider the objects which present the same colours as the rainbow; he mentions hexagonal crystals from Ireland and India, but he bids us not suppose that the hexagonal form is essential, for similar colours may be detected in many transparent stones. Drops of water scattered by the oar in the sun, the spray from a water-wheel, the dewdrops lying on the grass in the summer morning, all display a similar phenomenon. No sooner have we grouped together these apparently diverse instances, than we have begun to generalise, and have acquired a power of applying to one instance what we can detect of others. Even when we do not apply the knowledge gained to new objects, our comprehension of those already observed is greatly strengthened and deepened by learning to view them as particular cases of a more general property.

A second process, to which the name of generalisation is often given, consists in passing from a fact or partial law to a multitude of unexamined cases, which we believe to be subject to the same conditions. Instead of merely recognising similarity as it is brought before us, we predict its existence before our senses can detect it, so that generalisation of this kind endows us with a prophetic power of more or less probability. Having observed that many substances assume, like water and mercury, the three states of solid, liquid, and gas, and having assured ourselves by frequent trial that the greater the means we possess of heating and cooling, the more substances we can vaporise and freeze, we pass confidently in advance of fact, and assume that all substances are capable of these three forms. Such a generalisation was accepted by Lavoisier and Laplace before many of the corroborative facts now in our

possession were known. The reduction of a single comet
beneath the sway of gravity was considered sufficient
indication that all comets obey the same power. Few
persons doubted that the law of gravity extended over the
whole heavens; certainly the fact that a few stars out of
many millions manifest the action of gravity, is now held
to be sufficient evidence of its general extension over the
visible universe.

Value of Generalisation.

It might seem that if we know particular facts, there can
be little use in connecting them together by a general law.
The particulars must be more full of useful information
than an abstract general statement. If we know, for
instance, the properties of an ellipse, a circle, a parabola,
and hyperbola, what is the use of learning all these properties over again in the general theory of curves of the
second degree ? If we understand the phenomena of sound
and light and water-waves separately, what is the need of
erecting a general theory of waves, which, after all, is
inapplicable to practice until resolved again into particular
cases ? But, in reality, we never do obtain an adequate
knowledge of particulars until we regard them as cases of
the general. Not only is there a singular delight in discovering the many in the one, and the one in the many,
but there is a constant interchange of light and knowledge.
Properties which are unapparent in the hyperbola may be
readily observed in the ellipse. Most of the complex
relations which old geometers discovered in the circle will
be reproduced *mutatis mutandis* in the other conic sections.
The undulatory theory of light might have been unknown
at the present day, had not the theory of sound supplied
hints by analogy. The study of light has made known
many phenomena of interference and polarisation, the
existence of which had hardly been suspected in the case
of sound, but which may now be sought out, and perhaps
found to possess unexpected interest. The careful study
of water-waves shows how waves alter in form and velocity
with varying depth of water. Analogous changes may
some time be detected in sound waves. Thus there is
mutual interchange of aid.

" Every study of a generalisation or extension," De Morgan has well said,[1] "gives additional power over the particular form by which the generalisation is suggested. Nobody who has ever returned to quadratic equations after the study of equations of all degrees, or who has done the like, will deny my assertion that οὐ βλέπει Βλέπων may be predicated of any one who studies a branch or a case, without afterwards making it part of a larger whole. Accordingly it is always worth while to generalise, were it only to give power over the *particular*. This principle, of daily familiarity to the mathematician, is almost unknown to the logician."

Comparative Generality of Properties.

Much of the value of science depends upon the knowledge which we gradually acquire of the different degrees of generality of properties and phenomena of various kinds. The use of science consists in enabling us to act with confidence, because we can foresee the result. Now this foresight must rest upon the knowledge of the powers which will come into play. That knowledge, indeed, can never be certain, because it rests upon imperfect induction, and the most confident beliefs and predictions of the physicist may be falsified. Nevertheless, if we always estimate the probability of each belief according to the due teaching of the data, and bear in mind that probability when forming our anticipations, we shall ensure the minimum of disappointment. Even when he cannot exactly apply the theory of probabilities, the physicist may acquire the habit of making judgments in general agreement with its principles and results.

Such is the constitution of nature, that the physicist learns to distinguish those properties which have wide and uniform extension, from those which vary between case and case. Not only are certain laws distinctly laid down, with their extension carefully defined, but a scientific training gives a kind of tact in judging how far other laws are likely to apply under any particular circumstances. We learn by degrees that crystals exhibit phenomena de-

[1] *Syllabus of a Proposed System of Logic*, p. 34.

pending upon the directions of the axes of elasticity, which we must not expect in uniform solids. Liquids, compared even with non-crystalline · solids, exhibit laws of far less complexity and variety ; and gases assume, in many respects, an aspect of nearly complete uniformity. To trace out the branches of science in which varying degrees of generality prevail, would be an inquiry of great interest and importance ; but want of space, if there were no other reason, would forbid me to attempt it, except in a very slight manner.

Gases, so far as they are really gaseous, not only have exactly the same properties in all directions of space, but one gas exactly resembles other gases in many qualities. All gases expand by heat, according to the same law, and by nearly the same amount; the specific heats of equivalent weights are equal, and the densities are exactly proportional to the atomic weights. All such gases obey the general law, that the volume multiplied by the pressure, and divided by the absolute temperature, is constant or nearly so. The laws of diffusion and transpiration are the same in all cases, and, generally speaking, all physical laws, as distinguished from chemical laws, apply equally to all gases. Even when gases differ in chemical or physical properties, the differences are minor in degree. Thus the differences of viscosity are far less marked than in the liquid and solid states. Nearly all gases, again, are colourless, the exceptions being chlorine, the vapours of iodine, bromine, and a few other substances.

Only in one single point, so far as I am aware, do gases present distinguishing marks unknown or nearly so, in the solid and liquid states. I mean as regards the light given off when incandescent. Each gas when sufficiently heated, yields its own peculiar series of rays, arising from the free vibrations of the constituent parts of the molecules. Hence the possibility of distinguishing gases by the spectroscope. But the molecules of solids and liquids appear to be continually in conflict with each other, so that only a confused *noise* of atoms is produced, instead of a definite series of luminous chords. At the same temperature, accordingly, all solids and liquids give off nearly the same rays when strongly heated, and we have in this case an exception to the greater generality of properties in gases.

Liquids are in many ways intermediate in character between gases and solids. While incapable of possessing different elasticity in different directions, and thus denuded of the rich geometrical complexity of solids, they retain the variety of density, colour degrees of transparency great diversity in surface tension, viscosity, coefficients of expansion, compressibility, and many other properties which we observe in solids, but not for the most part in gases. Though our knowledge of the physical properties of liquids is much wanting in generality at present, there is ground to hope that by degrees laws connecting and explaining the variations may be traced out.

Solids are in every way contrasted to gases. Each solid substance has its own peculiar degree of density, hardness, compressibility, transparency, tenacity, elasticity, power of conducting heat and electricity, magnetic properties, capability of producing frictional electricity, and so forth. Even different specimens of the same kind of substance will differ widely, according to the accidental treatment received. And not only has each substance its own specific properties, but, when crystallised, its properties vary in each direction with regard to the axes of crystallisation. The velocity of radiation, the rate of conduction of heat, the coefficients of expansibility and compressibility, the thermo-electric properties, all vary in different crystallographic directions.

It is probable that many apparent differences between liquids, and even between solids, will be explained when we learn to regard them under exactly corresponding circumstances. The extreme generality of the properties of gases is in reality only true at an infinitely high temperature, when they are all equally remote from their condensing points. Now, it is found that if we compare liquids—for instance, different kinds of alcohols—not at equal temperatures, but at points equally distant from their respective boiling points, the laws and coefficients of expansion are nearly equal. The vapour-tensions of liquids also are more nearly equal, when compared at corresponding points, and the boiling-points appear in many cases to be simply related to the chemical composition. No doubt the progress of investigation will enable us to discover generality, where at present we only see variety and puzzling complexity.

In some cases substances exhibit the same physical properties in the liquid as in the solid state. Lead has a high
refractive power, whether in solution, or in solid salts,
crystallised or vitreous. The magnetic power of iron is
conspicuous, whatever be its chemical condition ; indeed,
the magnetic properties of substances, though varying
with temperature, seem not to be greatly affected by other
physical changes. Colour, absorptive power for heat or
light rays, and a few other properties are also often the
same in liquids and gases. Iodine and bromine possess a
deep colour whenever they are chemically uncombined.
Nevertheless, we can seldom argue safely from the properties of a substance in one condition to those in another
condition.   Ice is an insulator, water a conductor of
electricity, and the same contrast exists in most other
substances. The conducting power of a liquid for electricity increases with the temperature, while that of a solid
decreases.   By degrees we may learn to distinguish
between those properties of matter which depend upon the
intimate construction of the chemical molecule, and those
which depend upon the contact, conflict, mutual attraction,
or other relations of distinct molecules. The properties
of a substance with respect to light seem generally to
depend upon the molecule ; thus, the power of certain
substances to cause the plane of polarisation of a ray of
light to rotate, is exactly the same whatever .be its degree
of density, or the diluteness of the solution in which it is
contained. Taken as a whole, the physical properties of
substances and their quantitative laws, present a problem
of infinite complexity, and centuries must elapse before any
moderately complete generalisations on the subject become
possible.

Uniform Properties of all Matter.

Some laws are held to be true of all matter in the
universe absolutely, without exception, no instance to the
contrary having ever been noticed. This is the case with
the laws of motion, as laid down by Galileo and Newton.
It is also conspicuously true of the law of universal gravitation. The rise of modern physical science may perhaps
be considered as beginning at the time when Galileo

showed, in opposition to the Aristotelians, that matter is equally affected by gravity, irrespective of its form, magnitude, or texture. All objects fall with equal rapidity, when disturbing causes, such as the resistance of the air, are removed or allowed for. That which was rudely demonstrated by Galileo from the leaning tower of Pisa, was proved by Newton to a high degree of approximation, in an experiment which has been mentioned (p. 443).

Newton formed two pendulums, as nearly as possible the same in outward shape and size by taking two equal round wooden boxes, and suspending them by equal threads, eleven feet long. The pendulums were therefore equally subject to the resistance of the air. He filled one box with wood, and in the centre of oscillation of the other he placed an equal weight of gold. The pendulums were then equal in weight as well as in size ; and, on setting them simultaneously in motion, Newton found that they vibrated for a length of time with equal vibrations. He tried the same experiment with silver, lead, glass, sand, common salt, water, and wheat, in place of the gold, and ascertained that the motion of his pendulum was exactly the same whatever was the kind of matter inside.[1] He considered that a difference of a thousandth part would have been apparent. The reader must observe that the pendulums were made of equal weight only in order that they might suffer equal retardation from the air. The meaning of the experiment is that all substances manifest exactly equal acceleration from the force of gravity, and that therefore the inertia or resistance of matter to force, which is the only independent measure of mass known to us, is always proportional to gravity.

These experiments of Newton were considered conclusive up to very recent times, when certain discordances between the theory and observations of the movements of planets led Nicolai, in 1826, to suggest that the equal gravitation of different kinds of matter might not be absolutely exact. It is perfectly philosophical thus to call in question, from time to time, some of the best accepted laws. On this occasion Bessel carefully repeated the experiments of Newton with pendulums composed of

---

[1] *Principia*, bk. iii. Prop. VI.   Motte's translation, vol. ii. p. 220.

ivory, glass, marble, quartz, meteoric stones, &c., but was
unable to detect the least difference. This conclusion is
also confirmed by the ultimate agreement of all the calculations of physical astronomy based upon it. Whether
the mass of Jupiter be calculated from the motion of its
own satellites, from the effect upon the small planets,
Vesta, Juno, &c., or from the perturbation of Encke's
Comet, the results are closely accordant, showing that
precisely the same law of gravity applies to the most
different bodies which we can observe. The gravity of
a body, again, appears to be entirely independent of its
other physical conditions, being totally unaffected by
any alteration in the temperature, density, electric or
magnetic condition, or other physical properties of the
substance.

One paradoxical result of the law of equal gravitation
is the theorem of Torricelli, to the effect that all liquids
of whatever density fall or flow with equal rapidity. If
there be two equal cisterns respectively filled with mercury and water, the mercury, though thirteen times as
heavy, would flow from an aperture neither more rapidly
nor more slowly than the water, and the same would be
true of ether, alcohol, and other liquids, allowance being
made, however, for the resistance of the air, and the
differing viscosities of the liquids.

In its exact equality and its perfect independence of
all circumstances, except mass and distance, the force of
gravity stands apart from all the other forces and phenomena of nature, and has not yet been brought into any
relation with them except through the general principle
of the conservation of energy. Magnetic attraction, as
remarked by Newton, follows very different laws, depending upon the chemical quality and molecular structure of each particular substance.

We must remember that in saying " all matter gravitates," we exclude from the term matter the basis of light-
undulations, which is immensely more extensive in amount,
and obeys in many respects the laws of mechanics. This
adamantine substance appears, so far as can be ascertained,
to be perfectly uniform in its properties when existing in
space unoccupied by matter. Light and heat are conveyed
by it with equal velocity in all directions, and in all parts

of space so far as observation informs us. But the presence
of gravitating matter modifies the density and mechanical
properties of the so-called ether in a way which is yet
quite unexplained.[1]

Leaving gravity, it is somewhat difficult to discover
other laws which are equally true of all matter. Boerhaave was considered to have established that all bodies
expand by heat; but not only is the expansion very different in different substances, but we now know positive
exceptions. Many liquids and a few solids contract by
heat at certain temperatures. There are indeed other
relations of heat to matter which seem to be universal
and uniform; all substances begin to give off rays of light
at the same temperature, according to the law of Draper;
and gases will not be an exception if sufficiently condensed,
as in the experiments of Frankland. Grove considers it
to be universally true that all bodies in combining produce
heat; with the doubtful exception of sulphur and selenium,
all solids in becoming liquids, and all liquids in becoming
gases, absorb heat; but the quantities of heat absorbed
vary with the chemical qualities of the matter. Carnot's
Thermodynamic Law is held to be exactly true of all matter
without distinction; it expresses the fact that the amount
of mechanical energy which might be theoretically obtained
from a certain amount of heat energy depends only upon
the change of the temperatures, so that whether an engine
be worked by water, air, alcohol, ammonia, or any other
substance, the result would theoretically be the same, if
the boiler and condenser were maintained at similar
temperatures.

Variable Properties of Matter.

I have enumerated some of the few properties of matter,
which are manifested in exactly the same manner by all
substances, whatever be their differences of chemical or
physical constitution. But by far the greater number of

[1] Professor Lovering has pointed out how obscure and uncertain
the ideas of scientific men about this ether are, in his interesting
Presidential Address before the American Association at Hartford,
1874. *Silliman's Journal*, October 1874, p. 297. *Philosophical
Magazine*, vol. xlviii. p. 493.

qualities vary in degree; substances are more or less dense, more or less transparent, more or less compressible, more or less magnetic, and so on. One common result of the progress of science is to show that qualities supposed to be entirely absent from many substances are present only in so low a degree of intensity that the means of detection were insufficient. Newton believed that most bodies were quite unaffected by the magnet; Faraday and Tyndall have rendered it very doubtful whether any substance whatever is wholly devoid of magnetism, including under that term diamagnetism. We are rapidly learning to believe that there are no substances absolutely opaque, or non-conducting, non-electric, non-elastic, non-viscous, non-compressible, insoluble, infusible, or non-volatile. All tends to become a matter of degree, or sometimes of direction. There may be some substances oppositely affected to others, as ferro-magnetic substances are oppositely affected to diamagnetics, or as substances which contract by heat are opposed to those which expand; but the tendency is certainly for every affection of one kind of matter to be represented by something similar in other kinds. On this account one of Newton's rules of philosophising seems to lose all validity; he said, "Those qualities of bodies which are not capable of being heightened, and remitted, and which are found in all bodies on which experiment can be made, must be considered as universal qualities of all bodies." As far as I can see, the contrary is more probable, namely, that qualities variable in degree will be found in every substance in a greater or less degree.

It is remarkable that Newton whose method of investigation was logically perfect, seemed incapable of generalising and describing his own procedure. His celebrated "Rules of Reasoning in Philosophy," described at the commencement of the third book of the *Principia*, are of questionable truth, and still more questionable value.

Extreme Instances of Properties.

Although substances usually differ only in degree, great interest may attach to particular substances which manifest a property in a conspicuous and intense manner. Every branch of physical science has usually been developed from the attention forcibly drawn to some singular substance. Just as the loadstone disclosed magnetism and amber frictional electricity, so did Iceland spar show the existence of double refraction, and sulphate of quinine the phenomenon of fluorescence. When one such startling instance has drawn the attention of the scientific world, numerous less remarkable cases of the phenomenon will be detected, and it will probably prove that the property in question is actually universal to all matter. Nevertheless, the extreme instances retain their interest, partly in a historical point of view, partly because they furnish the most convenient substances for experiment.

Francis Bacon was fully aware of the value of such examples, which he called *Ostensive Instances* or Light-giving, Free and Predominant Instances. " They are those," he says,[1] " which show the nature under investigation naked, in an exalted condition, or in the highest degree of power; freed from impediments, or at least by its strength predominating over and suppressing them." He mentions quicksilver as an ostensive instance of weight or density, thinking it not much less dense than gold, and more remarkable than gold as joining density to liquidity. The magnet is mentioned as an ostensive instance of attraction. It would not be easy to distinguish clearly between these ostensive instances and those which he calls *Instantiae Monodicae,* or *Irregulares,* or *Heteroclitae,* under which he places whatever is extravagant in its properties or magnitude, or exhibits least similarity to other things, such as the sun and moon among the heavenly bodies, the elephant among animals, the letter *s* among letters, or the magnet among stones.[2]

In optical science great use has been made of the high dispersive power of the transparent compounds of lead, that is, the power of giving a long spectrum (p. 432). Dollond, having noticed this peculiar dispersive power in lenses made of flint glass, employed them to produce an achromatic arrangement. The element strontium presents a contrast to lead in this respect, being characterised by a remarkably low dispersive power; but I am not aware that this property has yet been turned to account.

[1] *Novum Organum,* bk. ii. Aphorisms, 24, 25.   [2] Ibid. Aph. 28.

Compounds of lead have both a high dispersive and
a high refractive index, and in the latter respect they
proved very useful to Faraday. Having spent much
labour in preparing various kinds of optical glass, Faraday happened to form a compound of lead, silica, and
boracic acid, now known as *heavy glass*, which possessed
an intensely high refracting power. Many years afterwards in attempting to discover the action of magnetism
upon light he failed to detect any effect, as has been
already mentioned, (p. 588), until he happened to test a
piece of the heavy glass. The peculiar refractive power of
this medium caused the magnetic strain to be apparent,
and the rotation of the plane of polarisation was discovered.

In almost every part of physical science there is some
substance of powers pre-eminent for the special purpose to
which it is put. Rock-salt is invaluable for its extreme
diathermancy or transparency to the least refrangible rays
of the spectrum. Quartz is equally valuable for its transparency, as regards the ultra-violet or most refrangible rays.
Diamond is the most highly refracting substance which is
at the same time transparent; were it more abundant and
easily worked it would be of great optical importance.
Cinnabar is distinguished by possessing a power of rotating
the plane of polarisation of light, from 15 to 17 times as
much as quartz. In electric experiments copper is employed for its high conducting powers and exceedingly low
magnetic properties; iron is of course indispensable for its
enormous magnetic powers; while bismuth holds a like
place as regards its diamagnetic powers, and was of much
importance in Tyndall's decisive researches upon the polar
character of the diamagnetic force.[1] In regard to
magne-crystallic action the mineral cyanite is highly
remarkable, being so powerfully affected by the earth's
magnetism, that, when delicately suspended, it assumes a
constant position with regard to the magnetic meridian,
and may almost be used like the compass needle. Sodium
is distinguished by its unique light-giving powers, which
are so extraordinary that probably one half of the whole
number of stars in the heavens have a yellow tinge in
consequence.

[1] *Philosophical Transactions* (1856) vol. cxlvi. p. 246.

It is remarkable that water, though the most common of all fluids, is distinguished in almost every respect by extreme qualities. Of all known substances water has the highest specific heat, being thus peculiarly fitted for the purpose of warming and cooling, to which it is often put. It rises by capillary attraction to a height more than twice that of any other liquid. In the state of ice it is nearly twice as dilatable by heat as any other known solid substance.[1] In proportion to its density it has a far higher surface tension than any other substance, being surpassed in absolute tension only by mercury; and it would not be difficult to extend considerably the list of its remarkable and useful properties.

Under extreme instances we may include cases of remarkably low powers or qualities. Such cases seem to correspond to what Bacon calls *Clandestine Instances*, which exhibit a given nature in the least intensity, and as it were in a rudimentary state.[2] They may often be important, he thinks, as allowing the detection of the cause of the property by difference. I may add that in some cases they may be of use in experiments. Thus hydrogen is the least dense of all known substances, and has the least atomic weight. Liquefied nitrous oxide has the lowest refractive index of all known fluids.[3] The compounds of strontium have the lowest dispersive power. It is obvious that a property of very low degree may prove as curious and valuable a phenomenon as a property of very high degree.

The Detection of Continuity.

We should bear in mind that phenomena which are in reality of a closely similar or even identical nature, may present to the senses very different appearances. Without a careful analysis of the changes which take place, we may often be in danger of widely separating facts and processes, which are actually instances of the same law. Extreme difference of degree or magnitude is a frequent cause of

[1] *Philosophical Magazine*, 4th Series, January 1870, vol. xxxix. p. 2.
[2] *Novum Organum*, bk. ii. Aphorism 25.
[3] Faraday's *Experimental Researches in Chemistry and Physics*, p. 93.

error.   It is truly difficult at the first moment to recognise
any similarity between the gradual rusting of a piece of
iron, and the rapid combustion of a heap of straw.   Yet
Lavoisier's chemical theory was founded upon the similarity
of the oxydising process in one case and the other.   We
have only to divide the iron into excessively small particles
to discover that it is really the more combustible of the
two, and that it actually takes fire spontaneously and burns
like tinder.   It is the excessive slowness of the process in
the case of a massive piece of iron which disguises its real
character.

If Xenophon reports truly, Socrates was misled by not
making sufficient allowance for extreme differences of degree and quantity.   Anaxagoras held that the sun is a fire,
but Socrates rejected this opinion, on the ground that we
can look at a fire, but not at the sun, and that plants grow
by sunshine while they are killed by fire.   He also pointed
out that a stone heated in a fire is not luminous, and soon
cools, whereas the sun ever remains equally luminous and
hot.[1]   All such mistakes evidently arise from not perceiving that difference of quantity may be so extreme as to
assume the appearance of difference of quality.   It is the
least creditable thing we know of Socrates, that after pointing out these supposed mistakes of earlier philosophers, he
advised his followers not to study astronomy.

Masses of matter of very different size may be expected
to exhibit apparent differences of conduct, arising from the
various intensity of the forces brought into play.   Many
persons have thought it requisite to imagine occult forces
producing the suspension of the clouds, and there have even
been absurd theories representing cloud particles as minute
water-balloons buoyed up by the warm air within them.
But we have only to take proper account of the enormous
comparative resistance which the air opposes to the fall of
minute particles, to see that all cloud particles are probably
constantly falling through the air, but so slowly that there
is no apparent effect.   Mineral matter again is always regarded as inert and incapable of spontaneous movement.
We are struck by astonishment on observing in a powerful
microscope, that every kind of solid matter suspended in

[1] *Memorabilia*, iv. 7.

extremely minute particles in pure water, acquires an oscillatory movement, often so marked as to resemble dancing or skipping. I conceive that this movement is due to the comparatively vast intensity of chemical action when exerted upon minute particles, the effect being 5,000 or 10,000 greater in proportion to the mass than in fragments of an inch diameter (p. 406).

Much that was formerly obscure in the science of electricity arose from the extreme differences of intensity and quantity in which this form of energy manifests itself. Between the brilliant explosive discharge of a thunder-cloud and the gentle continuous current produced by two pieces of metal and some dilute acid, there is no apparent analogy whatever. It was therefore a work of great importance when Faraday demonstrated the identity of the forces in action, showing that common frictional electricity would decompose water like that from the voltaic battery. The relation of the phenomena became plain when he succeeded in showing that it would require 800,000 discharges of his large Leyden battery to decompose one single grain of water. Lightning was now seen to be electricity of excessively high tension, but extremely small quantity, the difference being somewhat analogous to that between the force of one million gallons of water falling through one foot, and one gallon of water falling through one million feet. Faraday estimated that one grain of water acting on four grains of zinc, would yield electricity enough for a great thunderstorm.

It was long believed that electrical conductors and insulators belonged to two opposed classes of substances. Between the inconceivable rapidity with which the current passes through pure copper wire, and the apparently complete manner in which it is stopped by a thin partition of gutta-percha or gum-lac, there seemed to be no resemblance. Faraday again laboured successfully to show that these were but the extreme cases of a chain of substances varying in all degrees in their powers of conduction. Even the best conductors, such as pure copper or silver, offer resistance to the electric current. The other metals have considerably higher powers of resistance, and we pass gradually down through oxides and sulphides. The best insulators, on the other hand, allow of an atomic induction

which is the necessary antecedent of conduction. Hence
Faraday inferred that whether we can measure the effect or
not, all substances discharge electricity more or less.[1] One
consequence of this doctrine must be, that every discharge
of electricity produces an induced current. In the case of
the common galvanic current we can readily detect the induced current in any parallel wire or other neighbouring
conductor, and can separate the opposite currents which
arise at the moments when the original current begins and
ends. But a discharge of high tension electricity like
lightning, though it certainly occupies time and has a
beginning and an end, yet lasts so minute a fraction of a
second, that it would be hopeless to attempt to detect and
separate the two opposite induced currents, which are
nearly simultaneous and exactly neutralise each other.
Thus an apparent failure of analogy is explained away, and
we are furnished with another instance of a phenomenon
incapable of observation and yet theoretically known to
exist.[2]

Perhaps the most extraordinary case of the detection of
unsuspected continuity is found in the discovery of Cagniard de la Tour and Professor Andrews, that the liquid
and gaseous conditions of matter are only remote points in
a continuous course of change. Nothing is at first sight
more apparently distinct than the physical condition of
water and aqueous vapour. At the boiling-point there is
an entire breach of continuity, and the gas produced is subject to laws incomparably more simple than the liquid from
which it arose. But Cagniard de la Tour showed that if
we maintain a liquid under sufficient pressure its boiling
point may be indefinitely raised, and yet the liquid will
ultimately assume the gaseous condition with but a small
increase of volume. Professor Andrews, recently following
out this course of inquiry, has shown that liquid carbonic
acid may, at a particular temperature ($30°.92$ C.), and
under the pressure of 74 atmospheres, be at the same time
in a state indistinguishable from that of liquid and gas.
At higher pressures carbonic acid may be made to pass
from a palpably liquid state to a truly gaseous state without

[1] *Experimental Researches in Electricity*, Series xii. vol. i. p. 420.
[2] *Life of Faraday*, vol. ii. p. 7.

any abrupt change whatever. As the pressure is greater the abruptness of the change from liquid to gas gradually decreases, and finally vanishes. Similar phenomena or an approximation to them have been observed in other liquids, and there is little doubt that we may make a wide generalisation, and assert that, under adequate pressure, every liquid might be made to pass into a gas without breach of continuity.[1] The liquid state, moreover, is considered by Professor Andrews to be but an intermediate step between the solid and gaseous conditions. There are various indications that the process of melting is not perfectly abrupt ; and could experiments be made under adequate pressures, it is believed that every solid could be made to pass by insensible degrees into the state of liquid, and subsequently into that of gas.

These discoveries appear to open the way to most important and fundamental generalisations, but it is probable that in many other cases phenomena now regarded as discrete may be shown to be different degrees of the same process. Graham was of opinion that chemical affinity differs but in degree from the ordinary attraction which holds different particles of a body together. He found that sulphuric acid continued to evolve heat when mixed even with the fiftieth equivalent of water, so that there seemed to be no distinct limit to chemical affinity. He concludes, "There is reason to believe that chemical affinity passes in its lowest degree into the attraction of aggregation."[2]

The atomic theory is well established, but its limits are not marked out. As Grove points out, we may by selecting sufficiently high multipliers express any combination or mixture of elements in terms of their equivalent weights.[3] Sir W. Thomson has suggested that the power which vegetable fibre, oatmeal, and other substances possess of attracting and condensing aqueous vapour is probably continuous, or, in fact, identical with capillary attraction, which is capable of interfering with the pressure of aqueous vapour and aiding its condensation.[4] There are many cases of so-called catalytic or surface action, such as the extra-

[1] *Nature*, vol. ii. p. 278.
[2] *Journal of the Chemical Society*, vol. viii. p. 51.
[3] *Correlation of Physical Forces*, 3rd edit. p. 184.
[4] *Philosophical Magazine*, 4th Series, vol. xlii. p. 451.

ordinary power of animal charcoal for attracting organic matter, or of spongy platinum for condensing hydrogen, which can only be considered as exalted cases of a more general power of attraction. The number of substances which are decomposed by light in a striking manner is very limited; but many other substances, such as vegetable colours, are affected by long exposure; on the principle of continuity we might expect to find that all kinds of matter are more or less susceptible of change by the incidence of light rays.[1] It is the opinion of Grove that wherever an electric current passes there is a tendency to decomposition, a strain on the molecules, which when sufficiently intense leads to disruption. Even a metallic conducting wire may be regarded as tending to decomposition. Davy was probably correct in describing electricity as chemical affinity acting on masses, or rather, as Grove suggests, creating a disturbance through a chain of particles.[2] Laplace went so far as to suggest that all chemical phenomena may be results of the Newtonian law of attraction, applied to atoms of various mass and position; but the time is probably far distant when the progress of molecular philosophy and of mathematical methods will enable such a generalisation to be verified or refuted.

The Law of Continuity.

Under the title of the Law of Continuity we may place many applications of the general principle of reasoning, that what is true of one case will be true of similar cases, and probably true of what are probably similar. Whenever we find that a law or similarity is rigorously fulfilled up to a certain point in time or space, we expect with a high degree of probability that it will continue to be fulfilled at least a little further. If we see part only of a circle, we naturally expect that the circular form will be continued in the part hidden from us. If a body has moved uniformly over a certain space, we expect that it will continue to move uniformly. The ground of such inferences is doubtless identical with that of other inductive inferences.

---

[1] Grove, *Correlation of Physical Forces*, 3rd edit. p. 118.
[2] Ibid. pp. 166, 199, &c.

In continuous motion every infinitely small space passed over constitutes a separate constituent fact, and had we perfect powers of observation the smallest finite motion would include an infinity of information, which, by the principles of the inverse method of probabilities, would enable us to infer with certainty to the next infinitely small portion of the path. But when we attempt to infer from one finite portion of a path to another finite portion, inference will be only more or less probable, according to the comparative lengths of the portions and the accuracy of observation; the longer our experience is, the more probable our inference will be; the greater the length of time or space over which the inference extends, the less probable.

This principle of continuity presents itself in nature in a great variety of forms and cases. It is familiarly expressed in the dictum *Natura non agit per saltum.* As Graham expressed the maxim, there are in nature no abrupt transitions, and the distinctions of class are never absolute.[1] There is always some notice—some forewarning of every phenomenon, and every change begins by insensible degrees, could we observe it with perfect accuracy. The cannon ball, indeed, is forced from the cannon in an inappreciable portion of time; the trigger is pulled, the fuze fired, the powder inflamed, the ball expelled, all simultaneously to our senses. But there is no doubt that time is occupied by every part of the process, and that the ball begins to move at first with infinite slowness. Captain Noble is able to measure by his chronoscope the progress of the shot in a 300-pounder gun, and finds that the whole motion within the barrel takes place in something less than one 200th part of a second. It is certain that no finite force can produce motion, except in a finite space of time. The amount of momentum communicated to a body is proportional to the accelerating force multiplied by the time during which it acts uniformly. Thus a slight force produces a great velocity only by long-continued action. In a powerful shock, like that of a railway collision, the stroke of a hammer on an anvil, or the discharge of a gun, the

[1] *Philosophical Transactions,* 1861. *Chemical and Physical Researches,* p. 598.

time is very short, and therefore the accelerating forces
brought into play are exceedingly great, but never infinite.
In the case of a large gun the powder in exploding is said
to exert for a moment a force equivalent to at least 2,800,000
horses.

Our belief in some of the fundamental laws of nature
rests upon the principle of continuity. Galileo is held to
be the first philosopher who consciously employed this
principle in his arguments concerning the nature of motion,
and it is certain that we can never by mere experience
assure ourselves of the truth even of the first law of motion.
A material particle, we are told, *when not acted on by
extraneous forces will continue in the same state of rest or
motion.* This may be true, but as we can find no body
which is free from the action of extraneous causes, how are
we to prove it? Only by observing that the less the
amount of those forces the more nearly is the law found to
be true. A ball rolled along rough ground is soon stopped;
along a smooth pavement it continues longer in movement.
A delicately suspended pendulum is almost free from
friction against its supports, but it is gradually stopped by
the resistance of the air; place it in the vacuous receiver of
an air-pump and we find the motion much prolonged. A
large planet like Jupiter experiences almost infinitely less
friction, in comparison to its vast momentum, than we can
produce experimentally, and we find in such a case that
there is not the least evidence of the falsity of the law.
Experience, then, informs us that we may approximate
indefinitely to a uniform motion by sufficiently decreasing
the disturbing forces. It is an act of inference which
enables us to travel on beyond experience, and assert that,
in the total absence of any extraneous force, motion would
be absolutely uniform. The state of rest, again, is a
limiting case in which motion is infinitely small or zero,
to which we may attain, on the principle of continuity, by
successively considering cases of slower and slower motion.
There are many classes of phenomena, in which, by
gradually passing from the apparent to the obscure, we can
assure ourselves of the nature of phenomena which would
otherwise be a matter of great doubt. Thus we can sufficiently prove in the manner of Galileo, that a musical
sound consists of rapid uniform pulses, by causing strokes

to be made at intervals which we gradually diminish until the separate strokes coalesce into a uniform hum or note. With great advantage we approach, as Tyndall says, the sonorous through the grossly mechanical. In listening to a great organ we cannot fail to perceive that the longest pipes, or their partial tones, produce a tremor and fluttering of the building. At the other extremity of the scale, there is no fixed limit to the acuteness of sounds which we can hear; some individuals can hear sounds too shrill for other ears, and as there is nothing in the nature of the atmosphere to prevent the existence of undulations far more rapid than any of which we are conscious, we may infer, by the principle of continuity, that such undulations probably exist.

There are many habitual actions which we perform we know not how. So rapidly are acts of minds accomplished that analysis seems impossible. We can only investigate them when in process of formation, observing that the best formed habit is slowly and continuously acquired, and it is in the early stages that we can perceive the rationale of the process.

Let it be observed that this principle of continuity must be held of much weight only in exact physical laws, those which doubtless repose ultimately upon the simple laws of motion. If we fearlessly apply the principle to all kinds of phenomena, we may often be right in our inferences, but also often wrong. Thus, before the development of spectrum analysis, astronomers had observed that the more they increased the powers of their telescopes the more nebulæ they could resolve into distinct stars. This result had been so often found true that they almost irresistibly assumed that all nebulæ would be ultimately resolved by telescopes of sufficient power; yet Huggins has in recent years proved by the spectroscope, that certain nebulæ are actually gaseous, and in a truly nebulous state.

The principle of continuity must have been continually employed in the inquiries of Galileo, Newton, and other experimental philosophers, but it appears to have been distinctly formulated for the first time by Leibnitz. He at least claims to have first spoken of "the law of continuity" in a letter to Bayle, printed in the *Nouvelles de la Répub-lique des Lettres*, an extract from which is given in Erdmann's edition of Leibnitz's works, p. 104, under the title "Sur un Principe Général utile à l'explication des Lois de la Nature."[1] It has indeed been asserted that the doctrine of the *latens processus* of Francis Bacon involves the principle of continuity,[2] but I think that this doctrine, like that of the *natures* of substances, is merely a vague statement of the principle of causation.

Failure of the Law of Continuity.

There are certain cautions which must be given as to the application of the principle of continuity. In the first place, where this principle really holds true, it may seem to fail owing to our imperfect means of observation. Though a physical law may not admit of perfectly abrupt change, there is no limit to the approach which it may make to abruptness. When we warm a piece of very cold ice, the absorption of heat, the temperature, and the dilatation of the ice vary according to apparently simple laws until we come to the zero of the Centigrade scale. Everything is then changed; an enormous absorption of heat takes place without any rise of temperature, and the volume of the ice decreases as it changes into water. Unless carefully investigated, this change appears to be perfectly abrupt; but accurate observation seems to show that there is a certain forewarning; the ice does not turn into water all at once, but through a small fraction of a degree the change is gradual. All the phenomena concerned, if measured very exactly, would be represented not by angular lines, but continuous curves, undergoing rapid flexures; and we may probably assert with safety that between whatever points of temperature we examine ice, there would be found some indication, though almost infinitesimally small, of the apparently abrupt change which was to occur at a higher temperature. It might also be pointed out that the important and apparently simple physical laws, such as those of Boyle and Marriotte, Dalton and Gay-Lussac, &c., are only approximately true, and the divergences from the simple laws are forewarnings of abrupt changes, which would otherwise break the law of continuity.

[1] *Life of Sir W. Hamilton*, p. 439.
[2] Powell's *History of Natural Philosophy*, p. 201. *Novum Organum*, bk. ii. Aphorisms 5—7.

Secondly, it must be remembered that mathematical laws of some complexity will probably present singular cases or negative results, which may bear the appearance of discontinuity, as when the law of refraction suddenly yields us with perfect abruptness the phenomenon of total internal reflection. In the undulatory theory, however, there is no real change of law between refraction and reflection. Faraday in the earlier part of his career found so many substances possessing magnetic power, that he ventured on a great generalisation, and asserted that all bodies shared in the magnetic property of iron. His mistake, as he afterwards discovered, consisted in overlooking the fact that though magnetic in a certain sense, some substances have negative magnetism, and are repelled instead of being attracted by the magnet.

Thirdly, where we might expect to find a uniform mathematical law prevailing, the law may undergo abrupt change at singular points, and actual discontinuity may arise. We may sometimes be in danger of treating under one law phenomena which really belong to different laws. For instance, a spherical shell of uniform matter attracts an external particle of matter with a force varying inversely as the square of the distance from the centre of the sphere. But this law only holds true so long as the particle is external to the shell. Within the shell the law is wholly different, and the aggregate gravity of the sphere becomes zero, the force in every direction being neutralised by an exactly equal opposite force. If an infinitely small particle be in the superficies of a sphere, the law is again different, and the attractive power of the shell is half what it would be with regard to particles infinitely close to the surface of the shell. Thus in approaching the centre of a shell from a distance, the force of gravity shows double discontinuity in passing through the shell.[1]

It may admit of question, too, whether discontinuity is really unknown in nature. We perpetually do meet with events which are real breaks upon the previous law, though the discontinuity may be a sign that some independent cause has come into operation. If the ordinary course of

---

[1] Thomson and Tait, *Treatise on Natural Philosophy*, vol. i. pp. 346—351.

the tides is interrupted by an enormous irregular wave, we attribute it to an earthquake, or some gigantic natural disturbance. If a meteoric stone falls upon a person and kills him, it is clearly a discontinuity in his life, of which he could have had no anticipation. A sudden sound may pass through the air neither preceded nor followed by any continuous effect. Although, then, we may regard the Law of Continuity as a principle of nature holding rigorously true in many of the relations of natural forces, it seems to be a matter of difficulty to assign the limits within which the law is verified. Much caution is required in its application.

Negative Arguments on the Principle of Continuity.

Upon the principle of continuity we may sometimes found arguments of great force which prove an hypothesis to be impossible, because it would involve a continual repetition of a process *ad infinitum*, or else a purely arbitrary breach at some point. Bonnet's famous theory of reproduction represented every living creature as containing germs which were perfect representatives of the next generation, so that on the same principle they necessarily included germs of the next generation, and so on indefinitely. The theory was sufficiently refuted when once clearly stated, as in the following poem called the Universe,[1] by Henry Baker:—

> " Each seed includes a plant : that plant, again,
>   Has other seeds, which other plants contain :
>   Those other plants have all their seeds, and those
>   More plants again, successively inclose.

> " Thus, ev'ry single berry that we find,
>   Has, really, in itself whole forests of its kind,
>   Empire and wealth one acorn may dispense,
>   By fleets to sail a thousand ages hence."

The general principle of inference, that what we know of one case must be true of similar cases, so far as they are similar, prevents our asserting anything which we cannot apply time after time under the same circumstances.

---

[1] *Philosophical Transactions* (1740), vol. xli. p. 454.

On this principle Stevinus beautifully demonstrated that weights resting on two inclined planes and balancing each other must be proportional to the lengths of the planes between their apex and a horizontal plane. He imagined a uniform endless chain to be hung over the planes, and to hang below in a symmetrical festoon. If the chain were ever to move by gravity, there would be the same reason for its moving on for ever, and thus producing a perpetual motion. As this is absurd, the portions of the chain lying on the planes, and equal in length to the planes, must balance each other. On similar grounds we may disprove the existence of any *self-moving machine;* for if it could once alter its own state of motion or rest, in however small a degree, there is no reason why it should not do the like time after time *ad infinitum.* Newton's proof of his third law of motion, in the case of gravity, is of this character. For he remarks that if two gravitating bodies do not exert exactly equal forces in opposite directions, the one exerting the strongest pull will carry both away, and the two bodies will move off into space together with velocity increasing *ad infinitum.* But though the argument might seem sufficiently convincing, Newton in his characteristic way made an experiment with a loadstone and iron floated upon the surface of water.[1] In recent years the very foundation of the principle of conservation of energy has been placed on the assumption that it is impossible by any combination of natural bodies to produce force continually from nothing.[2] The principle admits of application in various subtle forms.

Lucretius attempted to prove, by a most ingenious argument of this kind, that matter must be indestructible. For if a finite quantity, however small, were to fall out of existence in any finite time, an equal quantity might be supposed to lapse in every equal interval of time, so that in the infinity of past time the universe must have ceased to exist.[3] But the argument, however ingenious, seems to fail at several points. If past time be infinite, why may not matter have been created infinite also? It would be most reasonable, again, to suppose the matter

[1] *Principia,* bk. i. Law iii. Corollary 6.
[2] Helmholtz, Taylor's *Scientific Memoirs* (1853), vol. vi. p. 118.
[3] *Lucretius,* bk. i. lines 232—264.

destroyed in any time to be proportional to the matter then remaining, and not to the original quantity ; under this hypothesis even a finite quantity of original matter could never wholly disappear from the universe. For like reasons we cannot hold that the doctrine of the conservation of energy is really proved, or can ever be proved to be absolutely true, however probable it may be regarded.

Tendency to Hasty Generalisation.

In spite of all the powers and advantages of generalisation, men require no incitement to generalise ; they are too apt to draw hasty and ill-considered inferences. As Francis Bacon said, our intellects want not wings, but rather weights of lead to moderate their course.[1] The process is inevitable to the human mind ; it begins with childhood and lasts through the second childhood. The child that has once been hurt fears the like result on all similar occasions, and can with difficulty be made to distinguish between case and case. It is caution and discrimination in the adoption of conclusions that we have chiefly to learn, and the whole experience of life is one continued lesson to this effect. Baden Powell has excellently described this strong natural propensity to hasty inference, and the fondness of the human mind for tracing resemblances real or fanciful. " Our first inductions," he says,[2] "are always imperfect and inconclusive ; we advance towards real evidence by successive approximations ; and accordingly we find false generalisation the besetting error of most first attempts at scientific research. The faculty to generalise accurately and philosophically requires large caution and long training, and is not fully attained, especially in reference to more general views, even by some who may properly claim the title of very accurate scientific observers in a more limited field. It is an intellectual habit which acquires immense and accumulating force from the contemplation of wider analogies."

Hasty and superficial generalisations have always been the bane of science, and there would be no difficulty in

---

[1] *Novum Organum,* bk. 1 Aphorism 104.
[2] *The Unity of Worlds and of Nature,* 2nd edit. p. 116.

finding endless illustrations. Between things which are the same in number there is a certain resemblance, namely in number ; but in the infancy of science men could not be persuaded that there was not a deeper resemblance implied in that of number. Pythagoras was not the inventor of a mystical science of number. In the ancient Oriental religions the seven metals were connected with the seven planets, and in the seven days of the week we still have, and probably always shall have, a relic of the septiform system ascribed by Dio Cassius to the ancient Egyptians. The disciples of Pythagoras carried the doctrine of the number seven into great detail. Seven days are mentioned in Genesis ; infants acquire their teeth at the end of seven months ; they change them at the end of seven years ; seven feet was the limit of man's height ; every seventh year was a climacteric or critical year, at which a change of disposition took place. Then again there were the seven sages of Greece, the seven wonders of the world, the seven rites of the Grecian games, the seven gates of Thebes, and the seven generals destined to conquer that city.

In natural science there were not only the seven planets, and the seven metals, but also the seven primitive colours, and the seven tones of music. So deep a hold did this doctrine take that we still have its results in many customs, not only in the seven days of the week, but the seven years' apprenticeship, puberty at fourteen years, the second climacteric, and legal majority at twenty-one years, the third climacteric. The idea was reproduced in the seven sacraments of the Roman Catholic Church, and the seven year periods of Comte's grotesque system of domestic worship. Even in scientific matters the loftiest intellects have occasionally yielded, as when Newton was misled by the analogy between the seven tones of music and the seven colours of his spectrum. Other numerical analogies, though rejected by Galileo, held Kepler in thraldom ; no small part of Kepler's labours during seventeen years was spent upon numerical and geometrical analogies of the most baseless character ; and he gravely held that there could not be more than six planets, because there were not more than five regular solids. Even the genius of Huyghens did not prevent him from inferring that but one satellite could belong to Saturn, because, with those of Jupiter and the Earth, it completed the perfect number of six. A whole series of other superstitions and fallacies attach to the numbers six and nine.

It is by false generalisation, again, that the laws of nature have been supposed to possess that perfection which we attribute to simple forms and relations. The heavenly bodies, it was held, must move in circles, for the circle was the perfect figure. Newton seemed to adopt the questionable axiom that nature always proceeds in the simplest way; in stating his first rule of philosophising, he adds : [1] " To this purpose the philosophers say, that nature does nothing in vain, when less will serve; for nature is pleased with simplicity, and affects not the pomp of superfluous causes." Keill lays down [2] as an axiom that " The causes of natural things are such, as are the most simple, and are sufficient to explain the phenomena : for nature always proceeds in the simplest and most expeditious method; because by this manner of operating the Divine Wisdom displays itself the more." If this axiom had any clear grounds of truth, it would not apply to proximate laws ; for even when the ultimate law is simple the results may be infinitely diverse, as in the various elliptic, hyperbolic, parabolic, or circular orbits of the heavenly bodies. Simplicity is naturally agreeable to a mind of limited powers, but to an infinite mind all things are simple.

Every great advance in science consists in a great generalisation, pointing out deep and subtle resemblances. The Copernican system was a generalisation, in that it classed the earth among the planets ; it was, as Bishop Wilkins expressed it, " the discovery of a new planet," but it was opposed by a more shallow generalisation. Those who argued from the condition of things upon the earth's surface, thought that every object must be attached to and rest upon something else. Shall the earth, they said, alone be free ? Accustomed to certain special results of gravity they could not conceive its action under widely different circumstances.[3] No hasty thinker could seize the deep analogy pointed out by Horrocks between a pen-

[1] *Principia*, bk. iii, *ad initium*.
[2] Keill, *Introduction to Natural Philosophy*, p. 89.
[3] Jeremie Horroccii *Opera Posthuma* (1673), pp. 26, 27

dulum and a planet, true in substance though mistaken in some details. All the advances of modern science rise from the conception of Galileo, that in the heavenly bodies, however apparently different their condition, we shall ultimately recognise the same fundamental principles of mechanical science which are true on earth.

Generalisation is the great prerogative of the intellect, but it is a power only to be exercised safely with much caution and after long training. Every mind must generalise, but there are the widest differences in the depth of the resemblances discovered and the care with which the discovery is verified. There seems to be an innate power of insight which a few men have possessed pre-eminently, and which enabled them, with no exemption indeed from labour or temporary error, to discover the one in the many. Minds of excessive acuteness may exist, which have yet only the powers of minute discrimination, and of storing up, in the treasure-house of memory, vast accumulations of words and incidents. But the power of discovery belongs to a more restricted class of minds. Laplace said that, of all inventors who had contributed the most to the advancement of human knowledge, Newton and Lagrange appeared to possess in the highest degree the happy tact of distinguishing general principles among a multitude of objects enveloping them, and this tact he conceived to be the true characteristic of scientific genius.[1]

[1] Young's *Works.* vol. ii. p. 564

CHAPTER XXVIII.

As we have seen in the previous chapter, generalisation passes insensibly into reasoning by analogy, and the difference is one of degree. We are said to generalise when we view many objects as agreeing in a few properties, so that the resemblance is extensive rather than deep. When we have only a few objects of thought, but are able to discover many points of resemblance, we argue by analogy that the correspondence will be even deeper than appears. It may not be true that the words are always used in such distinct senses, and there is great vagueness in the employment of these and many logical terms ; but if any clear discrimination can be drawn between generalisation and analogy, it is as indicated above.

It has been said, indeed, that analogy denotes not a resemblance between things, but between the relations of things. A pilot is a very different man from a prime minister, but he bears the same relation to a ship that the minister does to the state, so that we may analogically describe the prime minister as the pilot of the state. A man differs still more from a horse, nevertheless four men bear to three men the same relation as four horses bear to three horses. There is a real analogy between the tones of the Monochord, the Sages of Greece, and the Gates of Thebes, but it does not extend beyond the fact that they were all seven in number. Between the most discrete notions, as, for instance, those of time and space, analogy may exist, arising from the fact that the mathematical conditions of the lapse of time and of motion along a line are similar. There is no identity of nature between a word and the thing it signifies ; the substance *iron* is a heavy solid, the word *iron* is either a momentary disturbance of the air, or a film of black pigment on white paper ; but there is analogy between words and their significates. The substance iron is to the substance iron-carbonate, as the name iron is to the name iron-carbonate, when these names are used according to their scientific definitions. The whole structure of language and the whole utility of signs, marks, symbols, pictures, and representations of various kinds, rest upon analogy. I may hope perhaps to enter more fully upon this important subject at some future time, and to attempt to show how the invention of signs enables us to express, guide, and register our thoughts. It will be sufficient to observe here that the use of words constantly involves analogies of a subtle kind ; we should often be at a loss how to describe a notion, were we not at liberty to employ in a metaphorical sense the name of anything sufficiently resembling it. There would be no expression for the sweetness of a melody, or the brilliancy of an harangue, unless it were furnished by the taste of honey and the brightness of a torch.

A cursory examination of the way in which we popularly use the word analogy, shows that it includes all degrees of resemblance or similarity. The analogy may consist only in similarity of number or ratio, or in like relations of time and space. It may also consist in simple resemblance between physical properties. We should not be using the word inconsistently with custom, if we said that there was an analogy between iron, nickel, and cobalt, manifested in the strength of their magnetic powers. There is a still more perfect analogy between iodine and chlorine ; not that every property of iodine is identical with the corresponding property of chlorine ; for then they would be one and the same kind of substance, and not two substances ; but every property of iodine resembles in all but degree some property of chlorine. For almost every substance in which iodine forms a component, a corresponding substance may be discovered containing chlorine, so that we may confidently infer from the compounds of the one to the compounds of the other substance. Potassium iodide crystallises in cubes ; therefore it is to be expected that potassium chloride will also crystallise in cubes. The science of chemistry as now developed rests almost entirely upon a careful and extensive comparison of the properties of substances, bringing deep-lying analogies to light. When any new substance is encountered, the chemist is guided in his treatment of it by the analogies which it seems to present with previously known substances.

In this chapter I cannot hope to illustrate the all-pervading influence of analogy in human thought and science. All science, it has been said, at the outset, arises from the discovery of identity, and analogy is but one name by which we denote the deeper-lying cases of resemblance. I shall only try to point out at present how analogy between apparently diverse classes of phenomena often serves as a guide in discovery. We thus commonly gain the first insight into the nature of an apparently unique object, and thus, in the progress of a science, we often discover that we are treating over again, in a new form, phenomena which were well known to us in another form.

Analogy as a Guide in Discovery.

There can be no doubt that discovery is most frequently accomplished by following up hints received from analogy, as Jeremy Bentham remarked.[1] Whenever a phenomenon is perceived, the first impulse of the mind is to connect it with the most nearly similar phenomenon. If we could ever meet a thing wholly *sui generis*, presenting no analogy to anything else, we should be incapable of investigating its nature, except by purely haphazard trial. The probability of success by such a process is so slight, that it is preferable to follow up the faintest clue. As I have pointed out already (p. 418), the possible experiments are almost infinite in number, and very numerous also are the hypotheses upon which we may proceed. Now it is self-evident that, however slightly superior the probability of success by one course of procedure may be over another, the most probable one should always be adopted first.

[1] *Essay on Logic, Works,* vol. viii. p. 276.

The chemist having discovered what he believes to be a new element, will have before him an infinite variety of modes of treating and investigating it. If in any of its qualities the substance displays a resemblance to an aklaline metal, for instance, he will naturally proceed to try whether it possesses other properties of the alkaline metals. Even the simplest phenomenon presents so many points for notice that we have a choice from among many hypotheses.

It would be difficult to find a more instructive instance of the way in which the mind is guided by analogy than in the description by Sir John Herschel of the course of thought by which he was led to anticipate in theory one of Faraday's greatest discoveries. Herschel noticed that a screw-like form, technically called helicoidal dissymmetry, was observed in three cases, namely, in electrical helices, plagihedral quartz crystals, and the rotation of the plane of polarisation of light. As he said,[1] " I reasoned thus : Here are three phenomena agreeing in a *very strange peculiarity*. Probably, this peculiarity is a connecting link, physically speaking, among them. Now, in the case of the crystals and the light, this probability has been turned into certainty by my own experiments. Therefore, induction led me to conclude that a similar connection exists, and must turn up, somehow or other, between the electric current and polarised light, and that the plane of polarisation would be deflected by magneto-electricity." By this course of analogical thought Herschel had actually been led to anticipate Faraday's great discovery of the influence of magnetic strain upon polarised light. He had tried in 1822-25 to discover the influence of electricity on light, by sending a ray of polarised light through a helix, or near a long wire conveying an electric current. Such a course of inquiry, followed up with the persistency of Faraday, and with his experimental resources, would doubtless have effected the discovery. Herschel also suggests that the plagihedral form of quartz crystals must be due to a screw-like strain during crystallisation ; but the notion remains unverified by experiment.

[1] *Life of Faraday*, by Bence Jones, vol. ii. p. 206.

Analogy in the Mathematical Sciences.

Whoever wishes to acquire a deep acquaintance with
Nature must observe that there are analogies which connect whole branches of science in a parallel manner,
and enable us to infer of one class of phenomena what
we know of another. It has thus happened on several
occasions that the discovery of an unsuspected analogy
between two branches of knowledge has been the starting-
point for a rapid course of discovery. The truths readily
observed in the one may be of a different character from
those which present themselves in the other. The analogy,
once pointed out, leads us to discover regions of one
science yet undeveloped, to which the key is furnished by
the corresponding truths in the other science. An interchange of aid most wonderful in its results may thus
take place, and at the same time the mind rises to a higher
generalisation, and a more comprehensive view of nature.

No two sciences might seem at first sight more different
in their subject matter than geometry and algebra. The
first deals with circles, squares, parallelograms, and other
forms in space ; the latter with mere symbols of number.
Prior to the time of Descartes, the sciences were developed
slowly and painfully in almost entire independence of each
other. The Greek philosophers indeed could not avoid
noticing occasional analogies, as when Plato in the Thæe-
tetus describes a square number as *equally equal,* and a
number produced by multiplying two unequal factors
as *oblong.* Euclid, in the 7th and 8th books of his Elements, continually uses expressions displaying a consciousness of the same analogies, as when he calls a number
of two factors a *plane number,* ἐπίπεδος ἀριθμός, and
distinguishes a square number of which the two factors are
equal as an equal-sided and plane number, ἰσόπλευρος
καὶ ἐπίπεδος ἀριθμός. He also calls the root of a cubic
number its side, πλευρά. In the Diophantine algebra
many problems of a geometrical character were solved by
algebraic or numerical processes ; but there was no general
system, so that the solutions were of an isolated character.
In general the ancients were far more advanced in geometric
than symbolic methods ; thus Euclid in his 4th book gives

the means of dividing a circle by purely geometric means into 2, 3, 4, 5, 6, 8, 10, 12, 15, 16, 20, 24, 30 parts, but he was totally unacquainted with the theory of the roots of unity exactly corresponding to this division of the circle.

During the middle ages, on the contrary, algebra advanced beyond geometry, and modes of solving equations were gradually discovered by those who had no notion that at every step they were implicitly solving geometric problems. It is true that Regiomontanus, Tartaglia, Bombelli, and possibly other early algebraists, solved isolated geometrical problems by the aid of algebra, but particular numbers were always used, and no consciousness of a general method was displayed. Vieta in some degree anticipated the final discovery, and occasionally represented the roots of an equation geometrically, but it was reserved for Descartes to show, in the most general manner, that every equation may be represented by a curve or figure in space, and that every bend, point, cusp, or other peculiarity in the curve indicates some peculiarity in the equation. It is impossible to describe in any adequate manner the importance of this discovery. The advantage was two-fold : algebra aided geometry, and geometry gave reciprocal aid to algebra. Curves such as the well-known sections of the cone were found to correspond to quadratic equations ; and it was impossible to manipulate the equations without discovering properties of those all-important curves. The way was thus opened for the algebraic treatment of motions and forces, without which Newton's *Principia* could never have been worked out. Newton indeed was possessed by a strong infatuation in favour of the ancient geometrical methods ; but it is well known that he employed symbolic methods to discover his theorems, and he now and then, by some accidental use of algebraic expression, confessed its greater power and generality.

Geometry, on the other hand, gave great assistance to algebra, by affording concrete representations of relations which would otherwise be too abstract for easy comprehension. A curve of no great complexity may give the whole history of the variations of value of a troublesome mathematical expression. As soon as we know, too, that every regular geometrical curve represents some algebraic

equation, we are presented by observation of mechanical
movements with abundant suggestions towards the discovery of mathematical problems. Every particle of a
carriage-wheel when moving on a level road is constantly
describing a cycloidal curve, the curious properties of
which exercised the ingenuity of all the most skilful
mathematicians of the seventeenth century, and led to
important advancements in algebraic power. It may be
held that the discovery of the Differential Calculus was
mainly due to geometrical analogy, because mathematicians,
in attempting to treat algebraically the tangent of a curve,
were obliged to entertain the notion of infinitely small
quantities.[1] There can be no doubt that Newton's
fluxional, that is, geometrical mode of stating the differential calculus, however much it subsequently retarded
its progress in England, facilitated its apprehension at first,
and I should think it almost certain that Newton discovered
the principles of the calculus geometrically.

We may accordingly look upon this discovery of
analogy, this happy alliance, as Bossut calls it,[2] between
geometry and algebra, as the chief source of discoveries
which have been made for three centuries past in mathematical methods. This is certainly the opinion of Lagrange, who says, " So long as algebra and geometry have
been separate, their progress was slow, and their employment limited ; but since these two sciences have been
united, they have lent each other mutual strength, and
have marched together with a rapid step towards perfection."

The advancement of mechanical science has also been
greatly aided by analogy. An abstract and intangible
existence like force demands much power of conception,
but it has a perfect concrete representative in a line, the
end of which may denote the point of application, and the
direction the line of action of the force, while the length
can be made arbitrarily to denote the amount of the force.
Nor does the analogy end here ; for the moment of the
force about any point, or its product into the perpendicular distance of its line of action from the point, is

[1] Lacroix, *Traité Elémentaire de Calcul Différentiel et de Calcul
Intégral,* 5me édit. p. 699.
[2] *Histoire des Mathématiques,* vol. i. p. 298.

found to be represented by an area, namely twice the area of the triangle contained between the point and the ends of the line representing the force. Of late years a great generalisation has been effected; the Double Algebra of De Morgan is true not only of space relations, but of forces, so that the triangle of forces is reduced to a case of pure geometrical addition. Nay, the triangle of lines, the triangle of velocities, the triangle of forces, the triangle of couples, and perhaps other cognate theorems, are reduced by analogy to one simple theorem, which amounts to this, that there are two ways of getting from one angular point of a triangle to another, which ways, though different in length, are identical in their final results.[1] In the system of quaternions of the late Sir W. R. Hamilton, these analogies are embodied and carried out in the most general manner, so that whatever problem involves the threefold dimensions of space, or relations analogous to those of space, is treated by a symbolic method of the most comprehensive simplicity.

It ought to be added that to the discovery of analogy between the forms of mathematical and logical expressions, we owe the greatest advance in logical science. Boole based his extension of logical processes upon the notion that logic is an algebra of two quantities o and I. His profound genius for symbolic investigation led him to perceive by analogy that there must exist a general system of logical deduction, of which the old logicians had seized only a few fragments. Mistaken as he was in placing algebra as a higher science than logic, no one can deny that the development of the more complex and dependent science had advanced far beyond that of the simpler science, and that Boole, in drawing attention to the connection, made one of the most important discoveries in the history of science. As Descartes had wedded algebra and geo-

---

[1] See Goodwin, *Cambridge Philosophical Transactions* (1845), vol. viii. p. 269. O'Brien, "On Symbolical Statics," *Philosophical Magazine*, 4th Series, vol. i. pp. 491, &c. See also Professor Clerk Maxwell's delightful *Manual of Elementary Science*, called *Matter and Motion*, published by the Society for Promoting Christian Knowledge. In this admirable little work some of the most advanced results of mechanical and physical science are explained according to the method of quaternions, but with hardly any use of algebraic symbols.

metry, so did Boole accomplish the marriage of logic and algebra.

Analogy in the Theory of Undulations.

There is no class of phenomena which more thoroughly illustrates alike the power and weakness of analogy than the waves which agitate every kind of medium. All waves, whatsoever be the matter through which they pass, obey the principles of rhythmical or harmonic motion, and the subject therefore presents a fine field for mathematical generalisation. Each kind of medium may allow of waves peculiar in their conditions, so that it is a beautiful exercise in analogical reasoning to decide how, in making inferences from one kind of medium to another, we must make allowance for difference of circumstances. The waves of the ocean are large and visible, and there are the yet greater tidal waves which extend around the globe. From such palpable cases of rhythmical movement we pass to waves of sound, varying in length from about 32 feet to a small fraction of an inch. We have but to imagine, if we can, the fortieth octave of the middle C of a piano, and we reach the undulations of yellow light, the ultra-violet being about the forty-first octave. Thus we pass from the palpable and evident to that which is obscure, if not incomprehensible. Yet the same phenomena of reflection, interference, and refraction, which we find in some kinds of waves, may be expected to occur, *mutatis mutandis*, in other kinds.

From the great to the small, from the evident to the obscure, is not only the natural order of inference, but it is the historical order of discovery. The physical science of the Greek philosophers must have remained incomplete, and their theories groundless, because they did not understand the nature of undulations. Their systems were based upon the notion of movement of translation from place to place. Modern science tends to the opposite notion that all motion is alternating or rhythmical, energy flowing onwards but matter remaining comparatively fixed in position. Diogenes Laertius indeed correctly compared the propagation of sound with the spreading of waves on the surface of water when disturbed by a stone, and Vitruvius dis-

played a more complete comprehension of the same analogy.   It remained for Newton to create the theory of undulatory motion in showing by mathematical deductive
reasoning that the particles of an elastic fluid by vibrating
backwards and forwards, might carry a pulse or wave moving
from the source of disturbance, while the disturbed particles
return to their place of rest.   He was even able to make a
first approximation by theoretical calculation to the velocity
of sound-waves in the atmosphere.   His theory of sound
formed a hardly less important epoch in science than his far
more celebrated theory of gravitation.   It opened the way to
all the subsequent applications of mechanical principles to
the insensible motion of molecules.   He seems to have been,
too, upon the brink of another application of the same
principles which would have advanced science by a century
of progress, and made him the undisputed founder of all the
theories of matter.   He expressed opinions at various times
that light might be due to undulatory movements of a
medium occupying space, and in one intensely interesting
sentence remarks[1] that colours are probably vibrations of
different lengths, "much after the manner that, in the sense
of hearing, nature makes use of aërial vibrations of several
bignesses to generate sounds of divers tones, for the analogy
of nature is to be observed."   He correctly foresaw that
red and yellow light would consist of the longer undulations,
and blue and violet of the shorter, while white light would
be composed of an indiscriminate mixture of waves of
various lengths.   Newton almost overcame the strongest
apparent difficulty of the undulatory theory of light,
namely, the propagation of light in straight lines.   For he
observed that though waves of sound bend round an ob-
stacle to some extent, they do not do so in the same degree
as water-waves.[2]   He had but to extend the analogy
proportionally to light-waves, and not only would the
difficulty have vanished, but the true theory of diffraction
would have been open to him.   Unfortunately he had a
preconceived theory that rays of light are bent from and
not towards the shadow of a body, a theory which for once
he did not sufficiently compare with observation to detect

[1] Birch, *History of the Royal Society*, vol. iii. p. 262, quoted by
Young, *Works*, vol. i. p. 246.
[2] *Opticks*, Query 28, 3rd edit. p. 337.

its falsity. I am not aware, too, that Newton has, in any of his works, displayed an understanding of the phenomena of interference without which his notion of waves must have been imperfect.

While the general principles of undulatory motion will be the same in whatever medium the motion takes place, the circumstances may be excessively different. Between light travelling 186,000 miles per second and sound travelling in air only about 1,100 feet in the same time, or almost 900,000 times as slowly, we cannot expect a close outward resemblance. There are great differences, too, in the character of the vibrations. Gases scarcely admit of transverse vibration, so that sound travelling in air is a longitudinal wave, the particles of air moving backwards and forwards in the same line in which the wave moves onwards. Light, on the other hand, appears to consist entirely in the movement of points of force transversely to the direction of propagation of the ray. The light-wave is partially analogous to the bending of a rod or of a stretched cord agitated at one end. Now this bending motion may take place in any one of an infinite number of planes, and waves of which the planes are perpendicular to each other cannot interfere any more than two perpendicular forces can interfere. The complicated phenomena of polarised light arise out of this transverse character of the luminous wave, and we must not expect to meet analogous phenomena in atmospheric sound-waves. It is conceivable that in solids we might produce transverse sound undulations, in which phenomena of polarisation might be reproduced. But it would appear that even between transverse sound and light-waves the analogy holds true rather of the principles of harmonic motion than the circumstances of the vibrating medium; from experiment and theory it is inferred that the plane of polarisation in plane polarised light is perpendicular to instead of being coincident with the direction of vibration, as it would be in the case of transverse sound undulations. If so the laws of elastic forces are essentially different in application to the luminiferous ether and to ordinary solid bodies.[1]

---

[1] Rankine, *Philosophical Transactions* (1856), vol. cxlvi. p. 282.

Analogy in Astronomy.

We shall be much assisted in gaining a true appreciation of the value of analogy in its feebler degrees, by considering how much it has contributed to the progress of astronomical science. Our point of observation is so fixed with regard to the universe, and our means of examining distant bodies are so restricted, that we are necessarily guided by limited and apparently feeble resemblances. In many cases the result has been confirmed by subsequent direct evidence of the most forcible character.

While the scientific world was divided in opinion between the Copernican and Ptolemaic systems, it was analogy which furnished the most satisfactory argument. Galileo discovered, by the use of his new telescope, the four small satellites which circulate round Jupiter, and make a miniature planetary world. These four Medicean Stars, as they were called, were plainly seen to revolve round Jupiter in various periods, but approximately in one plane, and astronomers irresistibly inferred that what might happen on the smaller scale might also be found true of the greater planetary system. This discovery gave "the holding turn," as Herschel expressed it, to the opinions of mankind. Even Francis Bacon, who, little to the credit of his scientific sagacity, had previously opposed the Copernican views, now became convinced, saying "We affirm the solisequium of Venus and Mercury; since it has been found by Galileo that Jupiter also has attendants." Nor did Huyghens think it superfluous to adopt the analogy as a valid argument.[1] Even in an advanced stage of physical astronomy, the Jovian system has not lost its analogical interest; for the mutual perturbations of the four satellites pass through all their phases within a few centuries, and thus enable us to verify in a miniature case the principles of stability, which Laplace established for the great planetary system. Oscillations or disturbances which in the motions of the planets appear to be secular, because their periods extend over millions of years, can be watched, in the case of Jupiter's satellites, through complete revolutions within the historical period of astronomy.[2]

[1] *Cosmotheoros* (1699), p. 16.
[2] Laplace, *System of the World*, vol. ii. p. 316.

In obtaining a knowledge of the stellar universe we must sometimes depend upon precarious analogies. We still hold upon this ground the opinion, entertained by Bruno as long ago as 1591, that the stars may be suns attended by planets like our earth. This is the most probable first assumption, and it is supported by spectrum observations, which show the similarity of light derived from many stars with that of the sun. But at the same time we learn by the prism that there are nebulæ and stars in conditions widely different from anything known in our system. In the course of time the analogy may perhaps be restored to comparative completeness by the discovery of suns in various stages of nebulous condensation. The history of the evolution of our own world may be traced back in bodies less developed, or traced forwards in systems more advanced towards the dissipation of energy, and the extinction of life. As in a great workshop, we may perhaps see the material work of Creation as it has progressed through thousands of millions of years.

In speculations concerning the physical condition of the planets and their satellites, we depend upon analogies of a weak character. We may be said to know that the moon has mountains and valleys, plains and ridges, volcanoes and streams of lava, and, in spite of the absence of air and water, the rocky surface of the moon presents so many familiar appearances that we do not hesitate to compare them with the features of our globe. We infer with high probability that Mars has polar snow and an atmosphere absorbing blue rays like our own; Jupiter undoubtedly possesses a cloudy atmosphere, possibly not unlike a magnified copy of that surrounding the earth, but our tendency to adopt analogies receives a salutary correction in the recently discovered fact that the atmosphere of Uranus contains hydrogen.

Philosophers have not stopped at these comparatively safe inferences, but have speculated on the existence of living creatures in other planets. Huyghens remarked that as we infer by analogy from the dissected body of a dog to that of a pig and ox or other animal of the same general form, and as we expect to find the same viscera, the heart, stomach, lungs, intestines, &c., in corresponding positions, so when we notice the similarity of the planets

in many respects, we must expect to find them alike in
other respects.[1] He even enters into an inquiry whether
the inhabitants of other planets would possess reason and
knowledge of the same sort as ours, concluding in the
affirmative. Although the power of intellect might be
different, he considers that they would have the same
geometry if they had any at all, and that what is true
with us would be true with them.[2] As regards the sun,
he wisely observes that every conjecture fails. Laplace
entertained a strong belief in the existence of inhabitants
on other planets. The benign influence of the sun gives
birth to animals and plants upon the surface of the earth,
and analogy induces us to believe that his rays would tend
to have a similar effect elsewhere. It is not probable that
matter which is here so fruitful of life would be sterile
upon so great a globe as Jupiter, which, like the earth, has
its days and nights and years, and changes which indicate
active forces. Man indeed is formed for the temperature
and atmosphere in which he lives, and, so far as appears,
could not live upon the other planets. But there might
be an infinity of organisations relative to the diverse
constitutions of the bodies of the universe. The most
active imagination cannot form any idea of such various
creatures, but their existence is not unlikely.[3]

We now know that many metals and other elements
never found in organic structures are yet capable of forming compounds with substances of vegetable or animal
origin. It is therefore just possible that at different temperatures creatures formed of different yet analogous compounds might exist, but it would seem indispensable that
carbon should form the basis of organic structures. We
have no analogies to lead us to suppose that in the absence
of that complex element life can exist. Could we find
globes surrounded by atmospheres resembling our own in
temperature and composition, we should be almost forced
to believe them inhabited, but the probability of any analogical argument decreases rapidly as the condition of a
globe diverges from that of our own. The Cardinal
Nicholas de Cusa held long ago that the moon was

[1] *Cosmotheoros* (1699), p. 17.   [2] Ibid. p. 36.
[3] *System of the World*, vol. ii. p. 326.   *Essai Philosophique.* p. 87.

inhabited, but the absence of any appreciable atmosphere renders the existence of inhabitants highly improbable. Speculations resting upon weak analogies hardly belong to the scope of true science, and can only be tolerated as an antidote to the far worse dogmas which assert that the thousand million of persons on earth, or rather a small fraction of them, are the sole objects of care of the Power which designed this limitless Universe.

Failures of Analogy.

So constant is the aid which we derive from the use of analogy in all attempts at discovery or explanation, that it is most important to observe in what cases it may lead us into difficulties. That which we expect by analogy to exist

(1) May be found to exist;

(2) May seem not to exist, but nevertheless may really exist;

(3) May actually be non-existent.

In the second case the failure is only apparent, and arises from our obtuseness of perception, the smallness of the phenomenon to be noticed, or the disguised character in which it appears. I have already pointed out that the analogy of sound and light seems to fail because light does not apparently bend round a corner, the fact being that it does so bend in the phenomena of diffraction, which present the effect, however, in such an unexpected and minute form, that even Newton was misled, and turned from the correct hypothesis of undulations which he had partially entertained.

In the third class of cases analogy fails us altogether, and we expect that to exist which really does not exist. Thus we fail to discover the phenomena of polarisation in sound travelling through the atmosphere, since air is not capable of any appreciable transverse undulations. These failures of analogy are of peculiar interest, because they make the mind aware of its superior powers. There have been many philosophers who said that we can conceive nothing in the intellect which we have not previously received through the senses. This is true in the sense that we cannot *image* them to the mind in the concrete form of a shape or a colour; but we can speak of them and reason concerning them; in short, we often know them in everything but a sensuous manner. Accurate investigation shows that all material substances retard the motion of bodies through them by subtracting energy by impact. By the law of continuity we can frame the notion of a vacuous space in which there is no resistance whatever, nor need we stop there; for we have only to proceed by analogy to the case where a medium should accelerate the motion of bodies passing through it, somewhat in the mode which Aristotelians attributed falsely to the air. Thus we can frame the notion of *negative density*, and Newton could reason exactly concerning it, although no such thing exists.[1]

In every direction of thought we may meet ultimately with similar failures of analogy. A moving point generates a line, a moving line generates a surface, a moving surface generates a solid, but what does a moving solid generate? When we compare a polyhedron, or many-sided solid, with a polygon, or plane figure of many sides, the volume of the first is analogous to the area of the second; the face of the solid answers to the side of the polygon; the edge of the solid to the point of the figure; but the corner, or junction of edges in the polyhedron, is left wholly unrepresented in the plane of the polygon. Even if we attempted to draw the analogies in some other manner, we should still find a geometrical notion embodied in the solid which has no representative in the figure of two dimensions.[2]

Faraday was able to frame some notion of matter in a fourth condition, which should be to gas what gas is to liquid.[3] Such substance, he thought, would not fall far short of *radiant matter*, by which apparently he meant the supposed caloric or matter assumed to constitute heat, according to the corpuscular theory. Even if we could frame the notion, matter in such a state cannot be known to exist, and recent discoveries concerning the continuity

[1] *Principia*, bk. ii. Section ii. Prop. x.
[2] De Morgan, *Cambridge Philosophical Transactions* vol. xi. Part ii. p. 246.
[3] *Life of Faraday*, vol. i. p. 216.

of the solid, liquid, and gaseous states remove the basis
of the speculation.

From these and many other instances which might be
adduced, we learn that analogical reasoning leads us to
the conception of many things which, so far as we can
ascertain, do not exist. In this way great perplexities
have arisen in the use of language and mathematical
symbols. All language depends upon analogy; for we
join and arrange words so that they may represent the
corresponding junctions or arrangements of things and
their equalities. But in the use of language we are
obviously capable of forming many combinations of words
to which no corresponding meaning apparently exists.
The same difficulty arises in the use of mathematical
signs, and mathematicians have needlessly puzzled themselves about the square root of a negative quantity, which
is, in many applications of algebraic calculation, simply a
sign without any analogous meaning, there being a failure
of analogy.

CHAPTER XXIX.

IF science consists in the detection of identity and the recognition of uniformity existing in many objects, it follows that the progress of science depends upon the study of exceptional phenomena. Such new phenomena are the raw material upon which we exert our faculties of observation and reasoning, in order to reduce the new facts beneath the sway of the laws of nature, either those laws already well known, or those to be discovered. Not only are strange and inexplicable facts those which are on the whole most likely to lead us to some novel and important discovery, but they are also best fitted to arouse our attention. So long as events happen in accordance with our anticipations, and the routine of every-day observation is unvaried, there is nothing to impress upon the mind the smallness of its knowledge, and the depth of mystery, which may be hidden in the commonest sights and objects. In early times the myriads of stars which remained in apparently fixed relative positions upon the heavenly sphere, received less notice from astronomers than those few planets whose wandering and inexplicable motions formed a riddle. Hipparchus was induced to prepare the first catalogue of stars, because a single new star had been added to those nightly visible; and in the middle ages two brilliant but temporary stars caused more popular interest in astronomy than any other events, and to one of them we owe all the observations of Tycho Brahe, the mediæval Hipparchus.

In other sciences, as well as in that of the heavens,

exceptional events are commonly the points from which we start to explore new regions of knowledge. It has been beautifully said that Wonder is the daughter of Ignorance, but the mother of Invention; and though the most familiar and slight events, if fully examined, will afford endless food for wonder and for wisdom, yet it is the few peculiar and unlooked-for events which most often lead to a course of discovery. It is true, indeed, that it requires much philosophy to observe things which are too near to us.

The high scientific importance attaching, then, to exceptions, renders it desirable that we should carefully consider the various modes in which an exception may be disposed of; while some new facts will be found to confirm the very laws to which they seem at first sight clearly opposed, others will cause us to limit the generality of our previous statements. In some cases the exception may be proved to be no exception; occasionally it will prove fatal to our previous most confident speculations; and there are some new phenomena which, without really destroying any of our former theories, open to us wholly new fields of scientific investigation. The study of this subject is especially interesting and important, because, as I have before said (p. 587), no important theory can be built up complete and perfect all at once. When unexplained phenomena present themselves as objections to the theory, it will often demand the utmost judgment and sagacity to assign to them their proper place and force. The acceptance or rejection of a theory will depend upon discriminating the one insuperable contradictory fact from many, which, however singular and inexplicable at first sight, may afterwards be shown to be results of different causes, or possibly the most striking results of the very law with which they stand in apparent conflict.

I can enumerate at least eight classes or kinds of exceptional phenomena, to one or other of which any supposed exception to the known laws of nature can usually be referred; they may be briefly described as below, and will be sufficiently illustrated in the succeeding sections.

(1) Imaginary, or false exceptions, that is, facts, objects, or events which are not really what they are supposed to be.

(2) Apparent, but congruent exceptions, which, though apparently in conflict with a law of nature, are really in agreement with it.

(3) Singular exceptions, which really agree with a law of nature, but exhibit remarkable and unique results of it.

(4) Divergent exceptions, which really proceed from the ordinary action of known processes of nature, but which are excessive in amount or monstrous in character.

(5) Accidental exceptions, arising from the interference of some entirely distinct but known law of nature.

(6) Novel and unexplained exceptions, which lead to the discovery of a new series of laws and phenomena, modifying or disguising the effects of previously known laws, without being inconsistent with them.

(7) Limiting exceptions showing the falsity of a supposed law in some cases to which it had been extended, but not affecting its truth in other cases.

(8) Contradictory or real exceptions which lead us to the conclusion that a supposed hypothesis or theory is in opposition to the phenomena of nature, and must therefore be abandoned.

It ought to be clearly understood that in no case is a law of nature really thwarted or prevented from being fulfilled. The effects of a law may be disguised and hidden from our view in some instances: in others the law itself may be rendered inapplicable altogether; but if a law is applicable it must be carried out. Every law of nature must therefore be stated with the utmost generality of all the instances really coming under it. Babbage proposed to distinguish between *universal principles*, which do not admit of a single exception, such as that every number ending in 5 is divisible by five, and *general principles* which are more frequently obeyed than violated, as that " men will be governed by what they believe to be their interest."[1] But in a scientific point of view general principles must be universal as regards some distinct class of objects, or they are not principles at all. If a law to which exceptions exist is stated without allusion to those exceptions, the statement is erroneous. I have no right to say that " All liquids

---

[1] Babbage, *The Exposition of* 1851, p. 1.

expand by heat," if I know that water below 4° C. does not; I ought to say, "All liquids, except water below 4° C., expand by heat;" and every new exception discovered will falsify the statement until inserted in it. To speak of some laws as being *generally* true, meaning not universally but in the majority of cases, is a hurtful abuse of the word, but is quite usual. *General* should mean that which is true of a whole *genus* or class, and every true statement must be true of some assigned or assignable class.

Imaginary or False Exceptions.

When a supposed exception to a law of nature is brought to our notice, the first inquiry ought properly to be—Is there any breach of the law at all ? It may be that the supposed exceptional fact is not a fact at all, but a mere figment of the imagination. When King Charles requested the Royal Society to investigate the curious fact that a live fish put into a bucket of water does not increase the weight of the bucket and its contents, the Royal Society wisely commenced their deliberations by inquiring whether the fact was so or not. Every statement, however false, must have some cause or prior condition, and the real question for the Royal Society to investigate was, how the King came to think that the fact was so. Mental conditions, as we have seen, enter into all acts of observation, and are often a worthy subject of inquiry. But there are many instances in the history of science, in which trouble and error have been caused by false assertions carelessly made, and carelessly accepted without verification.

The reception of the Copernican theory was much impeded by the objection, that if the earth were moving, a stone dropped from the top of a high tower should be left behind, and should appear to move towards the west, just as a stone dropped from the mast-head of a moving ship would fall behind, owing to the motion of the ship. The Copernicans attempted to meet this grave objection in every way but the true one, namely, showing by trial that the asserted facts are not correct. In the first place, if a stone had been dropped with suitable precautions from the mast-head of a moving ship, it would have fallen close to the foot of the mast, because by the first law of motion, it would remain in the same state of horizontal motion communicated to it by the mast. As the anti-Copernicans had assumed the contrary result as certain to ensue, their argument would of course have fallen through. Had the Copernicans next proceeded to test with great care the other assertion involved, they would have become still better convinced of the truth of their own theory. A stone dropped from the top of a high tower, or into a deep well, would certainly not have been deflected from the vertical direction in the considerable degree required to agree with the supposed consequences of the Copernican views; but, with very accurate observation, they might have discovered, as Benzenberg subsequently did, a very small deflection towards the east, showing that the eastward velocity is greater at the top than the bottom. Had the Copernicans then been able to detect and interpret the meaning of the small divergence thus arising, they would have found in it corroboration of their own views.

Multitudes of cases might be cited in which laws of nature seem to be evidently broken, but in which the apparent breach arises from a misapprehension of the case. It is a general law, absolutely true of all crystals yet submitted to examination, that no crystal has a re-entrant angle, that is an angle which towards the axis of the crystal is greater than two right angles. Wherever the faces of a crystal meet they produce a projecting edge, and wherever edges meet they produce a corner. Many crystals, however, when carelessly examined, present exceptions to this law, but closer observation always shows that the apparently re-entrant angle really arises from the oblique union of two distinct crystals. Other crystals seem to possess faces contradicting all the principles of crystallography; but careful examination shows that the supposed faces are not true faces, but surfaces produced by the orderly junction of an immense number of distinct thin crystalline plates, each plate being in fact a separate crystal, in which the laws of crystallography are strictly observed. The roughness of the supposed face, the striæ detected by the microscope, or inference by continuity from other specimens where the true faces of the plates are clearly seen, prove the mistaken character of the supposed exceptions. Again, four of the faces of a regular octahedron may become so enlarged

in the crystallisation of iron pyrites and some other substances, that the other four faces become imperceptible and
a regular tetrahedron appears to be produced, contrary to
the laws of crystallographic symmetry. Many other crystalline forms are similarly modified, so as to produce a
series of what are called *hemihedral* forms.

In tracing out the isomorphic relations of the elements,
great perplexity has often been caused by mistaking one
substance for another. It was pointed out that though
arsenic was supposed to be isomorphous with phosphorus,
the arseniate of soda crystallised in a form distinct from
that of the corresponding phosphate. Some chemists held
this to be a fatal objection to the doctrine of isomorphism ;
but it was afterwards pointed out by Clarke, that the
arseniate and phosphate in question were not corresponding compounds, as they differed in regard to the water
of crystallisation.[1] Vanadium again appeared to be an
exception to the laws of isomorphism, until it was proved
by Professor Roscoe, that what Berzelius supposed to be
metallic vanadium was really an oxide of vanadium.[2]

Apparent but Congruent Exceptions.

Not unfrequently a law of nature will present results
in certain circumstances which appear to be entirely in
conflict with the law itself. Not only may the action of
the law be much complicated and disguised, but it may
in various ways be reversed or inverted, so that careless
observers are misled. Ancient philosophers generally
believed that while some bodies were heavy by nature,
others, such as flame, smoke, bubbles, clouds, &c., were
essentially light, or possessed a tendency to move upwards.
So acute an inquirer as Aristotle failed to perceive the
true nature of buoyancy, and the doctrine of intrinsic
lightness, expounded in his works, became the accepted
view for many centuries. It is true that Lucretius was
aware why flame tends to rise, holding that—

> " The flame has weight, though highly rare,
>   Nor mounts but when compelled by heavier air."

[1] Daubeny's *Atomic Theory*, p. 76.
[2] *Bakerian Lecture, Philosophical Transactions* (1868), vol. clviii
p. 2.

Archimedes also was so perfectly acquainted with the buoyancy of bodies immersed in water, that he could not fail to perceive the existence of a parallel effect in air. Yet throughout the early middle ages the light of true science could not contend with the glare of the Peripatetic doctrine. The genius of Galileo and Newton was required to convince people of the simple truth that all matter is heavy, but that the gravity of one substance may be overborne by that of another, as one scale of a balance is carried up by the preponderating weight in the opposite scale. It is curious to find Newton gravely explaining the difference of absolute and relative gravity, as if it were a new discovery proceeding from his theory.[1] More than a century elapsed before other apparent exceptions to the Newtonian philosophy were explained away.

Newton himself allowed that the motion of the apsides of the moon's orbit appeared to be irreconcilable with the law of gravity, and it remained for Clairaut to remove the difficulty by more complete mathematical analysis. There must always remain, in the motions of the heavenly bodies, discrepancies of some amount between theory and observation ; but such discrepancies have so often yielded in past times to prolonged investigation that physicists now regard them as merely apparent exceptions, which will afterwards be found to agree with the law of gravity.

The most beautiful instance of an apparent exception, is found in the total reflection of light, which occurs when a beam of light within a medium falls very obliquely upon the boundary separating it from a rarer medium. The general law is that when a ray strikes the limit between two media of different refractive indices, part of the light is reflected and part is refracted ; but when the obliquity of the ray within the denser medium passes beyond a certain point, there is a sudden apparent breach of continuity, and the whole of the light is reflected. A clear reason can be given for this exceptional conduct of the light. According to the law of refraction, the sine of the angle of incidence bears a fixed ratio to the sine of the angle of refraction, so that the greater of the two angles, which is always that in the less dense medium, may increase up to a right angle;

[1] *Principia*, bk. ii. Prop. 20. Corollaries, 5 and 6.

but when the media differ in refractive power, the less angle cannot become a right angle, as this would require the sine of an angle to be greater than the radius. It might seem that this is an exception of the kind described below as a limiting exception, by which a law is shown to be inapplicable beyond certain limits; but in the explanation of the exception according to the undulatory theory, we find that there is really no breach of the general law. When an undulation strikes a point in a bounding surface, spherical waves are produced and spread from the point. The refracted ray is the resultant of an infinite number of such spherical waves, and the bending of the ray at the common surface of two media depends upon the comparative velocities of propagation of the undulations in those media. But if a ray falls very obliquely upon the surface of a rarer medium, the waves proceeding from successive points of the surface spread so rapidly as never to intersect, and no resultant wave will then be produced. We thus perceive that from similar mathematical conditions arise distinct apparent effects.

There occur from time to time failures in our best grounded predictions. A comet, of which the orbit has been well determined, may fail, like Lexell's Comet, to appear at the appointed time and place in the heavens. In the present day we should not allow such an exception to our successful predictions to weigh against our belief in the theory of gravitation, but should assume that some unknown body had through the action of gravitation deflected the comet. As Clairaut remarked, in publishing his calculations concerning the expected reappearance of Halley's Comet, a body which passes into regions so remote, and which is hidden from our view during such long periods, might be exposed to the influence of forces totally unknown to us, such as the attraction of other comets, or of planets too far removed from the sun to be ever perceived by us. In the case of Lexell's Comet it was afterwards shown, curiously enough, that its appearance was not one of a regular series of periodical returns within the sphere of our vision, but a single exceptional visit never to be repeated, and probably due to the perturbing powers of Jupiter. This solitary visit became a strong confirmation of the law of gravity with which it seemed to be in conflict.

Singular Exceptions.

Among the most interesting of apparent exceptions are those which I call *singular exceptions*, because they are more or less analogous to the singular cases or solutions which occur in mathematical science. A general mathematical law embraces an infinite multitude of cases which perfectly agree with each other in a certain respect. It may nevertheless happen that a single case, while really obeying the general law, stands out as apparently different from all the rest. The rotation of the earth upon its axis gives to all the stars an apparent motion of rotation from east to west; but while countless thousands obey the rule, the Pole Star alone seems to break it. Exact observations indeed show that it also revolves in a small circle, but a star might happen for a short time to exist so close to the pole that no appreciable change of place would be caused by the earth's rotation. It would then constitute a perfect singular exception ; while really obeying the law, it would break the terms in which it is usually stated. In the same way the poles of every revolving body are singular points.

Whenever the laws of nature are reduced to a mathematical form we may expect to meet with singular cases, and, as all the physical sciences will meet in the mathematical principles of mechanics, there is no part of nature where we may not encounter them. In mechanical science the motion of rotation may be considered an exception to the motion of translation. It is a general law that any number of parallel forces, whether acting in the same or opposite directions, will have a resultant which may be substituted for them with like effect. This resultant will be equal to the algebraic sum of the forces, or the difference of those acting in one direction and the other; it will pass through a point which is determined by a simple formula, and which may be described as the mean point of all the points of application of the parallel forces (p. 364). Thus we readily determine the resultant of parallel forces except in one peculiar case, namely, when two forces are equal and opposite but not in the same straight line. Being equal and opposite the amount of the resultant is nothing, yet, as the forces are not in the same

straight line, they do not balance each other. Examining
the formula for the point of application of the resultant, we
find that it gives an infinitely great magnitude, so that the
resultant is nothing at all, and acts at an infinite distance,
which is practically the same as to say that there is no
resultant. Two such forces constitute what is known in
mechanical science as a *couple*, which occasions rotatory
instead of rectilinear motion, and can only be neutralised
by an equal and opposite couple of forces.

The best instances of singular exceptions are furnished
by the science of optics. It is a general law that in passing
through transparent media the plane of vibration of polarised light remains unchanged. But in certain liquids,
some peculiar crystals of quartz, and transparent solid
media subjected to a magnetic strain, as in Faraday's experiment (pp. 588, 630), the plane of polarisation is rotated
in a screw-like manner. This effect is so entirely *sui
generis*, so unlike any other phenomena in nature, as to
appear truly exceptional ; yet mathematical analysis shows
it to be only a single case of much more general laws. As
stated by Thomson and Tait,[1] it arises from the composition of two uniform circular motions. If while a point
is moving round a circle, the centre of that circle move
upon another circle, a great variety of curious curves will
be produced according as we vary the dimensions of the
circles, the rapidity or the direction of the motions. When
the two circles are exactly equal, the rapidities nearly so,
and the directions opposite, the point will be found to
move gradually round the centre of the stationary circle,
and describe a curious star-like figure connected with the
molecular motions out of which the rotational power of the
media rises. Among other singular exceptions in optics
may be placed the conical refraction of light, already
noticed (p. 540), arising from the peculiar form assumed
by a wave of light when passing through certain double-
refracting crystals. The laws obeyed by the wave are
exactly the same as in other cases, yet the results are
entirely *sui generis.* So far are such cases from contradicting the law of ordinary cases, that they afford the best
opportunities for verification.

[1] *Treatise on Natural Philosophy,* vol. i. p. 50.

In astronomy singular exceptions might occur, and in an approximate manner they do occur. We may point to the rings of Saturn as objects which, though undoubtedly obeying the law of gravity, are yet unique, as far as our observation of the universe has gone. They agree, indeed, with the other bodies of the planetary system in the stability of their movements, which never diverge far from the mean position. There seems to be little doubt that these rings are composed of swarms of small meteoric stones ; formerly they were thought to be solid continuous rings, and mathematicians proved that if so constituted an entirely exceptional event might have happened under certain circumstances. Had the rings been exactly uniform all round, and with a centre of gravity coinciding for a moment with that of Saturn, a singular case of unstable equilibrium would have arisen, necessarily resulting in the sudden collapse of the rings, and the fall of their debris upon the surface of the planet. Thus in one single case the theory of gravity would give a result wholly unlike anything else known in the mechanism of the heavens.

It is possible that we might meet with singular exceptions in crystallography. If a crystal of the second or dimetric system, in which the third axis is usually unequal to either of the other two, happened to have the three axes equal, it might be mistaken for a crystal of the cubic system, but would exhibit different faces and dissimilar properties. There is, again, a possible class of diclinic crystals in which two axes are at right angles and the third axis inclined to the other two. This class is chiefly remarkable for its non-existence, since no crystals have yet been proved to have such axes. It seems likely that the class would constitute only a singular case of the more general triclinic system, in which all three axes are inclined to each other at various angles. Now if the diclinic form were merely accidental, and not produced by any general law of molecular constitution, its actual occurrence would be infinitely improbable, just as it is infinitely improbable that any star should indicate the North Pole with perfect exactness.

In the curves denoting the relation between the temperature and pressure of water there is, as shown by Professor J. Thomson, one very remarkable point entirely unique, at which alone water can remain in the three conditions of gas, liquid, and solid in the same vessel. It is the triple point at which three lines meet, namely (1) the steam line, which shows at what temperatures and pressures water is just upon the point of becoming gaseous ; (2) the ice line, showing when ice is just about to melt ; and (3) the hoar-frost line, which similarly indicates the pressures and temperatures at which ice is capable of passing directly into the state of gaseous vapour.[1]

Divergent Exceptions.

Closely analogous to singular exceptions are those divergent exceptions, in which a phenomenon manifests itself in unusual magnitude or character, without becoming subject to peculiar laws.   Thus in throwing ten coins, it happened in four cases out of 2,048 throws, that all the coins fell with heads uppermost (p. 208) ; these would usually be regarded as very singular events, and, according to the theory of probabilities, they would be rare ; yet they proceed only from an unusual conjunction of accidental events, and from no really exceptional causes.   In all classes of natural phenomena we may expect to meet with similar divergencies from the average, sometimes due merely to the principles of probability, sometimes to deeper reasons.   Among every large collection of persons, we shall probably find some persons who are remarkably large or remarkably small, giants or dwarfs, whether in bodily or mental conformation. Such cases appear to be not mere *lusus naturæ*, since they occur with a frequency closely accordant with the law of error or divergence from an average, as shown by Quetelet and Mr. Galton.[2]   The rise of genius, and the occurrence of extraordinary musical or mathematical faculties, are attributed by Mr. Galton to the same principle of divergence.

When several distinct forces happen to concur together, we may have surprising or alarming results.   Great storms, floods, droughts, and other extreme deviations from the average condition of the atmosphere thus arise.   They must be expected to happen from time to time, and will yet be very infrequent compared with minor disturbances.

[1] Maxwell's *Theory of Heat*, (1871), p. 175.
[2] Galton, on the Height and Weight of Boys. *Journal of the Anthropological Institute*, 1875, p. 174.

They are not anomalous but only extreme events, analogous to extreme runs of luck. There seems, indeed, to be a fallacious impression in the minds of many persons, that the theory of probabilities necessitates uniformity in the happening of events, so that in the same space of time there will always be nearly the same number of railway accidents and murders. Buckle has superficially remarked upon the constancy of such events as ascertained by Quetelet, and some of his readers acquire the false notion that there is a mysterious inexorable law producing uniformity in human affairs. But nothing can be more opposed to the teachings of the theory of probability, which always contemplates the occurrence of unusual runs of luck. That theory shows the great improbability that the number of railway accidents per month should be always equal, or nearly so. The public attention is strongly attracted to any unusual conjunction of events, and there is a fallacious tendency to suppose that such conjunction must be due to a peculiar new cause coming into operation. Unless it can be clearly shown that such unusual conjunctions occur more frequently than they should do according to the theory of probabilities, we should regard them as merely divergent exceptions.

Eclipses and remarkable conjunctions of the heavenly bodies may also be regarded as results of ordinary laws which nevertheless appear to break the regular course of nature, and never fail to excite surprise. Such events vary greatly in frequency. One or other of the satellites of Jupiter is eclipsed almost every day, but the simultaneous eclipse of three satellites can only take place, according to the calculations of Wargentin, after the lapse of 1,317,900 years. The relations of the four satellites are so remarkable, that it is actually impossible, according to the theory of gravity, that they should all suffer eclipse simultaneously. But it may happen that while some of the satellites are really eclipsed by entering Jupiter's shadow, the others are either occulted or rendered invisible by passing over his disk. Thus on four occasions, in 1681, 1802, 1826, and 1843, Jupiter has been witnessed in the singular condition of being apparently deprived of satellites. A close conjunction of two planets always excites admiration, though such conjunctions must occur at intervals in the ordinary course of their motions. We cannot wonder that when

three or four planets approach each other closely, the event
is long remembered.   A most remarkable conjunction of
Mars, Jupiter, Saturn, and Mercury, which took place in
the year 2446 B.C., was adopted by the Chinese Emperor,
Chuen Hio, as a new epoch for the chronology of his
Empire, though there is some doubt whether the conjunction was really observed, or was calculated from the supposed
laws of motion of the planets.   It is certain that on the
11th November, 1524, the planets Venus, Jupiter, Mars,
and Saturn were seen very close together, while Mercury
was only distant by about 16° or thirty apparent diameters
of the sun, this conjunction being probably the most remarkable which has occurred in historical times.

Among the perturbations of the planets we find divergent
exceptions arising from the peculiar accumulation of effects,
as in the case of the long inequality of Jupiter and Saturn
(p. 455).   Leverrier has shown that there is one place between
the orbits of Mercury and Venus, and another between those
of Mars and Jupiter, in either of which, if a small planet
happened to exist, it would suffer comparatively immense
disturbance in the elements of its orbit.   Now between
Mars and Jupiter there do occur the minor planets, the
orbits of which are in many cases exceptionally divergent.[1]

Under divergent exceptions we might place all or nearly
all the instances of substances possessing physical properties in a very high or low degree, which were described
in the chapter on Generalisation (p. 607).   Quicksilver is
divergent among metals as regards its melting point, and
potassium and sodium as regards their specific gravities.
Monstrous productions and variations, whether in the animal
or vegetable kingdoms, should probably be assigned to this
class of exceptions.

It is worthy of notice that even in such a subject as
formal logic, divergent exceptions seem to occur, not of
course due to chance, but exhibiting in an unusual degree
a phenomenon which is more or less manifested in all
other cases.   I pointed out in p. 141 that propositions of
the general type $A = BC + bc$ are capable of expression
in six equivalent logical forms, so that they manifest in a
higher degree than any other proposition yet discovered
the phenomenon of logical equivalence.

[1] Grant's *History of Physical Astronomy*, p. 116.

Accidental Exceptions.

The third and largest class of exceptions contains those which arise from the casual interference of extraneous causes. A law may be in operation, and, if so, must be perfectly fulfilled ; but, while we conceive that we are examining its results, we may have before us the effects of a different cause, possessing no connexion with the subject of our inquiry. The law is not really broken, but at the same time the supposed exception is not illusory. It may be a phenomenon which cannot occur but under the condition of the law in question, yet there has been such interference that there is an apparent failure of science. There is, for instance, no subject in which more rigorous and invariable laws have been established than in crystallography. As a general rule, each chemical substance possesses its own definite form, by which it can be infallibly recognised ; but the mineralogist has to be on his guard against what are called *pseudomorphic* crystals. In some circumstances a substance, having assumed its proper crystalline form, may afterwards undergo chemical change ; a new ingredient may be added, a former one removed, or one element may be substituted for another. In calcium carbonate the carbonic acid is sometimes replaced by sulphuric acid, so that we find gypsum in the form of calcite; other cases are known where the change is inverted and calcite is found in the form of gypsum. Mica, talc, steatite, hematite, are other minerals subject to these curious transmutations. Sometimes a crystal embedded in a matrix is entirely dissolved away, and a new mineral is subsequently deposited in the cavity as in a mould. Quartz is thus found cast in many forms wholly unnatural to it. A still more perplexing case sometimes occurs. Calcium carbonate is capable of assuming two distinct forms of crystallisation, in which it bears respectively the names of calcite and arragonite. Now arragonite, while retaining its outward form unchanged, may undergo an internal molecular change into calcite, as indicated by the altered cleavage. Thus we may come across crystals apparently of arragonite, which seem to break all the laws of crystallography, by possessing the cleavage of a different system of crystallisation.

Some of the most invariable laws of nature are disguised by interference of unlooked-for causes. While the barometer was yet a new and curious subject of investigation, its theory, as stated by Torricelli and Pascal, seemed to be contradicted by the fact that in a well-constructed instrument the mercury would often stand far above 31 inches in height. Boyle showed[1] that mercury could be made to stand as high as 75 inches in a perfectly cleansed tube, or about two and a half times as high as could be due to the pressure of the atmosphere. Many theories about the pressure of imaginary fluids were in consequence put forth,[2] and the subject was involved in much confusion until the adhesive or cohesive force between glass and mercury, when brought into perfect contact, was pointed out as the real interfering cause. It seems to me, however, that the phenomenon is not thoroughly understood as yet.

Gay-Lussac observed that the temperature of boiling water was very different in some kinds of vessels from what it was in others. It is only when in contact with metallic surfaces or sharply broken edges that the temperature is fixed at 100° C. The suspended freezing of liquids is another case where the action of a law of nature appears to be interrupted. Spheroidal ebullition was at first sight a most anomalous phenomenon; it was almost incredible that water should not boil in a red-hot vessel, or that ice could actually be produced in a red-hot crucible. These paradoxical results are now fully explained as due to the interposition of a non-conducting film of vapour between the globule of liquid and the sides of the vessel. The feats of conjurors who handle liquid metals are accounted for in the same manner. At one time the *passive state* of steel was regarded as entirely anomalous. It may be assumed as a general law that when pieces of electro-negative and electro-positive metal are placed in nitric acid, and made to touch each other, the electro-negative metal will undergo rapid solution. But when iron is the electro-negative and platinum the electro-positive, the solution of the iron entirely and abruptly ceases. Faraday ingeniously proved

[1] *Discourse to the Royal Society*, 28th May, 1684.
[2] Robert Hooke's *Posthumous Works*, p. 365.

that this effect is due to a thin film of oxide of iron, which forms upon the surface of the iron and protects it.[1]

The law of gravity is so simple, and disconnected from the other laws of nature, that it never suffers any disturbance, and is in no way disguised, but by the complication of its own effects. It is otherwise with those secondary laws of the planetary system which have only an empirical basis. The fact that all the long known planets and satellites have a similar motion from west to east is not necessitated by any principles of mechanics, but points to some common condition existing in the nebulous mass from which our system has been evolved. The retrograde motions of the satellites of Uranus constituted a distinct breach in this law of uniform direction, which became all the more interesting when the single satellite of Neptune was also found to be retrograde. It now became probable, as Baden Powell well observed, that the anomaly would cease to be singular, and become a case of another law, pointing to some general interference which has taken place on the bounds of the planetary system. Not only have the satellites suffered from this perturbance, but Uranus is also anomalous in having an axis of rotation lying nearly in the ecliptic; and Neptune constitutes a partial exception to the empirical law of Bode concerning the distances of the planets, which circumstance may possibly be due to the same disturbance.

Geology is a science in which accidental exceptions are likely to occur. Only when we find strata in their original relative positions can we surely infer that the order of succession is the order of time. But it not uncommonly happens that strata are inverted by the bending and doubling action of extreme pressure. Landslips may carry one body of rock into proximity with an unrelated series, and produce results apparently inexplicable.[2] Floods, streams, icebergs, and other casual agents, may lodge remains in places where they would be wholly unexpected. Though such interfering causes have been sometimes wrongly supposed to explain important discoveries, the geologist must bear the possibility of interference in mind.

---

[1] *Experimental Researches in Electricity*, vol. ii. pp. 240--245.
[2] Murchison's *Silurian System*, vol. ii. p. 733, &c.

Scarcely more than a century ago it was held that fossils
were accidental productions of nature, mere forms into
which minerals had been shaped by no peculiar cause.
Voltaire appears not to have accepted such an explanation;
but fearing that the occurrence of fossil fishes on the Alps
would support the Mosaic account of the deluge, he did
not hesitate to attribute them to the remains of fishes
accidentally brought there by pilgrims. In archæological
investigations the greatest caution is requisite in allowing
for secondary burials in ancient tombs and tumuli, for
imitations, forgeries, casual coincidences, disturbance by
subsequent races or by other archæologists. In common
life extraordinary events will happen from time to time,
as when a shepherdess in France was astonished at an iron
chain falling out of the sky close to her, the fact being that
Gay-Lussac had thrown it out of his balloon, which was
passing over her head at the time.

Novel and Unexplained Exceptions.

When a law of nature appears to fail because some other
law has interfered with its action, two cases may present
themselves;—the interfering law may be a known one, or
it may have been previously undetected. In the first case,
which we have sufficiently considered in the preceding
section, we have nothing to do but calculate as exactly as
possible the amount of interference, and make allowance
for it; the apparent failure of the law under examination
should then disappear. But in the second case the results
may be much more important. A phenomenon which
cannot be explained by any known laws may indicate the
interference of undiscovered natural forces. The ancients
could not help perceiving that the general tendency of
bodies downwards failed in the case of the loadstone, nor
would the doctrine of essential lightness explain the exception, since the substance drawn upwards by the loadstone
is a heavy metal. We now see that there was no breach in
the perfect generality of the law of gravity, but that a new
form of energy manifested itself in the loadstone for the first
time.

Other sciences show us that laws of nature, rigorously
true and exact, may be developed by those who are

ignorant of more complex phenomena involved in their application. Newton's comprehension of geometrical optics was sufficient to explain all the ordinary refractions and reflections of light. The simple laws of the bending of rays apply to all rays, whatever the character of the undulations composing them. Newton suspected the existence of other classes of phenomena when he spoke of rays as *having sides;* but it remained for later experimentalists to show that light is a transverse undulation, like the bending of a rod or cord.

Dalton's atomic theory is doubtless true of all chemical compounds, and the essence of it is that the same compound will always be found to contain the same elements in the same definite proportions. Pure calcium carbonate contains 48 parts by weight of oxygen to 40 of calcium and 12 of carbon. But when careful analyses were made of a great many minerals, this law appeared to fail. What was unquestionably the same mineral, judging by its crystalline form and physical properties, would give varying proportions of its components, and would sometimes contain unusual elements which yet could not be set down as mere impurities. Dolomite, for instance, is a compound of the carbonates of magnesia and lime, but specimens from different places do not exhibit any fixed ratio between the lime and magnesia. Such facts could be reconciled with the laws of Dalton only by supposing the interference of a new law, that of Isomorphism.

It is now established that certain elements are related to each other, so that they can, as it were, step into each other's places without apparently altering the shapes of the crystals which they constitute. The carbonates of iron, calcium, and magnesium, are nearly identical in their crystalline forms, hence they may crystallise together in harmony, producing mixed minerals of considerable complexity, which nevertheless perfectly verify the laws of equivalent proportions. This principle of isomorphism once established, not only explains what was formerly a stumbling-block, but gives valuable aid to chemists in deciding upon the constitution of new salts, since compounds of isomorphous elements which have identical crystalline forms must possess corresponding chemical formulæ.

We may expect that from time to time extraordinary

phenomena will be discovered, and will lead to new views of nature. The recent observation, for instance, that the resistance of a bar of selenium to a current of electricity is affected in an extraordinary degree by rays of light falling upon the selenium, points to a new relation between light and electricity. The allotropic changes which sulphur, selenium, and phosphorus undergo by an alteration in the amount of latent heat which they contain, will probably lead at some future time to important inferences concerning the molecular constitution of solids and liquids. The curious substance ozone has perplexed many chemists, and Andrews and Tait thought that it afforded evidence of the decomposition of oxygen by the electric discharge. The researches of Sir B. C. Brodie negative this notion, and afford evidence of the real constitution of the substance,[1] which still, however, remains exceptional in its properties and relations, and affords a hope of important discoveries in chemical theory.

Limiting Exceptions.

We pass to cases where exceptional phenomena are actually irreconcilable with a law of nature previously regarded as true. Error must now be allowed to have been committed, but the error may be more or less extensive. It may happen that a law holding rigorously true of the facts actually under notice had been extended by generalisation to other series of facts then unexamined. Subsequent investigation may show the falsity of this generalisation, and the result must be to limit the law for the future to those objects of which it is really true. The contradiction to our previous opinions is partial and not total.

Newton laid down as a result of experiment that every ray of homogeneous light has a definite refrangibility, which it preserves throughout its course until extinguished. This is one case of the general principle of undulatory movement, which Herschel stated under the title " Principle of Forced Vibrations " (p. 451), and asserted to be absolutely without exception. But Herschel himself described in the *Philosophical Transactions* for 1845 a curious appearance in a

---

[1] *Philosophical Transactions* (1872), vol. clxii. No. 23.

solution of quinine; as viewed by transmitted light the solution appeared colourless, but in certain aspects it exhibited a beautiful celestial blue tint. Curiously enough the colour is seen only in the first portion of liquid which the light enters. Similar phenomena in fluor-spar had been described by Brewster in 1838. Professor Stokes, having minutely investigated the phenomena, discovered that they were more or less present in almost all vegetable infusions, and in a number of mineral substances. He came to the conclusion that this phenomenon, called by him Fluorescence, could only be explained by an alteration in the refrangibility of the rays of light; he asserts that light-rays of very short length of vibration in falling upon certain atoms excite undulations of greater length, in opposition to the principle of forced vibrations. No complete explanation of the mode of change is yet possible, because it depends upon the intimate constitution of the atoms of the substances concerned ; but Professor Stokes believes that the principle of forced vibrations is true only so long as the excursions of an atom are very small compared with the magnitude of the complex molecules.[1]

It is well known that in Calorescence the refrangibility of rays is increased and the wave-length diminished. Rays of obscure heat and low refrangibility may be concentrated so as to heat a solid substance, and make it give out rays belonging to any part of the spectrum, and it seems probable that this effect arises from the impact of distinct but conflicting atoms. Nor is it in light only that we discover limiting exceptions to the law of forced vibrations ; for if we notice gentle waves lapping upon the stones at the edge of a lake we shall see that each larger wave in breaking upon a stone gives rise to a series of smaller waves. Thus there is constantly in progress a degradation in the magnitude of water-waves. The principle of forced vibrations seems then to be too generally stated by Herschel, but it must be a difficult question of mechanical theory to discriminate the circumstances in which it does and does not hold true.

We sometimes foresee the possible existence of exceptions yet unknown by experience, and limit the statement of our discoveries accordingly. Extensive inquiries have shown

[1] *Philosophical Transactions* (1852), vol. cxlii. pp. 465, 548, &c.

that all substances yet examined fall into one of two classes ;
they are all either ferro-magnetic, that is, magnetic in the
same way as iron, or they are diamagnetic like bismuth.
But it does not follow that every substance must be ferro-
magnetic or diamagnetic. The magnetic properties are
shown by Sir W. Thomson[1] to depend upon the specific
inductive capacities of the substance in three rectangular
directions.   If these inductive capacities are all positive, we
have a ferro-magnetic substance ; if negative, a diamagnetic
substance ; but if the specific inductive capacity were
positive in one direction and negative in the others, we
should have an exception to previous experience, and
could not place the substance under either of the present
recognised classes.

So many gases have been reduced to the liquid state, and
so many solids fused, that scientific men rather hastily
adopted the generalisation that all substances could exist
in all three states.   A certain number of gases, such as
oxygen, hydrogen, and nitrogen, have resisted all efforts to
liquefy them, and it now seems probable from the experiments of Dr. Andrews that they are limiting exceptions.
He finds that above 31° C. carbonic acid cannot be liquefied
by any pressure he could apply, whereas below this temperature liquefaction is always possible.   By analogy it
becomes probable that even hydrogen might be liquefied if
cooled to a very low temperature.   We must modify our
previous views, and either assert that *below a certain critical
temperature* every gas may be liquefied, or else we must
assume that a highly condensed gas is, when above the
critical temperature, undistinguishable from a liquid.   At
the same time we have an explanation of a remarkable
exception presented by liquid carbonic acid to the general
rule that gases expand more by heat than liquids.   Liquid
carbonic acid was found by Thilorier in 1835 to expand
more than four times as much as air ; but by the light of
Andrews' experiments we learn to regard the liquid as
rather a highly condensed gas than an ordinary liquid, and
it is actually possible to reduce the gas to the apparently
liquid condition without any abrupt condensation.[2]

[1] *Philosophical Magazine*, 4th Series, vol. i. p. 182.
[2] Maxwell, *Theory of Heat*, p. 123.

Limiting exceptions occur most frequently in the natural sciences of Botany, Zoology, Geology, &c., the laws of which are empirical. In innumerable instances the confident belief of one generation has been falsified by the wider observation of a succeeding one. Aristotle confidently held that all swans are white,[1] and the proposition seemed true until not a hundred years ago black swans were discovered in Western Australia. In zoology and physiology we may expect a fundamental identity to exist in the vital processes, but continual discoveries show that there is no limit to the apparently anomalous expedients by which life is reproduced. Alternate generation, fertilisation for several successive generations, hermaphroditism, are opposed to all we should expect from induction founded upon the higher animals. But such phenomena are only limiting exceptions showing that what is true of one class is not true of another. In certain of the cephalopoda we meet the extraordinary fact that an arm of the male is cast off and lives independently until it encounters the female.

Real Exceptions to Supposed Laws.

The exceptions which we have lastly to consider are the most important of all, since they lead to the entire rejection of a law or theory before accepted. No law of nature can fail; there are no such things as real exceptions to real laws. Where contradiction exists it must be in the mind of the experimentalist. Either the law is imaginary or the phenomena which conflict with it; if, then, by our senses we satisfy ourselves of the actual occurrence of the phenomena, the law must be rejected as illusory. The followers of Aristotle held that nature abhors a vacuum, and thus accounted for the rise of water in a pump. When Torricelli pointed out the visible fact that water would not rise more than 33 feet in a pump, nor mercury more than about 30 inches in a glass tube, they attempted to represent these facts as limiting exceptions, saying that nature abhorred a vacuum to a certain extent and no further. But the Academicians del Cimento

---

[1] *Prior Analytics*, ii. 2, 8, and elsewhere

completed their discomfiture by showing that if we remove
the pressure of the surrounding air, and in proportion as
we remove it, nature's feelings of abhorrence decrease and
finally disappear altogether. Even Aristotelian doctrines
could not stand such direct contradiction.

Lavoisier's ideas concerning the constitution of acids
received complete refutation. He named oxygen the *acid
generator*, because he believed that all acids were compounds of oxygen, a generalisation based on insufficient
data. Berthollet, as early as 1789, proved by analysis that
hydrogen sulphide and prussic acid, both clearly acting
the part of acids, were devoid of oxygen ; the former might
perhaps have been interpreted as a limiting exception, but
when so powerful an acid as hydrogen chloride (muriatic
acid) was found to contain no oxygen the theory had to be
relinquished. Berzelius' theory of the dual formation of
chemical compounds met a similar fate.

It is obvious that all conclusive *experimenta crucis* constitute real exceptions to the supposed laws of the theory
which is overthrown. Newton's corpuscular theory of light
was not rejected on account of its absurdity or incon-
ceivability, for in these respects it is, as we have seen, far
superior to the undulatory theory. It was rejected because
certain small fringes of colour did not appear in the exact
place and of the exact size in which calculation showed
that they ought to appear according to the theory (pp. 516-
521). One single fact clearly irreconcilable with a theory
involves its rejection. In the greater number of cases,
what appears to be a fatal exception may be afterwards
explained away as a singular or disguised result of the
laws with which it seems to conflict, or as due to the interference of extraneous causes ; but if we fail thus to reduce
the fact to congruity, it remains more powerful than any
theories or any dogmas.

Of late years not a few of the favourite doctrines of
geologists have been rudely destroyed. It was the general
belief that human remains were to be found only in those
deposits which are actually in progress at the present day,
so that the creation of man appeared to have taken place
in this geological age. The discovery of a single worked
flint in older strata and in connexion with the remains of
extinct mammals was sufficient to explode such a doctrine.

Similarly, the opinions of geologists have been altered by the discovery of the Eozoön in the Laurentian rocks of Canada; it was previously held that no remains of life occurred in any older strata than those of the Cambrian system.   As the examination of the strata of the globe becomes more complete, our views of the origin and succession of life upon the globe must undergo many changes.

Unclassed Exceptions.

At every period of scientific progress there will exist a multitude of unexplained phenomena which we know not how to regard.   They are the outstanding facts upon which the labours of investigators must be exerted,—the ore from which the gold of future discovery is to be extracted.   It might be thought that, as our knowledge of the laws of nature increases, the number of such exceptions should decrease; but, on the contrary, the more we know the more there is yet to explain.   This arises from several reasons; in the first place, the principal laws and forces in nature are numerous, so that he who bears in mind the wonderfully large numbers developed in the doctrine of combinations, will anticipate the existence of immensely numerous relations of one law to another.   When we are once in possession of a law, we are potentially in possession of all its consequences; but it does not follow that the mind of man, so limited in its powers and capacities, can actually work them all out in detail.   Just as the aberration of light was discovered empirically, though it should have been foreseen, so there are multitudes of unexplained facts, the connexion of which with laws of nature already known to us, we should perceive, were we not hindered by the imperfection of our deductive powers.   But, in the second place, as will be more fully pointed out, it is not to be supposed that we have approximated to an exhaustive knowledge of nature's powers.   The most familiar facts may teem with indications of forces, now secrets hidden from us, because we have not mind-directed eyes to discriminate them.   The progress of science will consist in the discovery from time to time of new exceptional phenomena, and their assignment by degrees to one or other of the heads already described.   When a new fact proves to be merely a false, apparent, singular, divergent, or accidental exception, we gain a more minute and accurate acquaintance with the effects of laws already known to exist. We have indeed no addition to what was implicitly in our possession, but there is much difference between knowing the laws of nature and perceiving all their complicated effects. Should a new fact prove to be a limiting or real exception, we have to alter, in part or in whole, our views of nature, and are saved from errors into which we had fallen. Lastly, the new fact may come under the sixth class, and may eventually prove to be a novel phenomenon, indicating the existence of new laws and forces, complicating but not otherwise interfering with the effects of laws and forces previously known.

The best instance which I can find of an unresolved exceptional phenomenon, consists in the anomalous vapour-densities of phosphorus, arsenic, mercury, and cadmium. It is one of the most important laws of chemistry, discovered by Gay-Lussac, that equal volumes of gases exactly correspond to equivalent weights of the substances. Nevertheless phosphorus and arsenic give vapours exactly twice as dense as they should do by analogy, and mercury and cadmium diverge in the other direction, giving vapours half as dense as we should expect. We cannot treat these anomalies as limiting exceptions, and say that the law holds true of substances generally but not of these; for the properties of gases (p. 601), usually admit of the widest generalisations. Besides, the preciseness of the ratio of divergence points to the real observance of the law in a modified manner. We might endeavour to reduce the exceptions by doubling the atomic weights of phosphorus and arsenic, and halving those of mercury and cadmium. But this step has been maturely considered by chemists, and is found to conflict with all the other analogies of the substances and with the principle of isomorphism. One of the most probable explanations is, that phosphorus and arsenic produce vapour in an allotropic condition, which might perhaps by intense heat be resolved into a simpler gas of half the density ; but facts are wanting to support this hypothesis, and it cannot be applied to the other two exceptions without supposing that gases and vapours generally are capable of resolution into something simpler.

In short, chemists can at present make nothing of these anomalies. As Hofmann says, " Their philosophical interpretation belongs to the future . . . They may turn out to be typical facts, round which many others of the like kind may come hereafter to be grouped; and they may prove to be allied with special properties, or dependent on particular conditions as yet unsuspected." [1]

It would be easy to point out a great number of other unexplained anomalies. Physicists assert, as an absolutely universal law, that in liquefaction heat is absorbed;[2] yet sulphur is at least an apparent exception. The two substances, sulphur and selenium, are, in fact, very anomalous in their relations to heat. Sulphur may be said to have two melting points, for, though liquid like water at 120° C., it becomes quite thick and tenacious between 221° and 249°, and melts again at a higher temperature. Both sulphur and selenium may be thrown into several curious states, which chemists conveniently dispose of by calling them *allotropic*, a term freely used when they are puzzled to know what has happened. The chemical and physical history of iron, again, is full of anomalies; not only does it undergo inexplicable changes of hardness and texture in its alloys with carbon and other elements, but it is almost the only substance which conveys sound with greater velocity at a higher than at a lower temperature, the velocity increasing from 20° to 100° C., and then decreasing. Silver also is anomalous in regard to sound. These are instances of inexplicable exceptions, the bearing of which must be ascertained in the future progress of science.

When the discovery of new and peculiar phenomena conflicting with our theories of the constitution of nature is reported to us, it becomes no easy task to steer a philosophically correct course between credulity and scepticism. We are not to assume, on the one hand, that there is any limit to the wonders which nature can present to us. Nothing except the contradictory is really impossible, and many things which we now regard as common-place were considered as little short of the miraculous when first

---

[1] Hofmann's *Introduction to Chemistry*, p. 198.
[2] Stewart's *Elementary Treatise on Heat*, p. 80.

perceived. The electric telegraph was a visionary dream among mediæval physicists ;[1] it has hardly yet ceased to excite our wonder; to our descendants centuries hence it will probably appear inferior in ingenuity to some inventions which they will possess. Now every strange phenomenon may be a secret spring which, if rightly touched, will open the door to new chambers in the palace of nature. To refuse to believe in the occurrence of any- thing strange would be to neglect the most precious chances of discovery. We may say with Hooke, that " the believing strange things possible may perhaps be an occasion of taking notice of such things as another would pass by without regard as useless." We are not, therefore, to shut our ears even to such apparently absurd stories as those concerning second-sight, clairvoyance, animal magnetism, ode force, table-turning, or any of the popular delusions which from time to time are current. The facts recorded concerning these matters are facts in some sense or other, and they demand explanation, either as new natural phenomena, or as the results of credulity and imposture. Most of the supposed phenomena referred to have been, or by careful investigation would doubtless be, referred to the latter head, and the. absence of scientific ability in many of those who describe them is sufficient to cast a doubt upon their value.

It is to be remembered that according to the principle of the inverse method of probability, the probability of any hypothetical explanation is affected by the pro- bability of each other possible explanation. If no other reasonable explanation could be suggested, we should be forced to look upon spiritualist manifestations as indicating mysterious causes. But as soon as it is shown that fraud has been committed in several important cases, and that in other cases persons in a credulous and excited state of mind have deceived themselves, the probability becomes very con- siderable that similar explanations may apply to most like manifestations. The performances of conjurors sufficiently prove that it requires no very great skill to perform tricks the *modus operandi* of which shall entirely escape the

[1] Jevons, *Proceedings of the Manchester Literary and Philosophical Society,* 6th March, 1877, vol. xvi. p. 164. See also Mr. W. E. A. Axon's note on the same subject, ibid. p. 166.

notice of spectators.   It is on these grounds of probability that we should reject the so-called spiritualist
stories, and not simply because they are strange.

Certainly in the obscure phenomena of mind, those
relating to memory, dreams, somnambulism. and other
peculiar states of the nervous system, there are many
inexplicable and almost incredible facts, and it is equally
unphilosophical to believe or to disbelieve without clear
evidence.   There are many facts, too, concerning the
instincts of animals, and the mode in which they find
their way from place to place, which are at present quite
inexplicable.   No doubt there are many strange things
not dreamt of in our philosophy, but this is no reason
why we should believe in every strange thing which is
reported to have happened.

CHAPTER XXX.

CLASSIFICATION.

THE extensive subject of Classification has been deferred to a late part of this treatise, because it involves questions of difficulty, and did not seem naturally to fall into an earlier place. But it must not be supposed that, in now formally taking up the subject, we are for the first time entertaining the notion of classification. All logical inference involves classification, which is indeed the necessary accompaniment of the action of judgment. It is impossible to detect similarity between objects without thereby joining them together in thought, and forming an incipient class. Nor can we bestow a common name upon objects without implying the existence of a class. Every common name is the name of a class, and every name of a class is a common name. It is evident also that to speak of a general notion or concept is but another way of speaking of a class. Usage leads us to employ the word classification in some cases and not in others. We are said to form the *general notion* parallelogram when we regard an infinite number of possible four-sided rectilinear figures as resembling each other in the common property of possessing parallel sides. We should be said to form a *class*, Trilobite, when we place together in a museum a number of specimens resembling each other in certain defined characters. But the logical nature of the operation is the same in both cases. We form a *class* of figures called parallelograms and we form a *general notion* of trilobites.

Science, it was said at the outset, is the detection of identity, and classification is the placing together, either in

thought or in actual proximity of space, those objects between which identity has been detected. Accordingly, the
value of classification is co-extensive with the value of
science and general reasoning. Whenever we form a class
we reduce multiplicity to unity, and detect, as Plato said,
the one in the many. The result of such classification is
to yield generalised knowledge, as distinguished from the
direct and sensuous knowledge of particular facts. Of
every class, so far as it is correctly formed, the principle
of substitution is true, and whatever we know of one object
in a class we know of the other objects, so far as identity
has been detected between them. The facilitation and
abbreviation of mental labour is at the bottom of all mental
progress. The reasoning faculties of Newton were not
different in nature from those of a ploughman; the difference lay in the extent to which they were exerted, and
the number of facts which could be treated. Every thinking being generalises more or less, but it is the depth and
extent of his generalisations which distinguish the philosopher. Now it is the exertion of the classifying and
generalising powers which enables the intellect of man to
cope in some degree with the infinite number of natural
phenomena. In the chapters upon combinations and
permutations it was made evident, that from a few elementary differences immense numbers of combinations can be
produced. The process of classification enables us to resolve
these combinations, and refer each one to its place according
to one or other of the elementary circumstances out of which
it was produced. We restore nature to the simple conditions out of which its endless variety was developed. As
Professor Bowen has said,[1] "The first necessity which is
imposed upon us by the constitution of the mind itself, is
to break up the infinite wealth of Nature into groups and
classes of things, with reference to their resemblances and
affinities, and thus to enlarge the grasp of our mental
faculties, even at the expense of sacrificing the minuteness
of information which can be acquired only by studying
objects in detail. The first efforts in the pursuit of knowledge, then, must be directed to the business of classification.

[1] *A Treatise on Logic, or, the Laws of Pure Thought,* by Francis
Bowen, Professor of Moral Philosophy in Harvard College, Cambridge, United States, 1866, p. 315.

Perhaps it will be found in the sequel, that classification is not only the beginning, but the culmination and the end, of human knowledge."

Classification Involving Induction.

The purpose of classification is the detection of the laws of nature. However much the process may in some cases be disguised, classification is not really distinct from the process of perfect induction, whereby we endeavour to ascertain the connexions existing between properties.of the objects under treatment. There can be no use in placing an object in a class unless something more than the fact of being in the class is implied. If we arbitrarily formed a class of metals and placed therein a selection from the list of known metals made by ballot, we should have no reason to expect that the metals in question would resemble each other in any points except that they are metals, and have been selected by the ballot. But when chemists select from the list the five metals, potassium, sodium, cæsium, rubidium, and lithium and call them the Alkaline metals, a great deal is implied in this classification. On comparing the qualities of these substances they are all found to combine very energetically with oxygen, to decompose water at all temperatures, and to form strongly basic oxides, which are highly soluble in water, yielding powerfully caustic and alkaline hydrates from which water cannot be expelled by heat. Their carbonates are also soluble in water, and each metal forms only one chloride. It may also be expected that each salt of one of the metals will correspond to a salt of each other metal, there being a general analogy between the compounds of these metals and their properties.

Now in forming this class of alkaline metals, we have done more than merely select a convenient order of statement. We have arrived at a discovery of certain empirical laws of nature, the probability being very considerable that a metal which exhibits some of the properties of alkaline metals will also possess the others. If we discovered another metal whose carbonate was soluble in water, and which energetically combined with water at all temperatures, producing a strongly basic oxide, we should infer that it would form only a single chloride, and that generally speaking, it would enter into a series of compounds corresponding to the salts of the other alkaline metals. The formation of this class of alkaline metals then, is no mere matter of convenience; it is an important and successful act of inductive discovery, enabling us to register many undoubted propositions as results of perfect induction, and to make a great number of inferences depending upon the principles of imperfect induction.

An excellent instance as to what classification can do, is found in Mr. Lockyer's researches on the sun.[1] Wanting some guide as to what more elements to look for in the sun's photosphere, he prepared a classification of the elements according as they had or had not been traced in the sun, together with a detailed statement of the chief chemical characters of each element. He was then able to observe that the elements found in the sun were for the most part those forming stable compounds with oxygen. He then inferred that other elements forming stable oxides would probably exist in the sun, and he was rewarded by the discovery of five such metals. Here we have empirical and tentative classification leading to the detection of the correlation between existence in the sun, and the power of forming stable oxides and then leading by imperfect induction to the discovery of more coincidences between these properties.

Professor Huxley has defined the process of classification in the following terms.[2] " By the classification of any series of objects, is meant the actual or ideal arrangement together of those which are like and the separation of those which are unlike; the purpose of this arrangement being to facilitate the operations of the mind in clearly conceiving and retaining in the memory the characters of the objects in question."

This statement is doubtless correct, so far as it goes, but it does not include all that Professor Huxley himself implicitly treats under classification. He is fully aware that deep correlations, or in other terms deep uniformities or laws of nature, will be disclosed by any well chosen and profound system of classification. I should therefore propose to

---

[1] *Proceedings of the Royal Society*, November, 1873, vol. xxi. p. 512.
[2] *Lectures on the Elements of Comparative Anatomy*, 1864, p. 1.

modify the above statement, as follows:—"By the classification of any series of objects, is meant the actual or ideal arrangement together of those which are like and the separation of those which are unlike, the purpose of this arrangement being, primarily, to disclose the correlations or laws of union of properties and circumstances, and, secondarily, to facilitate the operations of the mind in clearly conceiving and retaining in the memory the characters of the objects in question."

Multiplicity of Modes of Classification.

In approaching the question how any given group of objects may be best classified, let it be remarked that there must generally be an unlimited number of modes of classifying a group of objects. Misled, as we shall see, by the problem of classification in the natural sciences, philosophers seem to think that in each subject there must be one essentially natural system of classification which is to be selected, to the exclusion of all others. This erroneous notion probably arises also in part from the limited powers of thought and the inconvenient mechanical conditions under which we labour. If we arrange the books in a library catalogue, we must arrange them in some one order; if we compose a treatise on mineralogy, the minerals must be successively described in some one arrangement; if we treat such simple things as geometrical figures, they must be taken in some fixed order. We shall naturally select that arrangement which appears to be most convenient and instructive for our principal purpose. But it does not follow that this method of arrangement possesses any exclusive excellence, and there will be usually many other possible arrangements, each valuable in its own way. A perfect intellect would not confine itself to one order of thought, but would simultaneously regard a group of objects as classified in all the ways of which they are capable. Thus the elements may be classified according to their atomicity into the groups of monads, dyads, triads, tetrads, pentads, and hexads, and this is probably the most instructive classification; but it does not prevent us from also classifying them according as they are metallic or non-metallic, solid liquid or gaseous at ordinary temperatures, useful or useless, abundant or scarce, ferro-magnetic or diamagnetic, and so on.

Mineralogists have spent a great deal of labour in trying to discover the supposed natural system of classification for minerals. They have constantly encountered the difficulty that the chemical composition does not run together with the crystallographic form, and the various physical pro perties of the mineral. Substances identical in the forms of their crystals, especially those belonging to the first or cubical system of crystals, are often found to have no resemblance in chemical composition. The same sub stance, again, is occasionally found crystallised in two essentially different crystallographic forms; calcium car bonate, for instance, appearing as calc-spar and arragonite. The simple truth is that if we are unable to discover any correspondence, or, as we may call it, any *correlation* between the properties of minerals, we cannot make any one arrange ment which will enable us to treat all these properties in a single system of classification. We must classify minerals in as many different ways as there are different groups of unrelated properties of sufficient importance. Even if, for the purpose of describing minerals successively in a treatise, we select one chief system, that, for instance, having regard to chemical composition, we ought mentally to regard the minerals as classified in all other useful modes.

Exactly the same may be said of the classification of plants. An immense number of different modes of classi fying plants have been proposed at one time or other, an exhaustive account of which will be found in the article on classification in Rees' "Cyclopædia," or in the introduc tion to Lindley's "Vegetable Kingdom." There have been the Fructists, such as Cæsalpinus, Morison, Hermann, Boerhaave or Gaertner, who arranged plants according to the form of the fruit. The Corollists, Rivinus, Ludwig, and Tournefort, paid attention chiefly to the number and arrangement of the parts of the corolla. Magnol selected the calyx as the critical part, while Sauvage arranged plants according to their leaves; nor are these instances more than a small selection from the actual variety of modes of classi fication which have been tried. Of such attempts it may be said that every system will probably yield some infor mation concerning the relations of plants and it is only

after trying many modes that it is possible to approximate
to the best.

Natural and Artificial Systems of Classification.

It has been usual to distinguish systems of classification as natural and artificial, those being called natural
which seemed to express the order of existing things as
determined by nature. Artificial methods of classification,
on the other hand, included those formed for the mere
convenience of men in remembering or treating natural
objects.

The difference, as it is commonly regarded, has been well
described by Ampére,[1] as follows : " We can distinguish
two kinds of classifications, the natural and the artificial.
In the latter kind, some characters, arbitrarily chosen,
serve to determine the place of each object; we abstract
all other characters, and the objects are thus found to be
brought near to or to be separated from each other, often
in the most bizarre manner. In natural systems of classification, on the contrary, we employ concurrently all the
characters essential to the objects with which we are
occupied, discussing the importance of each of them ; and
the results of this labour are not adopted unless the
objects which present the closest analogy are brought
most near together, and the groups of the several orders
which are formed from them are also approximated in proportion as they offer more similar characters. In this way
it arises that there is always a kind of connexion, more or
less marked, between each group and the group which
follows it."

There is much, however, that is vague and logically
false in this and other definitions which have been proposed by naturalists to express their notion of a natural
system. We are not informed how the *importance* of a
resemblance is to be determined, nor what is the measure
of the *closeness* of analogy. Until all the words employed
in a definition are made clear in meaning, the definition
itself is worse than useless. Now if the views concerning
classification here upheld are true, there can be no sharp

[1] *Essai sur la Philosophie des Sciences*, p. 9.

and precise distinction between natural and artificial systems. All arrangements which serve any purpose at all must be more or less natural, because, if closely enough scrutinised, they will involve more resemblances than those whereby the class was defined.

It is true that in the biological sciences there would be one arrangement of plants or animals which would be conspicuously instructive, and in a certain sense natural, if it could be attained, and it is that after which naturalists have been in reality striving for nearly two centuries, namely, that *arrangement which would display the genealogical descent of every form from the original life germ.* Those morphological resemblances upon which the classification of living beings is almost always based are inherited resemblances, and it is evident that descendants will usually resemble their parents and each other in a great many points.

I have said that a natural is distinguished from an arbitrary or artificial system only in degree. It will be found almost impossible to arrange objects according to any circumstance without finding that some correlation of other circumstances is thus made apparent. No arrangement could seem more arbitrary than the common alphabetical arrangement according to the initial letter of the name. But we cannot scrutinise a list of names of persons without noticing a predominance of Evans's and Jones's, under the letters E and J, and of names beginning with Mac under the letter M. The predominance is so great that we could not attribute it to chance, and inquiry would of course show that it arose from important facts concerning the nationality of the persons. It would appear that the Evans's and Jones's were of Welsh descent, and those whose names bear the prefix Mac of Keltic descent. With the nationality would be more or less strictly correlated many peculiarities of physical constitution, language, habits, or mental character. In other cases I have been interested in noticing the empirical inferences which are displayed in the most arbitrary arrangements. If a large register of the names of ships be examined it will often be found that a number of ships bearing the same name were built about the same time, a correlation due to the occurrence of some striking incident shortly previous to the building of the ships. The age of ships or other structures is usually correlated with their general form, nature of materials, &c, so that ships of the same name will often resemble each other in many points.

It is impossible to examine the details of some of the so-called artificial systems of classification of plants, without finding that many of the classes are natural in character. Thus in Tournefort's arrangement, depending almost entirely on the formation of the corolla, we find the natural orders of the Labiatæ, Cruciferæ, Rosaceæ, Umbelliferæ, Liliaceæ, and Papilionaceæ, recognised in his 4th, 5th, 6th, 7th, 9th, and 10th classes. Many of the classes in Linnæus' celebrated sexual system also approximate to natural classes.

Correlation of Properties.

Habits and usages of language are apt to lead us into the error of imagining that when we employ different words we always mean different things. In introducing the subject of classification nominally I was careful to draw the reader's attention to the fact that all reasoning and all operations of scientific method really involve classification, though we are accustomed to use the name in some cases and not in others. The name *correlation* requires to be used with the same qualification. Things are correlated (*con, relata*) when they are so related or bound to each other that *where one is the other is, and where one is not the other is not.* Throughout this work we have then been dealing with correlations. In geometry the occurrence of three equal angles in a triangle is correlated with the existence of three equal sides; in physics gravity is correlated with inertia; in botany exogenous growth is correlated with the possession of two cotyledons, or the production of flowers with that of spiral vessels. Wherever a proposition of the form $A = B$ is true there correlation exists. But it is in the classificatory sciences especially that the word correlation has been employed.

We find it stated that in the class Mammalia the possession of two occipital condyles, with a well-ossified basi-occipital, is correlated with the possession of mandibles, each ramus of which is composed of a single piece of bone, articulated with the squamosal element of the skull, and also with the possession of mammæ and non-nucleated red blood-corpuscles. Professor Huxley remarks [1] that this statement of the character of the class mammalia is something more than an arbitrary definition ; it is a statement of a law of correlation or co-existence of animal structures, from which most important conclusions are deducible. It involves a generalisation to the effect that in nature the structures mentioned are always found associated together.   This amounts to saying that the formation of the class mammalia involves an act of inductive discovery, and results in the establishment of certain empirical laws of nature. Professor Huxley has excellently expressed the mode in which discoveries of this kind enable naturalists to make deductions or predictions with considerable confidence, but he has also pointed out that such inferences are likely from time to time to prove mistaken. I will quote his own words :

" If a fragmentary fossil be discovered, consisting of no more than a ramus of a mandible, and that part of the skull with which it articulated, a knowledge of this law may enable the palæontologist to affirm, with great confidence, that the animal of which it formed a part suckled its young, and had non-nucleated red blood-corpuscles ; and to predict that should the back part of that skull be discovered, it will exhibit two occipital condyles and a well-ossified basi-occipital bone.

" Deductions of this kind, such as that made by Cuvier in the famous case of the fossil opossum of Montmartre, have often been verified, and are well calculated to impress the vulgar imagination ; so that they have taken rank as the triumphs of the anatomist. But it should carefully be borne in mind, that, like all merely empirical laws, which rest upon a comparatively narrow observational basis, the reasoning from them may at any time break down. If Cuvier, for example, had had to do with a fossil Thylacinus instead of a fossil Opossum, he would not have found the marsupial bones, though the inflected angle of the jaw would have been obvious enough.   And

<hr>

[1] *Lectures on the Elements of Comparative Anatomy, and on the Classification of Animals,* 1864, p. 3.

so, though, practically, any one who met with a characteristically mammalian jaw would be justified in expecting
to find the characteristically mammalian occiput associated with it; yet, he would be a bold man indeed, who
should strictly assert the belief which is implied in this
expectation, viz., that at no period of the world's history
did animals exist which combined a mammalian occiput
with a reptilian jaw, or *vice versâ*."

One of the most distinct and remarkable instances of
correlation in the animal world is that which occurs in
ruminating animals, and which could not be better stated
than in the following extract from the classical work of
Cuvier :[1]

" I doubt if any one would have divined, if untaught
by observation, that all ruminants have the foot cleft,
and that they alone have it. I doubt if any one would
have divined that there are frontal horns only in this
class : that those among them which have sharp canines
for the most part lack horns.

" However, since these relations are constant, they must
have some sufficient cause ; but since we are ignorant of
it, we must make good the defect of the theory by means
of observation : it enables us to establish empirical laws
which become almost as certain as rational laws when
they rest on sufficiently repeated observations ; so that
now whoso sees merely the print of a cleft foot may conclude that the animal which left this impression rumi-
nated, and this conclusion is as certain as any other in
physics or morals. This footprint alone then, yields, to
him who observes it, the form of the teeth, the form of
the jaws, the form of the vertebræ, the form of all the
bones of the legs, of the thighs, of the shoulders, and of
the pelvis of the animal which has passed by : it is a
surer mark than all those of Zadig."

We meet with a good instance of the purely empirical
correlation of circumstances when we classify the planets
according to their densities and periods of axial rotation.[2]
If we examine a table specifying the usual astronomical
elements of the solar system, we find that four planets

[1] *Ossemens Fossiles,* 4th edit. vol. i. p. 164. Quoted by Huxley,
Lectures, &c., p. 5.
[2] Chambers, *Descriptive Astronomy,* 1st edit. p. 23.

resemble each other very closely in the period of axial rotation, and the same four planets are all found to have high densities, thus :—

Name of Planet.	Period of Axial Rotation.			Density.
Mercury	24 hours	5 minutes	. . .	7·94
Venus	23 „	21 „	· · ·	5·33
Earth	23 „	56 „	· · ·	5·67
Mars	24 „	37 „	· · ·	5·84

A similar table for the other larger planets, is as follows :—

Jupiter	9 hours	55 minutes	. . .	1·36
Saturn	10 „	29 „	· · ·	·74
Uranus	9 „	30 „	· · ·	·97
Neptune	— „	—	. . .	1·02

It will be observed that in neither group is the equality of the rotational period or the density more than rudely approximate; nevertheless the difference of the numbers in the first and second group is so very well marked, the periods of the first being at least double and the densities four or five times those of the second, that the coincidence cannot be attributed to accident. The reader will also notice that the first group consists of the planets nearest to the sun; that with the exception of the earth none of them possess satellites; and that they are all comparatively small. The second group are furthest from the sun, and all of them possess several satellites, and are comparatively great. Therefore, with but slight exceptions, the following correlations hold true :—

Interior planets.	Long period.	Small size.	High Density.	No satellites.
Exterior „	Short „	Great „	Low „	Many „

These coincidences point with much probabilty to a difference in the origin of the two groups, but no further explanation of the matter is yet possible.

The classification of comets according to their periods by Mr. Hind and Mr. A. S. Davies, tends to establish the conclusion that distinct groups of comets have been brought into the solar system by the attractive powers of Jupiter, Uranus, or other planets.[1] The classification of nebulæ as commenced by the two Herschels, and continued

---

[1] *Philosophical Magazine*, 4th Series, vol. xxxix. p. 396 ; vol. xl. p. 183 ; vol. xli. p. 44. See also Proctor, *Popular Science Review*. October 1874, p. 350.

by Lord Rosse, Mr. Huggins, and others, will probably lead at some future time to the discovery of important empirical laws concerning the constitution of the universe. The minute examination and classification of meteorites, as carried on by Mr. Sorby and others, seems likely to afford us an insight into the formation of the heavenly bodies.

We should never fail to remember the slightest and most inexplicable correlations, for they may prove of importance in the future. Discoveries begin when we are least expecting them. It is a significant fact, for instance, that the greater number of variable stars are of a reddish colour. Not all variable stars are red, nor all red stars variable; but considering that only a small fraction of the observed stars are known to be variable, and only a small fraction are red, the number which fall into both classes is too great to be accidental.[1] It is also remarkable that the greater number of stars possessing great proper motion are double stars, the star 61 Cygni being especially noticeable in this respect.[2] The correlation in these cases is not without exception, but the preponderance is so great as to point to some natural connexion, the exact nature of which must be a matter for future investigation. Herschel remarked that the two double stars 61 Cygni and a Centauri of which the orbits were well ascertained, evidently belonged to the same family or genus.[3]

Classification in Crystallography.

Perhaps the most perfect and instructive instance of classification which we can find is furnished by the science of crystallography (p. 133). The system of arrangement now generally adopted is conspicuously natural, and is even mathematically perfect. A crystal consists in every part of similar molecules similarly related to the adjoining molecules, and connected with them by forces the nature of which we can only learn by their apparent effects. But these forces are exerted in space of three dimensions, so that there is a limited number of suppositions which can be entertained as to the relations of these forces. In one

[1] Humboldt, *Cosmos* (Bohn), vol. iii. p. 224.
[2] Baily, *British Association Catalogue*, p. 48.
[3] *Outlines of Astronomy*, § 850, 4th edit. p. 578.

case each molecule will be similarly related to all those which are next to it; in a second case, it will be similarly related to those in a certain plane, but differently related to those not in that plane. In the simpler cases the arrangement of molecules is rectangular; in the remaining cases oblique either in one or two planes.

In order to simplify the explanation and conception of the complicated phenomena which crystals exhibit, an hypothesis has been invented which is an excellent instance of the Descriptive Hypotheses before mentioned (p. 522). Crystallographers imagine that there are within each crystal certain axes, or lines of direction, by the comparative length and the mutual inclination of which the nature of the crystal is determined. In one class of crystals there are three such axes lying in one plane, and a fourth perpendicular to that plane; but in all the other classes there are imagined to be only three axes. Now these axes can be varied in three ways as regards length: they may be (1) all equal, or (2) two equal and one unequal, or (3) all unequal. They may also be varied in four ways as regards direction: (1) they may be all at right angles to each other; (2) two axes may be oblique to each other and at right angles to the third; (3) two axes may be at right angles to each other and the third oblique to both; (4) the three axes may be all oblique. Now, if all the variations as regards length were combined with those regarding direction, it would seem to be possible to have twelve classes of crystals in all, the enumeration being then logically and geometrically complete. But as a matter of empirical observation, many of these classes are not found to occur, oblique axes being seldom or never equal. There remain seven recognised classes of crystals, but even of these one class is not positively known to be represented in nature.

The first class of crystals is defined by possessing three equal rectangular axes, and equal elasticity in all directions. The primary or simple form of the crystals is the cube, but by the removal of the corners of the cube by planes variously inclined to the axes, we have the regular octohedron, the dodecahedron, and various combinations of these forms. Now it is a law of this class of crystals that as each axis is exactly like each other axis, every modification of any corner of a crystal must be repeated symmetrically with

regard to the other axes; thus the forms produced are
symmetrical or regular, and the class is called the *Regular
System* of crystals. It includes a great variety of substances,
some of them being elements, such as carbon in the form
of diamond, others more or less complex compounds, such
as rock-salt, potassium iodide and bromide, the several
kinds of alum, fluor-spar, iron bisulphide, garnet, spinelle,
&c. No correlation then is apparent between the form of
crystallisation and the chemical composition. But what
we have to notice is that the physical properties of the
crystallised substances with regard to light, heat, electricity,
&c., are closely similar. Light and heat undulations,wher-
ever they enter a crystal of the regular system, spread with
equal rapidity in all directions, just as they would in a uniform fluid. Crystals of the regular system accordingly do
not in any case exhibit the phenomena of double refraction,
unless by mechanical compression we alter the conditions
of elasticity. These crystals, again, expand equally in all
directions when heated, and if we could cut a sufficiently
large plate from a cubical crystal, and examine the sound
vibrations of which it is capable, we should find that they
indicated an equal elasticity in every direction. Thus we
see that a great number of important properties are correlated with that of crystallisation in the regular system, and
as soon as we know that the primary form of a substance
is the cube, we are able to infer with approximate certainty
that it possesses all these properties. The class of regular
crystals is then an eminently natural class, one disclosing
many general laws connecting together the physical and
mechanical properties of the substances classified.

In the second class of crystals, called the dimetric, square
prismatic, or pyramidal system, there are also three axes at
right angles to each other: two of the axes are equal, but
the third or principal axis is unequal, being either greater
or less than either of the other two. In such crystals.
accordingly the elasticity and other properties are alike
in all directions perpendicular to the principal axis, but
vary in all other directions. If a point within a crystal of
this system be heated, the heat spreads with equal rapidity
in planes perpendicular to the principal axis, but more or
less rapidly in the direction of this axis, so that the isothermal surface is an ellipsoid of revolution round that axis

Nearly the same statement may be made concerning the third or hexagonal or rhombohedral system of crystals, in which there are three axes lying in one plane and meeting at angles of 60°, while the fourth axis is perpendicular to the other three. The hexagonal prism and rhombohedron are the commonest forms assumed by crystals of this system, and in ice, quartz, and calc-spar, we have abundance of beautiful specimens of the various shapes produced by the modification of the primitive form. Calc-spar alone is said to crystallise in at least 700 varieties of form. Now of all the crystals belonging both to this and the dimetric class, we know that a ray of light passing in the direction of the principal axis will be refracted singly as in a crystal of the regular system; but in every other direction the light will suffer double refraction being separated into two rays, one of which obeys the ordinary law of refraction, but the other a much more complicated law. The other physical properties vary in an analogous manner. Thus calc-spar expands by heat in the direction of the principal axis, but contracts a little in directions perpendicular to it. So closely are the physical properties correlated that Mits-cherlich, having observed the law of expansion in calc-spar, was enabled to predict that the double refracting power of the substance would be decreased by a rise of temperature, as was proved by experiment to be the case.

In the fourth system, called the trimetric, rhombic, or right prismatic system, there are three axes, at right angles, but all unequal in length. It may be asserted in general terms that the mechanical properties vary in such crystals in every direction, and heat spreads so that the isothermal surface is an ellipsoid with three unequal axes.

In the remaining three classes, called the monoclinic, diclinic, and triclinic, the axes are more or less oblique, and at the same time unequal. The complication of phenomena is therefore greatly increased, and it need only be stated that there are always two directions in which a ray is singly refracted, but that in all other directions double refraction takes place. The conduction of heat is unequal in all directions, the isothermal surface being an ellipsoid of three unequal axes. The relations of such crystals to other phenomena are often very complicated, and hardly yet reduced to law. Some crystals, called pyro-electric, manifest vitreous electricity at some points of their surface, and resinous electricity at other points when rising in temperature, the character of the electricity being changed when the temperature sinks again. This production of electricity is believed to be connected with the hemihedral character of the crystals exhibiting it. The crystalline structure of a substance again influences its magnetic behaviour, the general law being that the direction in which the molecules of a crystal are most approximated tends to place itself axially or equatorially between the poles of a magnet, respectively as the body is magnetic or diamagnetic. Further questions arise if we apply pressure to crystals. Thus doubly refracting crystals with one principal axis acquire two axes when the pressure is perpendicular in direction to the principal axis.

All the phenomena peculiar to crystalline bodies are thus closely correlated with the formation of the crystal, or will almost certainly be found to be so as investigation proceeds. It is upon empirical observation indeed that the laws of connexion are in the first place founded, but the simple hypothesis that the elasticity and approximation of the particles vary in the directions of the crystalline axes allows of the application of deductive reasoning. The whole of the phenomena are gradually being proved to be consistent with this hypothesis, so that we have in this subject of crystallography a beautiful instance of successful classification, connected with a nearly perfect physical hypothesis. Moreover this hypothesis was verified experimentally as regards the mechanical vibrations of sound by Savart, who found that the vibrations in a plate of biaxial crystal indicated the existence of varying elasticity in varying directions.

Classification an Inverse and Tentative Operation.

If attempts at so-called natural classification are really attempts at perfect induction, it follows that they are subject to the remarks which were made upon the inverse character of the inductive process, and upon the difficulty of every inverse operation (pp. 11, 12, 122, &c.). There will be no royal road to the discovery of the best system, and it will even be impossible to lay down rules of procedure to assist those who are in search of a good arrangement. The only logical rule would be as follows :—Having given certain objects, group them in every way in which they can be grouped, and then observe in which method of grouping the correlation of properties is most conspicuously manifested. But this method of exhaustive classification will in almost every case be impracticable, owing to the immensely great number of modes in which a comparatively small number of objects may be grouped together. About sixty-three elements have been classified by chemists in six principal groups as monad, dyad, triad, &c., elements, the numbers in the classes varying from three to twenty elements. Now if we were to calculate the whole number of ways in which sixty-three objects can be arranged in six groups, we should find the number to be so great that the life of the longest lived man would be wholly inadequate to enable him to go through these possible groupings. The rule of exhaustive arrangement, then, is absolutely impracticable. It follows that mere haphazard trial cannot as a general rule give any useful result. If we were to write the names of the elements in succession upon sixty-three cards, throw them into a ballot-box, and draw them out haphazard in six handfuls time after time, the probability is excessively small that we should take them out in a specified order, that for instance at present adopted by chemists.

The usual mode in which an investigator proceeds to form a classification of a new group of objects seems to consist in tentatively arranging them according to their most obvious similarities. Any two objects which present a close resemblance to each other will be joined and formed into the rudiment of a class, the definition of which will at first include all the apparent points of resemblance. Other objects as they come to our notice will be gradually assigned to those groups with which they present the greatest number of points of resemblance, and the definition of a class will often have to be altered in order to admit them. The early chemists could hardly avoid classing together the common metals, gold, silver, copper, lead, and iron, which present such conspicuous points of similarity as regards density, metallic lustre, malleability,

&c. With the progress of discovery, however, difficulties
began to present themselves in such a grouping. Antimony, bismuth, and arsenic are distinctly metallic as
regards lustre, density, and some chemical properties, but
are wanting in malleability. The recently discovered
tellurium presents greater difficulties, for it has many of
the physical properties of metal, and yet all its chemical
properties are analogous to those of sulphur and selenium,
which have never been regarded as metals. Great chemical
differences again are discovered by degrees between the five
metals mentioned; and the class, if it is to have any chemical validity, must be made to include other elements,
having none of the original properties on which the class
was founded. Hydrogen is a transparent colourless gas,
and the least dense of all substances; yet in its chemical
analogies it is a metal, as suggested by Faraday [1] in 1838,
and almost proved by Graham; [2] it must be placed in
the same class as silver. In this way it comes to pass that
almost every classification which is proposed in the early
stages of a science will be found to break down as the
deeper similarities of the objects come to be detected. The
most obvious points of difference will have to be neglected.
Chlorine is a gas, bromine a liquid, and iodine a solid, and
at first sight these might have seemed formidable circumstances to overlook; but in chemical analogy the substances
are closely united. The progress of organic chemistry,
again, has yielded wholly new ideas of the similarities of
compounds. Who, for instance, would recognise without
extensive research a close similarity between glycerine and
alcohol, or between fatty substances and ether? The class
of paraffins contains three substances gaseous at ordinary
temperatures, several liquids, and some crystalline solids.
It required much insight to detect the analogy which exists
between such apparently different substances.

The science of chemistry now depends to a great extent
on a correct classification of the elements, as will be learnt
by consulting the able article on Classification by Professor G. C. Foster in Watts' *Dictionary of Chemistry*
But the present system of chemical classification was not

---

[1] *Life of Faraday*, vol. ii. p. 87.
[2] *Proceedings of the Royal Society*, vol. xvii. p. 212. *Chemical and
Physical Researches*, reprint, by Young and Angus Smith, p. 290.

reached until at least three previous false systems had been long entertained. And though there is much reason to believe that the present mode of classification according to atomicity is substantially correct, errors may yet be discovered in the details of the grouping.

Symbolic Statement of the Theory of Classification.

The theory of classification can be explained in the most complete and general manner, by reverting for a time to the use of the Logical Alphabet, which was found to be of supreme importance in Formal Logic.   That form expresses the necessary classification of all objects and ideas as depending on the laws of thought, and there is no point concerning the purpose and methods of classification which may not be stated precisely by the use of letter combinations, the only inconvenience being the abstract form in which the subject is thus represented.

If we pay regard only to three qualities in which things may resemble each other, namely, the qualities A, B, C, there are according to the laws of thought eight possible classes of objects, shown in the fourth column of the Logical Alphabet (p. 94).   If there exist objects belonging to all these eight classes, it follows that the qualities A, B, C, are subject to no conditions except the primary laws of thought and things (p. 5).   There is then no special law of nature to discover, and, if we arrange the objects in any one order rather than another, it must be for the purpose of showing that the combinations are logically complete.

Suppose, however, that there are but four kinds of objects possessing the qualities A, B, C, and that these kinds are represented by the combinations ABC, AbC, aBc, abc. The order of arrangement will now be of importance ; for if we place them in the order

$$\left\{ \begin{array}{l} \text{ABC} \\ a\text{B}c \end{array} \right. \qquad\qquad \left\{ \begin{array}{l} \text{A}b\text{C} \\ abc \end{array} \right.$$

placing the B's first and those which are b's last, we shall perhaps overlook the law of correlation of properties involved.   But if we arrange the combinations as follows

$$\left\{ \begin{array}{l} \text{ABC} \\ \text{A}b\text{C} \end{array} \right. \qquad\qquad \left\{ \begin{array}{l} a\text{B}c \\ abc \end{array} \right.$$

it becomes apparent at once that where A is, and only where A is, the property C is to be found, B being

indifferently present and absent. The second arrangement
then would be called a natural one, as rendering manifest the conditions under which the combinations exist.

As a further instance, let us suppose that eight objects
are presented to us for classification, which exhibit combinations of the five properties, A, B, C, D, E, in the following manner:—

ABC*d*E	*a*BC*d*E
AB*cde*	*a*B*cde*
A*b*CDE	*ab*CDE
A*bc*D*e*	*abc*D*e*

They are now classified, so that those containing A stand
first, and those devoid of A second, but no other property
seems to be correlated with A. Let us alter this arrangement and group the combinations thus :—

ABC*d*E	A*b*CDE
AB*cde*	A*bc*D*e*
*a*BC*d*E	*ab*CDE
*a*B*cde*	*abc*D*e*

It requires little examination to discover that in the first
group B is always present and D absent, whereas in the
second group, B is always absent and D present. This is
the result which follows from a law of the form $B = d$
(p. 136), so that in this mode of arrangement we readily
discover correlation between two letters. Altering the
groups again as follows :—

ABC*d*E	AB*cde*
*a*BC*d*E	*a*B*cde*
A*b*CDE	A*bc*D*e*
*ab*CDE	*abc*D*e*,

we discover another evident correlation between C and E.
Between A and the other letters, or between the two pairs
of letters B, D and C, E, there is no logical connexion.

This example may seem tedious, but it will be found
instructive in this way. We are classifying only eight
objects or combinations, in each of which only five qualities
are considered. There are only two laws of correlation
between four of those five qualities, and those aws are
of the simplest logical character. Yet the reader would
hardly discover what those laws are, and confidently assign
them by rapid contemplation of the combinations, as given
in the first group. Several tentative classifications must

probably be made before we can resolve the question. Let us now suppose that instead of eight objects and five qualities, we have, say, five hundred objects and fifty qualities. If we were to attempt the same method of exhaustive grouping which we before employed, we should have to arrange the five hundred objects in fifty different ways, before we could be sure that we had discovered even the simpler laws of correlation. But even the successive grouping of all those possessing each of the fifty properties would not necessarily give us all the laws. There might exist complicated relations between several properties simultaneously, for the detection of which no rule of procedure whatever can be given.

Bifurcate Classification.

Every system of classification ought to be formed on the principles of the Logical Alphabet. Each superior class should be divided into two inferior classes, distinguished by the possession and non-possession of a single specified difference. Each of these minor classes, again, is divisible by any other quality whatever which can be suggested, and thus every classification logically consists of an infinitely extended series of subaltern genera and species. The classifications which we form are in reality very small fragments of those which would correctly and fully represent the relations of existing things. But if we take more than four or five qualities into account, the number of subdivisions grows impracticably large. Our finite minds are unable to treat any complex group exhaustively, and we are obliged to simplify and generalise scientific problems, often at the risk of overlooking particular conditions and exceptions.

Every system of classes displayed in the manner of the Logical Alphabet may be called *bifurcate*, because every class branches out at each step into two minor classes, existent or imaginary. It would be a great mistake to regard this arrangement as in any way a peculiar or special method; it is not only a natural and important one, but it is the inevitable and only system which is logically perfect, according to the fundamental laws of thought. All other arrangements of classes correspond to the bifurcate arrangement, with the implication that some

of the minor classes are not represented among existing
things. If we take the genus A and divide it into the
species AB and AC, we imply two propositions, namely
that in the class A, the properties of B and C never occur
together, and that they are never both absent; these
propositions are logically equivalent to one, namely
$AB = Ac$. Our classification is then identical with the
following bifurcate one :—

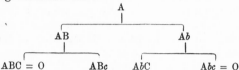

If, again, we divide the genus A into three species, AB,
AC, AD, we are either logically in error, or else we must
be understood to imply that, as regards the other letters,
there exist only three combinations containing A, namely
ABcd, AbCd, and AbcD.

The logical necessity of bifurcate classification has been
clearly and correctly stated in the *Outline of a New System
of Logic* by George Bentham, the eminent botanist, a work
of which the logical value has been quite overlooked until
lately. Mr. Bentham points out, in p. 113, that every
classification must be essentially bifurcate, and takes, as
an example, the division of vertebrate animals into four
sub-classes, as follows :—

Mammifera—endowed with mammæ and lungs.
Birds   without mammæ but with lungs and wings.
Fish   deprived of lungs.
Reptiles   deprived of mammæ and wings but with
             lungs.

We have, then, as Mr. Bentham says, three bifid divisions, thus represented :—

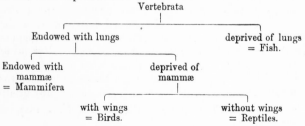

It is quite evident that according to the laws of thought even this arrangement is incomplete. The sub-class mammifera must either have wings or be deprived of them ; we must either subdivide this class, or assume that none of the mammifera have wings, which is, as a matter of fact, the case, the wings of bats not being true wings in the meaning of the term as applied to birds. Fish, again, ought to be considered with regard to the possession of mammæ and wings ; and in leaving them undivided we really imply that they never have mammæ nor wings, the wings of the flying-fish, again, being no exception. If we resort to the use of our letters and define them as follows—

A = vertebrata,
B = having lungs,
C = having mammæ,
D = having wings,

then there are four existent classes of vertebrata which appear to be thus described—

ABC   ABcD   ABcd   Ab.

But in reality the combinations are implied to be

ABCd = Mammifera,
ABcD = Birds,
ABcd = Reptiles,
Abcd = Fish,

and we imply at the same time that the other four conceivable combinations containing B, C, or D, namely ABCD, AbCD, AbCd, and AbcD, do not exist in nature.

Mr. Bentham points out [1] that it is really this method of classification which was employed by Lamarck and De Candolle in their so-called analytical arrangement of the French Flora. He gives as an example a table of the principal classes of De Candolle's system, as also a bifurcate arrangement of animals after the method proposed by Duméril in his *Zoologie Analytique*, this naturalist being distinguished by his clear perception of the logical importance of the method. A bifurcate classification of the animal kingdom may also be found in Professor Reay Greene's *Manual of the Cœlenterata*, p. 18.

The bifurcate form of classification seems to be needless when the quality according to which we classify any group

[1] *Essai sur la Nomenclature et la Classification,* Paris, 1823, pp. 107, 108.

of things admits of numerical discrimination. It would seem absurd to arrange things according as they have one degree of the quality or not one degree, two degrees or not two degrees, and so on. The elements are classified according as the atom of each saturates one, two, three, or more atoms of a monad element, such as chlorine, and they are called accordingly monad, dyad, triad, tetrad elements, and so on. It would be useless to apply the bifid arrangement, thus :—

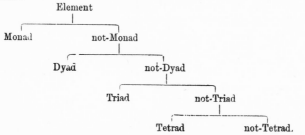

The reason of this is that, by the nature of number (p. 157) every number is logically discriminated from every other number. There can thus be no logical confusion in a numerical arrangement, and the series of numbers indefinitely extended is also exhaustive. Every thing admitting of a quality expressible in numbers must find its place somewhere in the series of numbers. The chords in music correspond to the simpler numerical ratios and must admit of complete exhaustive classification in respect to the complexity of the ratios forming them. Plane rectilinear figures may be classified according to the numbers of their sides, as triangles, quadrilateral figures, pentagons, hexagons, heptagons, &c. The bifurcate arrangement is not false when applied to such series of objects; it is even necessarily involved in the arrangement which we do apply, so that its formal statement is needless and tedious. The same may be said of the division of portions of space. Reid and Kames endeavoured to cast ridicule on the bifurcate arrangement[1] by proposing to classify the parts of England into Middlesex and what is not Middlesex, dividing the latter again into Kent and what is not Kent, Sussex and

---

[1] George Bentham, *Outline of a New System of Logic*, p. 115.

what is not Sussex ; and so on. This is so far, however, from being an absurd proceeding that it is requisite to assure us that we have made an exhaustive enumeration of the parts of England.

The Five Predicables.

As a rule it is highly desirable to consign to oblivion the ancient logical names and expressions, which have infested the science for many centuries past. If logic is ever to be a useful and progressive science, logicians must distinguish between logic and the history of logic. As in the case of any other science it may be desirable to examine the course of thought by which logic has, before or since the time of Aristotle, been brought to its present state; the history of a science is always instructive as giving instances of the mode in which discoveries take place. But at the same time we ought carefully to disencumber the statement of the science itself of all names and other vestiges of antiquity which are not actually useful at the present day.

Among the ancient expressions which may well be excepted from such considerations and retained in use, are the "Five Words" or "Five Predicables" which were described by Porphyry in his introduction to Aristotle's Organum. Two of them, *Genus* and *Species*, are the most venerable names in philosophy, having probably been first employed in their present logical meanings by Socrates. In the present day it requires some mental effort, as remarked by Grote, to see anything important in the invention of notions now so familiar as those of Genus and Species. But in reality the introduction of such terms showed the rise of the first germs of logic and scientific method; it showed that men were beginning to analyse their processes of thought.

The Five Predicables are Genus, Species, Difference, Property, and Accident. or in the original Greek, γένος, εἶδος, διαφορά, ἴδιον, συμβεβηκός. Of these, Genus may be taken to mean any class of objects which is regarded as broken up into two minor classes, which form Species of it. The genus is defined by a certain number of qualities or circumstances which belong to all objects included in the class, and which are sufficient to mark out these objects from all others which we do not intend to include. Interpreted as regards intension, then, the genus is a group of qualities; interpreted as regards extension, it is a group of objects possessing those qualities. If another quality be taken into account which is possessed by some of the objects and not by the others, this quality becomes a difference which divides the genus into two species. We may interpret the species either in intension or extension; in the former respect it is more than the genus as containing one more quality, the difference: in the latter respect it is less than the genus as containing only a portion of the group constituting the genus. We may say, then, with Aristotle, that in one sense the genus is in the species, namely in intension, and in another sense the species is in the genus, namely in extension. The difference, it is evident, can be interpreted in intension only.

A Property is a quality which belongs to the whole of a class, but does not enter into the definition of that class. A ·generic property belongs to every individual object contained in the genus. It is a property of the genus parallelogram that the opposite angles are equal. If we regard a rectangle as a species of parallelogram, the difference being that *one* angle is a right angle, it follows as a specific property that all the angles are right angles. Though a property in the strict logical sense must belong to each of the objects included in the class of which it is a property, it may or may not belong to other objects. The property of having the opposite angles equal may belong to many figures besides parallelograms, for instance, regular hexagons. It is a property of the circle that all triangles constructed upon the diameter with the apex upon the circumference are right-angled triangles, and *vice versâ*, all curves of which this is true must be circles. A property which thus belongs to the whole of a class and only to that class, corresponds to the ἴδιον of Aristotle and Porphyry; we might conveniently call it *a peculiar property*. Every such property enables us to make a statement in the form of a simple identity (p. 37). Thus we know it to be a peculiar property of the circle that for a given length of perimeter it encloses a greater area than any other possible curve ; hence we may say—

Curve of equal curvature = curve of greatest area.

It is a peculiar property of equilateral triangles that they are equiangular, and *vice versâ*, it is a peculiar property of equiangular triangles that they are equilateral. It is a property of crystals of the regular system that they are devoid of the power of double refraction, but this is not a property peculiar to them, because liquids and gases are devoid of the same property.

An Accident, the fifth and last of the Predicables, is any quality which may or may not belong to certain objects, and which has no connexion with the classification adopted. The particular size of a crystal does not in the slightest degree affect the form of the crystal, nor does the manner in which it is grouped with other crystals ; these, then, are accidents as regards a crystallographic classification. With respect to the chemical composition of a substance, again, it is an accident whether the substance be crystallised or not, or whether it be organised or not. As regards botanical classification the absolute size of a plant is an accident. Thus we see that a logical accident is any quality or circumstance which is not known to be correlated with those qualities or circumstances forming the definition of the species.

The meanings of the Predicables can be clearly explained by our symbols. Let A be any definite group of qualities and B another quality or group of qualities; then A will constitute a genus, and AB, Ab will be species of it, B being the difference. Let C, D and E be other qualities or groups of qualities, and on examining the combinations in which A, B, C, D, E occur let them be as follows :—

$$ABCDE \qquad AbCdE$$
$$ABCDe \qquad AbCde.$$

Here we see that wherever A is we also find C, so that C is a generic property; D occurs always with B, so that it constitutes a specific property, while E is indifferently present and absent, so as not to be related to any other letter; it represents, therefore, an accident. It will now be seen that the Logical Alphabet represents an interminable series of subordinate genera and species; it is but a concise symbolic statement of what was involved in the ancient doctrine of the Predicables.

Summum Genus and Infima Species.

As a genus means any class whatever which is regarded as composed of minor classes or species, it follows that the same class will be a genus in one point of view and a species in another. Metal is a genus as regards alkaline metal, a species as regards element, and any extensive system of classes consists of a series of subordinate, or as they are technically called, *subaltern* genera and species. The question, however, arises, whether such a chain of classes has a definite termination at either end. The doctrine of the old logicians was to the effect that it terminated upwards in a *genus generalissimum* or *summum genus*, which was not a species of any wider class. Some very general notion, such as substance, object, or thing, was supposed to be so comprehensive as to include all thinkable objects, and for all practical purposes this might be so. But as I have already explained (p. 74), we cannot really think of any object or class without thereby separating it from what is not that object or class. All thinking is relative, and implies discrimination, so that every class and every logical notion must have its negative. If so, there is no such thing as a *summum genus;* for we cannot frame the requisite notion of a class forming it without implying the existence of another class discriminated from it; add this new negative class to the supposed *summum genus,* and we form a still higher genus, which is absurd.

Although there is no absolute summum genus, nevertheless relatively to any branch of knowledge or any particular argument, there is always some class or notion which bounds our horizon as it were. The chemist restricts his view to material substances and the forces manifested in them; the mathematician extends his view so as to comprehend all notions capable of numerical discrimination. The biologist, on the other hand, has a narrower sphere containing only organised bodies, and of these the botanist and the zoologist take parts. In other subjects there may be a still narrower summum genus, as when the lawyer regards only reasoning beings of his own country together with their property.

In the description of the Logical Alphabet it was pointed out (p. 93) that every series of combinations is really the

development of a single class, denoted by X, which letter
was accordingly placed in the first column of the table on
p. 94. This is the formal acknowledgment of the principle
clearly stated by De Morgan, that all reasoning proceeds
within an assumed summum genus. But at the same time
the fact that X as a logical term must have its negative
x, shows that it cannot be an absolute summum genus.

There arises, again, the question whether there be any
such thing as an *infima species*, which cannot be divided
into minor species. The ancient logicians were of opinion
that there always was some assignable class which could
only be divided into individuals, but this doctrine appears
to be theoretically incorrect, as Mr. George Bentham
long ago stated.[1] We may put an arbitrary limit to the
subdivision of our classes at any point convenient to our
purpose. The crystallographer would not generally treat
as different species crystalline forms which differ only
in the degree of development of the faces. The naturalist
overlooks innumerable slight differences between animals
which he refers to the same species. But in a strictly
logical point of view classification might be carried on as
long as there is a difference, however minute, between
two objects, and we might thus go on until we arrive at
individual objects which are numerically distinct in the
logical sense attributed to that expression in the chapter
upon Number. Either, then, we must call the individual
the *infima species* or allow that there is no such thing at all.

The Tree of Porphyry.

Both Aristotle and Plato were acquainted with the value
of bifurcate classification, which they occasionally employed
in an explicit manner. It is impossible too that Aristotle
should state the laws of thought, and employ the predicables
without implicitly recognising the logical necessity of that
method. It is, however, in Porphyry's remarkable and in
many respects excellent *Introduction to the Categories of
Aristotle* that we find the most distinct account of it.
Porphyry not only fully and accurately describes the
Predicables, but incidentally introduces an example for

---

[1] *Outline of a New System of Logic*, 1827, p. 117.

illustrating those predicables, which constitutes a good
specimen of bifurcate classification. Translating his words[1]
freely we may say that he takes Substance as the genus to
be divided, under which are successively placed as Species—
Body, Animated Body, Animal, Rational Animal, and Man.
Under Man, again, come Socrates, Plato, and other particular men.   Now of these notions Substance is the genus
generalissimum, and is a genus only, not a species.   Man,
on the other hand, is the species specialissima (infima
species), and is a species only, not a genus.   Body is a
species of substance, but a genus of animated body, which,
again, is a species of body but a genus of animal.
Animal is a species of animated body, but a genus of
rational animal, which, again, is a species of animal, but a
genus of man.   Finally, man is a species of rational animal,
but is a species merely and not a genus, being divisible
only into particular men.

Porphyry proceeds at some length to employ his example
in further illustration of the predicables. We do not
find in Porphyry's own work any scheme or diagram
exhibiting this curious specimen of classification, but some
of the earlier commentators and epitome writers drew what
has long been called the Tree of Porphyry.   This diagram,
which may be found in most elementary works on Logic,[2]
is also called the Ramean Tree, because Ramus insisted
much upon the value of Dichotomy.   With the exception
of Jeremy Bentham[3] and George Bentham, hardly any
modern logicians have shown an appreciation of the value
of bifurcate classification.   The latter author has treated
the subject, both in his *Outline of a New System of Logic*
(pp. 105-118), and in his earlier work entitled *Essai sur la
Nomenclature et la Classification des Principales Branches
d'Art-et-Science* (Paris, 1823), which consists of a free
translation or improved version of his uncle's Essay on
Classification in the *Chrestomathia*.   Some interest attaches
to the history of the Tree of Porphyry and Ramus, because it
is the prototype of the Logical Alphabet which lies at the
basis of logical method.   Jeremy Bentham speaks truly

---

[1] *Porphyrii Isagoge*, Caput ii. 24.
[2] Jevons, *Elementary Lessons in Logic*, p. 104
[3] *Chrestomathia ; being a Collection of Papers, &c.* London, 1816,
Appendix V.

of "the matchless beauty of the Ramean Tree." After
fully showing its logical value as an exhaustive method of
classification, and refuting the objections of Reid and
Kames, on a wrong ground, as I think, he proceeds to
inquire to what length it may be carried. He correctly
points out two objections to the extensive use of bifid
arrangements, (1) that they soon become impracticably
extensive and unwieldy, and (2) that they are unecono-
mical. In his day the recorded number of different species
of plants was 40,000, and he leaves the reader to estimate
the immense number of branches and the enormous area of
a bifurcate table which should exhibit all these species in
one scheme. He also points out the apparent loss of
labour in making any large bifurcate classification; but
this he considers to be fully recompensed by the logical
value of the result, and the logical training acquired in its
execution. Jeremy Bentham, then, fully recognises the
value of the Logical Alphabet under another name, though
he apprehends also the limit to its use placed by the
finiteness of our mental and manual powers.

Does Abstraction imply Generalisation?

Before we can acquire a sound comprehension of the
subject of classification we must answer the very difficult
question whether logical abstraction does or does not imply
generalisation. It comes to exactly the same thing if we
ask whether a species may be coextensive with its genus,
or whether, on the other hand, the genus must contain
more than the species. To abstract logically is (p. 27),
to overlook or withdraw our notice from some point of
difference. Whenever we form a class we abstract, for the
time being, the differences of the objects so united in respect
of some common quality. If we class together a great
number of objects as dwelling-houses, we overlook the fact
that some dwelling-houses are constructed of stone, others
of brick, wood, iron, &c. Often at least the abstraction of a
circumstance increases the number of objects included
under a class according to the law of the inverse relation
of the quantities of extension and intension (p. 26).
Dwelling-house is a wider term than brick-dwelling-house.
House is more general than dwelling-house. But the

question before us is, whether abstraction *always* increases
the number of objects included in a class, which amounts to
asking whether the law of the inverse relation of logical
quantities is *always* true. The interest of the question
partly arises from the fact, that so high a philosophical
authority as Mr. Herbert Spencer has denied that generalisation is implied in abstraction,[1] making this doctrine
the ground for rejecting previous methods of classifying
the sciences, and for forming an ingenious but peculiar
method of his own. The question is also a fundamental
one of the highest logical importance, and involves subtle
difficulties which have made me long hesitate in forming
a decisive opinion.

Let us attempt to answer the question by examination of
a few examples. Compare the two classes *gun* and *iron
gun*. It is certain that there are many guns which are not
made of iron, so that abstraction of the circumstance " made
of iron " increases the extent of the notion. Next compare
gun and *metallic gun*. All guns made at the present day
consist of metal, so that the two notions seem to be co-
extensive; but guns were at first made of pieces of wood
bound together like a tub, and as the logical term *gun*
takes no account of time, it must include all guns that
have ever existed. Here again extension increases as intension decreases. Compare once more " steam-locomotive
engine " and " locomotive engine." In the present day, as
far as I am aware, all locomotives are worked by steam, so
that the omission of that qualification might seem not to
widen the term; but it is quite possible that in some future
age a different motive power may be used in locomotives ;
and as there is no limitation of time in the use of logical
terms, we must certainly assume that there is a class of
locomotives not worked by steam, as well as a class that is
worked by steam. When the natural class of Euphorbiaceæ
was originally formed, all the plants known to belong to it
were devoid of corollas; it would have seemed therefore
that the two classes " Euphorbiaceæ," and " Euphorbiaceæ
devoid of Corollas," were of equal extent. Subsequently a
number of plants plainly belonging to the same class were
found in tropical countries, and they possessed bright

---

[1] *The Classification of the Sciences,* &c., 3rd edit. p. 7. *Essays :
Scientific, Political, and Speculative,* vol. iii. p. 13.

coloured corollas. Naturalists believe with the utmost confidence that "Ruminants" and "Ruminants with cleft feet "
are identical terms, because no ruminant has yet been discovered without cleft feet. But we can see no impossibility
in the conjunction of rumination with uncleft feet, and it
vould be too great an assumption to say that we are
certain that an example of it will never be met with.
Instances can be quoted, without end, of objects being
ultimately discovered combining properties which had never
before been seen together. In the animal kingdom the
Black Swan, the Ornithorhynchus Paradoxus, and more
recently the singular fish called Ceratodus Forsteri, all
discovered in Australia, have united characters never
previously known to coexist. At the present time deep-
sea dredging is bringing to light many animals of an un-
precedented nature. Singular exceptional discoveries may
certainly occur in other branches of science. When Davy
first discovered metallic potassium, it was a well established
empirical law that all metallic substances possessed a high
specific gravity, the least dense of the metals then known
being zinc, of which the specific gravity is 7·1. Yet to
the surprise of chemists, potassium was found to be an
undoubted metal of less density than water, its specific
gravity being 0·865.

It is hardly requisite to prove by further examples that
our knowledge of nature is incomplete, so that we cannot
safely assume the non-existence of new combinations.
Logically speaking, we ought to have a place open for
animals which ruminate but are without cleft feet, and
for every possible intermediate form of animal, plant, or
mineral. A purely logical classification must take account
not only of what certainly does exist, but of what may in
after ages be found to exist.

I will go a step further, and say that we must have
places in our scientific classifications for purely imaginary
existences. A large proportion of the mathematical functions which are conceivable have no application to the circumstances of this world. Physicists certainly do investigate the nature and consequences of forces which nowhere
exist. Newton's *Principia* is full of such investigations.
In one chapter of his *Mécanique Céleste* Laplace indulges
in a remarkable speculation as to what the laws of motion

would have been if momentum, instead of varying simply
as the velocity, had been a more complicated function of
it. I have already mentioned (p. 223) that Airy contemplated the existence of a world in which the laws of force
should be such that a perpetual motion would be possible,
and the Law of Conservation of Energy would not hold
true.

Thought is not bound down to the limits of what is
materially existent, but is circumscribed only by those
Fundamental Laws of Identity, Contradiction and Duality,
which were laid down at the outset. This is the point at
which I should differ from Mr. Spencer. He appears to
suppose that a classification is complete if it has a place
for every existing object, and this may perhaps seem to be
practically sufficient; but it is subject to two profound
objections. Firstly, we do not know all that exists, and
therefore in limiting our classes we are erroneously omitting
multitudes of objects of unknown form and nature which
may exist either on this earth or in other parts of space
Secondly, as I have explained, the powers of thought are
not limited by material existences, and we may, or, for some
purposes, must imagine objects which probably do not
exist, and if we imagine them we ought to find places for
them in the classifications of science.

The chief difficulty of this subject, however, consists in
the fact that mathematical or other certain laws may
entirely forbid the existence of some combinations. The
circle may be defined as a plane curve of equal curvature,
and it is a property of the circle that it contains the greatest
area within the least possible perimeter. May we then
contemplate mentally a circle not a figure of greatest possible area? Or, to take a still simpler example, a parallelogram possesses the property of having the opposite angles
equal. May we then mentally divide parallelograms into
two classes according as they do or do not have their opposite angles equal? It might seem absurd to do so, because
we know that one of the two species of parallelogram
would be non-existent. But, then, unless the student had
previously contemplated the existence of both species as
possible, what is the meaning of the thirty-fourth proposition of Euclid's first book? We cannot deny or disprove
the existence of a certain combination without thereby in

a certain way recognising, that combination as an object of thought.

The conclusion at which I arrive is in opposition to that of Mr. Spencer. I think that whenever we abstract a quality or circumstance we do generalise or widen the notion from which we abstract. Whatever the terms A, B, and C may be, I hold that in strict logic AB is mentally a wider term than ABC, because AB includes the two species ABC and AB*c*. The term A is wider still, for it includes the four species ABC, AB*c*, A*b*C, A*bc*. The Logical Alphabet, in short, is the only limit of the classes of objects which we must contemplate in a purely logical point of view. Whatever notions be brought before us, we must mentally combine them in all the ways sanctioned by the laws of thought and exhibited in the Logical Alphabet, and it is a matter for after consideration to determine how many of these combinations exist in outward nature, or how many are actually forbidden by the conditions of space. A classification is essentially a mental, not a material thing.

Discovery of Marks or Characteristics.

Although the chief purpose of classification is to disclose the deepest and most general resemblances of the objects classified, yet the practical value of a system will depend partly upon the ease with which we can refer an object to its proper class, and thus infer concerning it all that is known generally of that class. This operation of discovering to which class of a system a certain 'specimen or case belongs, is generally called *Diagnosis*, a technical term familiarly used by physicians, who constantly require to diagnose or determine the nature of the disease from which a patient is suffering. Now every class is defined by certain specified qualities or circumstances, the whole of which are present in every object contained in the class, and *not all present* in any object excluded from it. These defining circumstances ought to consist of the deepest and most important circumstances, by which we vaguely mean those probably forming the conditions with which the minor circumstances are correlated. But it will often happen that the so-called important points of an object are not those which can

most readily be observed. Thus the two great classes of
phanerogamous plants are defined respectively by the
possession of two cotyledons or seed-leaves, and one coty-
ledon. But when a plant comes to our notice and we
want to refer it to the right class, it will often happen
that we have no seed at all to examine, in order to discover whether there be one seed-leaf or two in the germ.
Even if we have a seed it will often be small, and a careful
dissection under the microscope will be requisite to ascertain the number of cotyledons. Occasionally the examination of the germ would mislead us, for the cotyledons may
be obsolete, as in Cuscuta, or united together, as in Clin-
tonia. Botanists therefore seldom actually refer to the
seed for such information. Certain other characters of a
plant are correlated with the number of seed-leaves ; thus
monocotyledonous plants almost always possess leaves with
parallel veins like those of grass, while dicotyledonous
plants have leaves with reticulated veins like those of an
oak leaf. In monocotyledonous plants, too, the parts of the
flower are most often three or some multiple of three in
number, while in dicotyledonous plants the numbers four
and five and their multiples prevail. Botanists, therefore,
by a glance at the leaves and flowers can almost certainly
refer a plant to its right class, and can infer not only the
number of cotyledons which would be found in the seed or
young plant, but also the structure of the stem and other
general characters.

Any conspicuous and easily discriminated property
which we thus select for the purpose of deciding to which
class an object belongs, may be called a *characteristic*. The
logical conditions of a good characteristic mark are very
simple, namely, that it should be possessed by all objects
entering into a certain class, and by none others. Every
characteristic should enable us to assert a simple identity ;
if A is a characteristic, and B, viewed intensively, the class
of objects of which it is the mark, then A = B ought to be
true. The characteristic may consist either of a single
quality or circumstance, or of a group of such, provided
that they all be constant and easily detected. Thus in the
classification of mammals the teeth are of the greatest
assistance, not because a slight variation in the number
and form of the teeth is of importance in the general

economy of the animal, but because such variations are
proved by empirical observation to coincide with most important differences in the general affinities. It is found
that the minor classes and genera of mammals can be
discriminated accurately by their teeth, especially by the
foremost molars and the hindmost pre-molars. Some teeth,
indeed, are occasionally missing, so that zoologists prefer to
trust to those characteristic teeth which are most constant,[1]
and to infer from them not only the arrangement of the
other teeth, but the whole conformation of the animal.

It is a very difficult matter to mark out a boundary-line
between the animal and vegetable kingdoms, and it may
even be doubted whether a rigorous boundary can be established. The most fundamental and important difference of
a vegetable as compared with an animal substance probably
consists in the absence of nitrogen from the constituent
membranes. Supposing this to be the case, the difficulty
arises that in examining minute organisms we cannot ascertain directly whether they contain nitrogen or not. Some
minor but easily detected circumstance is therefore needed
to discriminate between animals and vegetables, and this is
furnished to some extent by the fact that the production
of starch granules is restricted to the vegetable kingdom.
Thus the Desmidiaceæ may be safely assigned to the vegetable kingdom, because they contain starch. But we
must not employ this characteristic negatively ; the Diatomaceæ are probably vegetables, though they do not produce starch.

Diagnostic Systems of Classification.

We have seen that diagnosis is the process of discovering the place in any system of classes, to which an object
has been referred by some previous investigation, the
object being to avail ourselves of the information relating
to such an object which has been accumulated and recorded. It is obvious that this is a matter of great importance, for, unless we can recognise, from time to time,
objects or substances which have been investigated, recorded
discoveries would lose their value. Even a single investi-

---

[1] Owen, *Essay on the Classification and Geographical Distribution
of the Mammalia,* p. 20.

gator must have means of recording and systematising his observations of any large groups of objects like the vegetable and animal kingdoms.

Now whenever a class has been properly formed, a definition must have been laid down, stating the qualities and circumstances possessed by all the objects which are intended to be included in the class, and not possessed *completely* by any other objects. Diagnosis, therefore, consists in comparing the qualities of a certain object with the definitions of a series of classes; the absence in the object of any one quality stated in the definition excludes it from the class thus defined; whereas, if we find every point of a definition exactly fulfilled in the specimen, we may at once assign it to the class in question. It is of course by no means certain that everything which has been affirmed of a class is true of all objects afterwards referred to the class; for this would be a case of imperfect inference, which is never more than matter of probability. A definition can only make known a finite number of the qualities of an object, and it always remains possible that objects agreeing in those assigned qualities will differ in others. *An individual cannot be defined,* and can only be made known by the exhibition of the individual itself, or by a material specimen exactly representing it. But this and other questions relating to definition must be treated when I am able to take up the subject of language in another work.

Diagnostic systems of classification should, as a general rule, be arranged on the bifurcate method explicitly. Any quality may be .hosen which divides the whole group of objects into two distinct parts, and each part may be subdivided successively by any prominent and well-marked circumstance which is present in a large part of the genus and not in the other. To refer an object to its proper place in such an arrangement we have only to note whether it does or does not possess the successive critical differentiæ. Dana devised a classification of this kind[1] by which to refer a crystal to its place in the series of six or seven classes already described. If a crystal has all its edges modified alike or the angles replaced by three or six similar planes,

[1] Dana's *Mineralogy,* vol. i. p. 123 ; quoted in Watts' *Dictionary if Chemistry,* vol. ii. p. 166.

it belongs to the monometric system ; if not, we observe
whether the number of similar planes at the extremity of
the crystal is three or some multiple of three, in which
case it is a crystal of the hexagonal system ; and so we
proceed with further successive discriminations. To ascertain the name of a mineral by examination with the blowpipe, an arrangement more or less evidently on the bifurcate
plan, has been laid down by Von Kobell.[1] Minerals
are divided according as they possess or do not possess
metallic lustre ; as they are fusible or not fusible, according as they do or do not on charcoal give a metallic bead,
and so on.

Perhaps the best example to be found of an arrangement devised simply for the purpose of diagnosis, is
Mr. George Bentham's *Analytical Key to the Natural
Orders and Anomalous Genera of the British Flora*, given
in his *Handbook of the British Flora*.[2] In this scheme,
the great composite family of plants, together with the
closely approximate genus Jasione, are first separated
from all other flowering plants by the compound character
of their flowers. The remaining plants are sub-divided
according as the perianth is double or single. Since no
plants are yet known in which the perianth can be said
to have three or more distinct rings, this division becomes
practically the same as one into double and not-double.
Flowers with a double perianth are next discriminated
according as the corolla does or does not consist of one
piece ; according as the ovary is free or not free ; as it is
simple or not simple ; as the corolla is regular or irregular ;
and so on. On looking over this arrangement, it will
be found that numerical discriminations often occur, the
numbers of petals, stamens, capsules, or other parts being
the criteria, in which cases, as already explained (p. 697),
the actual exhibition of the bifid division would be tedious.

Linnæus appears to have been perfectly acquainted
with the nature and uses of diagnostic classification, which
he describes under the name of Synopsis, saying:[3]—

---

[1] *Instructions for the Discrimination of Minerals by Simple Chemical Experiments*, by Franz von Kobell, translated from the German
by R. C. Campbell. Glasgow, 1841.

[2] Edition of 1866, p. lxiii.

[3] *Philosophia Botanica* (1770), § 154, p. 98.

" Synopsis tradit Divisiones arbitrarias, longiores aut brevi-
ores, plures aut pauciores : a Botanicis in genere non
agnoscenda.   Synopsis est dichotomia arbitraria, quæ
instar viæ ad Botanicem ducit.   Limites autem non de-
terminat."

The rules and tables drawn out by chemists to facilitate
the discovery of the nature of a substance in qualitative
analysis are usually arranged on the bifurcate method,
and form excellent examples of diagnostic classification,
the qualities of the substances produced in testing being
in most cases merely characteristic properties of little importance in other respects.   The chemist does not detect
potassium by reducing it to the state of metallic potassium, and then observing whether it has all the principal
qualities belonging to potassium.   He selects from among
the whole number of compounds of potassium that salt,
namely the compound of platinum tetra-chloride, and
potassium chloride, which has the most distinctive appearance, as it is comparatively insoluble and produces
a peculiar yellow and highly crystalline precipitate.   Accordingly, potassium is present whenever this precipitate
can be produced by adding platinum chloride to a solution.   The fine purple or violet colour which potassium
salts communicate to the blowpipe flame, had long been
used as a characteristic mark.   Some other elements were
readily detected by the colouring of the blowpipe flame,
barium giving a pale yellowish green, and salts of strontium a bright red.   By the use of the spectroscope the
coloured light given off by an incandescent vapour is made
to give perfectly characteristic marks of the elements contained in the vapour.

Diagnosis seems to be identical with the process termed
by the ancient logicians *abscissio infiniti*, the cutting off
of the infinite or negative part of a genus when we discover by observation that an object possesses a particular
difference.   At every step in a bifurcate division, some
objects possessing the difference will fall into the affirmative part or species ; all the remaining objects in the world
fall into the negative part, which will be infinite in extent.
Diagnosis consists in the successive rejection from further
notice of those infinite classes with which the specimen in
question does not agree.

Index Classifications.

Under classification we may include all arrangements of objects or names, which we make for saving labour in the discovery of an object. Even alphabetical indices are real classifications. No such arrangement can be of use unless it involves some correlation of circumstances, so that knowing one thing we learn another. If we merely arrange letters in the pigeon-holes of a secretaire we establish a correlation, for all letters in the first hole will be written by persons, for instance, whose names begin with A, and so on. Knowing then the initial letter of the writer's name, we know also the place of the letter, and the labour of search is thus reduced to one twenty-sixth part of what it would be without arrangement.

Now the purpose of a catalogue is to discover the place in which an object is to be found; but the art of cataloguing involves logical considerations of some importance. We want to establish a correlation between the place of an object and some circumstance about the object which shall enable us readily to refer to it; this circumstance therefore should be that which will most readily dwell in the memory of the searcher. A piece of poetry will be best remembered by the first line of the piece, and the name of the author will be the next most definite circumstance ; a catalogue of poetry should therefore be arranged alphabetically according to the first word of the piece, or the name of the author, or, still better, in both ways. It would be impossible to arrange poems according to their subjects, so vague and mixed are these found to be when the attempt is made.

It is a matter of considerable literary importance to decide upon the best mode of cataloguing books, so that any required book in a library shall be most readily found. Books may be classified in a great number of ways, according to subject, language, date, or place of publication, size, the initial words of the text or title-page, or colophon, the author's name, the publisher's name, the printer's name, the character of the type, and so on. Every one of these modes of arrangement may be useful, for we may happen to remember one circumstance about a book when we have forgotten all others ; but as we cannot usually go to the expense of forming more than two or three indices, we must select those circumstances which will lead to the discovery of a book most frequently. Many of the criteria mentioned are evidently inapplicable.

The language in which a book is written is definite enough, provided that the whole book is written in the same language ; but it is obvious that language gives no means for the subdivision and arrangement of the literature of any one people. Classification by subjects would be an exceedingly useful method if it were practicable, but experience shows it to be a logical absurdity. It is a very difficult matter to classify the sciences, so complicated are the relations between them. But with books the complication is vastly greater, since the same book may treat of different sciences, or it may discuss a problem involving many branches of knowledge. A good account of the steam-engine will be antiquarian, so far as it traces out the earliest efforts at discovery ; purely scientific, as regards the principles of thermodynamics involved; technical, as regards the mechanical means of applying those principles; economical, as regards the industrial results of the invention; biographical, as regards the lives of the inventors. A history of Westminster Abbey might belong either to the history of architecture, the history of the Church, or the history of England. If we abandon the attempt to carry out an arrangement according to the natural classification of the sciences, and form comprehensive practical groups, we shall be continually perplexed by the occurrence of intermediate cases, and opinions will differ *ad infinitum* as to the details. If, to avoid the difficulty about Westminster Abbey, we form a class of books devoted to the History of Buildings, the question will then arise whether Stonehenge is a building, and if so, whether cromlechs, mounds, and monoliths are so. We shall be uncertain whether to include lighthouses, monuments, bridges, &c. In regard to literary works, rigorous classification is still less possible. The same work may partake of the nature of poetry, biography, history, philosophy, or if we form a comprehensive class of Belles-lettres, nobody can say exactly what does or does not come under the term.

My own experience entirely bears out the opinion of De Morgan, that classification according to the name of the author is the only one practicable in a large library, and this method has been admirably carried out in the great catalogue of the British Museum. The name of the author is the most precise circumstance concerning a book, which usually dwells in the memory. It is a better characteristic of the book than anything else. In an alphabetical arrangement we have an exhaustive classification, including a place for every name. The following remarks [1] of De Morgan seem therefore to be entirely correct. " From much, almost daily use, of catalogues for many years, I am perfectly satisfied that a classed catalogue is more difficult to use than to make. It is one man's theory of the subdivision of knowledge, and the chances are against its suiting any other man. Even if all doubtful works were entered under several different heads, the frontier of the dubious region would itself be a mere matter of doubt. I never turn from a classed catalogue to an alphabetical one without a feeling of relief and security. With the latter I can always, by taking proper pains, make a library yield its utmost ; with the former I can never be satisfied that I have taken proper pains, until I have made it, in fact, as many different catalogues as there are different headings, with separate trouble for each. Those to whom bibliographical research is familiar, know that they have much more frequently to hunt an author than a subject : they know also that in searching for a subject, it is never safe to take another person's view, however good, of the limits of that subject with reference to their own particular purposes."

It is often desirable, however, that a name catalogue should be accompanied by a subordinate subject catalogue, but in this case no attempt should be made to devise a theoretically complete classification. Every principal subject treated in a book should be entered separately in an alphabetical list, under the name most likely to occur

---

[1] *Philosophical Magazine,* 3rd Series (1845), vol. xxvi. p. 522. See also De Morgan's evidence before the Royal Commission on the British Museum in 1849, Report (1850), Questions, 5704*—5815*, 6481—6513. This evidence should be studied by every person who wishes to understand the elements of Bibliography.

to the searcher, or under several names. This method was partially carried out in Watts' *Bibliotheca Britannica*, but it was excellently applied in the admirable subject index to the *British Catalogue of Books*, and equally well in the *Catalogue of the Manchester Free Library* at Campfield, drawn up under the direction of Mr. Crestadoro, this latter being the most perfect model of a printed catalogue with which I am acquainted. The Catalogue of the London Library is also in the right form, and has a useful index of subjects, though it is too much condensed and abbreviated. The public catalogue of the British Museum is arranged as far as possible according to the alphabetical order of the authors' names, but in writing the titles for this catalogue several copies are simultaneously produced by a manifold writer, so that a catalogue according to the order of the books on the shelves, and another according to the first words of the title-page, are created by a mere rearrangement of the spare copies. In the *English Cyclopædia* it is suggested that twenty copies of the book titles might readily have been utilised in forming additional catalogues, arranged according to the place of publication, the language of the book, the general nature of the subject, and so forth.[1] An excellent suggestion has also been made to the effect that each book when published should have a fly-leaf containing half a dozen printed copies of the title, drawn up in a form suitable for insertion in catalogues. Every owner of a library could then easily make accurate printed catalogues to suit his own purposes, by merely cutting out these titles and pasting them in books in any desirable order.

It will hardly be a digression to point out the enormous saving of labour, or, what comes to the same thing, the enormous increase in our available knowledge, both literary and scientific, which arises from the formation of extensive indices. The " State Papers," containing the whole history of the nation, were practically sealed to literary inquirers until the Government undertook the task of calendaring and indexing them. The British Museum Catalogue is another national work, of which the importance in advancing knowledge cannot be overrated. The Royal

---

[1] *English Cyclopædia, Arts and Sciences.* vol. v. p. 233.

Society is doing great service in publishing a complete catalogue of memoirs upon physical science. The time will perhaps come when our views upon this subject will be extended, and either Government or some public society will undertake the systematic cataloguing and indexing of masses of historical and scientific information which are now almost closed against inquiry.

Classification in the Biological Sciences.

The great generalisations established in the works of Herbert Spencer and Charles Darwin have thrown much light upon other sciences, and have removed several difficulties out of the way of the logician. The subject of classification has long been studied in almost exclusive reference to the arrangement of animals and plants. Systematic botany and zoology have been commonly known as the Classificatory Sciences, and scientific men seemed to suppose that the methods of arrangement, which were suitable for living creatures, must be the best for all other classes of objects. Several mineralogists, especially Mohs, have attempted to arrange minerals in genera and species, just as if they had been animals capable of reproducing their kind with variations. This confusion of ideas between the relationship of living forms and the logical relationship of things in general prevailed from the earliest times, as manifested in the etymology of words. We familiarly speak of a *kind* of things meaning a class of things, and the kind consists of those things which are *akin*, or come of the same race. When Socrates and his followers wanted a name for a class regarded in a philosophical light, they adopted the analogy in question, and called it a γένος, or race, the root γεν- being connected with the notion of generation.

So long as species of plants and animals were believed to proceed from distinct acts of Creation, there was no apparent reason why methods of classification suitable to them should not be treated as a guide to the classification of other objects generally. But when once we regard these resemblances as hereditary in their origin, we see that the sciences of systematic botany and zoology have a special character of their own. There is no reason to suppose that the same kind of natural classification which is best in biology will apply also in mineralogy, in chemistry, or in astronomy. The logical principles which underlie all classification are of course the same in natural history as in the sciences of lifeless matter, but the special resemblances which arise from the relation of parent and offspring will not be found to prevail between different kinds of crystals or mineral bodies.

The genealogical view of the relations of animals and plants leads us to discard all notions of a regular progression of living forms, or any theory as to their symmetrical relations. It was at one time a question whether the ultimate scheme of natural classification would lead to arrangement in a simple line, or a circle, or a combination of circles. Macleay's once celebrated system was a circular one, and each class-circle was composed of five order-circles, each of which was composed again of five tribe-circles, and so on, the subdivision being at each step into five minor circles. Macleay held that in the animal kingdom there are five sub-kingdoms—the Vertebrata, Annulosa, Radiata, Acrita, and Mollusca. Each of these was again divided into five—the Vertebrata, consisting of Mammalia, Reptilia, Pisces, Amphibia, and Aves.[1] It is evident that in such a symmetrical system the animals were made to suit themselves to the classes instead of the classes being suited to the animals.

We now perceive that the ultimate system will have the form of an immensely extended genealogical tree, which will be capable of representation by lines on a plane surface of sufficient extent. Strictly speaking, this genealogical tree ought to represent the descent of each individual living form now existing or which has existed. It should be as personal and minute in its detail of relations, as the Stemma of the Kings of England. We must not assume that any two forms are exactly alike, and in any case they are numerically distinct. Every parent then must be represented at the apex of a series of divergent lines, representing the generation of so many children. Any complete system of classification must regard individuals as the infimæ species. But as in the lower races of animals

[1] Swainson, "Treatise on the Geography and Classification of Animals," *Cabinet Cyclopædia*, p. 201.

and plants the differences between individuals are slight
and apparently unimportant, while the numbers of such
individuals are immensely great, beyond all possibility of
separate treatment, scientific men have always stopped at
some convenient but arbitrary point, and have assumed
that forms so closely resembling each other as to present
no constant difference were all of one kind. They have,
in short, fixed their attention entirely upon the main
features of family difference. In the genealogical tree
which they have been unconsciously aiming to construct,
diverging lines meant races diverging in character, and
the purpose of all efforts at so-called natural classification
was to trace out the descents between existing groups of
plants or animals.

Now it is evident that hereditary descent may have in
different cases produced very different results as regards
the problem of classification. In some cases the differentiation of characters may have been very frequent, and
specimens of all the characters produced may have
been transmitted to the present time. A living form
will then have, as it were, an almost infinite number of
cousins of various degrees, and there will be an immense
number of forms finely graduated in their resemblances.
Exact and distinct classification will then be almost
impossible, and the wisest course will be not to attempt
arbitrarily to distinguish forms closely related in nature,
but to allow that there exist transitional forms of every
degree, to mark out if possible the extreme limits of the
family relationship, and perhaps to select the most
generalised form, or that which presents the greatest
number of close resemblances to others of the family, as
the *type* of the whole.

Mr. Darwin, in his most interesting work upon Orchids,
points out that the tribe of Malaxeæ are distinguished from
Epidendreæ by the absence of a caudicle to the pollinia;
but as some of the Malaxeæ have a minute caudicle, the
division really breaks down in the most essential point.
"This is a misfortune," he remarks,[1] "which every naturalist encounters in attempting to classify a largely
developed or so-called natural group, in which, relatively

---

[1] Darwin, *Fertilisation of Orchids*, p. 159.

to other groups, there has been little extinction. In order
that the naturalist may be enabled to give precise and
clear definitions of his divisions, whole ranks of intermediate or gradational forms must have been utterly swept
away : if here and there a member of the intermediate
ranks has escaped annihilation, it puts an effectual bar to
any absolutely distinct definition."

In other cases a particular plant or animal may perhaps
have transmitted its form from generation to generation
almost unchanged, or, what comes to the same result, those
forms which diverged in character from the parent stock
may have proved unsuitable to their circumstances, and
perished. We shall then find a particular form standing
apart from all others, and marked by many distinct
characters. Occasionally we may meet with specimens of
a race which was formerly far more common but is now
undergoing extinction, and is nearly the last of its kind.
Thus we explain the occurrence of exceptional forms such
as are found in the Amphioxus. The Equisetaceæ perplex
botanists by their want of affinity to other orders of Acro-
genous plants. This doubtless indicates that their genealogical connection with other plants must be sought for in
the most distant ages of geological development.

Constancy of character, as Mr. Darwin has said,[1] is
what is chiefly valued and sought after by naturalists ;
that is to say, naturalists wish to find some distinct family
mark, or group of characters, by which they may clearly
recognise the relationship of descent between a large
group of living forms. It is accordingly a great relief to
the mind of the naturalist when he comes upon a defi-
nitely marked group, such as the Diatomaceæ, which are
clearly separated from their nearest neighbours the Desmidiaceæ by their siliceous framework and the absence of
chlorophyll. But we must no longer think that because
we fail in detecting constancy of character the fault is
in our classificatory sciences. Where gradation of character really exists, we must devote ourselves to defining and
registering the degrees and limits of that gradation. The
ultimate natural arrangement will often be devoid of strong
lines of demarcation.

[1] *Descent of Man*, vol. i. p. 214.

Let naturalists, too, form their systems of natural classification with all care they can, yet it will certainly happen from time to time that new and exceptional forms of animals or vegetables will be discovered and will require the modification of the system. A natural system is directed, as we have seen, to the discovery of empirical laws of correlation, but these laws being purely empirical will frequently be falsified by more extensive investigation. From time to time the notions of naturalists have been greatly widened, especially in the case of Australian animals and plants, by the discovery of unexpected combinations of organs, and such events must often happen in the future. If indeed the time shall come when all the forms of plants are discovered and accurately described, the science of Systematic Botany will then be placed in a new and more favourable position, as remarked by Alphonse Decandolle.[1]

It ought to be remembered that though the genealogical classification of plants or animals is doubtless the most instructive of all, it is not necessarily the best for all purposes. There may be correlations of properties important for medicinal, or other practical purposes, which do not correspond to the correlations of descent. We must regard the bamboo as a tree rather than a grass, although it is botanically a grass. For legal purposes we may continue with advantage to treat the whale, seal, and other cetaceæ, as fish. We must also class plants according as they belong to arctic, alpine, temperate, sub-tropical or tropical regions. There are causes of likeness apart from hereditary relationship, and *we must not attribute exclusive excellence to any one method of classification.*

Classification by Types.

Perplexed by the difficulties arising in natural history from the discovery of intermediate forms, naturalists have resorted to what they call classification by types. Instead of forming one distinct class defined by the invariable possession of certain assigned properties, and rigidly including or excluding objects according as they do or do not

[1] *Laws of Botanical Nomenclature,* p. 16.

possess all these properties, naturalists select a typical specimen, and they group around it all other specimens which resemble this type more than any other selected type. "The type of each genus," we are told,[1] "should be that species in which the characters of its group are best exhibited and most evenly balanced." It would usually consist of those descendants of a form which had undergone little alteration, while other descendants had suffered slight differentiation in various directions.

It would be a great mistake to suppose that this classification by types is a logically distinct method. It is either not a real method of classification at all, or it is merely an abbreviated mode of representing a complicated system of arrangement. A class must be defined by the invariable presence of certain common properties. If, then, we include an individual in which one of these properties does not appear, we either fall into logical contradiction, or else we form a new class with a new definition. Even a single exception constitutes a new class by itself, and by calling it an exception we merely imply that this new class closely resembles that from which it diverges in one or two points only. Thus in the definition of the natural order of Rosaceæ, we find that the seeds are one or two in each carpel, but that in the genus Spiræa there are three or four; this must mean either that the number of seeds is not a part of the fixed definition of the class, or else that Spiræa does not belong to that class, though it may closely approximate to it. Naturalists continually find themselves between two horns of a dilemma; if they restrict the number of marks specified in a definition so that every form intended to come within the class shall possess all those marks, it will then be usually found to include too many forms; if the definition be made more particular, the result is to produce so-called anomalous genera, which, while they are held to belong to the class, do not in all respects conform to its definition. The practice has hence arisen of allowing considerable latitude in the definition of natural orders. The family of Cruciferæ, for instance, forms an exceedingly well-marked natural order, and among its characters we find it

[1] Waterhouse, quoted by Woodward in his *Rudimentary Treatise of Recent and Fossil Shells*, p. 61.

specified that the fruit is a pod, divided into two cells by a thin partition, from which the valves generally separate at maturity ; but we are also informed that, in a few genera, the pod is one-celled, or indehiscent, or separates transversely into several joints.[1] Now this must either mean that the formation of the pod is not an essential point in the definition of the family, or that there are several closely associated families.

The same holds true of typical classification. The type itself is an individual, not a class, and no other object can be exactly like the type. But as soon as we abstract the individual peculiarities of the type and thus specify a finite number of qualities in which other objects may resemble the type, we immediately constitute a class. If some objects resemble the type in some points, and others in other points, then each definite collection of points of resemblance constitutes intensively a separate class. The very notion of classification by types is in fact erroneous in a logical point of view. The naturalist is constantly occupied in endeavouring to mark out definite groups of living forms, where the forms themselves do not in many cases admit of such rigorous lines of demarcation. A certain laxity of logical method is thus apt to creep in, the only remedy for which will be the frank recognition of the fact, that, according to the theory of hereditary descent, gradation of characters is probably the rule, and precise demarcation between groups the exception.

Natural Genera and Species.

One important result of the establishment of the theory of evolution is to explode all notions about natural groups constituting separate creations. Naturalists long held that every plant belongs to some species, marked out by invariable characters, which do not change by difference of soil, climate, cross-breeding, or other circumstances. They were unable to deny the existence of such things as subspecies, varieties, and hybrids, so that a species of plants was often subdivided and classified within itself. But then the differences upon which this sub-classification

[1] Bentham's *Handbook of the British Flora* (1866), p. 25.

depended were supposed to be variable, and thus distinguished from the invariable characters imposed upon the
whole species at its creation. Similarly a natural genus
was a group of species, and was marked out from other
genera by eternal differences of still greater importance.

We now, however, perceive that the existence of any
such groups as genera and species is an arbitrary creation
of the naturalist's mind. All resemblances of plants are
natural so far as they express hereditary affinities; but this
applies as well to the variations within the species as to
the species itself, or to the larger groups. All is a matter
of degree. The deeper differences between plants have
been produced by the differentiating action of circumstances during millions of years, so that it would naturally
require millions of years to undo this result, and prove
experimentally that the forms can be approximated again.
Sub-species may sometimes have arisen within historical
times, and varieties approaching to sub-species may often
be produced by the horticulturist in a few years. Such
varieties can easily be brought back to their original forms,
or, if placed in the original circumstances, will themselves
revert to those forms; but according to Darwin's views
all forms are capable of unlimited change, and it might
possibly be, unlimited reversion if suitable circumstances
and sufficient time be granted.

Many fruitless attempts have been made to establish a
rigorous criterion of specific and generic difference, so that
these classes might have a definite value and rank in all
branches of biology. Linnæus adopted the view that the
species was to be defined as a distinct creation, saying,[1]
" Species tot numeramus, quot diversæ formæ in principio
sunt creatæ ; " or again, " Species tot sunt, quot diversas
formas ab initio produxit Infinitum Ens ; quæ formæ,
secundum generationis inditas leges, produxere plures, at
sibi semper similes." Of genera he also says,[2] " Genus
omne est naturale, in primordio tale creatum." It was a
common doctrine added to and essential to that of distinct
creation that these species could not produce intermediate
and variable forms, so that we find Linnæus obliged by the
ascertained existence of hybrids to take a different view

---

[1] *Philosophia Botanica* (1770), § 157, p. 99.
[2] *Ibid.* § 159, p. 100.

in another work; he says,[1] "Novas species immo et genera
ex copula diversarum specierum in regno vegetabilium oriri
primo intuitu paradoxum videtur; interim observationes sic
fieri non ita dissuadent." Even supposing in the present
day that we could assent to the notion of a certain number
of distinct creational acts, this notion would not help us in
the theory of classification. Naturalists have never pointed
out any method of deciding what are the results of distinct
creations, and what are not. As Darwin says,[2] "the definition must not include an element which cannot possibly
be ascertained, such as an act of creation." It is, in fact,
by investigation of forms and classification that we should
ascertain what were distinct creations and what were not;
this information would be a result and not a means of
classification.

Agassiz seemed to consider that he had discovered an important principle, to the effect that general plan or structure
is the true ground for the discrimination of the great classes
of animals, which may be called branches of the animal
kingdom.[3] He also thought that genera are definite and
natural groups. "Genera," he says,[4] "are most closely
allied groups of animals, differing neither in form, nor in
complication of structure, but simply in the ultimate structural peculiarities of some of their parts; and this is, I believe, the best definition which can be given of genera."
But it is surely apparent that there are endless degrees both
of structural peculiarity and of complication of structure.
It is impossible to define the amount of structural peculiarity which constitutes the genus as distinguished from
the species.

The form which any classification of plants or animals
tends to take is that of an unlimited series of subaltern
classes. Originally botanists confined themselves for the
most part to a small number of such classes. Linnæus
adopted Class, Order, Genus, Species, and Variety, and even
seemed to think that there was something essentially natural in a five-fold arrangement of groups.[5]

[1] *Amœnitates Academicæ* (1744), vol. i. p. 70. Quoted in *Edinburgh Review*, October 1868, vol. cxxviii. pp. 416, 417.
[2] *Descent of Man*, vol. i. p. 228.
[3] Agassiz, *Essay on Classification*, p. 219.   [4] *Ibid.* p. 249.
[5] *Philosophia Botanica*, § 155, p. 98.

With the progress of botany intermediate and additional groups have gradually been introduced. According to the Laws of Botanical Nomenclature adopted by the International Botanical Congress, held at Paris [1] in August 1867, no less than twenty-one names of classes are recognised—namely, Kingdom, Division, Sub-division, Class, Sub-class, Cohort, Sub-cohort, Order, Sub-order, Tribe, Sub-tribe, Genus, Sub-genus, Section, Sub-section, Species, Sub-species, Variety, Sub-variety, Variation, Sub-variation. It is allowed by the authors of this scheme, that the rank or degree of importance to be attributed to any of these divisions may vary in a certain degree according to individual opinion. The only point on which botanists are not allowed discretion is as to the order of the successive sub-divisions ; any inversion of the arrangement, such as division of a genus into tribes, or of a tribe into orders, is quite inadmissible. There is no reason to suppose that even the above list is complete and inextensible. The Botanical Congress itself recognised the distinction between variations according as they are Seedlings, Half-breeds, or *Lusus Naturæ*. The complication of the inferior classes is increased again by the existence of *hybrids*, arising from the fertilisation of one species by another deemed a distinct species, nor can we place any limit to the minuteness of discrimination of degrees of breeding short of an actual pedigree of individuals.

It will be evident to the reader that in the remarks upon classification as applied to the Natural Sciences, given in this and the preceding sections, I have not in the least attempted to treat the subject in a manner adequate to its extent and importance. A volume would be insufficient for tracing out the principles of scientific method specially applicable to these branches of science. What more I may be able to say upon the subject will be better said, if ever, when I am able to take up the closely-connected subjects of Scientific Nomenclature, Terminology, and Descriptive Representation. In the meantime, I have wished to show, in a negative point of view, that natural classification in the animal and vegetable kingdoms is a special problem, and that the particular methods and

---

[1] *Laws of Botanical Nomenclature*, by Alphonse Decandolle, translated from the French, 1868, p. 19.

difficulties to which it gives rise are not those common to all cases of classification, as so many physicists have supposed. Genealogical resemblances are only a special case of resemblances in general.

Unique or Exceptional Objects.

In framing a system of classification in almost any branch of science, we must expect to meet with unique or peculiar objects, which stand alone, having comparatively few analogies with other objects. They may also be said to be *sui generis*, each unique object forming, as it were, a genus by itself; or they are called *nondescript*, because from thus standing apart it is difficult to find terms in which to describe their properties. The rings of Saturn, for instance, form a unique object among the celestial bodies. We have indeed considered this and many other instances of unique objects in the preceding chapter on Exceptional Phenomena. Apparent, Singular, and Divergent Exceptions especially, are analogous to unique objects.

In the classification of the elements, Carbon stands apart as a substance entirely unique in its powers of producing compounds. It is considered to be a quadrivalent element, and it obeys all the ordinary laws of chemical combination. Yet it manifests powers of affinity in such an exalted degree that the substances in which it appears are more numerous than all the other compounds known to chemists. Almost the whole of the substances which have been called organic contain carbon, and are probably held together by the carbon atoms, so that many chemists are now inclined to abandon the name Organic Chemistry, and substitute the name Chemistry of the Carbon Compounds. It used to be believed that the production of organic compounds could be effected only by the action of vital force, or of some inexplicable cause involved in the phenomena of life; but it is now found that chemists are able to commence with the elementary materials, pure carbon, hydrogen, and oxygen, and by strictly chemical operations to combine these so as to form complicated organic compounds. So many substances have already been formed that we might be inclined to generalise and infer that all organic compounds might ultimately be produced without the agency of living beings. Thus the distinction between the organic and the inorganic kingdoms seems to be breaking down, but our wonder at the peculiar powers of carbon must increase at the same time.

In considering generalisation, the law of continuity was applied chiefly to physical properties capable of mathematical treatment. But in the classificatory sciences, also, the same important principle is often beautifully exemplified. Many objects or events seem to be entirely exceptional and abnormal, and in regard to degree or magnitude they may be so termed; but it is often easy to show that they are connected by intermediate links with ordinary cases. In the organic kingdoms there is a common groundwork of similarity running through all classes, but particular actions and processes present themselves conspicuously in particular families and classes. Tenacity of life is most marked in the Rotifera, and some other kinds of microscopic organisms, which can be dried and boiled without loss of life. Reptiles are distinguished by torpidity, and the length of time they can live without food. Birds, on the contrary, exhibit ceaseless activity and high muscular power. The ant is as conspicuous for intelligence and size of brain among insects as the quadrumana and man among vertebrata. Among plants the Leguminosæ are distinguished by a tendency to sleep, folding their leaves at the approach of night. In the genus Mimosa, especially the Mimosa pudica, commonly called the sensitive plant, the same tendency is magnified into an extreme irritability, almost resembling voluntary motion. More or less of the same irritability probably belongs to vegetable forms of every kind, but it is of course to be investigated with special ease in such an extreme case. In the Gymnotus and Torpedo, we find that organic structures can act like galvanic batteries. Are we to suppose that such animals are entirely anomalous exceptions; or may we not justly expect to find less intense manifestations of electric action in all animals?

Some extraordinary differences between the modes of reproduction of animals have been shown to be far less than was at first sight apparent. The lower animals seem to differ entirely from the higher ones in the power of reproducing lost limbs. A kind of crab has the habit of casting portions of its claws when much frightened, but they soon grow again. There are multitudes of smaller animals which, like the Hydra, may be cut in two and yet live and develop into new complete individuals. No mammalian animal can reproduce a limb, and in appearance there is no analogy. But it was suggested by Blumenbach that the healing of a wound in the higher animals really represents in a lower degree the power of reproducing a limb. That this is true may be shown by adducing a multitude of intermediate cases, each adjoining pair of which are clearly analogous, so that we pass gradually from one extreme to the other. Darwin holds, moreover, that any such restoration of parts is closely connected with that perpetual replacement of the particles which causes every organised body to be after a time entirely new as regards its constituent substance. In short, we approach to a great generalisation under which all the phenomena of growth, restoration, and maintenance of organs are effects of one and the same power.[1] It is perhaps still more surprising to find that the complicated process of reproduction in the higher animals may be gradually traced down to a simpler and simpler form, which at last becomes undistinguishable from the budding out of one plant from the stem of another. By a great generalisation we may regard all the modes of reproduction of organic life as alike in their nature, and varying only in complexity of development.[2]

Limits of Classification.

Science can extend only so far as the power of accurate classification extends. If we cannot detect resemblances, and assign their exact character and amount, we cannot have that generalised knowledge which constitutes science; we cannot infer from case to case. Classification is the opposite process to discrimination. If we feel that two tastes differ, the tastes of two kinds of wine for instance, the mere fact of difference existing prevents inference. The detection of the difference saves us, indeed, from false

---

[1] Darwin, *The Variation of Animals and Plants*, vol. ii. pp. 293, 359, &c. ; quoting Paget, *Lectures on Pathology*, 1853, pp. 152, 164.
[2] *Ibid.* vol. ii. p. 372.

inference, because so far as difference exists, inference is impossible. But classification consists in detecting resemblances of all degrees of generality, and ascertaining exactly how far such resemblances extend, while assigning precisely the points at which difference begins. It enables us, then, to generalise, and make inferences where it is possible, and it saves us at the same time from going too far. A full classification constitutes a complete record of all our knowledge of the objects or events classified, and the limits of exact knowledge are identical with the limits of classification.

It must by no means be supposed that every group of natural objects will be found capable of rigorous classification. There may be substances which vary by insensible degrees, consisting, for instance, in varying mixtures of simpler substances. Granite is a mixture of quartz, felspar, and mica, but there are hardly two specimens in which the proportions of these three constituents are alike, and it would be impossible to lay down definitions of distinct species of granite without finding an infinite variety of intermediate species. The only true classification of granites, then, would be founded on the proportions of the constituents present, and a chemical or microscopic analysis would be requisite, in order that we might assign a specimen to its true position in the series. Granites vary, again, by insensible degrees, as regards the magnitude of the crystals of felspar and mica. Precisely similar remarks might be made concerning the classification of other plutonic rocks, such as syenite, basalt, pumice-stone, lava.

The nature of a ray of homogeneous light is strictly defined, either by its place in the spectrum or by the corresponding wave-length, but a ray of mixed light admits of no simple classification; any of the infinitely numerous rays of the continuous spectrum may be present or absent, or present in various intensities, so that we can only class and define a mixed colour by defining the intensity and wave-length of each ray of homogeneous light which is present in it. Complete spectroscopic analysis and the determination of the intensity of every part of the spectrum yielded by a mixed ray is requisite for its accurate classification. Nearly the same may be said of complex sounds. A simple sound undulation, if we could meet with such a sound, would admit of precise and exhaustive classification as regards pitch, the length of wave, or the number of waves reaching the ear per second being a sufficient criterion. But almost all ordinary sounds, even those of musical instruments, consist of complex aggregates of undulations of different pitches, and in order to classify the sound we should have to measure the intensities of each of the constituent sounds, a work which has been partially accomplished by Helmholtz, as regards the vowel sounds. The different tones of voice distinctive of different individuals must also be due to the intermixture of minute waves of various pitch, which are yet quite beyond the range of experimental investigation. We cannot, then, at present attempt to classify the different kinds or *timbres* of sound.

The difficulties of classification are still greater when a varying phenomenon cannot be shown to be a mixture of simpler phenomena. If we attempt to classify tastes, we may rudely group them according as they are sweet, bitter, saline, alkaline, acid, astringent or fiery ; but it is evident that these groups are bounded by no sharp lines of definition. Tastes of mixed or intermediate character may exist almost *ad infinitum*, and what is still more troublesome, the tastes clearly united within one class may differ more or less from each other, without our being able to arrange them in subordinate genera and species. The same remarks may be made concerning the classification of odours, which may be roughly grouped according to the arrangement of Linnæus as, aromatic, fragrant, ambrosiac, alliaceous, fetid, virulent, nauseous. Within each of these vague classes, however, there would be infinite shades of variety, and each class would graduate into other classes. The odours which can be discriminated by an acute nose are infinite ; every rock, stone, plant, or animal has some slight smell, and it is well known that dogs, or even blind men, can discriminate persons by a slight distinctive odour which usually passes unnoticed.

Similar remarks may be made concerning the feelings of the human mind, called emotions. We know what is anger, grief, fear, hatred, love ; and many systems for classifying these feelings have been proposed. They may be roughly distinguished according as they are pleasurable or painful, prospective or retrospective, selfish or sympathetic, active or passive, and possibly in many other ways; but each mode of arrangement will be indefinite and unsatisfactory when followed into details. As a general rule, the emotional state of the mind at any moment will be neither pure anger nor pure fear, nor any one pure feeling, but an indefinite and complex aggregate of feelings. It may be that the state of mind is really a sum of several distinct modes of agitation, just as a mixed colour is the sum of the several rays of the spectrum. In this case there may be more hope of some method of analysis being successfully applied at a future time. But it may be found that states of mind really graduate into each other so that rigorous classification would be hopeless.

A little reflection will show that there are whole worlds of existences which in like manner are incapable of logical analysis and classification. One friend may be able to single out and identify another friend by his countenance among a million other countenances. Faces are capable of infinite discrimination, but who shall classify and define them, or say by what particular shades of feature he does judge ? There are of course certain distinct types of face, but each type is connected with each other type by infinite intermediate specimens. We may classify melodies according to the major or minor key, the character of the time, and some other distinct points; but every melody has, independently of such circumstances, its own distinctive character and effect upon the mind. We can detect differences between the styles of literary, musical, or artistic compositions. We can even in some cases assign a picture to its painter, or a symphony to its composer, by a subtle feeling of resemblances or differences which may be felt, but cannot be described.

Finally, it is apparent that in human character there is unfathomable and inexhaustible diversity. Every mind is more or less like every other mind; there is always a basis of similarity, but there is a superstructure of feelings, impulses, and motives which is distinctive for each person. We can sometimes predict the general character of the feelings and actions which will be produced by a given external event in an individual well known to us; but we also know that we are often inexplicably at fault in our inferences. No one can safely generalise upon the subtle variations of temper and emotion which may arise even in a person of ordinary character. As human knowledge and civilisation progress, these characteristic differences tend to develop and multiply themselves, rather than decrease. Character grows more many-sided. Two well educated Englishmen are far better distinguished from each other than two common labourers, and these are better distinguished than two Australian aborigines. The complexities of existing phenomena probably develop themselves more rapidly than scientific method can overtake them. In spite of all the boasted powers of science, we cannot really apply scientific method to our own minds and characters, which are more important to us than all the stars and nebulæ.

BOOK VI.

CHAPTER XXXI.

REFLECTIONS ON THE RESULTS AND LIMITS OF
SCIENTIFIC METHOD.

BEFORE concluding a work on the Principles of Science,
it will not be inappropriate to add some remarks upon
the limits and ultimate bearings of the knowledge which
we may acquire by the employment of scientific method.
All science consists, it has several times been stated, in the
detection of identities in the action of natural agents.   The
purpose of inductive inquiry is to ascertain the apparent
existence of necessary connection between causes and
effects, expressed in the form of natural laws.   Now so far
as we thus learn the invariable course of nature, the future
becomes the necessary sequel of the present, and we are
brought beneath the sway of powers with which nothing
can interfere.

By degrees it is found, too, that the chemistry of
organised substances is not entirely separated from, but is
continuous with, that of earth and stones.   Life seems to
be nothing but a special form of energy which is manifested in heat and electricity and mechanical force.   The
time may come, it almost seems, when the tender mechanism of the brain will be traced out, and every thought
reduced to the expenditure of a determinate weight of

nitrogen and phosphorus.   No apparent limit exists to the success of scientific method in weighing and measuring, and reducing beneath the sway of law, the phenomena both of matter and of mind.   And if mental phenomena be thus capable of treatment by the balance and the micrometer, can we any longer hold that mind is distinct from matter? Must not the same inexorable reign of law which is apparent in the motions of brute matter be extended to the subtle feelings of the human heart ?   Are not plants and animals, and ultimately man himself, merely crystals, as it were, of a complicated form ?   If so, our boasted free will becomes a delusion, moral responsibility a fiction, spirit a mere name for the more curious manifestations of material energy.   All that happens, whether right or wrong, plea- surable or painful, is but the outcome of the necessary relations of time and space and force.

Materialism seems, then, to be the coming religion, and resignation to the nonentity of human will the only duty. Such may not generally be the reflections of men of science, but I believe that we may thus describe the secret feelings of fear which the constant advance of scientific investigation excites in the minds of many.   Is science, then, essentially atheistic and materialistic in its tendency ?   Does the uniform action of material causes, which we learn with an ever-increasing approximation to certainty, preclude the hypothesis of a benevolent Creator, who has not only designed the existing universe, but who still retains the power to alter its course from time to time?

To enter upon actual theological discussions would be evidently beyond the scope of this work.   It is with the scientific method common to all the sciences, and not with any of the separate sciences, that we are concerned. Theology therefore would be at least as much beyond my scope as chemistry or geology.   But I believe that grave misapprehensions exist as regards the very nature of scientific method.   There are scientific men who assert that the interposition of Providence is impossible, and prayer an absurdity, because the laws of nature are in- ductively proved to be invariable.   Inferences are drawn not so much from particular sciences as from the logical nature of science itself, to negative the impulses and

hopes of men. Now I may state that my own studies in
logic lead me to call in question such negative inferences.
Laws of nature are uniformities observed to exist in the action of certain material agents, but it is logically impossible
to show that all other agents must behave as these do.
The too exclusive study of particular branches of physical
science seems to generate an over-confident and dogmatic
spirit. Rejoicing in the success with which a few groups
of facts are brought beneath the apparent sway of laws, the
investigator hastily assumes that he is close upon the ultimate springs of being. A particle of gelatinous matter is
found to obey the ordinary laws of chemistry; yet it moves
and lives. The world is therefore asked to believe that
chemistry can resolve the mysteries of existence.

The Meaning of Natural Law.

Pindar speaks of Law as the Ruler of the Mortals and
the Immortals, and it seems to be commonly supposed
that the so-called Laws of Nature, in like manner, rule
man and his Creator. The course of nature is regarded
as being determined by invariable principles of mechanics
which have acted since the world began, and will act for
evermore. Even if the origin of all things is attributed
to an intelligent creative mind, that Being is regarded as
having yielded up arbitrary power, and as being subject like
a human legislator to the laws which he has himself
enacted. Such notions I should describe as superficial and
erroneous, being derived, as I think, from false views of
the nature of scientific inference, and the degree of certainty
of the knowledge which we acquire by inductive investigation.
A law of nature, as I regard the meaning of the
expression, is not a uniformity which must be obeyed by
all objects, but merely a uniformity which is as a matter of
fact obeyed by those objects which have come beneath
our observation. There is nothing whatever incompatible with logic in the discovery of objects which should
prove exceptions to any law of nature. Perhaps the best
established law is that which asserts an invariable correlation to exist between gravity and inertia, so that all
gravitating bodies are found to possess inertia, and all

bodies possessing inertia are found to gravitate. But it would be no reproach to our scientific method, if something were ultimately discovered to possess gravity without inertia. Strictly defined and correctly interpreted, the law itself would acknowledge the possibility ; for with the statement of every law we ought properly to join an esti- mate of the number of instances in which it has been observed to hold true, and the probability thence calcu- lated, that it will hold true in the next case. Now, as we found (p. 259), no finite number of instances can warrant us in expecting with certainty that the next instance will be of like nature ; in the formulas yielded by the inverse method of probabilities a unit always appears to represent the probability that our inference will be mistaken. I demur to the assumption that there is any necessary truth even in such fundamental laws of nature as the Indestruc- tibility of Matter, the Conservation of Energy, or the Laws of Motion. Certain it is that men of science have recog- nised the conceivability of other laws, and even investigated their mathematical consequences. Airy investigated the mathematical conditions of a perpetual motion (p. 223), and Laplace and Newton discussed imaginary laws of forces inconsistent with those observed to operate in the universe (pp. 642, 706).

The laws of nature, as I venture to regard them, are simply general propositions concerning the correlation of properties which have been observed to hold true of bodies hitherto observed. On the assumption that our experience is of adequate extent, and that no arbitrary interference takes place, we are then able to assign the probability, always less than certainty, that the next object of the same apparent nature will conform to the same laws.

Infiniteness of the Universe.

We may safely accept as a satisfactory scientific hypo- thesis the doctrine so grandly put forth by Laplace, who asserted that a perfect knowledge of the universe, as it existed at any given moment, would give a perfect know- ledge of what was to happen thenceforth and for ever after. Scientific inference is impossible, unless we may regard the present as the outcome of what is past, and the cause of what is to come. To the view of perfect intelligence nothing is uncertain. The astronomer can calculate the positions of the heavenly bodies when thousands of generations of men shall have passed away, and in this fact we have some illustration, as Laplace remarks, of the power which scientific prescience may attain. Doubtless, too, all efforts in the investigation of nature tend to bring us nearer to the possession of that ideally perfect power of intelligence. Nevertheless, as Laplace with profound wisdom adds,[1] we must ever remain at an infinite distance from the goal of our aspirations.

Let us assume, for a time at least, as a highly probable hypothesis, that whatever is to happen must be the outcome of what is ; there then arises the question, What is ? Now our knowledge of what exists must ever remain imperfect and fallible in two respects. Firstly, we do not know all the matter that has been created, nor the exact manner in which it has been distributed through space. Secondly, assuming that we had that knowledge, we should still be wanting in a perfect knowledge of the way in which the particles of matter will act upon each other. The power of scientific prediction extends at the most to the limits of the data employed. Every conclusion is purely hypothetical and conditional upon the non-interference of agencies previously undetected. The law of gravity asserts that every body tends to approach towards every other body, with a certain determinate force ; but, even supposing the law to hold true, it does not assert that the body *will* approach. No single law of nature can warrant us in making an absolute prediction. We must know all the laws of nature and all the existing agents acting according to those laws before we can say what will happen. To assume, then, that scientific method can take everything within its cold embrace of uniformity, is to imply that the Creator cannot outstrip the intelligence of his creatures, and that the existing Universe is not infinite in extent and complexity, an assumption for which I see no logical basis whatever.

---

[1] *Théorie Analytique des Probabilités,* quoted by Babbage, *Ninth Bridgewater Treatise,* p. 173.

The Indeterminate Problem of Creation.

A second and very serious misapprehension concerning the import of a law of nature may now be pointed out. It is not uncommonly supposed thåt a law determines the character of the results which shall take place, as, for instance, that the law of gravity determines what force of gravity shall act upon a given particle. Surely a little reflection must render it plain that a law by itself determines nothing. It is *law plus agents obeying law which has results*, and it is no function of law to govern or define the number and place of its own agents. Whether a particle of matter shall gravitate, depends not only upon the law of Newton, but also upon the distribution of surrounding particles. The theory of gravitation may perhaps be true throughout all time and in all parts of space, and the Creator may never find occasion to create those possible exceptions to it which I have asserted to be conceivable. Let this be as it may ; our science cannot certainly determine the question. Certain it is, that the law of gravity does not alone determine the forces which may be brought to bear at any point of space. The force of gravitation acting upon any particle depends upon the mass, distance, and relative position of all the other particles of matter within the bounds of space at the instant in question. Even assuming that all matter when once distributed through space at the Creation was thenceforth to act in an invariable manner without subsequent interference, yet the actual configuration of matter at any moment, and the consequent results of the law of gravitation, must have been entirely a matter of free choice.

Chalmers has most distinctly pointed out that the existing *collocations* of the material world are as important as the laws which the objects obey. He remarks that a certain class of writers entirely overlook the distinction, and forget that mere laws without collocations would have afforded no security against a turbid and disorderly chaos.[1] Mill has recognised[2] the truth of Chalmers' statement, without drawing the proper inferences from

[1] *First Bridgewater Treatise* (1834), pp. 16-24.
[2] *System of Logic*, 5th edit. bk. III. chap. V. § 7 ; chap. XVI. § 3.

it. He says[1] of the distribution of matter through space,
" We can discover nothing regular in the distribution itself;
we can reduce it to no uniformity, to no law." More lately
the Duke of Argyll in his well-known work on the *Reign
of Law* has drawn attention to the profound distinction
between laws and collocations of causes.

The original conformation of the material universe, as
far as we can tell, was free from all restriction. There
was unlimited space in which to frame it, and an unlimited
number of material particles, each of which could be placed
in any one of an infinite number of different positions. It
should be added, that each particle might be endowed
with any one of an infinite number of quantities of *vis
viva* acting in any one of an infinite number of different
directions. The problem of Creation was, then, what a
mathematician would call *an indeterminate problem*, and it
was indeterminate in a great number of ways. Infinitely
numerous and various universes might then have been
fashioned by the various distribution of the original
nebulous matter, although all the particles of matter
should obey the law of gravity.

Lucretius 'tells us how in the original rain of atoms
some of these little bodies diverged from the rectilinear
direction, and coming into contact with other atoms gave
rise to the various combinations of substances which exist.
He omitted to tell us whence the atoms came, or by what
force some of them were caused to diverge; but surely
these omissions involve the whole question. I accept the
Lucretian conception of creation when properly supple-
mented. Every atom which existed in any point of space
must have existed there previously, or must have been
created there by a previously existing Power. When
placed there it must have had a definite mass and a
definite energy. Now, as before remarked, an unlimited
number of atoms can be placed in unlimited space in an
unlimited number of modes of distribution. Out of infinitely infinite choices which were open to the Creator,
that one choice must have been made which has yielded
the Universe as it now exists.

It would be a mistake, indeed, to suppose that the law

[1] *System of Logic*, vol. i. p. 384.

of gravity, when it holds true, is no restriction on the
distribution of force. That law is a geometrical law, and
it would in many cases be mathematically impossible, as
far as we can see, that the force of gravity acting on one
particle should be small while that on a neighbouring
particle is great. We cannot conceive that even Omni-
potent Power should make the angles of a triangle greater
than two right angles. The primary laws of thought and
the fundamental notions of the mathematical sciences do
not seem to admit of error or alteration. Into the metaphysical origin and meaning of the apparent necessity
attaching to such laws I have not attempted to inquire in
this work, and it is not requisite for my present purpose.
If the law of gravity were the only law of nature and the
Creator had chosen to render all matter obedient to that
law, there would doubtless be restrictions upon the effects
derivable from any one distribution of matter.

Hierarchy of Natural Laws.

A further consideration presents itself. A natural law
like that of gravity expresses a certain uniformity in the
action of agents submitted to it, and this produces, as we
have seen, certain geometrical restrictions upon the effects
which those agents may produce. But there are other
forces and laws besides gravity. One force may override
another, and two laws may each be obeyed and may each
disguise the action of the other. In the intimate constitution of matter there may be hidden springs which, while
acting in accordance with their own fixed laws, may lead
to sudden and unexpected changes. So at least it has
been found from time to time in the past, and so there
is every reason to believe it will be found in the future.
To the ancients it seemed incredible that one lifeless stone
could make another leap towards it. A piece of iron
while it obeys the magnetic force of the loadstone does
not the less obey the law of gravity. A plant gravitates
downwards as regards every constituent cell or fibre, and
yet it persists in growing upwards. Life is altogether an
exception to the simpler phenomena of mineral substances,
not in the sense of disproving those laws, but in superadding
forces of new and inexplicable character. Doubtless no

law of chemistry is broken by the action of the nervous cells, and no law of physics by the pulses of the nervous fibres, but something requires to be added to our sciences in order that we may explain these subtle phenomena.

Now there is absolutely nothing in science or in scientific method to warrant us in assigning a limit to this hierarchy of laws. When in many undoubted cases we find law overriding law, and at certain points in our experience producing unexpected results, we cannot venture to affirm that we have exhausted the strange phenomena which may have been provided for in the original constitution of matter. The Universe might have been so designed that it should go for long intervals through the same round of unvaried existence, and yet that events of exceptional character should be produced from time to time. Babbage showed in that most profound and eloquent work, *The Ninth Bridgewater Treatise*, that it was theoretically possible for human artists to design a machine, consisting of metallic wheels and levers, which should work invariably according to a simple law of action during any finite number of steps, and yet at a fixed moment, however distant, should manifest a single breach of law. Such an engine might go on counting, for instance, the natural numbers until they would reach a number requiring for its expression a hundred million digits. " If every letter in the volume now before the reader's eyes," says Babbage,[1] " were changed into a figure, and if all the figures contained in a thousand such volumes were arranged in order, the whole together would yet fall far short of the vast induction the observer would have had in favour of the truth of the law of natural numbers. . . Yet shall the engine, true to the prediction of its director, after the lapse of myriads of ages, fulfil its task, and give that one, the first and only exception to that time-sanctioned law. What would have been the chances against the appearance of the excepted case, immediately prior to its occurrence ? "

As Babbage further showed,[2] a calculating engine, after proceeding through any required number of motions according to a first law, may be made suddenly to suffer a change, so that it shall then commence to calculate

---

[1] *Ninth Bridgewater Treatise*, p. 140.
[2] *Ibid.* pp. 34-43.

according to a wholly new law. After giving the natural
numbers for a finite time, it might suddenly begin to give
triangular, or square, or cube numbers, and these changes
might be conceived theoretically as occurring time after
time. Now if such occurrences can be designed and foreseen by a human artist, it is surely within the capacity of
the Divine Artist to provide for analogous changes of law
in the mechanism of the atom, or the construction of the
heavens.

Physical science, so far as its highest speculations can
be trusted, gives some indication of a change of law in
the past history of the Universe. According to Sir W.
Thomson's deductions from Fourier's *Theory of Heat*, we
can trace down the dissipation of heat by conduction and
radiation to an infinitely distant time when all things will
be uniformly cold. But we cannot similarly trace the
heat-history of the Universe to an infinite distance in the
past. For a certain negative value of the time the formulæ
give impossible values, indicating that there was some
initial distribution of heat which could not have resulted,
according to known laws of nature,[1] from any previous
distribution.[2] There are other cases in which a consideration of the dissipation of energy leads to the conception of
a limit to the antiquity of the present order of things.[3]
Human science, of course, is fallible, and some oversight
or erroneous simplification in these theoretical calculations
may afterwards be discovered; but as the present state of
scientific knowledge is the only ground on which erroneous
inferences from the uniformity of nature and the supposed
reign of law are founded, I am right in appealing to the
present state of science in opposition to these inferences.
Now the theory of heat places us in the dilemma either of

[1] Professor Clifford, in his most interesting lecture on "The First
and Last Catastrophe" (*Fortnightly Review*, April 1875, p. 480, reprint by the Sunday Lecture Society, p. 24), objects that I have
erroneously substituted "known laws of nature" for "known laws
of conduction of heat." I quite admit the error, without admitting
all the conclusions which Professor Clifford proceeds to draw; but I
maintain the paragraph unchanged, in order that it may be discussed
in the Preface.

[2] Tait's *Thermodynamics*, p. 38.   *Cambridge Mathematical Journal*,
vol. iii. p. 174.

[3] Clerk Maxwell's *Theory of Heat*, p. 245.

believing in Creation at an assignable date in the past, or else of supposing that some inexplicable change in the working of natural laws then took place. Physical science gives no countenance to the notion of infinite duration of matter in one continuous course of existence. And if in time past there has been a discontinuity of law, why may there not be a similar event awaiting the world in the future? Infinite ingenuity could have implanted some agency in matter so that it might never yet have made its tremendous powers manifest. We have a very good theory of the conservation of energy, but the foremost physicists do not deny that there may possibly be forms of energy, neither kinetic nor potential, and therefore of unknown nature.[1]

We can imagine reasoning creatures dwelling in a world where the atmosphere was a mixture of oxygen and inflammable gas like the fire-damp of coal-mines. If devoid of fire, they might have lived through long ages unconscious of the tremendous forces which a single spark would call into play. In the twinkling of an eye new laws might come into action, and the poor reasoning creatures, so confident about their knowledge of the reign of law in their world, would have no time to speculate upon the overthrow of all their theories. Can we with our finite knowledge be sure that such an overthrow of our theories is impossible?

The Ambiguous Expression, "Uniformity of Nature."

I have asserted that serious misconception arises from an erroneous interpretation of the expression Uniformity of Nature. Every law of nature is the statement of a certain uniformity observed to exist among phenomena, and since the laws of nature are invariably obeyed, it seems to follow that the course of nature itself is uniform, so that we can safely judge of the future by the present. This inference is supported by some of the results of physical astronomy. Laplace proved that the planetary system is stable, so that no perturbation which planet produces upon planet can become so great as to cause disruption and permanent alteration of the planetary orbits. A full comprehension

---

[1] Maxwell's *Theory of Heat*, p. 92

of the law of gravity shows that all such disturbances are essentially periodic, so that after the lapse of millions of years the planets will return to the same relative positions, and a new cycle of disturbances will then commence.

As other branches of science progress, we seem to gain assurance that no great alteration of the world's condition is to be expected.   Conflict with a comet has long been the cause of fear, but now it is credibly asserted that we have passed through a comet's tail without the fact being known at the time, or manifested by any more serious a phenomenon than a slight luminosity of the sky.   More recently still the earth is said to have touched the comet Biela, and the only result was a beautiful and perfectly harmless display of meteors.   A decrease in the heating power of the sun seems to be the next most probable circumstance from which we might fear the extinction of life on the earth. But calculations founded on reasonable physical data show that no appreciable change can be going on, and experimental data to indicate a change are wholly wanting. Geological investigations show indeed that there have been extensive variations of climate in past times; vast glaciers and icebergs have swept over the temperate regions at one time, and tropical vegetation has flourished near the poles at another time.   But here again the vicissitudes of climate assume a periodic character, so that the stability of the earth's condition does not seem to be threatened.

All these statements may be reasonable, but they do not establish the Uniformity of Nature in the sense that extensive alterations or sudden catastrophes are impossible.   In the first place, Laplace's theory of the stability of the planetary system is of an abstract character, as paying regard to nothing but the mutual gravitation of the planetary bodies and the sun.   It overlooks several physical causes of change and decay in the system which were not so well known in his day as at present, and it also presupposes the absence of any interruption of the course of things by conflict with foreign astronomical bodies.

It is now acknowledged by astronomers that there are at least two ways in which the *vis viva* of the planets and satellites may suffer loss.   The friction of the tides upon the earth produces a small quantity of heat which is radiated into space, and this loss of energy must result in a decrease of the rotational velocity, so that ultimately the terrestrial day will become identical with the year, just as the periods of revolution of the moon upon its axis and around the earth have already become equal. Secondly, there can be little doubt that certain manifestations of electricity upon the earth's surface depend upon the relative motions of the planets and the sun, which give rise to periods of increased intensity. Such electrical phenomena must result in the production and dissipation of heat, the energy of which must be drawn, partially at least, from the moving bodies. This effect is probably identical (p. 570) with the loss of energy of comets attributed to the so-called resisting medium. But whatever be the theoretical explanation of these phenomena, it is almost certain that there exists a tendency to the dissipation of the energy of the planetary system, which will, in the indefinite course of time, result in the fall of the planets into the sun.

It is hardly probable, however, that the planetary system will be left undisturbed throughout the enormous interval of time required for the dissipation of its energy in this way. Conflict with other bodies is so far from being improbable, that it becomes approximately certain when we take very long intervals of time into account. As regards cometary conflicts, I am by no means satisfied with the negative conclusions drawn from the remarkable display on the evening of the 27th of November, 1872. We may often have passed through the tail of a comet, the light of which is probably an electrical manifestation no more substantial than the aurora borealis. Every remarkable shower of shooting stars may also be considered as proceeding from a cometary body, so that we may be said to have passed through the thinner parts of innumerable comets. But the earth has probably never passed, in times of which we have any record, through the nucleus of a comet, which consists perhaps of a dense swarm of small meteorites. We can only speculate upon the effects which might be produced by such a conflict, but it would probably be a much more serious event than any yet registered in history. The probability of its occurrence, too, cannot be assigned; for though the probability of conflict with any one cometary nucleus is almost infinitesimal, yet the number of comets is immensely great (p. 408).

It is far from impossible, again, that the planetary system may be invaded by bodies of greater mass than comets. The sun seems to be placed in so extensive a portion of empty space that its own proper motion would not bring it to the nearest known star (*a* Centauri) in less than 139,200 years. But in order to be sure that this interval of undisturbed life is granted to our globe, we must prove that there are no stars moving so as to meet us, and no dark bodies of considerable size flying through intervening space unknown to us. The intrusion of comets into our system, and the fact that many of them have hyperbolic paths, is sufficient to show that the surrounding parts of space are occupied by multitudes of dark bodies of some size. It is quite probable that small suns may have cooled sufficiently to become non-luminous; for even if we discredit the theory that the variation of brightness of periodic stars is due to the revolution of dark companion stars, yet there is in our own globe an unquestionable example of a smaller body which has cooled below the luminous point.

Altogether, then, it is a mere assumption that the uniformity of nature involves the unaltered existence of our own globe. There is no kind of catastrophe which is too great or too sudden to be theoretically consistent with the reign of law. For all that our science can tell, human history may be closed in the next instant of time. The world may be dashed to pieces against a wandering star; it may be involved in a nebulous atmosphere of hydrogen to be exploded a second afterwards; it may be scorched up or dissipated into vapour by some great explosion in the sun; there might even be within the globe itself some secret cause of disruption, which only needs time for its manifestation.

There are some indications, as already noticed (p. 660), that violent disturbances have actually occurred in the history of the solar system. Olbers sought for the minor planets on the supposition that they were fragments of an exploded planet, and he was rewarded with the discovery of some of them. The retrograde motion of the satellites of the more distant planets, the abnormal position of the poles of Uranus and the excessive distance of Neptune, are other indications of some violent event, of which we have no other evidence. I adduce all these facts and arguments, not to show that there is any considerable probability, as far as we can judge, of interruption within the scope of human history, but to prove that the Uniformity of Nature is theoretically consistent with the most unexpected events of which we can form a conception.

Possible States of the Universe.

When we give the rein to scientific imagination, it becomes apparent that conflict of body with body must not be regarded as the rare exception, but as the general rule and the inevitable fate of each star system. So far as we can trace out the results of the law of gravitation, and of the dissipation of energy, the universe must be regarded as undergoing gradual condensation into a single cold solid body of gigantic dimensions. Those who so frequently use the expression Uniformity of Nature seem to forget that the Universe might exist consistently with the laws of nature in the most diverse conditions. It might consist, on the one hand, of a glowing nebulous mass of gaseous substances. The heat might be so intense that all elements, even carbon and silicon, would be in the state of gas, and all atoms, of whatever nature, would be flying about in chemical independence, diffusing themselves almost uniformly in the neighbouring parts of space. There would then be no life, unless we can apply that name to the passage through each part of space of similar average trains of atoms, the particular succession of atoms being governed only by the theory of probability, and the law of divergence from a mean exhibited in the Arithmetical Triangle. Such a universe would correspond partially to the Lucretian rain of atoms, and to that nebular hypothesis out of which Laplace proposed philosophically to explain the evolution of the planetary system.

According to another extreme supposition, the intense heat-energy of this nebulous mass might be radiated away into the unknown regions of outer space. The attraction of gravity would exert itself between each two particles, and the energy of motion thence arising would, by incessant conflicts, be resolved into heat and dissipated.

Inconceivable ages might be required for the completion of this process, but the dissipation of energy thus proceeding could end only in the production of a cold and motionless universe. The relation of cause and effect, as we see it manifested in life and growth, would degenerate into the constant existence of every particle in a fixed position relative to every other particle. Logical and geometrical resemblances would still exist between atoms, and between groups of atoms crystallised in their appropriate forms for evermore. But time, the great variable, would bring no variation, and as to human hopes and troubles, they would have gone to eternal rest.

Science is not really adequate to proving that such is the inevitable fate of the universe, for we can seldom trust our best-established theories far from their data. Nevertheless, the most probable speculations which we can form as to the history, especially of our own planetary system, is that it originated in a heated revolving nebulous mass of gas, and is in a state of excessively slow progress towards the cold and stony condition. Other speculative hypotheses might doubtless be entertained. Every hypothesis is pressed by difficulties. If the whole universe be cooling, whither does the heat go ? If we are to get rid of it entirely, outer space must be infinite in extent, so that it shall never be stopped and reflected back. But not to speak of metaphysical difficulties, if the medium of heat undulations be infinite in extent, why should not the material bodies placed in it be infinite also in number and aggregate mass ? It is apparent that we are venturing into speculations which surpass our powers of scientific inference. But then I am arguing negatively; I wish to show that those who speak of the uniformity of nature, and the reign of law, misinterpret the meaning involved in those expressions. Law is not inconsistent with extreme diversity, and, so far as we can read the history of this planetary system, it did probably originate in heated nebulous matter, and man's history forms but a brief span in its progress towards the cold and stony condition. It is by doubtful and speculative hypotheses alone that we can avoid such a conclusion, and I depart least from undoubted facts and well-established laws when I assert that, whatever uniformities may underlie the phenomena of nature, constant variety and ever-progressing change is the real outcome.

Speculations on the Reconcentration of Energy.

There are unequivocal indications, as I have said, that the material universe, as we at present see it, is progressing from some act of creation, or some discontinuity of existence of which the date may be approximately fixed by scientific inference. It is progressing towards a state in which the available energy of matter will be dissipated through infinite surrounding space, and all matter will become cold and lifeless. This constitutes, as it were, the historical period of physical science, that over which our scientific foresight may more or less extend. But in this, as in other cases, we have no right to interpret our experience negatively, so as to infer that because the present state of things began at a particular time, there was no previous existence. It may be that the present period of material existence is but one of an indefinite series of like periods. All that we can see, and feel, and infer, and reason about may be, as it were, but a part of one single pulsation in the existence of the universe.

After Sir W. Thomson had pointed out the preponderating tendency which now seems to exist towards the conversion of all energy into heat-energy, and its equal diffusion by radiation throughout space, the late Professor Rankine put forth a remarkable speculation. He suggested that the ethereal, or, as I have called it, the *adamantine* medium in which all the stars exist, and all radiation takes place, may have bounds, beyond which only empty space exists. All heat undulations reaching this boundary will be totally reflected, according to the theory of undulations, and will be reconcentrated into foci situated in various parts of the medium. Whenever a cold and extinct star happens to pass through one of these foci, it will be instantly ignited and resolved by intense heat into its constituent elements. Discontinuity will occur in the history of that portion of matter, and the star will begin its history afresh with a renewed store of energy.

[1] *Report of the British Association* (1852), Report of Sections, p. 12.

This is doubtless a mere speculation, practically incapable of verification by observation, and almost free from restrictions afforded by present knowledge. We might attribute various shapes to the adamantine medium, and the consequences would be various. But there is this value in such speculations, that they draw attention to the finiteness of our knowledge. We cannot deny the possible truth of such an hypothesis, nor can we place a limit to the scientific imagination in the framing of other like hypotheses. It is impossible, indeed, to follow out our scientific inferences without falling into speculation. If heat be radiated into outward space, it must either proceed *ad infinitum*, or it must be stopped somewhere. In the latter case we fall upon Rankine's hypothesis. But if the material universe consist of a finite collection of heated matter situated in a finite portion of an infinite adamantine medium, then either this universe must have existed for a finite time, or else it must have cooled down during the infinity of past time indefinitely near to the absolute zero of temperature. I objected to Lucretius' argument against the destructibility of matter, that we have no knowledge whatever of the laws according to which it would undergo destruction. But we do know the laws according to which the dissipation of heat appears to proceed, and the conclusion inevitably is that a finite heated material body placed in a perfectly cold infinitely extended medium would in an infinite time sink to zero of temperature. Now our own world is not yet cooled down near to zero, so that physical science seems to place us in the dilemma of admitting either the finiteness of past duration of the world, or else the finiteness of the portion of medium in which we exist. In either case we become involved in metaphysical and mechanical difficulties surpassing our mental powers.

The Divergent Scope for New Discovery.

In the writings of some recent philosophers, especially of Auguste Comte, and in some degree John Stuart Mill, there is an erroneous and hurtful tendency to represent our knowledge as assuming an approximately complete character. At least these and many other writers fail to

impress upon their readers a truth which cannot be too
constantly borne in mind, namely, that the utmost successes
which our scientific method can accomplish will not enable
us to comprehend more than an infinitesimal fraction of
what there doubtless is to comprehend.[1] Professor Tyndall
seems to me open to the same charge in a less degree. He
remarks [2] that we can probably never bring natural phenomena completely under mathematical laws, because the
approach of our sciences towards completeness may be
asymptotic, so that however far we may go, there may
still remain some facts not subject to scientific explanation.
He thus likens the supply of novel phenomena to a con-
vergent series, the earlier and larger terms of which have
been successfully disposed of, so that comparatively minor
groups of phenomena alone remain for future investigators
to occupy themselves upon.

On the contrary, as it appears to me, the supply of new
and unexplained facts is divergent in extent, so that the
more we have explained, the more there is to explain.
The further we advance in any generalisation, the more
numerous and intricate are the exceptional cases still
demanding further treatment. The experiments of Boyle,
Mariotte, Dalton, Gay-Lussac, and others, upon the physical
properties of gases, might seem to have exhausted that
subject by showing that all gases obey the same laws
as regards temperature, pressure, and volume. But in
reality these laws are only approximately true, and the
divergences afford a wide and quite unexhausted field for
further generalisation. The recent discoveries of Professor
Andrews have summed up some of these exceptional facts
under a wider generalisation, but in reality they have
opened to us vast new regions of interesting inquiry, and
they leave wholly untouched the question why one gas
behaves differently from another.

[1] Mr. C. J. Monroe objects that in this statement I do injustice
to Comte, who, he thinks, did impress upon his readers the inadequacy of our mental powers compared with the vastness of the subject
matter of science. The error of Comte, he holds, was in maintaining
that science had been carried about as far as it is worth while to
carry it, which is a different matter. In either case, Comte's position
is so untenable that I am content to leave the question undecided.
[2] *Fragments of Science*, p. 362.

The science of crystallography is that perhaps in which the most precise and general laws have been detected, but it would be untrue to assert that it has lessened the area of future discovery. We can show that each one of the seven or eight hundred forms of calcite is derivable by geometrical modifications from an hexagonal prism; but who has attempted to explain the molecular forces producing these modifications, or the chemical conditions in which they arise? The law of isomorphism is an important generalisation, for it establishes a general resemblance between the forms of crystallisation of natural classes of elements. But if we examine a little more closely we find that these forms are only approximately alike, and the divergence peculiar to each substance is an unexplained exception.

By many similar illustrations it might readily be shown that in whatever direction we extend our investigations and successfully harmonise a few facts, the result is only to raise up a host of other unexplained facts. Can any scientific man venture to state that there is less opening now for new discoveries than there was three centuries ago? Is it not rather true that we have but to open a scientific book and read a page or two, and we shall come to some recorded phenomenon of which no explanation can yet be given? In every such fact there is a possible opening for new discoveries, and it can only be the fault of the investigator's mind if he can look around him and find no scope for the exercise of his faculties.

Infinite Incompleteness of the Mathematical Sciences.

There is one privilege which a certain amount of knowledge should confer; it is that of becoming aware of the weakness of our powers compared with the tasks which they might undertake if stronger. To the poor savage who cannot count twenty the arithmetical accomplishments of the schoolboy are miraculously great. The schoolboy cannot comprehend the vastly greater powers of the student, who has acquired facility in algebraic processes. The student can but look with feelings of surprise and reverence at the powers of a Newton or a Laplace. But the question at once suggests itself, Do the powers of the highest human intellect bear a finite ratio to the things which are to be understood and calculated ? How many further steps must we take in the rise of mental ability and the extension of mathematical methods before we begin to exhaust the knowable ?

I am inclined to find fault with mathematical writers because they often exult in what they can accomplish, and omit to point out that what they do is but an infinitely small part of what might be done. They exhibit a general inclination, with few exceptions, not to do so much as mention the existence of problems of an impracticable character. This may be excusable as far as the immediate practical result of their researches is in question, but the custom has the effect of misleading the general public into the fallacious notion that mathematics is a *perfect* science, which accomplishes what it undertakes in a complete manner. On the contrary, it may be said that if a mathematical problem were selected by chance out of the whole number which might be proposed, the probability is infinitely slight that a human mathematician could solve it. Just as the numbers we can count are nothing compared with the numbers which might exist, so the accomplishments of a Laplace or a Lagrange are, as it were, the little corner of the multiplication-table, which has really an infinite extent.

I have pointed out that the rude character of our observations prevents us from being aware of the greater number of effects and actions in nature. It must be added that, if we perceive them, we should usually be incapable of including them in our theories from want of mathematical power. Some persons may be surprised that though nearly two centuries have elapsed since the time of Newton's discoveries, we have yet no general theory of molecular action. Some approximations have been made towards such a theory. Joule and Clausius have measured the velocity of gaseous atoms, or even determined the average distance between the collisions of atom and atom. Thomson has approximated to the number of atoms in a given bulk of substance. Rankine has formed some reasonable hypotheses as to the actual constitution of atoms. It would be a mistake to suppose that these ingenious results of theory and experiment form any appreciable approach to a complete solution of molecular motions.

There is every reason to believe, judging from the spectra of the elements, their atomic weights and other data, that chemical atoms are very complicated structures.   An atom of pure iron is probably a far more complicated system than that of the planets and their satellites.   A compound atom may perhaps be compared with a stellar system, each star a minor system in itself.   The smallest particle of solid substance will consist of a great number of such stellar systems united in regular order, each bounded by the other, communicating with it in some manner yet wholly incomprehensible.   What are our mathematical powers in comparison with this problem ?

After two centuries of continuous labour, the most gifted men have succeeded in calculating the mutual effects of three bodies each upon the other, under the simple hypothesis of the law of gravity.   Concerning these calculations we must further remember that they are purely approximate, and that the methods would not apply where four or more bodies are acting, and all produce considerable effects upon each other.   There is reason to believe that each constituent of a chemical atom goes through an orbit in the millionth part of the twinkling of an eye.   In each revolution it is successively or simultaneously under the influence of many other constituents, or possibly comes into collision with them.   It is no exaggeration to say that mathematicians have the least notion of the way in which they could successfully attack so difficult a problem of forces and motions.   As Herschel has remarked,[1] each of these particles is for ever solving differential equations, which, if written out in full, might belt the earth.

Some of the most extensive calculations ever made were those required for the reduction of the measurements executed in the course of the Trigonometrical Survey of Great Britain.   The calculations arising out of the principal triangulation occupied twenty calculators during three or four years, in the course of which the computers had to solve simultaneous equations involving seventy-seven unknown quantities.   The reduction of the levellings required the solution of a system of ninety-one equations. But these vast calculations present no approach whatever to

---

[1] *Familiar Lectures on Scientific Subjects,* p. 458.

what would be requisite for the complete treatment of any one physical problem. The motion of glaciers is supposed to be moderately well understood in the present day. A glacier is a viscid, slowly yielding mass, neither absolutely solid nor absolutely rigid, but it is expressly remarked by Forbes,[1] that not even an approximate solution of the mathematical conditions of such a moving mass can yet be possible. "Every one knows," he says, "that such problems are beyond the compass of exact mathematics;" but though mathematicians may know this, they do not often enough impress that knowledge on other people.

The problems which are solved in our mathematical books consist of a small selection of those which happen from peculiar conditions to be solvable. But the very simplest problem in appearance will often give rise to impracticable calculations. Mr. Todhunter [2] seems to blame Condorcet, because in one of his memoirs he mentions a problem to solve which would require a great and impracticable number of successive integrations. Now, if our mathematical sciences are to cope with the problems which await solution, we must be prepared to effect an unlimited number of successive integrations; yet at present, and almost beyond doubt for ever, the probability that an integration taken haphazard will come within our powers is exceedingly small.

In some passages of that remarkable work, the ·Ninth Bridgewater Treatise (pp. 113—115), Babbage has pointed out that if we had power to follow and detect the minutest effects of any disturbance, each particle of existing matter would furnish a register of all that has happened. "The track of every canoe—of every vessel that has yet disturbed the surface of the ocean, whether impelled by manual force or elemental power, remains for ever registered in the future movement of all succeeding particles which may occupy its place. The furrow which it left is, indeed, instantly filled up by the closing waters; but they draw after them other and larger portions of the surrounding element, and these again, once moved, communicate motion to others in endless succession." We may even say that "The air itself is one vast library, on whose pages are for ever written all that

[1] *Philosophical Magazine*, 3rd Series, vol. xxvi. p. 406.
[2] *History of the Theory of Probability*, p. 398.

man has ever said or even whispered. There, in their
mutable but unerring characters, mixed with the earliest
as well as the latest sighs of mortality, stand for ever
recorded, vows unredeemed, promises unfulfilled, perpe-
tuating in the united movements of each particle the
testimony of man's changeful will."

When we read reflections such as these, we may con-
gratulate ourselves that we have been endowed with minds
which, rightly employed, can form some estimate of their
incapacity to trace out and account for all that proceeds
in the simpler actions of material nature. It ought to be
added that, wonderful as is the extent of physical phenomena open to our investigation, intellectual phenomena are
yet vastly more extensive. Of this I might present one
satisfactory proof were space available by pointing out that
the mathematical functions employed in the calculations
of physical science form an infinitely small fraction of the
functions which might be invented. Common trigonometry
consists of a great series of useful formulæ, all of which arise
out of the relation of the sine and cosine expressed in one
equation, $\sin {}^2x + \cos {}^2x = 1$. But this is not the only
trigonometry which may exist; mathematicians also recognise hyperbolic trigonometry, of which the fundamental
equation is $\cos {}^2x - \sin {}^2x = 1$. De Morgan has pointed
out that the symbols of ordinary algebra form but three
of an interminable series of conceivable systems.[1] As the
logarithmic operation is to addition or addition to multiplication, so is the latter to a higher operation, and so on
without limit.

We may rely upon it that immense, and to us inconceivable, advances will be made by the human intellect, in
the absence of any catastrophe to the species or the globe.
Within historical periods we can trace the rise of mathematical science from its simplest germs. We can prove
our descent from ancestors who counted only on their
fingers. How infinitely is a Newton or a Laplace above
those simple savages. Pythagoras is said to have sacrificed
a hecatomb when he discovered the forty-seventh proposition of Euclid, and the occasion was worthy of the sacrifice.
Archimedes was beside himself when he first perceived

• *Trigonometry and Double Algebra* chap. ix

in the denominators of the binomial expansion (p. 190), which are reproduced in the natural constant ϵ, or

$$1 + \frac{1}{1} + \frac{1}{1 . 2} + \frac{1}{1 . 2 . 3} + \ldots$$

and in many results of mathematical analysis. I now perceive, as already explained (pp. 33, 160, 383), that they arise out of the fact that the relations of space do not apply to the logical conditions governing the numbers of combinations as contrasted to those of permutations. So far am I from accepting Kant's doctrine that space is a necessary form of thought, that I regard it as an accident, and an impediment to pure logical reasoning. Material existences must exist in space, no doubt, but intellectual existences may be neither in space nor out of space; they may have no relation to space at all, just as space itself has no relation to time. For all that I can see, then, there may be intellectual existences to which both time and space are nullities.

Now among the most unquestionable rules of scientific method is that first law that *whatever phenomenon is, is.* We must ignore no existence whatever; we may variously interpret or explain its meaning and origin, but, if a phenomenon does exist, it demands some kind of explanation. If then there is to be competition for scientific recognition, the world without us must yield to the undoubted existence of the spirit within. Our own hopes and wishes and determinations are the most undoubted phenomena within the sphere of consciousness. If men do act, feel, and live as if they were not merely the brief products of a casual conjunction of atoms, but the instruments of a far-reaching purpose, are we to record all other phenomena and pass over these? We investigate the instincts of the ant and the bee and the beaver, and discover that they are led by an inscrutable agency to work towards a distant purpose. Let us be faithful to our scientific method, and investigate also those instincts of the human mind by which man is led to work as if the approval of a Higher Being were the aim of life.

his beautiful mode of determining specific gravities. Yet these great discoveries are the commonplaces of our school books. Step by step we can trace upwards the acquirement of new mental powers. What could be more wonderful than Napier's discovery of logarithms, a new mode of calculation which has multiplied perhaps a hundredfold the working powers of every computer, and has rendered easy calculations which were before impracticable ? Since the time of Newton and Leibnitz worlds of problems have been solved which before were hardly conceived as matters of inquiry. In our own day extended methods of mathematical reasoning, such as the system of quaternions, have been brought into existence. What intelligent man will doubt that the recondite speculations of a Cayley, a Sylvester, or a Clifford may lead to some new development of new mathematical power, at the simplicity of which a future age will wonder, and yet wonder more that to us they were so dark and difficult. May we not repeat the words of Seneca : " Veniet tempus, quo ista quæ nunc latent, in lucem dies extrahat, et longioris ævi diligentia : ad inquisitionem tantorum ætas una non sufficit. Veniet tempus, quo posteri nostri tam aperta nos nescisse mirentur."

The Reign of Law in Mental and Social Phenomena.

After we pass from the so-called physical sciences to those which attempt to investigate mental and social phenomena, the same general conclusions will hold true. No one will be found to deny that there are certain uniformities of thinking and acting which can be detected in reasoning beings, and so far as we detect such laws we successfully apply scientific method. But those who attempt to establish social or moral sciences soon become aware that they are dealing with subjects of enormous perplexity. Take as an instance the science of political economy. If a science at all, it must be a mathematical science, because it deals with quantities of commodities. But as soon as we attempt to draw out the equations expressing the laws of demand and supply, we discover that they have a complexity entirely surpassing our powers of mathematical treatment. We may lay down the general form of the equations, expressing the demand and supply

for two or three commodities among two or three trading
bodies, but all the functions involved are so complicated in
character that there is not much fear of scientific method
making rapid progress in this direction. If such be the
prospects of a comparatively formal science, like political
economy, what shall we say of moral science? Any
complete theory of morals must deal with quantities of
pleasure and pain, as Bentham pointed out, and must sum
up the general tendency of each kind of action upon the
good of the community. If we are to apply scientific
method to morals, we must have a calculus of moral effects,
a kind of physical astronomy investigating the mutual perturbations of individuals. But as astronomers have not
yet fully solved the problem of three gravitating bodies,
when shall we have a solution of the problem of three
moral bodies ?

The sciences of political economy and morality are comparatively abstract and general, treating mankind from
simple points of view, and attempting to detect general
principles of action. They are to social phenomena what
the abstract sciences of chemistry, heat, and electricity
are to the concrete science of meteorology. Before we can
investigate the actions of any aggregate of men, we must
have fairly mastered all the more abstract sciences applying
to them, somewhat in the way that we have acquired a
fair comprehension of the simpler truths of chemistry and
physics. But all our physical sciences do not enable us to
predict the weather two days hence with any great probability, and the general problem of meteorology is almost
unattempted as yet. What shall we say then of the general
problem of social science, which shall enable us to predict
the course of events in a nation ?

Several writers have proposed to lay the foundations of
the science of history. Buckle undertook to write the
History of Civilisation in England, and to show how the
character of a nation could be explained by the nature of
the climate and the fertility of the soil. He omitted to
explain the contrast between the ancient Greek nation and
the present one ; there must have been an extraordinary
revolution in the climate or the soil. Auguste Comte
detected the simple laws of the course of development
through which nations pass. There are always three

phases of intellectual condition,—the theological, the metaphysical, and the positive ; applying this general law of progress to concrete cases, Comte was enabled to predict that in the hierarchy of European nations, Spain would necessarily hold the highest place. Such are the parodies of science offered to us by the *positive* philosophers.

A science of history in the true sense of the term is an absurd notion. A nation is not a mere sum of individuals whom we can treat by the method of averages ; it is an organic whole, held together by ties of infinite complexity. Each individual acts and re-acts upon his smaller or greater circle of friends, and those who acquire a public position exert an influence on much larger sections of the nation. There will always be a few great leaders of exceptional genius or opportunities, the unaccountable phases of whose opinions and inclinations sway the whole body. From time to time arise critical situations, battles, delicate negotiations, internal disturbances, in which the slightest incidents may change the course of history. A rainy day may hinder a forced march, and change the course of a campaign ; a few injudicious words in a despatch may irritate the national pride ; the accidental discharge of a gun may precipitate a collision the effects of which will last for centuries. It is said that the history of Europe depended at one moment upon the question whether the look-out man upon Nelson's vessel would or would not descry a ship of Napoleon's expedition to Egypt which was passing not far off. In human affairs, then, the smallest causes may produce the greatest effects, and the real application of scientific method is out of the question.

The Theory of Evolution.

Profound philosophers have lately generalised concerning the production of living forms and the mental and moral phenomena regarded as their highest development. Herbert Spencer's theory of evolution purports to explain the origin of all specific differences, so that not even the rise of a Homer or a Beethoven would escape from his broad theories. The homogeneous is unstable and must differentiate itself, says Spencer, and hence comes the variety of human institutions and characters. In order that a living form shall continue to exist and propagate its kind, says Darwin, it must be suitable to its circumstances, and the most suitable forms will prevail over and extirpate those which are less suitable. From these fruitful ideas are developed theories of evolution and natural selection which go far towards accounting for the existence of immense numbers of living creatures—plants, and animals. Apparent adaptations of organs to useful purposes, which Paley regarded as distinct products of creative intelligence, are now seen to follow as natural effects of a constantly acting tendency. Even man, according to these theories, is no distinct creation, but rather an extreme case of brain development. His nearest cousins are the apes, and his pedigree extends backwards until it joins that of the lowliest zoophytes.

The theories of Darwin and Spencer are doubtless not demonstrated; they are to some extent hypothetical, just as all the theories of physical science are to some extent hypothetical, and open to doubt. Judging from the immense numbers of diverse facts which they harmonise and explain, I venture to look upon the theories of evolution and natural selection in their main features as two of the most probable hypotheses ever proposed. I question whether any scientific works which have appeared since the *Principia* of Newton are comparable in importance with those of Darwin and Spencer, revolutionising as they do all our views of the origin of bodily, mental, moral, and social phenomena.

Granting all this, I cannot for a moment admit that the theory of evolution will destroy theology. That theory embraces several laws or uniformities which are observed to be true in the production of living forms; but these laws do not determine the size and figure of living creatures, any more than the law of gravitation determines the magnitudes and distances of the planets. Suppose that Darwin is correct in saying that man is descended from the Ascidians: yet the precise form of the human body must have been influenced by an infinite train of circumstances affecting the reproduction, growth, and health of the whole chain of intermediate beings. No doubt, the circumstances being what they were, man could not be otherwise than he is, and if in any other part of the universe an exactly similar earth, furnished with exactly similar germs of life, existed, a race must have grown up there exactly similar to the human race.

By a different distribution of atoms in the primeval world a different series of living forms on this earth would have been produced. From the same causes acting according to the same laws, the same results will follow; but from different causes acting according to the same laws, different results will follow. So far as wé can see, then, infinitely diverse living creatures might have been created consistently with the theory of evolution, and the precise reason why we have a backbone, two hands with opposable thumbs, an erect stature, a complex brain, about 223 bones, and many other peculiarities, is only to be found in the original act of creation. I do not, any less than Paley, believe that the eye of man manifests design. I believe that the eye was gradually developed, and we can in fact trace its gradual development from the first germ of a nerve affected by light-rays in some simple zoophyte. In proportion as the eye became a more accurate instrument of vision, it enabled its possessor the better to escape destruction, but the ultimate result must have been contained in the aggregate of the causes, and these causes, as far as we can see, were subject to the arbitrary choice of the Creator.

Although Agassiz was clearly wrong in holding that every species of living creature appeared on earth by the immediate intervention of the Creator, which would amount to saying that no laws of connection between forms are discoverable, yet he seems to be right in asserting that living forms are distinct from those produced by purely physical causes. " The products of what are commonly called physical agents," he says,[1] " are everywhere the same (*i.e.* upon the whole surface of the earth), and have always been the same (*i.e.* during all geological periods); while organised beings are everywhere different and have differed in all ages. Between two such series of phenomena there can be no causal or genetic connection." Living forms as we now regard them are essentially variable, but from constant mechanical causes constant effects would ensue. If vegetable cells are formed on geometrical principles

---

[1] Agassiz, *Essay on Classification*, p. 75.

being first spherical, and then by mutual compression dodecahedral, then all cells should have similar forms. In the Foraminifera and some other lowly organisms, we seem to observe the production of complex forms on geometrical principles. But from similar causes acting according to similar laws only similar results could be produced. If the original life-germ of each creature is a simple particle of protoplasm, unendowed with any distinctive forces, then the whole of the complex phenomena of animal and vegetable life are effects without causes. Protoplasm may be chemically the same substance, and the germ-cell of a man and of a fish may be apparently the same, so far as the microscope can decide; but if certain cells produce men, and others as uniformly produce a species of fish, there must be a hidden constitution determining the extremely different results. If this were not so, the generation of every living creature from the uniform germ would have to be regarded as a distinct act of creation.

Theologians have dreaded the establishment of the theories of Darwin and Huxley and Spencer, as if they thought that those theories could explain everything upon the purest mechanical and material principles, and exclude all notions of design. They do not see that those theories have opened up more questions than they have closed. The doctrine of evolution gives a complete explanation of no single living form. While showing the general principles which prevail in the variation of living creatures, it only points out the infinite complexity of the causes and circumstances which have led to the present state of things. Any one of Mr. Darwin's books, admirable though they all are, consists but in the setting forth of a multitude of indeterminate problems. He proves in the most beautiful manner that each flower of an orchid is adapted to some insect which frequents and fertilises it, and these adaptations are but a few cases of those immensely numerous ones which have occurred in the lives of plants and animals. But why orchids should have been formed so differently from other plants, why anything, indeed, should be as it is, rather than in some of the other infinitely numerous possible modes of existence, he can never show. The origin of everything that exists is wrapped up in the past history of the universe. At some one or more points in past time there

must have been arbitrary determinations which led to the
production of things as they are.

Possibility of Divine Interference.

I will now draw the reader's attention to pages 149 to 152.
I there pointed out that all inductive inference involves
the assumption that our knowledge of what exists is complete, and that the conditions of things remain unaltered
between the time of our experience and the time to which
our inferences refer. Recurring to the illustration of a
ballot-box, employed in the chapter on the inverse method
of probabilities, we assume when predicting the probable
nature of the next drawing, firstly, that our previous
drawings have been sufficiently numerous to give us
knowledge of the contents of the box; and, secondly, that
no interference with the ballot-box takes place between
the previous and the next drawings. The results yielded
by the theory of probability are quite plain. No finite
number of casual drawings can give us sure knowledge of
the contents of the box, so that, even in the absence of all
disturbance, our inferences are merely the best which can
be made, and do not approach to infallibility. If, however,
interference be possible, even the theory of probability
ceases to be applicable, for, the amount and nature of that
interference being arbitrary and unknown, there ceases to
be any connection between premises and conclusion. Many
years of reflection have not enabled me to see the way of
avoiding this hiatus in scientific certainty. The conclusions
of scientific inference appear to be always of a hypothetical
and provisional nature. Given certain experience, the
theory of probability yields us the true interpretation of
that experience and is the surest guide open to us. But
the best calculated results which it can give are never
absolute probabilities; they are purely relative to the extent
of our information. It seems to be impossible for us to
judge how far our experience gives us adequate information
of the universe as a whole, and of all the forces and phenomena which can have place therein.

I feel that I cannot in the space remaining at my command in the present volume, sufficiently follow out the
lines of thought suggested, or define with precision my

own conclusions. This chapter contains merely *Reflections* upon subjects of so weighty a character that I should myself wish for many years—nay for more than a lifetime of further reflection. My purpose, as I have repeatedly said, is the purely negative one of showing that atheism and materialism are no necessary results of scientific method. From the preceding reviews of the value of our scientific knowledge, I draw one distinct conclusion, that we cannot disprove the possibility of Divine interference in the course of nature. Such interference might arise, so far as our knowledge extends, in two ways. It might consist in the disclosure of the existence of some agent or spring of energy previously unknown, but which effects a given purpose at a given moment. Like the pre-arranged change of law in Babbage's imaginary calculating machine, there may exist pre-arranged surprises in the order of nature, as it presents itself to us. Secondly, the same Power, which created material nature, might, so far as I can see, create additions to it, or annihilate portions which do exist. Such events are in a certain sense inconceivable to us; yet they are no more inconceivable than the existence of the world as it is. The indestructibility of matter, and the conservation of energy, are very probable scientific hypotheses, which accord satisfactorily with experiments of scientific men during a few years past, but it would be gross misconception of scientific inference to suppose that they are certain in the sense that a proposition in geometry is certain. Philosophers no doubt hold that *de nihilo nihil fit*, that is to say, their senses give them no means of imagining to the mind how creation can take place. But we are on the horns of a trilemma; we must either deny that anything exists, or we must allow that it was created out of nothing at some moment of past time, or that it existed from eternity. The first alternative is absurd; the other two seem to me equally conceivable.

Conclusion.

It may seem that there is one point where our specu-lations must end, namely where contradiction begins. The laws of Identity and Difference and Duality were the

INDEX.

SCIENCE AND METHOD
by Henri Poincare

Written by Henri Poincare, who has been termed the last mathematical universalist and the greatest mathematician since Gauss, this volume is concerned with the basic methodology and psychology of scientific discovery, especially in mathematics and mathematical physics. It explains how the scientist analyzes and selects facts with which he must work, and analyzes the nature of experimentation, theory, and the human mind, as they are applied to the acquisition of organized knowledge.

Examples from many fields of science illustrate Poincare's discussion of the germination of ideas. Besides special topics, this volume also contains Poincare's famous discussion of his own idea-creating mental processes, and the use of the unconscious mind. Especially valuable for the modern mathematician or logician is a searching examination of the ideas of Whitehead, Hilbert, and Russell.

"Vivid . . . immense clarity . .. the product of a brilliant and extremely forceful intellect," JOURNAL OF THE ROYAL NAVAL SCIENTIFIC SERVICE. "Still a sheer joy to read," MATHEMATICAL GAZETTE. "Should be read by any student, teacher or researcher in mathematics," MATHEMATICS TEACHER.

Table of contents. THE SCIENTIST AND SCIENCE. Selection of facts. The future of mathematics. Mathematical discovery. Chance. MATHEMATICAL REASONING. Relativity of space. Mathematical difinitions and education. Mathematicians and logic. The new logics. The last efforts of the logisticians. THE NEW MECHANICS. Mechanics and radium. Mechanics and optics. The new mechanics and astronomy. ASTRONOMICAL SCIENCE. The Milky Way and the theory of gases. French geodesy. Conclusions.

Translated by Francis Maitland. 288pp.

S222 Paperbound **$1.25**

EXPERIMENT AND THEORY IN PHYSICS
by Max Born

This is an expanded version of a famous address given by Max Born, Nobel Prize winner, at King's College, Newcastle-on-Tyne, in 1943. It examines the nature of experiment and theory in theoretical physics, discussing conflicting opinions as to their relative values, weight, claims. It then analyzes in detail the two types of theoretical scientific advance — synthetic and analytical — showing that each is really based firmly upon experimental data.

Dr. Born also offers careful analyses of actual theoretical and mathematical advances made by the great physicists and mathematical physicists of our day: Einstein, Heisenberg, Bohr, Planck, Dirac, and others. These analyses are not mere inference (as might be the case with a historian standing outside the field of physics), but are analytical narrative, with scientific background, of the actual idea-flights as they occurred, as witnessed by a participant. A special discussion then follows of the a priori theories of Eddington and Milne, in which each is examined in terms of validity of scientific method.

This modern classic is invaluable to anyone interested in either theoretical physics in its widest application, or in scientific method, the psychological logic of science, or the creative process in science.

44pp. 5⅜ x 8.   S308 Paperbound 60¢

THE BIRTH AND DEVELOPMENT OF THE GEOLOGICAL SCIENCES

by Frank Dawson Adams

This famous 200,000-word text traces the history of the geological sciences from Greek and Roman times, through the Middle Ages, the Renaissance and the modern era, up to the mid-19th century. It is not a dull coverage of obsolete ideas but a truly fascinating account of how dozens of curious, colorful systems evolved into modern geology.

In his extremely thorough coverage of the subject, the late Professor Adams discusses the work of over 300 different authorities, analyzing in detail the ideas of such men as William Smith, Agricola, Geikie, Hutton, Werner, Aristotle, Becher, Cuvier, Kircher, and many others. He recreates the birth of modern mineralogy, paleontology and historical geology; treats the origin of metals and their ores, mountains and earthquakes, springs and rivers; describes Becher's metallic tree at the center of the earth, Greek concepts of vulcanology, Sherley's view that metals grow from seeds, da Vinci's theory of fossils, and many other quaint stories and beliefs that will delight any reader interested in geology or mineralogy.

"Geologists owe Professor Adams a profound debt of gratitude," JOURNAL OF GEOLOGY. "Should be in every biological library," BIOLOGIST.

Unabridged republication of 1st edition. 632 footnotes, mostly bibliographical. Index. 110 illustrations, including many medieval and renaissance woodcuts, portraits of eminent early geologists. 506pp. 5⅜ x 8.

T5 Paperbound $2.00

THE EVOLUTION OF SCIENTIFIC THOUGHT FROM NEWTON TO EINSTEIN
by A. d'Abro

This is the best detailed semi-popular account of the special and general theories of relativity. It is not a watered-down popularization, but a scientifically impeccable account, written, however, in the language of intelligent laymen. It is both valuable as a broad survey for the specialist and as introduction to the layman.

The first portion describes those parts of classical mathematical physics which were affected by relativity, analyzing those new developments which demanded a new cosmology. It describes fully Euclidean and Riemannian geometry, space, time, distance, mechanics, electromagnetism, and the concept of ether — and the evolution which each was undergoing.

The second part analyzes Einstein's special theory with all its implications, the work of Fitzgerald and Minkowski, and Whitehead's criticism of Einstein; de Sitter, Lemaitre, Weyl, Eddington are also examined in detail. The final part of this work is concerned with the philosophy of science and scientific method. In more than 100 pages the author analyzes assumptions, logical method, and techniques.

"A model of semi-popular exposition," NEW REPUBLIC. "Here at last we have a book on relativity that is thoroughly good," JOURNAL OF PHILOSOPHY. "Probably no other book covers so thoroughly and so lucidly its broad range of subject matter," ISIS.

Second enlarged edition. 36 illustrations. 482pp. 5⅜ x 8.

Paperbound **$2.00**

THE COMMON SENSE OF THE EXACT SCIENCES
by W. K. Clifford

For seventy years this book has been used as the general reader's guide to classical scientific and mathematical thought. It explains with unusual clarity such basic concepts as the extension of meaning of symbols, characteristics of surface boundaries, properties of plane figures, measurement of quantities, vectors, the Cartesian method of determining position, bending of space, uniform and variable motion, mass and force, and the laws of motion. Individual chapters examine in great detail Number, Space, Quantity, Position, and Motion. A bibliography of the writings of W. K. Clifford is appended.

"Clifford possessed an art of clarity such as belongs only to a very few great men — not the pseudo-clarity of the popularizer, which is achieved by ignoring or glozing over the difficult points, but the clarity that comes of profound and orderly understanding, by virtue of which principles become luminous and deductions look easy. . . . . Clifford's book may not only still be read with great profit by young people interested in mathematics, but should also be studied with diligent admiration by all who are engaged in trying to make difficult ideas intelligible." BERTRAND RUSSELL.

Preface by Bertrand Russell. Biographical and critical introduction by James R. Newman. Preface by Karl Pearson. 123 figures have been redrawn and corrected. lxvi + 249pp. 5⅜ x 8.

T61 Paperbound **$1.60**

FOUNDATIONS OF SCIENCE:
THE PHILOSOPHY OF THEORY AND EXPERIMENT
by N. R. Campbell

In this volume, formerly entitled PHYSICS: THE ELEMENTS, Dr. Campbell provides a critique of the most fundamental concepts of science in general and of physics in particular. His point of view is that of the experimental physicist rather than the mathematician. This, combined with his knowledge of the entire field of physics, allows his investigation to proceed along unique lines.

This book has three purposes. (1) To discover why certain propositions of science are accepted without question. These include the use of hypothesis and theory, induction, application of "numbers" to phenomena, dimensional analysis, etc. (2) To demarcate science from philosophy, and to discuss attempts to make one a branch of the other. (3) To clarify our understanding of the tools of science (theory, probability, measurement), to prevent errors in their use, and to extend our understanding of the phenomena which we investigate by their means. The author draws upon the work of countless predecessors, ranging from Euclid and Aristotle to Maxwell, Planck, Poincaré, Bergson, and scores of others.

FOUNDATIONS OF SCIENCE is divided into two parts. The first part analyzes the presuppositions upon which scientific thought is based. Subject matter of science; the nature, discovery, proof of laws; theories; chance and probability; science and philosophy are discussed, and the physical nature of the world is studied in relation to problems suggested by mechanics, thermodynamics, gas theory, and electrical phenomena. In the second part the author covers the nature of experiment and the application of mathematics; measurement; magnitudes, fractional and negative; units and dimensions; errors of measurement etc. are all considered. An appendix covers problems that arise from relativity, force, motion, space & time.

This is not an elementary work. It is written for the reader who has a good background in the physical sciences and it has been accepted as a classic in its field. It is difficult to conceive that anyone interested in the sciences would not profit by studying this monumental work.

Index. xii + 565pp. 5⅜ x 8.

S372 Paperbound $2.95